Log on.

Tune in.

Succeed.

Your steps to success.

STEP 1: Register

All you need to get started is a valid email address and the access code below. To register, simply:

1. Go to www.mybiology.com
2. Click the appropriate book cover.
   Cover must match the textbook edition being used for your class.
3. Click **"Register"** under **"First-Time User?"**
4. Leave **"No, I Am a New User"** selected.
5. Using a coin, scratch off the silver coating below to reveal your access code.
   Do not use a knife or other sharp object, which can damage the code.
6. Follow the on-screen instructions to complete registration. You may want to click Log In Now on your registration confirmation screen and bookmark that page.

   During registration, you will establish a personal login name and password to use for logging into the website. You will also be sent a registration confirmation email that contains your login name and password.

Your Access Code is:

ACCT ID: 2517 4817
USERNAME: audris.Korth
PN: 11lanbel19

USWCCE-FROMM-LEVEL-SCRAN-TOPAZ-JADES

Note: If there is no silver foil covering the access code, it may already have been redeemed, and therefore may no longer be valid. In that case, you can purchase access online using a major credit card. To do so, go to www.mybiology.com and click "Buy Access" and follow the on-screen instructions.

STEP 2: Log in

1. Go to www.mybiology.com and **"Log In."**
2. Click your book cover and under enter the login name and password that you created during registration. Cover must match the textbook edition being used for your class. If unsure of this information, refer to your registration confirmation email.
3. Click **"Log In."**

STEP 3: (Optional) Join a class

Instructors have the option of creating an online class for you to use with this website. If your instructor decides to do this, you'll need to complete the following steps using the Class ID your instructor provides you. By "joining a class," you enable your instructor to view the scored results of your work on the website in his or her online gradebook.

To join a class:

1. Log into the website. For instructions, see "STEP 2: Log in."
2. Click **"Join a Class"** near the top right.
3. Enter your instructor's **"Class ID"** and then click **"Next."**
4. At the Confirm Class page you will see your instructor's name and class information. If this information is correct, click Next.
5. Click **"Enter Class Now"** from the Class Confirmation page.
* To confirm your enrollment in the class, check for your instructor and class name at the top right of the page. You will be sent a class enrollment confirmation email.
* As you complete quizzes on the website from now through the class end date, your results will post to your instructor's gradebook, in addition to appearing in your personal view of the Results Reporter.

To log into the class later, follow the instructions under "STEP 2: Log in."

Got technical questions?

Customer Technical Support: To obtain support, please visit us online anytime at http://247.aw.com where you can search our knowledgebase for common solutions, view product alerts, and review all options for additional assistance.

SITE REQUIREMENTS

For the latest updates on Site Requirements, go to www.mybiology.com, choose your text cover, and click Site Reqs.

WINDOWS
OS: Windows XP
Resolution: 1024 x 768
Plugins: Latest version of Flash/QuickTime/Shockwave (as needed)
Browsers: Internet Explorer 6.0 (XP only); Internet Explorer 7.0; Firefox 2.0.
Internet connection: 56K minimum

MACINTOSH
OS: 10.3.x; 10.4
Resolution: 1024 x 768
Plugins: Latest version of Flash/QuickTime/Shockwave (as needed)
Browsers: Safari 1.3 (10.3.x only); Safari 2.0 (10.4.x only); Firefox 2.0
Internet connection: 56K minimum

Register and log in

Join a class

Important: Please read the Subscription and End-User License agreement, accessible from the book website's login page, before using the *myBiology* website. By using the website or CD-ROM, you indicate that you have read, understood, and accepted the terms of this agreement.

Features of the Student Website for *Biology: Concepts & Connections,* **Sixth Edition**

Chapter Guide
The Chapter Guide organizes media under central concepts that correlate directly to the text.

Bioflix™
These 3-D animations and interactive, self-paced tutorials bring difficult biological concepts to life. Topics include cellular respiration, mitosis, and meiosis. Prepare for exams by completing a tutorial, printing a personal review sheet, and taking a quiz.

MP3 Tutors
Study anytime, anywhere, with these downloadable audio tutorials narrated by the author, Eric Simon. Nineteen new MP3 Tutors focus on tough terms and provide a unique alternative to flashcards.

The New York Times Current Event Articles
Current articles are posted monthly along with quiz questions to help you link the topics you study in the course to the latest news coverage.

Discovery Channel Video Clips
These brief two-five minutes video clips from the Discovery Channel cover topics from fighting cancer to antibiotic resistance to introduced species.

Activities
Explore approximately 200 activities, including animations, interactive review exercises, and videos. Test your knowledge with Activities Quizzes.

Process of Science Investigations
Perform fifty-six virtual investigations that develop data collection and analysis skills.

Quizzes
Assess your understanding with over 3,600 multiple-choice questions. Each chapter includes a Pre-Test to diagnose current knowledge, an Activities Quiz with graphics that tests understanding of the media activities in the chapter, and a comprehensive Post-Test (50 questions per chapter on average). Each quiz has hints, immediate feedback, grading, and e-mailable results.

Cumulative Quizzes
Create customized tests on multiple chapters at once by choosing the chapters and number of questions.

E-book
Navigate the on-line e-Book to electronically view and search the textbook and related images.

Art and Videos
View all the art from the textbook and a collection of 85 videos.

Word Study Tools
Use electronic Flash Cards to test your knowledge of the key terms and definitions for each chapter or multiple chapters. Includes audio pronunciations for selected terms. Key Terms allow you to study the list of key terms for each chapter, looking up definitions and hearing selected audio pronunciations. Word roots are also provided to improve vocabulary skills. The Glossary provides definitions of boldface terms and selected audio pronunciations.

Web Links and References
Organized by chapter, Web Links and References allow you to extend your knowledge through links to relevant websites, access news links on recent developments in biology, and consult an archive of relevant biology news articles and lists of further readings for each chapter.

BIOLOGY
Concepts & Connections

NEIL A. CAMPBELL · JANE B. REECE · MARTHA R. TAYLOR
ERIC J. SIMON · JEAN L. DICKEY

A CUSTOM EDITION FOR EVERETT COMMUNITY COLLEGE

Taken from:

Biology: Concepts and Connections, Sixth Edition
by Neil A. Campbell, Jane B. Reece, Martha R. Taylor, Eric J. Simon, and Jean L. Dickey

Custom Publishing

New York   Boston   San Francisco
London   Toronto   Sydney   Tokyo   Singapore   Madrid
Mexico City   Munich   Paris   Cape Town   Hong Kong   Montreal

Cover Art: Courtesy of PhotoDisc/Getty Images, brandXpictures

Taken from:

Biology: Concepts and Connections, Sixth Edition
by Neil A. Campbell, Jane B. Reece, Martha R. Taylor, Eric J. Simon, and Jean L. Dickey
Copyright © 2009 by Pearson Education, Inc.
Published by Benjamin Cummings
San Francisco, California 94111

This special edition published in cooperation with Pearson Custom Publishing.

Printed in the United States of America

10 9 8 7 6 5 4

2008140477

CA

**Pearson
Custom Publishing**
is a division of

www.pearsonhighered.com

ISBN 10: 0-555-04545-5
ISBN 13: 978-0-555-04545-9

About the Authors

Neil A. Campbell (1946–2004) taught general biology for over 30 years and with Dr. Reece coauthored *Biology,* now in its eighth edition and the most widely used text for biology majors. His enthusiasm for sharing the fun of science with students stemmed from his own undergraduate experience. He began at Long Beach State College as a history major, but switched to zoology after general education requirements "forced" him to take a science course. Following a B.S. from Long Beach, he earned an M.A. in zoology from UCLA and a Ph.D. in plant biology from the University of California, Riverside. He published numerous articles on how certain desert plants thrive in salty soil and how the sensitive plant (*Mimosa*) and other legumes move their leaves. His diverse teaching experiences included courses for nonbiology majors at Cornell University, Pomona College, and San Bernardino Valley College, where he received the first Outstanding Professor Award in 1986. For many years, Dr. Campbell was a visiting scholar in the Department of Botany and Plant Sciences at UC Riverside, which recognized him as the university's Distinguished Alumnus for 2001. In addition to *Biology,* Dr. Campbell coauthored *Essential Biology* and *Essential Biology with Physiology.* Neil Campbell died in October of 2004. While he is greatly missed by his many friends throughout the biology community, his coauthors remain inspired by his visionary dedication to education and committed to searching for ever better ways to engage students in the wonders of biology.

Jane B. Reece has worked in biology publishing since 1978, when she joined the editorial staff of Benjamin Cummings. Her education includes an A.B. in biology from Harvard University (where she was initially a philosophy major), an M.S. in microbiology from Rutgers University, and a Ph.D. in bacteriology from the University of California, Berkeley. At UC Berkeley, and later as a postdoctoral fellow in genetics at Stanford University, her research focused on genetic recombination in bacteria. Dr. Reece taught biology at Middlesex County College (New Jersey) and Queensborough Community College (New York). During her 12 years as an editor at Benjamin Cummings, she played a major role in a number of successful textbooks. She is a coauthor of *Biology, Essential Biology,* and *Essential Biology with Physiology.*

Martha R. Taylor has been teaching biology for over 30 years. She earned her B.A. in biology from Gettysburg College. After teaching biology in high school and community college, she went on to earn her M.S. and Ph.D. in science education from Cornell University. She was assistant director of the Office of Instructional Support at Cornell for seven years. She has taught introductory biology for both majors and nonmajors at Cornell University for many years. Based on her experiences working with students in classrooms, laboratories, and tutorials, Dr. Taylor is committed to helping students create their own knowledge of and appreciation for biology. She has been the author of the *Student Study Guide* for all eight editions of *Biology* by Drs. Campbell and Reece.

Eric J. Simon is an associate professor of biology at New England College in Henniker, New Hampshire. He teaches introductory biology to both science majors and nonscience majors, as well as upper-level courses in genetics, microbiology, and molecular biology. Dr. Simon received a B.A. in biology and computer science and an M.A. in biology from Wesleyan University and a Ph.D. in biochemistry from Harvard University. His research focuses on innovative ways to use technology to improve teaching and learning in the science classroom, particularly for nonscience majors. Dr. Simon is also a coauthor of *Essential Biology* and *Essential Biology with Physiology.*

Jean L. Dickey is a professor of biology at Clemson University. She had no idea that science was interesting until her senior year in high school, when a scheduling problem landed her in advanced biology. Abandoning plans to study English or foreign languages, she enrolled in Kent State University as a biology major. After receiving her B.S. in biology, she went on to earn a Ph.D. in ecology and evolution from Purdue University. Since joining the faculty at Clemson in 1984, Dr. Dickey has specialized in teaching nonscience majors, including a course designed for preservice elementary teachers and workshops for in-service teachers. She also developed an investigative laboratory curriculum for general biology and is the author of *Laboratory Investigations for Biology.*

To the student: *How to use this book*

Introduce yourself to the chapter.

Find out where you're going. Use the ***chapter outline*** to preview the chapter.

Focus on what's most important.

Get the big picture. Look for the ***main headings*** (orange bars) that organize the chapter into major sections.

Understand biology one concept at a time. Each module features a ***central concept***, announced in its heading.

Use both text and figures as you study. The ***figures*** illuminate the text and vice versa. Text and figures are always together—so you'll never have to turn a page to find what you need.

chapter 1

Biology: *Exploring Life*

Themes in the Study of Biology

1.1 In life's hierarchy of organization, new properties emerge at each level

1.2 Living organisms interact with their environments, exchanging matter and energy

1.3 Cells are the structural and functional units of life

Evolution, the Core Theme of Biology

1.4 The unity of life: All forms of life have common features

1.5 The diversity of life can be arranged into three domains

1.6 Evolution explains the unity and diversity of life

The Process of Science

1.7 Scientists use two main approaches to learn about nature

1.8 With hypothesis-based science, we pose and test hypotheses

Biology and Everyday Life

1.9 Biology, technology, and society are connected in important ways

1.10 Evolution is connected to our everyday lives

Cloning of Plants and Animals

11.14 **Plant cloning shows that differentiated cells may retain all of their genetic potential**

One of the most important "take home lessons" from this chapter is that differentiated cells express only a small percentage of their genes. So then how do we know that all the genes are still present? And if all the genes are still there, do differentiated cells retain the potential to express them?

One way to approach these questions is to see if a differentiated cell can generate a whole new organism. In plants, this ability is common, as was first demonstrated during the 1950s by F. C. Steward and his students at Cornell University. As shown in Figure 11.14, they found that when they transferred cells from a carrot to a culture medium, a single cell could begin dividing and eventually grow into an adult plant, a genetic replica of the parent plant. The fact that a mature plant cell can dedifferentiate (reverse its differentiation) and then give rise to all the different kinds of specialized cells of a new plant shows that differentiation does not necessarily involve irreversible changes in the plant's DNA.

Plant cloning is now used extensively in agriculture. For some plants, such as orchids, cloning is the only commercially practical means of reproducing plants. In other cases, cloning has been used to reproduce a plant with valuable characteristics, such as the ability to resist a plant pathogen. You yourself may be a plant cloner if you have ever grown a new plant from a cutting.

But is this sort of cloning possible in animals? An indication that differentiation need not impair an animal's genetic potential is the natural process of **regeneration**, the regrowth of lost body parts. When a salamander loses a leg, for example, certain cells in the leg stump dedifferentiate, divide, and then

redifferentiate, giving rise to a new leg. Many animals can regenerate lost parts, especially among the invertebrates, and in a few relatively simple animals, isolated differentiated cells can dedifferentiate and then develop into an organism. Further evidence for the complete genetic potential of animal cells comes from cloning experiments, our next topic.

? How does the cloning of plants from differentiated cells support the view that differentiation is based on the control of gene expression rather than on irreversible changes in the genome?

Root of carrot plant

Single cell

Root cells cultured in nutrient medium   Cell division in culture   Plantlet   Adult plant

Figure 11.14 Growth of a carrot plant from a differentiated root cell

■ Cloning shows that all the genes of a fully differentiated plant are still present, but some may be turned off.

Dining in the Trees

A female leopard (*Panthera pardus*) and her young daughter have just killed a duiker, a small antelope and a preferred leopard meal. The pair could start their feast on the spot. But the mother instinctively knows that eating in the open might allow other predators, such as lions or hyenas, to steal their kill. The duiker is best consumed up in a tree, out of reach of thieves. The older leopard has hauled the family's prey up into the branches many times before. But this afternoon, the cub follows her mother's example and carries the meal herself. The mother, featured on the cover of this book, looks up from below. She'll wait to eat, watching first to see how well her daughter has learned the lessons she'll need to survive.

Leopards are the strongest climbers among the big cats that make up the genus *Panthera*. Scientific evidence indicates that members of *Panthera*, which include leopards, lions, tigers, and jaguars, last shared a common ancestor about 6 million years ago. This linkage still shows in these cats' large size, hunting prowess, and unique ability to roar. The leopard species, which is found across Africa and Asia, has the widest distribution of these big cats and displays many adaptations that enhance its survival.

African leopards, for example, have features that help them thrive alongside Africa's regal lion. Leopards tend to be nocturnal hunters, whereas lions hunt during the day. And leopards take a

much larger variety of prey ite[...]
of about 58 kilograms (128 p[...]
(84 pounds) for females, Afri[...]
the size of a typical lion. But [...]
running speeds of 64 kilomet[...]
superior jumping skills that p[...]
through the air horizontally an[...]
an exceptional climber. Power[...]
give the leopard the ability to p[...]
and the additional strength n[...]
times dragging a carcass as hig[...]

Other characteristics of th[...]
vival. With the exception of [...]
generally loners and maintair[...]
ries. Thus, they do not compet[...]
whiskers on the face and head[...]
vegetation while hunting at ni[...]
coat, often an array of black[...]

ochre fur, provides excellent camouflage in the dry grasses of the African plains. Leopards also thrive in desert areas, hilly country, or jungle terrain, and their coat color can vary from pale cream to deep gold, enabling them to blend in with their surroundings.

This habitat flexibility of leopards is linked to their amazing diet flexibility. Leopards consume everything from beetles and birds to baboons, hares, and smaller cats. Antelopes such as the duiker or the larger impala are a frequent favorite among leopards living in the African savannah. Observers have noted leopards killing impala larger than themselves and still managing to drag the carcass high into tree branches.

So far, the African leopard has fared better in the modern era

[1]You can review metric measurement[...]

Discover. The *opening essays* introduce the chapter topic through stories that will pique your curiosity.

Never get lost. *Figures* describing a process take you through a series of numbered steps keyed to explanations in the text.

Interact. *Media references* direct you to related media resources including BioFlix™ 3-D Animations, MP3 Tutors, and Web Activities.

Test yourself. Get immediate feedback with a *checkpoint question* at the end of each module.

11.7 Small RNAs play multiple roles in controlling gene expression

Recall that only 1.5% of the human genome—and a similarly small percentage of the genomes of many other multicellular eukaryotes—codes for proteins. Another very small fraction of DNA consists of genes for ribosomal RNA and transfer RNA. Until recently, most of the remaining DNA was considered to be "noncoding," meaning that it neither coded for proteins nor was transcribed into functional RNA of the few known types. In other words, it was thought not to contain meaningful genetic information. However, a flood of recent data has contradicted this view. Biologists currently think that a significant amount of the genome may be transcribed into non-protein-coding RNAs, including a variety of small RNAs. While many questions about the functions of these RNAs remain unanswered, researchers are uncovering more evidence of their biological roles every day.

In 1993, researchers discovered small single-stranded RNA molecules, called microRNAs (miRNAs), that can bind to complementary sequences on mRNA molecules (Figure 11.7). Each miRNA, typically about 20 nucleotides long, ❶ associates with a large protein complex. The complex can ❷ bind to any mRNA molecule with the complementary sequence. Then the miRNA-protein complex either ❸ degrades the target mRNA or ❹ blocks its translation. It has been estimated that miRNAs may regulate the expression of up to one-third of all human genes, a striking figure given that miRNAs were unknown a mere 20 years ago.

Researchers can take advantage of the miRNA mechanism to artificially control gene expression. For example, injecting miRNAs into a cell can turn off expression of a gene with a sequence that matches the miRNA. This procedure is called **RNA interference (RNAi).** As you learned in Chapter 10, some viruses that infect cells have double-stranded RNA genomes. The RNAi pathway may have evolved as a natural defense against infection by such viruses.

Biologists are excited about these recent discoveries, which hint at a large, diverse population of RNA molecules in the cell

that play crucial roles in regulating gene expression—and have gone largely unnoticed until now. Clearly, we must revise the long-standing view that because they code for proteins, mRNAs are the most important RNAs in terms of cellular function.

Figure 11.7 The mechanism of RNA interference

MP3 Tutor *Control of Gene Expression*

? If a gene has the sequence AATTCGCG, what would be the sequence of an miRNA that turns off the gene?

■ The gene will be transcribed as the mRNA sequence UUAAGCGC; an miRNA of sequence AAUUCGCG would bind to and disable this mRNA.

To the student: *How to use this book*
(CONTINUED)

Learn about biology in your world.

Make a connection. *Connection modules* relate biology to your life and interests—from global warming to blood doping to sperm motility to sustainable agriculture.

Understand how evolution works. NEW! *Evolution Connection modules in every chapter* relate evolution to a wide spectrum of biology topics and help explain the mechanisms underlying evolution and the evidence for it.

Meet the people behind the science. Scientists discuss their careers, their research, and their thoughts about the future in *Talking About Science modules.*

Connection

7.13 Photosynthesis moderates global warming

The greenhouse in Figure 7.13A is used to grow plants where the weather outside is too cold. The glass or plastic walls of a greenhouse allow solar radiation to pass through. The sunlight heats the soil, which in turn warms the air. The walls trap the warm air, raising the temperature inside.

An analogous process, called the **greenhouse effect**, operates on a global scale (Figure 7.13B). Solar radiation reaching Earth's atmosphere includes ultraviolet radiation and visible light. As we discuss in the next module, the ozone layer filters out most of the damaging UV radiation. Visible light passes through and is absorbed by the planet's surface, warming it. Heat is radiated by the warmed planet, and these longer, infrared wavelengths are absorbed by gases in the atmosphere, which then reflect some of the heat back to Earth. This natural heating effect is highly beneficial. Without it, Earth would be much colder and much less hospitable to life.

The gases in the atmosphere that absorb heat radiation are called greenhouse gases. Some occur naturally, such as water vapor, carbon dioxide (CO_2), and methane (CH_4), while others are synthetic, such as chlorofluorocarbons (CFCs). Human activities are adding to the levels of these greenhouse gases.

Carbon dioxide is one of the most important greenhouse gases. You have just learned that CO_2 is a raw material for photosynthesis and a waste product of cellular respiration. These two processes, taking place in microscopic chloroplasts and mitochondria, keep carbon cycling between inorganic and organic compounds on a global scale. Photosynthetic organisms absorb billions of tons of CO_2 each year. Most of that fixed carbon returns to the atmosphere via cellular respiration, the action of decomposers, and fires. But much of it remains locked in large tracts of forests and undecomposed organisms. And large amounts of carbon are in long-term storage in fossil fuels buried deep under Earth's surface.

Before 1850, carbon dioxide was estimated to make up less than 0.03% of the air we breathe. Since the start of the Industrial Revolution, the atmospheric concentration of CO_2 has increased about 40%, mostly due to the combustion of carbon-based fossil fuels, such as coal, oil, and gasoline.

Increasing concentrations of greenhouse gases have been linked to **global warming,** a slow but steady rise in Earth's surface temperature. Predicted changes of just a few degrees over the next 50 years may have dramatic and wide-ranging consequences. These would likely include melting of polar ice, rising [sea levels], weather patterns, droughts, and the spread [of disease].

[...] the rise in atmospheric CO_2 levels during the [...] added with widespread deforestation, which [...] al warming problem by reducing an effec- [...] forests are cleared for lumber or agriculture, [...] growth increases the demand for fossil fuels,

Figure 7.13A Plants growing in a greenhouse

Figure 7.13B CO_2 in the atmosphere and global warming

CO_2 levels will continue to rise. We discuss global warming in more detail in Module 38.5.

Can photosynthesis help mitigate this increase in atmospheric CO_2? As you read in the chapter introduction, "energy plantations" hold out the promise of a cleaner, renewable fuel source. Recent studies show that increasing CO_2 levels will increase plant production somewhat, but far less than predicted even a decade ago. Slowing the destruction of forests will sustain their photosynthetic and carbon-storing contributions. Taking a lesson from plants, we can explore technologies that utilize solar energy for some of our energy needs. Almost all life on Earth depends on the ability of plants and other photosynthetic organisms to convert light energy to the chemical energy of food molecules. Their contribution to life on Earth may also come to include increased removal of CO_2 from the atmosphere.

? Explain the greenhouse effect.

■ Sunlight warms Earth's surface, which radiates heat to the atmosphere. CO_2 and other greenhouse gases absorb and radiate some heat back to Earth.

Chapter 7 *Photosynthesis: Using Light to Make Food* **119**

Evolution Connection

22.5 The evolution of lungs facilitated the movement of tetrapods onto land

The colonization of land by vertebrates was one of the pivotal milestones in the history of life. The evolution of legs from fins may be the most obvious change in body design, but the refinement of lung breathing was just as important. And while skeletal changes were undoubtedly required in the transition from fins to legs, the evolution of lungs for breathing on land also required skeletal changes. Interestingly, current fossil evidence supports the hypothesis that the beginning changes in the front fins and shoulder girdle of tetrapod ancestors may actually have been breathing adaptations that enabled the kind of push up needed in shallow water for a fish to gulp air.

Paleontologists have uncovered numerous transitional forms in tetrapod evolution (see Module 19.4). It now seems clear that tetrapods first evolved in shallow water from what some researchers jokingly call "fishapods." These ancient forms had both gills and lungs. The adaptations for air-breathing evident in their fossils include a stronger and elongated snout and a muscular neck that enabled the animal to lift the head clear of water and into the unsupportive air. Strengthening of the lower jaw may have facilitated the pumping motion presumed to be used by early air-breathing tetrapods and still employed by frogs to inflate their lungs. The recently discovered 375 million year old fossil of *Tiktaalik* (Figure 22.5) illustrates some of these air-breathing adaptations.

The first tetrapods on land diverged into three major lineages: amphibians, reptiles (including birds), and mammals. Most amphibians have small lungs and rely heavily on the diffusion of gases across body surfaces. Reptiles (including all

Figure 22.5 A cast of a fossil of *Tiktaalik*. Note the elongated snout and strong shoulder support.

birds) and mammals rely o[n] [...] general, the size and complex[ity] [...] an animal's metabolic rate (an[d] [...] ple, the lungs of birds and [...] temperatures are maintained b[y] [...] greater area of exchange surf[ace] [...] sized amphibians and nonbi[rds] [...] lower metabolic rate.

We explore the mammalian [...]

? How might adaptations [...] the evolution of tetrapod [...]

[...] s in the shoulder girdle and limb [...] ancestors lift their heads above water

---

Talking About Science

18.16 Sean Carroll talks about the evolution of animal diversity

. . . from so simple a beginning endless forms most beautiful and most wonderful have been, and are being evolved.

—Charles Darwin, *The Origin of Species*

This chapter, a brief tour of invertebrate life, introduced you to some of the immense variety of animal bodies—flower-like sea anemones, echinoderms in the shapes of stars and cucumbers, and arthropods with countless configurations of appendages and color patterns, to name just a few. Data from molecular biology are providing new insights into the evolutionary relationships among these animal groups (see Module 18.15). But how can we explain the evolution of such strikingly different forms from a common protistan ancestor? Dr. Sean Carroll (Figure 18.16) of the Howard Hughes Medical Institute and the University of Wisconsin-Madison is a pioneer in the field of evolutionary developmental biology ("evo devo"). His book *Endless Forms Most Beautiful: The New Science of Evo Devo*, details the new understanding of the evolution of diversity that emerged when exciting new discoveries in the genetics and evolution of development were integrated with existing lines of evidence from the fossil record, comparative anatomy, and molecular biology. In a recent interview, Dr. Carroll described how surprising revelations forced scientists to think differently about the evolution of animal diversity.

The conventional wisdom was that humans were very complex and really—in terms of genetic material—fundamentally different from things like fruit flies, butterflies, or worms. Maybe we'd have something more in common with a mouse or an ape, but not necessarily with the rest of the animal kingdom. But the huge discovery of evo devo was that the genes that build the bodies and body parts [...]

Figure 18.16 Sean Carroll, talking with Jane Reece

control the events that lead to the different body forms of different animals. How is that possible? Dr. Carroll explains.

It turns out that these body-building genes have very sophisticated and extensive sets of regulatory instructions [control sequences in the DNA that regulate gene expression; see Module 11.5] that surround them or are embedded within them.

The key genetic differences are not in the segments of DNA that are transcribed and translated into proteins, but in the segments of DNA that control when and where genes are transcribed and translated into proteins, or expressed (see Module 11.5). Given different sets of instructions, the same gene can direct the formation of a fly eye or a human eye. The [...]

Reviewing the Concepts

An Overview of Photosynthesis (Introduction–7.5)

Photosynthesis is summarized by the following equation:

$$6 CO_2 + 6 H_2O + Light energy \rightarrow C_6H_{12}O_6 + 6 O_2$$

Plants, algae, and some bacteria are photoautotrophs, the producers of food consumed by virtually all organisms. Chloroplasts appear to have evolved from an endosymbiotic photosynthetic prokaryote (**Introduction–7.1**). In plants, photosynthesis occurs primarily in the leaves, within chloroplasts, which contain stroma and stacks of thylakoids called grana (**7.2**).

The Two Stages of Photosynthesis. The O_2 liberated by photosynthesis comes from H_2O (**7.3**). In photosynthesis, H_2O is oxidized and CO_2 is reduced (**7.4**). The light reactions convert light energy to chemical energy and produce O_2. The Calvin cycle assembles sugar molecules from CO_2 using ATP and NADPH from the light reactions (**7.5**).

The Light Reactions: Converting Solar Energy to Chemical Energy (7.6–7.9)

Photosystems. Certain wavelengths of visible light, absorbed by pigments such as chlorophyll and carotenoids, drive photosynthesis (**7.6**). Thylakoid membranes contain multiple photosystems, each consisting of light-harvesting complexes of pigments and a reaction center complex with a primary electron acceptor that receives excited electrons from a reaction center chlorophyll *a* (**7.7**).

The Light Reactions. Two photosystems absorb photons and transfer energy to chlorophyll P680 and P700. Their excited electrons are passed from primary electron acceptors to electron transport chains. Electrons shuttle from photosystem II to I, providing energy to make ATP. Electrons from photosystem I reduce NADP⁺ to NADPH. Photosystem II regains electrons by splitting water, releasing O_2 (**7.8**).

Photophosphorylation. ATP is synthesized by chemiosmosis. The electron transport chain pumps H⁺ into the thylakoid space. The concentration gradient drives H⁺ back across the membrane through ATP synthase and powers the phosphorylation of ADP to produce ATP (**7.9**).

The Calvin Cycle: Converting CO₂ to Sugars (7.10)

The Calvin cycle, occurring in the stroma, consists of carbon fixation, reduction, release of G3P, and regeneration of RuBP. Using carbon from CO_2, electrons from NADPH, and energy from ATP, the cycle constructs G3P, which is used to build glucose and other organic molecules (**7.10**).

Photosynthesis Reviewed and Extended (7.11–7.12)

A summary diagram of the two stages of photosynthesis is shown at the top of the next column (**7.11**).

C₃, C₄, and CAM plants. In C₃ plants, a drop in CO_2 and rise in O_2 when stomata close on hot, dry days divert the Calvin cycle to photorespiration. C₄ plants first fix CO_2 into a four-carbon compound that provides CO_2 to the Calvin cycle. CAM plants open stomata at night, making a four-carbon compound used as a CO_2 source during the day (**7.12**).

Photosynthesis, Solar Radiation, and Earth's Atmosphere (7.13–7.14)

Excess CO_2 is contributing to global warming. Photosynthesis, which removes CO_2 from the atmosphere, moderates this warming (**7.13**). Solar radiation converts O_2 high in the atmosphere to ozone (O_3), which shields organisms from damaging UV radiation. Industrial chemicals called CFCs have caused dangerous thinning of the ozone layer, but international restrictions on CFC use is allowing recovery (**7.14**).

Connecting the Concepts

1. This diagram compares the chemiosmotic synthesis of ATP in mitochondria and chloroplasts. In both cases, label the structures involved and indicate which side of the membrane has the higher H⁺ concentration. Then label on the right the locations within the chloroplast.

Mitochondrion structure

Intermembrane space

Membrane

Matrix

a.

b.

Chloroplast structure

c.

d.

e.

2. Continue your comparison of chemiosmosis and electron transport in mitochondria and chloroplasts. In each case:
   a. where do the electrons come from?
   b. where do the electrons get their energy?
   c. what picks up the electrons at the end of the chain?
   d. how is the energy given up by the electrons used?

3. Complete this summary map of photosynthesis.

Testing Your Knowledge

Multiple Choice

4. Photosynthesis consumes _____ and produces _____.
   a. $O_2 \ldots H_2O$
   b. $H_2O \ldots CO_2$
   c. $CO_2 \ldots$ chlorophyll
   d. $H_2O \ldots O_2$
   e. glucose $\ldots O_2$

5. Which of the following are produced by reactions that take place in the thylakoids and consumed by reactions in the stroma?
   a. CO_2 and H_2O
   b. NADP⁺ and ADP
   c. ATP and NADPH
   d. ATP, NADPH, and O_2
   e. CO_2 and ATP

6. In photosynthesis, _____ is oxidized and _____ is reduced.
   a. glucose . . . oxygen
   b. carbon dioxide . . . water
   c. water . . . carbon dioxide
   d. glucose . . . carbon dioxide
   e. water . . . oxygen

7. Why is it difficult for most plants to carry out photosynthesis in very hot, dry environments such as deserts?
   a. The light is too intense and overpowers the pigment molecules.
   b. The closing of stomata keeps CO_2 from entering and O_2 from leaving the plant.
   c. They must rely on photorespiration to make ATP.
   d. Global warming is intensified in the leaves, blocking carbon fixation.
   e. CO_2 builds up in the leaves, blocking carbon fixation.

8. When light strikes chlorophyll molecules, they lose electrons, which are ultimately replaced by
   a. splitting water.
   b. breaking down ATP.
   c. oxidizing NADPH.
   d. fixing carbon.
   e. oxidizing glucose.

9. What is the role of NADP⁺ in photosynthesis?
   a. It assists chlorophyll in capturing light.
   b. It acts as the primary electron acceptor for the photosystems.
   c. As part of the electron transport chain, it helps to synthesize ATP.
   d. It assists photosystem II in the splitting of water.
   e. It accepts electrons and carries them to the Calvin cycle.

10. The reactions of the Calvin cycle are not directly dependent on light, but they usually do not occur at night. Why? (Explain your answer.)
    a. It is often too cold at night for these reactions to take place.
    b. Carbon dioxide concentrations decrease at night.
    c. The Calvin cycle depends on products of the light reactions.
    d. Plants usually close their stomata at night.
    e. Most plants do not make four-carbon compounds, which they would need for the Calvin cycle at night.

11. How many "turns" of the Calvin cycle are required to produce one molecule of glucose? (Assume one CO_2 is fixed in each turn of the cycle.)
    a. 1   b. 2   c. 3   d. 6   e. 12

12. Which of the following does *not* occur during the Calvin cycle?
    a. carbon fixation
    b. oxidation of NADPH
    c. consumption of ATP
    d. regeneration of RuBP, the CO_2 acceptor
    e. release of oxygen

Describing, Comparing, and Explaining

13. What are the major inputs and outputs of the two stages of photosynthesis?

14. What do plants do with the sugar they produce in photosynthesis?

Applying the Concepts

15. Most experts now agree that global warming is occurring, and in response to its potential threat, a number of countries have made a commitment to reduce CO_2 emissions significantly. However, some countries oppose taking strong action at this time. Several reasons are cited: First, a few experts think that the apparent warming trend may be just a random fluctuation in temperature. Second, if the temperature increase is real, it has yet to be shown that it is caused by increased CO_2. Some people also believe that it would be difficult to cut CO_2 emissions without sacrificing economic growth. Do you think we should have more evidence before taking action? Or is it better to play it safe and act now to reduce CO_2 emissions? What are the possible costs and benefits of each of these two strategies?

16. The use of biomass energy (see chapter introduction) avoids many of the problems associated with gathering, refining, transporting, and burning fossil fuels. Yet biomass energy is not without its own set of problems. What challenges do you think would arise from a large-scale conversion to biomass energy? How do these challenges compare with those encountered with fossil fuels? Which set of challenges do you think is more likely to be overcome eventually? Do you think any one type of energy has more benefits and fewer costs than the others? Which one, and why?

Answers to all questions can be found in Appendix 4.

For Practice Quizzes, BioFlix, MP3 Tutors, and Activities, go to www.mybiology.com.

Feel confident going into the test.

Review the main points. *Reviewing the Concepts* helps you do just that, with helpful summary diagrams and references back to the text.

Connect the chapter's key concepts. *Connecting the Concepts* activities test your ability to link topics from different modules and include concept mapping, labeling, and categorizing exercises.

Prepare for the test using the multiple-choice questions that appear in the *Testing Your Knowledge* section.

Test your understanding with *questions that ask you to describe, compare, and explain.* If you can restate a concept in your own words, you've probably learned it.

Get involved. *Applying the Concepts* questions help connect biology to your life and society.

Check your knowledge by comparing your answers to those found in *Appendix 4*.

Get a personal study plan by doing the *chapter pre-test or post-test*.

Make the most of your study time with mybiology.com

mybiology is a comprehensive resource that helps you study more efficiently and provides all of the study tools you need, including quizzes, an integrated eBook, MP3 Tutors, and BioFlix™—movie-quality animations that tackle the toughest topics in biology.

The 4-step structure of **mybiology** allows you to identify what you don't know, select the appropriate learning activity to match your learning style, and practice outside of lecture.

① *Focus Your Effort* uses a pre-test as a roadmap to identify your study needs.

② *Direct Your Learning* utilizes the resources that support the various learning styles, from MP3 Tutors for auditory learners to BioFlix for visual learners and the eBook for those who prefer to read.

③ *Test Yourself* offers a post-test to check your understanding and prepare for exams.

④ *Extend Your Knowledge* allows you to go beyond the chapter material by exploring case studies in the process of science and viewing Discovery Channel videos, etc.

Also located on mybiology.com

*Bio*Flix

NEW! BioFlix are interactive, self-paced tutorials that help you master the toughest topics in biology. You can prepare for exams by viewing a 3-D animation, completing the tutorial, printing a personal review sheet, and taking a quiz.

BioFlix Tutorial Topics
- Tour of an Animal Cell
- Tour of a Plant Cell
- Cellular Respiration
- Photosynthesis
- Mitosis
- Meiosis
- Protein Synthesis
- How Neurons Work

MP3 Tutors
Expanded! *MP3 Tutor Sessions* are downloadable audio tutorials, narrated by author Eric Simon, allowing you to study anytime, anywhere. **NEW!** *19 MP3 Tutors* focus on tough terms and provide a unique alternative to flashcards.

Preface

Inspired by the enthusiastic responses of the many users of the fifth edition, we authors have worked closely together to create a new, sixth edition that reflects current progress in biology and the evolving needs of today's courses and students. For this edition, the author team is fortunate to include Jean Dickey of Clemson University. Jean brings a wealth of experience teaching introductory biology, superb communication skills, and special expertise in ecology. She is also the author of the popular lab manual *Laboratory Investigations for Biology,* which has accompanied our book since its first edition.

The aim of *Biology: Concepts & Connections* has always been to engage students from a wide variety of majors in the wonders of the living world. Most of these students will not become biologists themselves, but their lives will be touched by biology every day. Today, understanding the concepts of biology and their connections to our lives is more important than ever. Whether we're concerned with our own health or the health of our planet, a familiarity with biology is essential. This basic knowledge and an appreciation for how science works have become elements of good citizenship in an era when informed evaluations of health issues, environmental problems, and applications of new technology are critical.

The "connections" to which the title of this book refers include many such practical applications of biology—and go beyond them. Biology has important connections with the other natural sciences and with the humanities and social sciences as well. And the study of life has no coherence without an understanding of the connections between the different areas of biology and an appreciation of the grand unifying theme of evolution. From its first edition, the hallmarks of this book have included an emphasis on connections within biology and between biology and other fields. In this sixth edition, we have increased the emphasis on connections to our everyday world while also doing more to help students connect the concepts of biology to evolution.

We could not have hoped to meet our ambitious goals for this book without extensive discussions with teaching colleagues around the world and feedback from many of the hundreds of instructors and hundreds of thousands of students who have used our earlier editions. We have been gratified by their enthusiasm for the book and have paid close attention to their thoughtful suggestions for improvement. For this edition, we set out to create a book that would be more effective than ever as a learning tool and would also integrate smoothly with the rich program of supporting materials at **mybiology**.

How can we help students learn—and enjoy—biology? How can we help instructors teach biology? Our responses to these questions are reflected in the teaching strategies we bring to the book. Below we describe our main strategies as they are embodied in *Biology: Concepts & Connections,* Sixth Edition.

Focus Students on the Main Ideas of Biology

Biology is a vast subject that gets bigger every year, but an introductory biology course is still only one or two terms long. In that brief time, we explore all of life, from molecules to ecosystems, while also trying to share the excitement of research breakthroughs. For beginning students confronting this avalanche of information, it can seem as important to memorize all the scientific terms and facts as it is to master and apply the major ideas. This situation changes, however, when students acquire a framework of key biological concepts into which they can fit the many new things they learn. It is this framework of concepts that will serve them long after they have forgotten specific facts and terms.

Concept Modules *Biology: Concepts & Connections* was the first introductory biology textbook to use concept modules to help students recognize and focus on the main ideas of each chapter. The heading of each module is not simply a topic title but a carefully crafted statement of a biological concept. Each concept heading serves as a focal point for a module, and the module's text and illustrations converge on that concept with explanation and, often, evidence. For example, "Sensory receptors convert stimulus energy to action potentials" announces a key concept in Chapter 29 (Module 29.2). The text and illustrations introduce the general principles of sensory reception and transduction, using the human sense of taste as an example. In this and other modules, we integrate the words and pictures to an unprecedented degree: The text walks the student through the illustrations, just as an instructor would do in class. In teaching a sequential process, such as the functioning of the taste-bud receptor cells (Figure 29.2), we number the steps in the text to correspond to numbered steps in the figure. The synergy between a module's verbal and graphic components transforms the concept heading into an idea with meaning to the student, serving both visual and nonvisual learners.

Integrated Media Relevant modules feature references to the BioFlix™ 3-D animations with tutorials, MP3 Tutors, Web Activities, and Web Process of Science Investigations available at **mybiology**. You can read about these valuable learning tools on page xx.

Checkpoint Questions The checkpoint question at the end of each module encourages students to test themselves as they proceed through a chapter. Some questions simply ask the student to restate the main concept or a corollary; others test understanding of the supporting evidence or ask the student to connect the concept to another concept in the book; still others require the student to carry out a calculation using information in the module. Feedback is provided on the spot: The answer is printed upside down beneath the question.

Help Students Connect the Concepts

How do we help students see the connections between concepts? First, we group the modules under prominent main headings, printed on orange bars, which form an overarching framework for the chapter. Students first see these main headings and their subordinate concepts and connections in the outline at the beginning of the chapter. Within the chapter, we often make use of overviews and reviews, and explanatory transitions at the beginnings or ends of modules help the modules flow as a continuous story. The chapter summary at the end of the chapter is organized using the main chapter headings. This Reviewing the Concepts section includes helpful visuals. Following the summary, a section called Connecting the Concepts helps students tie the chapter's concepts together for themselves. This section includes concept maps for students to complete and other graphic activities.

Relate Biological Concepts to Everyday Life

Connection Modules Students are more motivated to study biology when they can connect it to their own lives and interests—for example, to health issues, economic problems, environmental quality, ethical controversies, and social responsibility. In this edition, gold Connection tabs mark the numerous application modules that go beyond the core biological concepts. You can preview the Connection module headings on the front endpapers of the book.

Chapter-Opening Essays Most of the illustrated essays that introduce the chapters discuss topics that relate to readers' lives and interests. For example, Chapter 3, "The Molecules of Cells," opens with an essay on lactose intolerance. And a new essay for Chapter 26, "Hormones and the Endocrine System," discusses endocrine disruption caused by pollutants in the environment. Other introductory essays continue our earlier tradition of featuring a nonhuman organism and describing how it is adapted to its environment. One example is our new essay for Chapter 1, which focuses on African leopards, our cover organism. Our hope is that essays like this one will nurture students' appreciation for biological diversity.

Applying the Concepts Many of the questions in Applying the Concepts, found at the end of every chapter, encourage students to use the concepts they have learned in thinking about various social and environmental issues.

Adapt This Book to Fit Your Course

Though a biology textbook's table of contents must be linear, biology itself is more like a web of related concepts without a single starting point or prescribed path. Courses can navigate this network starting with molecules, with ecology, or somewhere in between, and most courses omit some topics. *Biology: Concepts & Connections* is uniquely suited to serve this variety of courses. The seven units of the book are largely self-contained, and in a number of the units, chapters can be assigned in a different order without much loss of coherence.

Moreover, the modular format of the chapters makes it easy to omit or to relocate modules within a syllabus.

Relate Biological Concepts to Evolution

The history of life on Earth goes back more than 3.5 billion years, and this past is the key to the present diversity of organisms. As the unifying theme of this textbook, evolution elevates biology from a collection of facts to a coherent study of changing life on a changing planet. In *Biology: Concepts & Connections*, students study the structure, function, and behavior of organisms in an evolutionary context. And throughout the book, students learn to view the unity and diversity of life—the similarities and differences among organisms—as the dual consequences of descent with modification. Our reorganized and enhanced coverage of evolution in Unit Three of this edition strengthens this unifying theme.

In addition, this edition has a new feature called Evolution Connections. In every chapter, one or more modules, identified by rust-colored tabs, highlight the relevance of evolution to some aspect of the chapter content. Examples include Module 12.21 on what genome sequences reveal about evolution and Module 20.2 on how the body forms of aquatic animals reflect natural selection.

Help Students Learn the Process of Science

A biology course should familiarize students with the scientific process—in particular, with the posing and testing of hypotheses. With a solid introduction to the process of science in Chapter 1, students will be equipped to appreciate the many examples throughout the book of how scientific concepts emerge from observations and experimental evidence. The book also puts human faces on science with Talking About Science modules, marked with teal tabs.

Many of the questions in Applying the Concepts, at the end of each chapter, give students personal practice with science as a process. At **mybiology**, students can access a wealth of interactive activities, including Process of Science Investigations, YouDecide, and GraphIt! In fact, this book will work best for students who participate actively in learning about biological concepts and their applications.

■ ■ ■

Introductory biology is the only science course that many students will take during their college years. Long after today's students have forgotten most of the specific content of their biology course, they will be left with general impressions and attitudes about science and scientists. We hope that this new edition of *Biology: Concepts & Connections* helps make those impressions positive and supports instructors' goals for sharing the fun of biology. To help us produce an even better text in the next edition, please send your comments and suggestions to us in care of our editor, Chalon Bridges, at Pearson Benjamin Cummings, 1301 Sansome Street, San Francisco, CA 94111. You can also send e-mail to chalon.bridges@pearson.com.

Jane Reece, Martha Taylor, Eric Simon, and Jean Dickey

New to This Edition

In preparing this new edition, we had ambitious goals for improvement in four main areas. The first major goal was to strengthen our coverage of evolution, the all-important core theme of biology. To more clearly relate evolution to *all* of biology and to address common misconceptions about its scope and relevance, we decided to include Evolution Connection modules in each and every chapter. We also worked to restructure Unit Three, "Concepts of Evolution," to better emphasize Darwin's theory, microevolution, speciation, and macroevolution. In Unit Four, "The Evolution of Biological Diversity," we continued our quest to tell the story of diversity in an evolutionary context by, among other changes, presenting the evolution of vertebrates and invertebrates in separate chapters. Our second major goal was to improve our presentation of ecology, an area of increasing practical importance and interest to students; we wanted to infuse Unit Seven with current content and interesting new examples and applications. Our third major goal was, as always, to improve the book's pedagogy in every chapter to make learning biology more fun as well as more successful. Finally, we sought to update the science in a way that would give students an understanding of the exciting field that biology is today.

Below are just a few highlights of new content and organizational improvements in *Biology: Concepts & Connections*, Sixth Edition.

Chapter 1, "Biology: Exploring Life," has a new opening essay on the African leopard, pictured on the cover of this book. In addition to emphasizing the core biological theme of evolution, the chapter now highlights three other themes: emergent properties (Module 1.1), interactions between organisms and their environments (Module 1.2), and cells as a prime example of the correlation of biological structure and function (Module 1.3).

Unit One, The Life of the Cell,
the book's introduction to the basic chemistry, structure, and energetics of cells, has benefited from a number of improvements. Chapter 2 now includes an abbreviated periodic table to help illustrate atomic structure and chemical behavior. (Appendix 2 contains a complete periodic table.) Chapters 4 and 5 have been revised to more clearly introduce the important topic of cellular membranes: New Module 4.5, in the "Tour of the Cell" chapter, introduces the structure and function of membranes, formerly in Chapter 5, "The Working Cell." Chapter 5 now begins with a more detailed exploration of membranes and then proceeds to major sections on energy and enzymes. This new organization better fits the location of Chapter 5 between Chapter 4 (on cells) and Chapter 6 (on cellular respiration). Chapter 5 also features an Evolution Connection on the evolution of membranes.

Unit Two, Cellular Reproduction and Genetics,
incorporates important recent advances in the field. Chapter 10, "Molecular Biology of the Gene," has a new module (10.21) on prions and viroids. Chapter 11, now entitled "How Genes Are Controlled," has been reorganized to improve flow and enhance understanding; it includes a streamlined discussion of development and new coverage of microRNAs and RNA interference (Module 11.7). Chapter 12, "DNA Technology and Genomics," has been extensively revised. For example, it has a new module (12.14) on STR (short tandem repeat) analysis and its use in DNA profiling. Within the genomics section of the chapter, new Module 12.18 explains the main findings of the Human Genome Project and discusses how that information is being used. New Figure 12.12 shows how primers are used to amplify specific DNA sequences during the polymerase chain reaction (PCR). Chapter 12 also includes a new Module 12.20 on proteomics and an Evolution Connection (Module 12.21) on what genome studies reveal about evolution.

Unit Three, Concepts of Evolution,
has been restructured, as mentioned in the first paragraph. In Chapter 13, "How Populations Evolve," changes include a new Figure 13.4H showing gradual transition of land-dwelling ancestors of whales to life in the sea—an example of fossil evidence for evolution. Also, the new Module 13.6 introduces evolutionary (phylogenetic) trees and shows how biologists use them to show patterns of evolution. Common misconceptions about evolution are explicitly addressed. Chapter 14, "The Origin of Species," now focuses on speciation (material on macroevolution has been moved to Chapter 15). A new opening essay tells the story of the dramatic speciation of cichlids in Lake Victoria only 100,000 years ago and the dramatic decline in species in the past 30 years, and the cichlid example is used throughout the chapter. Chapter 15, "Tracing Evolutionary History," has been revised to provide a cohesive presentation of all the material on macroevolution (some moved from Chapter 14 and some from 16). The chapter retains the modules on phylogeny. New Module 15.4 gives an overview of the major events in life's history. Module 15.11 has new material on the important role of developmental genes in evolution; a new figure on gene expression in threespine stickleback fish is used to illustrate differences in gene regulation. Module 15.16 has interesting new material on using phylogenetic trees to make inferences about a common ancestor, pointing out that dinosaurs may have brooded their eggs and "sung." Module 15.18 has been dedicated to the discussion of molecular clocks, which can help track evolutionary time; it includes a figure showing how scientists have dated the origin of HIV infection in humans.

Unit Four, The Evolution of Biological Diversity,
has been significantly restructured. Modules about the origin of life have been moved into Unit Three, where they are integrated with other material on the history of life. Chapter 18, which included all of animal diversity in previous editions, now includes only invertebrates and features a new opening essay on

octopuses. Chapter 19 now covers vertebrate diversity as well as human evolution (formerly the sole topic of Chapter 19). Throughout the unit, the presentation of key concepts has been improved, and new and revised modules provide compelling evolutionary explanations for some of the most striking organismal diversity. Chapter 16, "The Origin and Evolution of Microbial Life: Prokaryotes and Protists," is now more focused on diversity. New Module 16.12 "Secondary endosymbiosis is the key to protist diversity" builds on new Module 4.16, "Mitochondria and chloroplasts evolved by endosymbiosis," to explain the current hypothesis for protist evolution. Revised Module 16.5 includes increased coverage of biofilms, aggregates of bacteria whose significance in infectious disease and other fields is just beginning to be recognized. In Chapter 17, "Plants, Fungi, and the Colonization of Land," Module 17.12 now describes adaptations that attract and reward pollinators, and considers the effect of these adaptations on the reproductive success of flowering plants. Chapter 18, "The Evolution of Invertebrate Diversity," is now more limited in scope. New Module 18.12 highlights features that have made insects the most numerous and diverse group of animals, and the role of homeotic genes in the evolution of insect diversity. In new Talking About Science Module 18.16, leading researcher Sean Carroll reflects on how recent discoveries in evolutionary developmental biology (evo-devo) have led to astonishing insights into the process of animal evolution. Chapter 19, "The Evolution of Vertebrate Diversity," now includes the vertebrate diversity from Chapter 18 in the previous edition as well as our coverage of human evolution. New Evolution Connection Module 19.4, on tetrapod evolution, tracks transitional fossil forms related to the ancient tetrapod Tiktaalik—the "missing link" between water and land animals. Modules 19.12 and 19.13, on the evolution of our upright posture and enlarged brain, have been updated to include recent fossil evidence. A heavily revised Module 19.14 on the divergence of Neanderthals and *Homo sapiens* includes discussion of Neanderthals in popular culture, analysis of DNA from Neanderthal bones, and recent sequencing of Neanderthal DNA. New Figure 19.15 illustrates the global spread of *Homo sapiens*. New Table 19.17 helps students see the relationships between UV radiation and vitamin deficiencies that probably influenced the evolution of differences in human skin pigmentation. Throughout Unit IV, phylogenetic trees are rendered in a graceful new style that is more attractive and easier for students to interpret.

Unit Five, Animals: Form and Function, has been

updated throughout. In addition, Chapter 20, "Unifying Concepts of Animal Structure and Function," includes a new Module 20.12 on the integumentary system. Chapter 21, "Nutrition and Digestion," has a new Module 21.11 on the liver, emphasizing the hepatic portal vein and liver functions related to digestion (including material that was formerly in Chapter 25). In Chapter 27, "Reproduction and Embryonic Development," our discussion of sexual and asexual reproduction is split into separate modules (27.1 and 27.2) to help students better compare and contrast the two modes of reproduction. In the same chapter, the coverage of STDs and contraception has been expanded and updated, and "Principles of

Embryonic Development" has been streamlined. Chapter 28, "Nervous Systems," includes a new Module 28.18 on fMRI (functional magnetic resonance imaging). Chapter 30, "How Animals Move," has a new opening essay on the "Man vs. Horse" race (which compares human and horse anatomy and function), improved coverage of the vertebrate skeleton and its evolution (Module 30.3), and a new Connection module (30.12) on how muscle fiber characteristics affect athletic performance.

Unit Six, Plants: Form and Function, has been refined

and revised to make this subject more interesting to students. The first chapter, Chapter 31, opens with a new essay on the use of "extreme tree climbing" in studying the world's tallest plants, and Module 31.1 is a new Connection on the link between the cultivation of wheat and the development of civilization. Other additions include mention of how tree rings can provide data on global climate change (Module 31.8). Chapter 32, "Plant Nutrition and Transport," has a new opening essay connecting to environmental action in the wake of Hurricane Katrina, and new coverage of composting and the use of fertilizer.

Unit Seven, Ecology, has been extensively revised. The

opening to the first chapter, Chapter 34, introduces the biosphere with examples of life in two extreme environments: the snow leopard in a Himalayan alpine meadow and the Yeti crab, which lives around hydrothermal vents at the bottom of the ocean near Easter Island. Heavily revised Module 34.1, with new figures, explains what ecologists study and how organisms interact with their environment at several levels. Module 34.6, also heavily revised, emphasizes the roles of sunlight and substrate in marine ecosystems; new Figure 34.6A, showing ocean zones, includes examples of organisms that live in each zone. The water cycle diagram formerly in Chapter 37 is now Figure 34.17. The revision of Module 34.8, on terrestrial biomes, includes mention of global warming effects. Chapter 35, "Behavioral Adaptations to the Environment," has a new opener on the monogamous prairie vole, and modules within the chapter weave in examples relating to this animal. For example, the heavily revised Module 35.3, "Behavior is the result of both genetic and environmental factors," explains the genetic basis of vole mating, as well as cross-fostering experiments using rats. New Module 35.23 discusses how studies of animal behavior (including vole mating) can help explain some aspects of human behavior. Chapter 36, "Population Ecology" (formerly "Population Dynamics"), has a new opening essay on the invasive Nile perch in Lake Victoria and the extinction of cichlid species. In Module 36.4, new data tables help students understand models of population growth. Module 36.9, on human population growth, has been reorganized and revised to better emphasize major concepts and to help students apply the lessons of Module 36.4. New Connection Module 36.10 uses age structure diagrams to show the effect of the post–World War II baby boom on the future of programs such as Medicare and Social Security; the accompanying figure shows age structures for the United States in 1974, 2000, and 2025. New Connection

Module 36.11, on the ecological footprint concept, emphasizes in words and pictures that overconsumption is potentially as damaging to the Earth as overpopulation. In Chapter 37, the new opener discusses the Mzima Springs ecosystem, where hippo dung plays a central role. The chapter's major section on community ecology has been reorganized for greater effectiveness. New Module 37.2, "Interspecific interactions are fundamental to community structure," briefly introduces categories of interspecific interactions and includes a table showing the effect of each category on the interacting individuals. The five modules that follow (all either new or revised) explain and give examples of competition, mutualism, predation, herbivory, and parasitism and disease. New

Module 37.7, "Parasites and pathogens can affect community composition," uses chestnut blight—one of the few examples where disease impact has been studied in a natural system—to describe the consequences of a disease epidemic on a forest community. Sudden oak death, an epidemic that is still in its early stages, brings the topic into the present day. Revised Module 37.11, on keystone species, uses the high-interest topic of coral reefs to show the effect of a keystone species on its community. Chapter 38, "Conservation Biology," provides new information on global climate change from the 2007 report by the IPCC (Intergovernmental Panel on Climate Change). Our chapter now has four new modules that cover the latest findings in this crucial area: Modules 38.5–38.8.

Acknowledgments

Biology: Concepts & Connections, Sixth Edition, results from the combined efforts of many people, and the authors wish to extend heartfelt thanks to all those who contributed to this and previous editions. Our work on this edition was shaped by input from the biologists acknowledged in the Sixth Edition reviewer list on p. xv, who shared with us their experiences teaching introductory biology and provided specific suggestions for improving the book. In particular, we would like to thank Ed Zalisko, Blackburn College, and Jon Hoekstra, Gainesville College. The unsolicited comments and suggestions we received from other biologists and from biology students were also extremely helpful. In addition, this book has benefited in countless ways from the stimulating contacts we had with numerous biologists during the recent preparation of the larger text, Biology, Eighth Edition.

Eric Simon would like to thank Mark J. Daly, Ph.D. (Center for Human Genetic Research, Harvard Medical School), Kevin McMahon (New Hampshire State Police Forensics Laboratory), Marshall Simon, Dr. Michael C. Ain (Johns Hopkins Children's Center), Jamey Barone, Amanda Marsh, the Cystic Fibrosis Foundation, and Emily Posner of the Meg Perry Healthy Soil Project of the Common Ground Collective. Dr. James Newcomb, New England College, provided expert content and pedagogical advice for a number of chapters. EJS would also like to thank his colleagues at New England College for their support: Lori Bergeron, Amanda and Giulia Bussone, Sachie Howard, Mark Mitch, Maria Colby, Ed Cooper, Shannan Hudgins, and Linden Jackett. Jean Dickey thanks her colleagues at Clemson University for their support and assistance.

The superb publishing team for this edition was headed up by editor-in-chief Beth Wilbur and senior acquisitions editor Chalon Bridges. We cannot thank them enough for their unstinting efforts on behalf of the book and for their commitment to excellence in biology education. We are fortunate to have had the contributions of executive director of development Deborah Gale and senior editorial manager Ginnie Simione Jutson. Directing the project on a daily basis was our beloved editorial project manager Mary Douglas. We enormously appreciate her dedication to this project, her firm yet gentle guidance, and her positive approach to this work and to life. We are similarly grateful to our exceptional senior developmental editor Evelyn Dahlgren for her thoughtful and steadfast commitment to quality and her leadership of the talented developmental editorial team of Susan Teahan and Debbie Hardin. We thank them for their thoroughness and hard work; the book is far better than it would have been without their efforts. Thanks also to senior supplements project editor Susan Berge for her oversight of the supplements program and to assistant editor Rebecca Johnson for her efficient and calm support of the editorial team and her coordination of various supplements. We wish to express our appreciation to Linda Davis, president of Pearson Math, Economics, and Science, and Paul Corey, president of Pearson Science, for their ongoing support.

This book and all the other components of the teaching package are both attractive and pedagogically effective in large part because of the hard work and creativity of the production professionals on our team. We wish to thank the managing editor for production, Michael Early, and our very talented and hard-working production supervisor, Lori Newman. We thank Heather Meledin and Crystal Clifton of Progressive Publishing Alternatives for overseeing production, copyediting, and indexing and Progressive Information Technologies for composition. We are also grateful to permissions editor Sue Ewing.

For users of this book, the illustrations and photos are as important as the prose. We thank developmental artist Andrew Recher and his team at Precision Graphics for illustrations. We are indebted to senior photo editor Donna Kalal and photo researcher Kristin Piljay. In addition, we thank design director Mark Ong and designer Jana Anderson for the text design. And many thanks go to Yvo Riezebos for his patient and creative work on our beautiful cover.

The value of Concepts & Connections as a learning tool is greatly enhanced by the talents of outside contributors. Our thanks to April Lynch for writing the chapter opening essay for Chapter 1 and the back cover story. We much appreciate the hard work and creativity of the following supplements contributors: Ed Zalisko (Instructor's Guide to Text and Media); Richard Liebaert (Student Study Guide); David Reid, Jon Hoekstra, Richard Myers, Linda Brooke Stabler, Mimi Bres, Arnold Weisshaar, and David Mirman (Test Bank contributors); and Sarah Alvanipour, Richard Myers, Chris Romero, and Jennifer Katcher (Test Bank accuracy checkers). We thank the many contributors to the wonderful package of electronic media that accompanies the book: James Newcomb (author of new MP3 Tutor scripts and questions); Dawn Keller (selector of monthly New York Times articles and author of accompanying quiz questions); Martin Zahn, Helen Walter, Sarah Alvanipour, Richard Myers, Jon Hoekstra, and Dawn Keller (authors of website questions); Michael Wenzel (website accuracy checker); Jan McDearmon (website copyeditor); and Nina Lewallen Hufford (correlator of all Concepts media for text and website). Playing key roles in the development and production of the electronic supplements were media producer Ericka O'Benar and media project editor Brienn Buchanan. Thank you, one and all!

For their important roles in marketing the book, we are very grateful to Lauren Harp, executive marketing manager, and Jay Jenkins, senior marketing manager. The members of the Pearson Science sales team have continued to help us connect with biology instructors and their teaching needs. We thank them for all their hard work and enthusiastic support.

Finally, we are deeply grateful to our families and friends for their support, encouragement, and patience throughout this project. Our special thanks to: Paul, Dan, Maria, Armelle, and Sean (J.R.); Josie, Alice, Jack, David, Paul, and Ava (M.T.); Amanda, Reed, and Forest (E.S.); and Katherine and Jessie (J.D.).

Jane Reece, Martha Taylor, Eric Simon, and Jean Dickey

Reviewers

Reviewers of the Sixth Edition

Tanveer Abidi, *Kean University*
John Aliff, *Georgia Perimeter College*
Yael Avissar, *Rhode Island College*
Andrei Barkovskii, *Georgia College and State University*
Michael Battaglia, *Greenville Technical College*
Dennis Bogyo, *Valdosta State University*
Robert Boyd, *Auburn University*
Chad Brommer, *Emory University*
Ray Burton, *Germanna Community College*
Beth Campbell, *Itawamba Community College*
John Campbell, *University of Central Oklahoma*
John Capeheart, *University of Houston–Downtown*
David Chambers, *Northeastern University*
Craig Clifford, *Northeastern State University, Tahlequah*
Richard Cobb, *South Maine Community College*
Mary Colavito, *Santa Monica College*
Jennifer Cooper, *Itawamba Community College*
Jessica Crowe, *South Georgia College*
Jean DeSaix, *University of North Carolina at Chapel Hill*
Mary Dettman, *Seminole Community College*
Kathy Diamond, *College of San Mateo*
Lee Edwards, *Greenville Technical College*
William Ezell, *University of North Carolina at Pembroke*
Edward Fliss, *St. Louis Community College, Florissant Valley*
Linda Flora, *Montgomery County Community College*
Linda Gardner, *San Diego Mesa College*
Janet Gaston, *Troy University*
Bagie George, *Georgia Gwinnett College*
Laura Grayson-Roselli, *Burlington County College*
Reba Harrell, *Hinds Community College*
Jon Hoekstra, *Gainesville State College*
Kelly Hogan, *University of North Carolina at Chapel Hill*
Barbara Hunnicutt, *Seminole Community College*
Robert Iwan, *Inver Hills Community College*
Charles Jacobs, *Henry Ford Community College*
Roishene Johnson, *Bossier Parish Community College*
Jennifer Katcher, *Pima Community College*
Cindy Klevickis, *James Madison University*
MaryLynne LaMantia, *Golden West College*
Thomas Lammers, *University of Wisconsin–Oshkosh*
Peggy Lepley, *Cincinnati State University*
Eric Lovely, *Arkansas Tech University*
Paul Lurquin, *Washington State University*
Juan Morata, *Miami Dade College*
James Newcomb, *New England College*
Mark Paulissen, *Northeastern State University, Tahlequah*
John Peters, *College of Charleston*
Michael Read, *Germanna Community College*
Erin Rempala, *San Diego Mesa College*
Tim Revell, *Mt. San Antonio College*
Laura Ritt, *Burlington County College*

Lynn Rivers, *Henry Ford Community College*
Lynette Rushton, *South Puget Sound Community College*
Connie Rye, *East Mississippi Community College*
Beverly Schieltz, *Wright State University*
Daniela Shebitz, *Kean University*
Cara Shillington, *Eastern Michigan University*
Marc Smith, *Sinclair Community College*
Michael Smith, *Western Kentucky University*
Ralph Sorensen, *Gettysburg College*
Ruth Sporer, *Rutgers University*
Linda Brooke Stabler, *University of Central Oklahoma*
Christopher Tabit, *University of West Georgia*
Franklin Te, *Miami Dade College*
Gene Thomas, *Solano Community College*
Ken Thomas, *Northern Essex Community College*
Virginia Turner, *Harper College*
Cinnamon VanPutte, *Southwestern Illinois College*
Rani Vajravelu, *University of Central Florida*
Martin Vaughan, *Indiana University–Purdue University*
Mark Venable, *Appalachian State University*
Lura Williamson, *University of New Orleans*
Robert Wise, *University of Wisconsin–Oshkosh*
Mary Wisgirda, *San Jacinto College*
Michael Womack, *Macon State University*
Maury Wrightson, *Germanna Community College*
Tumen Wuliji, *Langston University*
Mark Wygoda, *McNeese State University*
Gregory Zagursky, *Radford University*
Martin Zahn, *Thomas Nelson Community College*
Edward Zalisko, *Blackburn College*
David Zeigler, *University of North Carolina at Pembroke*

Reviewers of Previous Editions

Michael Abbott, *Westminster College*
Daryl Adams, *Mankato State University*
Dawn Adrian Adams, *Baylor University*
Olushola Adeyeye, *Duquesne University*
Shylaja Akkaraju, *Bronx Community College*
Felix Akojie, *Paducah Community College*
Dan Alex, *Chabot College*
Sylvester Allred, *Northern Arizona University*
Jane Aloi-Horlings, *Saddleback College*
Loren Ammerman, *University of Texas at Arlington*
Dennis Anderson, *Oklahoma City Community College*
Marjay Anderson, *Howard University*
Bert Atsma, *Union County College*
Gail Baker, *LaGuardia Community College*
Mark Barnby, *Ohlone College*
Chris Barnhart, *University of San Diego*
Stephen Barnhart, *Santa Rosa Junior College*
William Barstow, *University of Georgia*
Kirk A. Bartholomew, *Central Connecticut State University*
Gail Baughman, *Mira Costa College*
Jane Beiswenger, *University of Wyoming*
Tania Beliz, *College of San Mateo*
Lisa Bellows, *North Central Texas College*
Ernest Benfield, *Virginia Polytechnic Institute*

Rudi Berkelhamer, *University of California, Irvine*
Harry Bernheim, *Tufts University*
Richard Bliss, *Yuba College*
Lawrence Blumer, *Morehouse College*
Mehdi Borhan, *Johnson County Community College*
Kathleen Bossy, *Bryant College*
William Bowen, *University of Arkansas at Little Rock*
Robert Boyd, *Auburn University*
Bradford Boyer, *State University of New York, Suffolk County Community College*
Paul Boyer, *University of Wisconsin–Parkside*
William Bradshaw, *Brigham Young University*
Agnello Braganza, *Chabot College*
James Bray, *Blackburn College*
Peggy Brickman, *University of Georgia*
Chris Brinegar, *San Jose State University*
Becky Brown-Watson, *Santa Rosa Junior College*
Charles Brown, *Santa Rosa Junior College*
Carole Browne, *Wake Forest University*
Virginia Buckner, *Johnson County Community College*
Joseph C. Bundy, Jr., *University of North Carolina at Greensboro*
Warren Buss, *University of Northern Colorado*
Michael Bucher, *College of San Mateo*
Linda Butler, *University of Texas at Austin*
Jerry Button, *Portland Community College*
Carolee Caffrey, *University of California, Los Angeles*
George Cain, *University of Iowa*
James Cappuccino, *Rockland Community College*
M. Carabelli, *Broward Community College*
Cathryn Cates, *Tyler Junior College*
Russell Centanni, *Boise State University*
Van Christman, *Ricks College*
Ruth Chesnut, *Eastern Illinois University*
Vic Chow, *San Francisco City College*
Mary Colavito-Shepanski, *Santa Monica College*
Bob Cowling, *Ouachita Technical College*
Don Cox, *Miami University*
Robert Creek, *Western Kentucky University*
Hillary Cressey, *George Mason University*
Norma Criley, *Illinois Wesleyan University*
Judy Daniels, *Monroe Community College*
Michael Davis, *Central Connecticut State University*
Lewis Deaton, *University of Louisiana–Lafayette*
Lawrence DeFilippi, *Lurleen B. Wallace College*
James Dekloe, *Solano Community College*
Loren Denney, *Southwest Missouri State University*
Jean DeSaix, *University of North Carolina at Chapel Hill*
Veronique Delesalle, *Gettysburg College*
Mary Dettman, *Seminole Community College*
Kathleen Diamond, *College of San Mateo*
Alfred Diboll, *Macon College*
Jean Dickey, *Clemson University*
Stephen Dina, *St. Louis University*
Robert P. Donaldson, *George Washington University*
Gary Donnermeyer, *Iowa Central Community College*
Charles Duggins, *University of South Carolina*
Susan Dunford, *University of Cincinnati*
Betty Eidemiller, *Lamar University*
Jamin Eisenbach, *Eastern Michigan University*

Norman Ellstrand, *University of California, Riverside*
Thomas Emmel, *University of Florida*
Cindy Erwin, *City College of San Francisco*
David Essar, *Winona State University*
Gerald Esch, *Wake Forest University*
Cory Etchberger, *Longview Community College*
Nancy Eyster-Smith, *Bentley College*
Laurie Faber, *Grand Rapids Community College*
Terence Farrell, *Stetson University*
Shannon Kuchel Fehlberg, *Colorado Christian University*
Jerry Feldman, *University of California, Santa Cruz*
Eugene Fenster, *Longview Community College*
Dino Fiabane, *Community College of Philadelphia*
Kathleen Fisher, *San Diego State University*
Dennis Forsythe, *The Citadel Military College of South Carolina*
Robert Frankis, *College of Charleston*
James French, *Rutgers University*
Bernard Frye, *University of Texas at Arlington*
Anne Galbraith, *University of Wisconsin–LaCrosse*
Robert Galbraith, *Crafton Hills College*
Rosa Gambier, *State University of New York, Suffolk County Community College*
George Garcia, *University of Texas at Austin*
Sandi Gardner, *Triton College*
Gail Gasparich, *Towson University*
Shelley Gaudia, *Lane Community College*
Douglas Gayou, *University of Missouri–Columbia*
Robert Gendron, *Indiana University of Pennsylvania*
Rebecca German, *University of Cincinnati*
Grant Gerrish, *University of Hawaii*
Frank Gilliam, *Marshall University*
Patricia Glas, *The Citadel Military College of South Carolina*
David Glenn-Lewin, *Wichita State University*
Robert Grammer, *Belmont University*
Peggy Green, *Broward Community College*
Miriam L. Greenberg, *Wayne State University*
Sylvia Greer, *City University of New York*
Dana Griffin, *University of Florida*
Richard Groover, *J. Sargeant Reynolds Community College*
Peggy Guthrie, *University of Central Oklahoma*
Maggie Haag, *University of Alberta*
Richard Haas, *California State University, Fresno*
Martin Hahn, *William Paterson College*
Leah Haimo, *University of California, Riverside*
James Hampton, *Salt Lake Community College*
Blanche Haning, *North Carolina State University*
Richard Hanke, *Rose State College*
Laszlo Hanzely, *Northern Illinois University*
David Harbster, *Paradise Valley Community College*
Jim Harris, *Utah Valley Community College*
Mary Harris, *Louisiana State University*
Chris Haynes, *Shelton State Community College*
Janet Haynes, *Long Island University*
Jean Helgeson, *Collin County Community College*
Ira Herskowitz, *University of California, San Francisco*
Paul Hertz, *Barnard College*
Margeret Hicks, *David Lipscomb University*
Jean Higgins-Fonda, *Prince George's Community College*
Phyllis Hirsch, *East Los Angeles College*
William Hixon, *St. Ambrose University*
Carl Hoagstrom, *Ohio Northern University*
Kim Hodgson, *Longwood College*
John Holt, *Michigan State University*

Laura Hoopes, *Occidental College*
Lauren Howard, *Norwich University*
Robert Howe, *Suffolk University*
George Hudock, *Indiana University*
Michael Hudecki, *State University of New York, Buffalo*
Kris Hueftle, *Pensacola Junior College*
Catherine Hurlbut, *Florida Community College*
Charles Ide, *Tulane University*
Mark Ikeda, *San Bernardino Valley College*
Georgia Ineichen, *Hinds Community College*
Charles Jacobs, *Henry Ford Community College*
Fred James, *Presbyterian College*
Ursula Jander, *Washburn University*
Alan Jaworski, *University of Georgia*
R. Jensen, *Saint Mary's College*
Russell Johnson, *Ricks College*
Florence Juillerat, *Indiana University–Purdue University at Indianapolis*
Tracy Kahn, *University of California, Riverside*
Hinrich Kaiser, *Victor Valley College*
Klaus Kalthoff, *University of Texas at Austin*
Tom Kantz, *California State University, Sacramento*
Jennifer Katcher, *Pima Community College*
Marlene Kayne, *The College of New Jersey*
Judy Kaufman, *Monroe Community College*
Mahlon Kelly, *University of Virginia*
Kenneth Kerrick, *University of Pittsburgh at Johnstown*
Joyce Kille-Marino, *College of Charleston*
Joanne Kilpatrick, *Auburn University, Montgomery*
Stephen Kilpatrick, *University of Pittsburgh at Johnstown*
Lee Kirkpatrick, *Glendale Community College*
Peter Kish, *Southwestern Oklahoma State University*
Robert Koch, *California State University, Fullerton*
Eliot Krause, *Seton Hall University*
Kevin Krown, *San Diego State University*
Mary Rose Lamb, *University of Puget Sound*
Carmine Lanciani, *University of Florida*
Vic Landrum, *Washburn University*
Deborah Langsam, *University of North Carolina at Charlotte*
Geneen Lannom, *University of Central Oklahoma*
Brenda Latham, *Merced College*
Steven Lebsack, *Linn-Benton Community College*
Karen Lee, *University of Pittsburgh at Johnstown*
Tom Lehman, *Morgan Community College*
Richard Liebaert, *Linn-Benton Community College*
Kevin Lien, *Portland Community College*
Harvey Liftin, *Broward Community College*
Ivo Lindauer, *University of Northern Colorado*
William Lindsay, *Monterey Peninsula College*
Kirsten Lindstrom, *Santa Rosa Junior College*
Melanie Loo, *California State University, Sacramento*
Dave Loring, *Johnson County Community College*
James Mack, *Monmouth University*
David Magrane, *Morehead State University*
Joan Maloof, *Salisbury State University*
Joseph Marshall, *West Virginia University*
Presley Martin, *Drexel University*
William McComas, *University of Iowa*
Steven McCullagh, *Kennesaw State College*
Mitchell McGinnis, *North Seattle Community College*
James McGivern, *Gannon University*
Colleen McNamara, *Albuquerque TVI Community College*
Scott Meissner, *Cornell University*

Joseph Mendelson, *Utah State University*
Timothy Metz, *Campbell University*
Iain Miller, *University of Cincinnati*
Robert Miller, *University of Dubuque*
V. Christine Minor, *Clemson University*
Brad Mogen, *University of Wisconsin–River Falls*
James Moné, *Millersville University*
Richard Mortensen, *Albion College*
Henry Mulcahy, *Suffolk University*
Christopher Murphy, *James Madison University*
James Nivison, *Mid Michigan Community College*
Peter Nordloh, *Southeastern Community College*
Stephen Novak, *Boise State University*
Bette Nybakken, *Hartnell College*
Michael O'Donnell, *Trinity College*
Karen Olmstead, *University of South Dakota*
Steven Oliver, *Worcester State College*
Steven O'Neal, *Southwestern Oklahoma State University*
Lowell Orr, *Kent State University*
William Outlaw, *Florida State University*
Kevin Padian, *University of California at Berkeley*
Kay Pauling, *Foothill College*
Debra Pearce, *Northern Kentucky University*
David Pearson, *Bucknell University*
Patricia Pearson, *Western Kentucky University*
Kathleen Pelkki, *Saginaw Valley State University*
Andrew Penniman, *Georgia Perimeter College*
Gary Peterson, *South Dakota State University*
Margaret Peterson, *Concordia Lutheran College*
Russell I. Peterson, *Indiana University of Pennsylvania*
Paula Piehl, *Potomac State College*
Ben Pierce, *Baylor University*
Barbara Pleasants, *Iowa State University*
Kathryn Podwall, *Nassau Community College*
Judith Pottmeyer, *Columbia Basin College*
Donald Potts, *University of California, Santa Cruz*
Nirmala Prabhu, *Edison Community College*
James Pru, *Belleville Area College*
Rongsun Pu, *Kean University*
Charles Pumpuni, *Northern Virginia Community College*
Rebecca Pyles, *East Tennessee State University*
Bob Ratterman, *Jamestown Community College*
Jill Raymond, *Rock Valley College*
Brian Reeder, *Morehead State University*
Bruce Reid, *Kean College*
David Reid, *Blackburn College*
Stephen Reinbold, *Longview Community College*
Michael Renfroe, *James Madison University*
Douglas Reynolds, *Central Washington University*
Fred Rhoades, *Western Washington University*
John Rinehart, *Eastern Oregon University*
Laura Ritt, *Burlington County College*
Lynn Rivers, *Henry Ford Community College*
Bruce Robart, *University of Pittsburgh at Johnstown*
Jennifer Roberts, *Lewis University*
Laurel Roberts, *University of Pittsburgh*
Duane Rohlfing, *University of South Carolina*
Jeanette Rollinger, *College of the Sequoias*
Steven Roof, *Fairmont State College*
Jim Rosowski, *University of Nebraska*
Stephen Rothstein, *University of California, Santa Barbara*
Donald Roush, *University of North Alabama*
Lynette Rushton, *South Puget Sound Community College*

Linda Sabatino, *State University of New York, Suffolk County Community College*
Douglas Schamel, *University of Alaska, Fairbanks*
Douglas Schelhaas, *University of Mary*
Fred Schindler, *Indian Hills Community College*
Robert Schoch, *Boston University*
Brian Scholtens, *College of Charleston*
Julie Schroer, *Bismarck State College*
Fayla Schwartz, *Everett Community College*
Judy Shea, *Kutztown University of Pennsylvania*
Thomas Shellberg, *Henry Ford Community College*
Lisa Shimeld, *Crafton Hills College*
Brian Shmaefsky, *Kingwood College*
Mark Shotwell, *Slippery Rock University*
Jane Shoup, *Purdue University*
Michele Shuster, *New Mexico State University*
Linda Simpson, *University of North Carolina at Charlotte*
Gary Smith, *Tarrant County Junior College*
Phil Snider, *University of Houston*
Gary Sojka, *Bucknell University*
Ralph Sorensen, *Gettysburg College*
David Stanton, *Saginaw Valley State University*

Amanda Starnes, *Emory University*
John Stolz, *Duquesne University*
Ross Strayer, *Washtenaw Community College*
Donald Streuble, *Idaho State University*
Mark Sugalski, *New England College*
Gerald Summers, *University of Missouri–Columbia*
Marshall Sundberg, *Louisiana State University*
Christopher Tabit, *State University of West Georgia*
David Tauck, *Santa Clara University*
Hilda Taylor, *Acadia University*
Kenneth Thomas, *Hillsborough Community College*
Kathy Thompson, *Louisiana State University*
Laura Thurlow, *Jackson Community College*
Anne Tokazewski, *Burlington County College*
Bruce Tomlinson, *State University of New York, Fredonia*
Nancy Tress, *University of Pittsburgh at Titusville*
Donald Trisel, *Fairmont State College*
Kimberly Turk, *Mitchell Community College*
Michael Twaddle, *University of Toledo*
Leslie VanderMolen, *Humboldt State University*
John Vaughan, *Georgetown College*

Ann Vernon, *St. Charles County Community College*
Rukmani Viswanath, *Laredo Community College*
Mary Beth Voltura, *State University of New York, Cortland*
Jerry Waldvogel, *Clemson University*
Robert Wallace, *Ripon College*
Patricia Walsh, *University of Delaware*
James Wee, *Loyola University*
Harrington Wells, *University of Tulsa*
Larry Williams, *University of Houston*
Mary Jo Witz, *Monroe Community College*
Neil Woffinden, *University of Pittsburgh at Johnstown*
Mark Wygoda, *McNeese State University*
William Yurkiewicz, *Millersville University of Pennsylvania*
Ray S. Williams, *Appalachian State University*
Sandra Winicur, *Indiana University, South Bend*
Patrick Woolley, *East Central College*
Tony Yates, *Seminole State College*
William Yurkiewicz, *Millersville University*
Edward J. Zalisko, *Blackburn College*
Uko Zylstra, *Calvin College*

Supplements for the Instructor

Lectures

Instructor Resource CD/DVD Set for *Biology: Concepts & Connections,* Sixth Edition

(0-321-54824-8/978-0-321-54824-5)
The instructor media for *Biology: Concepts & Connections,* Sixth Edition, is combined into one chapter-by-chapter resource along with a Quick Reference Guide. CD/DVDs provide convenient one-stop access to all the visual media for each chapter. Assets are now organized by chapter folders, making it easier to access files. The CD/DVDs include the following:

Prepared PowerPoint™ Tools

The following lecture tools are provided in Powerpoint™ format.

- **Lecture Presentations for every chapter** allow instructors to lecture immediately and with confidence, supported by a rich array of content, including additional notes and examples not found in the text, plus links to videos and animations, including BioFlix™ 3-D animations.

- **Art and Photos** includes all the art, photos, and tables from the book embedded in PowerPoint™. All figure labels are editable and selected figures are layered for step-by-step presentation.

- More than 100 **Extra Animations** on topics across all units provide additional lecture resources.

- **Introductory Biology Lecture Launcher (Discovery Channel™) Videos** bring biology to life and show scientists in action. Questions before and after each video elicit student input and teaching tips in the Notes field provide alternative questions to spark discussions.

- **Active Lecture Questions** for use with and without clickers help prompt classroom discussions and elicit student input.

- **Lectures accompanying** *Current Issues in Biology* (volumes 1–5) **articles from** *Scientific American* features concept summaries, class response questions, and art and images from every article to enhance class discussions on issues of interest to students.

- **Quiz Show** offers unit-level quizzes in an interactive game show format.

JPEGs of Art and Photos

- All the art, photos, and tables from the book with and without labels are provided.

- More than 270 extra photos provide additional resources for your lectures.

Animation and Video Files

- BioFlix™ 3-D Animations invigorate lectures with movie-quality 3-D animations. Topics include: Tour of an Animal Cell, Tour of a Plant Cell, Cellular Respiration, Photosynthesis, Mitosis, Meiosis, Protein Synthesis, and How Neurons Work.

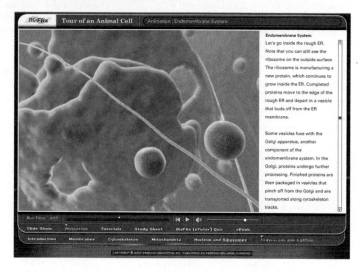

- Over 200 animations in Flash format

- 90 videos in Flash and MPEG formats

Also available in the Instructor Resource CD/DVD set is the *Instructor Guide* in Word format. The **Test Bank CD-ROM** includes test bank questions in Pearson's exclusive TestGen software, which allows instructors to make use of the same high-quality questions on Course Compass™, Blackboard, and WebCT, with results that flow instantly into their online GradeBooks. The Test Bank is also available in Word format.

Instructor's Guide to Text and Media, Sixth Edition

(0-321-54783-7/978-0-321-54783-5)
Edward Zalisko, *Blackburn College*
This newly streamlined guide provides an outstanding set of resources, including objectives, a guide to teaching resources, teaching tips and activities, and a section devoted to student misconceptions about subject matter, for each chapter. References to all media resources available to instructors and students, plus lists of key terms and relevant word roots, are also provided.

Transparency Acetates for *Biology: Concepts & Connections,* Sixth Edition

(0-321-54731-4/978-0-321-54731-6)
More than 650 full-color acetates include all illustrations and tables from the text, many of which incorporate photographs. Selected figures illustrating key concepts are broken down into layers for step-by-step lecture presentation.

Assessment

Printed Test Bank for *Biology: Concepts & Connections,* Sixth Edition

(0-3215-4792-6/978-0-321-54792-7)

Thoroughly revised and updated, and carefully reviewed for accuracy, the test bank features 40–70 multiple-choice questions per chapter, authored by instructors who are experts in each subject area. Chapters now also feature brand-new, art-based scenario questions to stimulate visual and critical thinking. The Test Bank is also available as part of the Instructor Resource CD/DVD in Pearson's exclusive TestGen software.

Course Management

CourseCompass™ with eBook for *Biology: Concepts & Connections,* Sixth Edition

(0-321-54785-3/978-0-321-54785-9)

URL: http://cmc.aw.com/coursecompass

CourseCompass™ combines the strength of Benjamin Cummings content with state-of-the-art eLearning tools, including a complete electronic version of the text. CourseCompass™ is a nationally hosted, dynamic, interactive online course management system powered by Blackboard, leaders in the development of Internet-based learning tools. This easy-to-use and customizable program enables instructors to tailor content and functionality to meet individual course needs. Every CourseCompass™ course includes a range of preloaded content, such as testing and assessment question pools, chapter-level objectives, chapter summaries, photos, illustrations, videos, animations, and web activities—all designed to help students master core course objectives.

CourseCompass™ for *Biology: Concepts & Connections,* Sixth Edition

(0-321-54779-9/, 978-0-321-54779-8)

CourseCompass™ Student Access Kit for *Biology: Concepts & Connections,* Sixth Edition

(0-321-54784-5/978-0-321-54784-2)

WebCT Premium for *Biology: Concepts & Connections,* Sixth Edition

(0-321-54787-X/978-0-321-54787-3)

WebCT Student Access Kit for *Biology: Concepts & Connections,* Sixth Edition

(0-321-54823-X/978-0-321-54823-8)

WebCT Open Access for *Biology: Concepts & Connections,* Sixth Edition

(0-321-54780-2/978-0-321-54780-4)

Blackboard Premium for *Biology: Concepts & Connections,* Sixth Edition

(0-321-54781-0/978-0-321-54781-1)

Blackboard Open Access for *Biology: Concepts & Connections,* Sixth Edition

(0-321-54782-9/978-0-321-54782-8)

Blackboard Student Access Kit for *Biology: Concepts & Connections,* Sixth Edition

(0-321-54823-X/978-0-321·54823-8)

Biology: Concepts & Connections, Sixth Edition, CourseSmart eTextbook

(0-321-54447-1/978-0-321-54447-6)

CourseSmart is an exciting new *choice* for students looking to save money. As an alternative to purchasing the print textbook, students can purchase an electronic version of the same content and save up to 50% off the suggested list price of the print text. With a CourseSmart eTextbook, students can search the text, make notes online, print out reading assignments that incorporate lecture notes, and bookmark important passages for later review. For more information, or to purchase access to the CourseSmart eTextbook, visit www.coursesmart.com.

Labs

Annotated Instructor's Edition for Laboratory Investigations for Biology, Second Edition

(0-8053-6792-6/978-0-805-36792-8)

Jean L. Dickey, *Clemson University*

The *Annotated Instructor's Edition* includes margin notes with teacher overviews, time requirements, helpful hints, and suggestions for extending or supplementing labs; answers to questions in the Student Edition; and suggestions for adapting the labs to a 2-hour period.

Preparation Guide for Laboratory Investigations for Biology, Second Edition

(0-8053-6771-3/978-0-805-36771-3)

Jean L. Dickey, *Clemson University*

This guide provides complete instructions on how to order materials and plan, set up, and run labs smoothly.

Symbiosis Lab Authoring Kit

Build a customized lab manual, choosing the labs you want, importing artwork from our graphics library, and even adding your own notes, syllabi, or other material.

Instructor's Lab Manual for BiologyLabs On-Line

(0-8053-7018-8/978-0-805-37018-8)

URL: http://www.biologylabsonline.com

This printed manual provides the individual and group assignments from the Student Lab Manual for BiologyLabs On-Line. Includes a subscription to BiologyLabs On-Line.

Explorations in Basic Biology, Eleventh Edition

(0-132-22913-7/978-0-132-22913-5)

Stanley E. Gunstream

Thinking About Biology: An Introductory Laboratory Manual, Third Edition

(0-132-30736-7/978-0-132-30736-9)

Kathleen T. McWhorter, *Niagara County Community College;* Mimi Bres, *Prince George's Community College;* Arnold Weisshaar, *Prince George's Community College*

Supplements for the Student

Books a la Carte for *Biology: Concepts & Connections,* Sixth Edition

(0-321-54789-6/978-0-321-54789-7)

Study Tools

 mybiology for *Biology: Concepts & Connections,* **Sixth Edition**

(www.mybiology.com)

mybiology is a comprehensive study resource that provides all of the study tools students need, including quizzes, an integrated eBook, MP3 Tutors, and BioFlix™ movie-quality animations that tackle the toughest topics in biology. The four-step structure of **mybiology** allows students to identify what they don't know, select the appropriate learning activity to match their learning style, and practice outside of lecture. This edition includes 19 additional MP3 Tutors on tough terms, narrated by co-author Eric Simon, providing a unique alternative to flashcards.

NEW! BioFlix are interactive, self-paced tutorials that help you master the toughest topics in biology. You can prepare for exams by viewing a 3-D animation, completing the tutorial, printing a personal review sheet, and taking a quiz.

BioFlix Tutorial Topics

- Tour of an Animal Cell
- Tour of a Plant Cell
- Cellular Respiration
- Photosynthesis
- Mitosis
- Meiosis
- Protein Synthesis

mybiology.com Premium Website

(0-321-54728-4/978-0-321-54728-6)

mybiology.com Website with eBook

(0-321-54729-2/978-0-321-54729-3)

Study Guide for *Biology: Concepts & Connections,* Sixth Edition

(0-321-54825-6/978-0-321-54825-2)

Richard Liebaert, *Linn-Benton Community College*

Students can master key concepts and earn a better grade with the thought-provoking exercises found in this study guide. A wide range of questions and activities help students test their understanding of biology. The study guide also includes key terms, word roots, and a listing of student media activities at **mybiology**.

Study Card for *Biology: Concepts & Connections,* Sixth Edition

(0-321-54777-2/978-0-321-54777-4)

This fold-out quick-reference card provides students with an overview of the entire book, helping them see the connections between topics and understand the big picture.

Current Topics in Biology

Exclusive to Benjamin Cummings and free when bundled with Benjamin Cummings' nonmajors biology texts, each volume of *Current Issues* contains a set of timely and accessible articles from *Scientific American* that are sure to stimulate thought among students. Volume 5, the most recent edition, includes articles on deciphering diet advice, the genetics of alcoholism, and the role of plants in global warming, among others. Each article ends with a set of questions that allow students to test their comprehension, practice their writing skills, and apply their imagination to the topic.

Current Issues in Biology, Vol 1

(0-805-37507-4/978-0-805-37507-7)

Current Issues in Biology, Vol 2

(0-805-37108-7/978-0-805-37108-6)

Current Issues in Biology, Vol 3

(0-805-37527-9/978-0-805-37527-5)

Current Issues in Biology, Vol 4

(0-805-33566-8/978-0-805-33566-8)

Current Issues in Biology, Vol 5

(0-321-54187-1/978-0-321-54187-1)

Special Topics in Biology (booklets)

- *Alzheimer's Disease*
  (978-0-1318-3834-5/0-1318-3834-2)

- *Biological Terrorism*
  (978-0-8053-4868-2/0-8053-4868-9)

- *Biology of Cancer*
  (978-0-8053-4867-5/0-8053-4867-0)

- *Emerging Infectious Diseases*
  (978-0-8053-3955-0/0-8053-3955-8)

- *Gene Therapy*
  (978-0-8053-3819-5/0-8053-3819-5)

- *Genetic Testimony: A Guide to Forensic DNA Profiling*
  (978-0-1314-2338-1/0-1314-2338-X)

- *HIV and AIDS*
  (978-0-8053-3956-7/0-8053-3956-6)

- *Mad Cows and Cannibals: A Guide to the Transmissible Spongiform Encephalopathies*
  (978-0-1314-2339-8/0-1314-2339-8)

- *Stem Cells and Cloning*
  (978-0-8053-4864-4/0-8053-4864-6)

- *Understanding the Human Genome Project*
  (978-0-8053-4877-4/0-8053-4877-8)

Labs

Laboratory Investigations for Biology, Second Edition

(0-8053-6789-6/978-0-805-36789-8)

Jean L. Dickey, *Clemson University*

An investigative approach actively involves students in the process of scientific discovery by allowing them to make observations, devise techniques, and draw conclusions. Twenty carefully chosen laboratory topics encourage students to use their critical thinking skills to solve problems using the scientific method.

Student Lab Manual for BiologyLabs On-Line, First Edition

(0-8053-7017-X/978-0-805-37017-1)

This printed student manual provides background information, instructions, assignments, and group assignments for Biology-Labs On-Line. Includes a subscription to BiologyLabs On-Line.

Explorations in Basic Biology, Eleventh Edition

(0-132-22913-7/978-0-132-22913-5)

Stanley E. Gunstream

Thinking About Biology: An Introductory Laboratory Manual, Third Edition

(0-132-30736-7/978-0-132-30736-9)

Kathleen T. McWhorter, Niagara County Community College; Mimi Bres, Prince George's Community College; Arnold Weisshaar, Prince George's Community College

Detailed Contents

1 Biology: Exploring Life 1

ESSAY Dining in the Trees 1

Themes in the Study of Biology 2
1.1 In life's hierarchy of organization, new properties emerge at each level 2
1.2 Living organisms interact with their environments, exchanging matter and energy 3
1.3 Cells are the structural and functional units of life 4

Evolution, the Core Theme of Biology 4
1.4 The unity of life: All forms of life have common features 4
1.5 The diversity of life can be arranged into three domains 6
1.6 Evolution explains the unity and diversity of life 8

The Process of Science 9
1.7 Scientists use two main approaches to learn about nature 9
1.8 With hypothesis-based science, we pose and test hypotheses 10

Biology and Everyday Life 12
1.9 Connection Biology, technology, and society are connected in important ways 12
1.10 Evolution Connection Evolution is connected to our everyday lives 12

Chapter Review 13

UNIT ONE The Life of the Cell

2 The Chemical Basis of Life 16

ESSAY Who Tends This Garden? 17

Elements, Atoms, and Molecules 18
2.1 Living organisms are composed of about 25 chemical elements 18
2.2 Connection Trace elements are common additives to food and water 18
2.3 Elements can combine to form compounds 19
2.4 Atoms consist of protons, neutrons, and electrons 20
2.5 Connection Radioactive isotopes can help or harm us 21
2.6 Electron arrangement determines the chemical properties of an atom 22
2.7 Ionic bonds are attractions between ions of opposite charge 22
2.8 Covalent bonds join atoms into molecules through electron sharing 23
2.9 Unequal electron sharing creates polar molecules 24
2.10 Hydrogen bonds are weak bonds important in the chemistry of life 24

Water's Life-Supporting Properties 25
2.11 Hydrogen bonds make liquid water cohesive 25
2.12 Water's hydrogen bonds moderate temperature 25
2.13 Ice is less dense than liquid water 26
2.14 Water is the solvent of life 26
2.15 The chemistry of life is sensitive to acidic and basic conditions 27
2.16 Connection Acid precipitation and ocean acidification threaten the environment 28
2.17 Evolution Connection The search for extraterrestrial life centers on the search for water 28

Chemical Reactions 29
2.18 Chemical reactions make and break bonds, changing the composition of matter 29

Chapter Review 30

3 The Molecules of Cells 32

ESSAY Got Lactose? 33

Introduction to Organic Compounds 34
3.1 Life's molecular diversity is based on the properties of carbon 34
3.2 Characteristic chemical groups help determine the properties of organic compounds 35
3.3 Cells make a huge number of large molecules from a small set of small molecules 36

Carbohydrates 37
3.4 Monosaccharides are the simplest carbohydrates 37
3.5 Cells link two single sugars to form disaccharides 38
3.6 Connection What is high-fructose corn syrup and is it to blame for obesity? 38
3.7 Polysaccharides are long chains of sugar units 39

Lipids 40
3.8 Fats are lipids that are mostly energy-storage molecules 40

3.9   Phospholipids and steroids are important lipids
        with a variety of functions   41

3.10   Connection Anabolic steroids pose health risks   41

Proteins   42

3.11   Proteins are essential to the structures and functions
        of life   42

3.12   Proteins are made from amino acids linked by
        peptide bonds   42

3.13   A protein's specific shape determines its function   43

3.14   A protein's shape depends on four levels of
        structure   44

3.15   Talking About Science Linus Pauling contributed
        to our understanding of the chemistry of life   46

Nucleic Acids   46

3.16   Nucleic acids are information-rich polymers
        of nucleotides   46

3.17   Evolution Connection Lactose tolerance is a recent
        event in human evolution   47

Chapter Review   48

4   A Tour of the Cell   50

ESSAY Cells on the Move   51

Introduction to the Cell   52

4.1   Microscopes reveal the world of the cell   52

4.2   Most cells are microscopic   54

4.3   Prokaryotic cells are structurally simpler than
        eukaryotic cells   55

4.4   Eukaryotic cells are partitioned into functional
        compartments   56

4.5   The structure of membranes correlates with their
        functions   58

Cell Structures Involved in Manufacturing and Breakdown   58

4.6   The nucleus is the cell's genetic control center   58

4.7   Ribosomes make proteins for use in the cell
        and export   59

4.8   Overview: Many cell organelles are connected through
        the endomembrane system   59

4.9   The endoplasmic reticulum is a biosynthetic
        factory   60

4.10   The Golgi apparatus finishes, sorts, and ships
        cell products   61

4.11   Lysosomes are digestive compartments within a cell   62

4.12   Vacuoles function in the general maintenance
        of the cell   62

4.13   A review of the structures involved in manufacturing
        and breakdown   63

Energy-Converting Organelles   63

4.14   Mitochondria harvest chemical energy from food   63

4.15   Chloroplasts convert solar energy to chemical
        energy   64

4.16   Evolution Connection Mitochondria and chloroplasts
        evolved by endosymbiosis   64

Internal and External Support: The Cytoskeleton and Cell Surfaces   65

4.17   The cell's internal skeleton helps organize its structure
        and activities   65

4.18   Cilia and flagella move when microtubules bend   66

4.19   Connection Problems with sperm motility may be
        environmental or genetic   67

4.20   The extracellular matrix of animal cells functions in
        support, movement, and regulation   67

4.21   Three types of cell junctions are found in animal
        tissues   68

4.22   Cell walls enclose and support plant cells   68

Functional Categories of Cell Structures   69

4.23   Review: Eukaryotic cell structures can be grouped
        on the basis of four basic functions   69

Chapter Review   70

5   The Working Cell   72

ESSAY Turning on the Lights to
Be Invisible   73

Membrane Structure and Function   74

5.1   Membranes are a fluid mosaic of
        phospholipids and proteins   74

5.2   Evolution Connection
        Membranes form spontaneously, a
        critical step in the origin of life   75

5.3   Passive transport is diffusion
        across a membrane with no energy investment   75

5.4   Osmosis is the diffusion of water across a membrane   76

5.5   Water balance between cells and their surroundings is
        crucial to organisms   76

5.6   Transport proteins may facilitate diffusion across
        membranes   77

5.7   Talking About Science Peter Agre talks about
        aquaporins, water-channel proteins found in some cells   78

5.8   Cells expend energy in the active transport of a solute
        against its concentration gradient   78

5.9   Exocytosis and endocytosis transport large molecules
        across membranes   79

Energy and the Cell   80

5.10   Cells transform energy as they perform work   80

5.11   Two laws govern energy transformations   81

5.12   Chemical reactions either release or store energy   82

5.13   ATP shuttles chemical energy and drives
        cellular work   83

How Enzymes Function   84

5.14   Enzymes speed up the cell's chemical reactions
        by lowering energy barriers   84

5.15   A specific enzyme catalyzes each cellular reaction   84

5.16   Enzyme inhibitors block enzyme action and can
        regulate enzyme activity in a cell   85

Chapter Review   86

6 How Cells Harvest Chemical Energy 88

ESSAY How Is a Marathoner Different from a Sprinter? 89

Introduction to Cellular Respiration 90
6.1 Photosynthesis and cellular respiration provide energy for life 90
6.2 Breathing supplies oxygen to our cells for use in cellular respiration and removes carbon dioxide 90
6.3 Cellular respiration banks energy in ATP molecules 91
6.4 Connection The human body uses energy from ATP for all its activities 91
6.5 Cells tap energy from electrons "falling" from organic fuels to oxygen 92

Stages of Cellular Respiration and Fermentation 93
6.6 Overview: Cellular respiration occurs in three main stages 93
6.7 Glycolysis harvests chemical energy by oxidizing glucose to pyruvate 94
6.8 Pyruvate is chemically groomed for the citric acid cycle 96
6.9 The citric acid cycle completes the oxidation of organic molecules, generating many NADH and $FADH_2$ molecules 96
6.10 Most ATP production occurs by oxidative phosphorylation 98
6.11 Connection Certain poisons interrupt critical events in cellular respiration 99
6.12 Review: Each molecule of glucose yields many molecules of ATP 100
6.13 Fermentation enables cells to produce ATP without oxygen 101
6.14 Evolution Connection Glycolysis evolved early in the history of life on Earth 102

Interconnections Between Molecular Breakdown and Synthesis 102
6.15 Cells use many kinds of organic molecules as fuel for cellular respiration 102
6.16 Food molecules provide raw materials for biosynthesis 103

Chapter Review 104

7 Photosynthesis: Using Light to Make Food 106

ESSAY Plant Power 107

An Overview of Photosynthesis 108
7.1 Autotrophs are the producers of the biosphere 108
7.2 Photosynthesis occurs in chloroplasts in plant cells 109
7.3 Plants produce O_2 gas by splitting water 110
7.4 Photosynthesis is a redox process, as is cellular respiration 110
7.5 Overview: The two stages of photosynthesis are linked by ATP and NADPH 111

The Light Reactions: Converting Solar Energy to Chemical Energy 112
7.6 Visible radiation drives the light reactions 112
7.7 Photosystems capture solar power 113
7.8 Two photosystems connected by an electron transport chain generate ATP and NADPH 114
7.9 Chemiosmosis powers ATP synthesis in the light reactions 115

The Calvin Cycle: Converting CO_2 to Sugars 116
7.10 ATP and NADPH power sugar synthesis in the Calvin cycle 116

Photosynthesis Reviewed and Extended 117
7.11 Review: Photosynthesis uses light energy, CO_2, and H_2O to make food molecules 117
7.12 Evolution Connection Adaptations that save water in hot, dry climates evolved in C_4 and CAM plants 118

Photosynthesis, Solar Radiation, and Earth's Atmosphere 119
7.13 Connection Photosynthesis moderates global warming 119
7.14 Talking About Science Mario Molina talks about Earth's protective ozone layer 120

Chapter Review 121

UNIT TWO Cellular Reproduction and Genetics

8 The Cellular Basis of Reproduction and Inheritance 124

ESSAY Rain Forest Rescue 125

Connections Between Cell Division and Reproduction 126
8.1 Like begets like, more or less 126
8.2 Cells arise only from preexisting cells 127
8.3 Prokaryotes reproduce by binary fission 127

The Eukaryotic Cell Cycle and Mitosis   128

8.4   The large, complex chromosomes of eukaryotes duplicate with each cell division   128

8.5   The cell cycle multiplies cells   129

8.6   Cell division is a continuum of dynamic changes   130

8.7   Cytokinesis differs for plant and animal cells   132

8.8   Anchorage, cell density, and chemical growth factors affect cell division   133

8.9   Growth factors signal the cell cycle control system   134

8.10   Connection Growing out of control, cancer cells produce malignant tumors   135

8.11   Review: Mitosis provides for growth, cell replacement, and asexual reproduction   136

Meiosis and Crossing Over   136

8.12   Chromosomes are matched in homologous pairs   136

8.13   Gametes have a single set of chromosomes   137

8.14   Meiosis reduces the chromosome number from diploid to haploid   138

8.15   Mitosis and meiosis have important similarities and differences   140

8.16   Independent orientation of chromosomes in meiosis and random fertilization lead to varied offspring   141

8.17   Homologous chromosomes can carry different versions of genes   142

8.18   Crossing over further increases genetic variability   142

Alterations of Chromosome Number and Structure   144

8.19   A karyotype is a photographic inventory of an individual's chromosomes   144

8.20   Connection An extra copy of chromosome 21 causes Down syndrome   145

8.21   Accidents during meiosis can alter chromosome number   146

8.22   Connection Abnormal numbers of sex chromosomes do not usually affect survival   146

8.23   Evolution Connection New species can arise from errors in cell division   147

8.24   Connection Alterations of chromosome structure can cause birth defects and cancer   148

Chapter Review   149

9   Patterns of Inheritance   152

ESSAY Barking Up the Genetic Tree   153

Mendel's Laws   154

9.1   The science of genetics has ancient roots   154

9.2   Experimental genetics began in an abbey garden   154

9.3   Mendel's law of segregation describes the inheritance of a single character   156

9.4   Homologous chromosomes bear the alleles for each character   157

9.5   The law of independent assortment is revealed by tracking two characters at once   158

9.6   Geneticists use the testcross to determine unknown genotypes   159

9.7   Mendel's laws reflect the rules of probability   160

9.8   Connection Genetic traits in humans can be tracked through family pedigrees   161

9.9   Connection Many inherited disorders in humans are controlled by a single gene   162

9.10   Connection New technologies can provide insight into one's genetic legacy   164

Variations on Mendel's Laws   166

9.11   Incomplete dominance results in intermediate phenotypes   166

9.12   Many genes have more than two alleles in the population   167

9.13   A single gene may affect many phenotypic characters   168

9.14   A single character may be influenced by many genes   169

9.15   The environment affects many characters   170

The Chromosomal Basis of Inheritance   170

9.16   Chromosome behavior accounts for Mendel's laws   170

9.17   Genes on the same chromosome tend to be inherited together   172

9.18   Crossing over produces new combinations of alleles   172

9.19   Geneticists use crossover data to map genes   174

Sex Chromosomes and Sex-Linked Genes   174

9.20   Chromosomes determine sex in many species   174

9.21   Sex-linked genes exhibit a unique pattern of inheritance   176

9.22   Connection Sex-linked disorders affect mostly males   177

9.23   Evolution Connection The Y Chromosome provides clues about human male evolution   177

Chapter Review   178

10 Molecular Biology of the Gene 180

ESSAY Sabotage Inside Our Cells 181

The Structure of the Genetic Material 182
10.1 Experiments showed that DNA is the genetic material 182

10.2 DNA and RNA are polymers of nucleotides 184

10.3 DNA is a double-stranded helix 186

DNA Replication 188
10.4 DNA replication depends on specific base pairing 188

10.5 DNA replication proceeds in two directions at many sites simultaneously 189

The Flow of Genetic Information from DNA to RNA to Protein 190
10.6 The DNA genotype is expressed as proteins, which provide the molecular basis for phenotypic traits 190

10.7 Genetic information written in codons is translated into amino acid sequences 191

10.8 The genetic code is the Rosetta stone of life 192

10.9 Transcription produces genetic messages in the form of RNA 193

10.10 Eukaryotic RNA is processed before leaving the nucleus 194

10.11 Transfer RNA molecules serve as interpreters during translation 194

10.12 Ribosomes build polypeptides 196

10.13 An initiation codon marks the start of an mRNA message 196

10.14 Elongation adds amino acids to the polypeptide chain until a stop codon terminates translation 197

10.15 Review: The flow of genetic information in the cell is DNA → RNA → protein 198

10.16 Mutations can change the meaning of genes 199

Microbial Genetics 200
10.17 Viral DNA may become part of the host chromosome 200

10.18 Connection Many viruses cause disease in animals and plants 201

10.19 Evolution Connection Emerging viruses threaten human health 202

10.20 The AIDS virus makes DNA on an RNA template 203

10.21 Viroids and prions are formidable pathogens in plants and animals 203

10.22 Bacteria can transfer DNA in three ways 204

10.23 Bacterial plasmids can serve as carriers for gene transfer 205

Chapter Review 206

11 How Genes Are Controlled 208

ESSAY Cloning to the Rescue? 209

Control of Gene Expression 210
11.1 Proteins interacting with DNA turn prokaryotic genes on or off in response to environmental changes 210

11.2 Differentiation results from the expression of different combinations of genes 212

11.3 DNA packing in eukaryotic chromosomes helps regulate gene expression 212

11.4 In female mammals, one X chromosome is inactive in each somatic cell 213

11.5 Complex assemblies of proteins control eukaryotic transcription 214

11.6 Eukaryotic RNA may be spliced in more than one way 214

11.7 Small RNAs play multiple roles in controlling gene expression 215

11.8 Translation and later stages of gene expression are also subject to regulation 216

11.9 Review: Multiple mechanisms regulate gene expression in eukaryotes 217

11.10 Cascades of gene expression direct the development of an animal 218

11.11 Connection DNA microarrays test for the transcription of many genes at once 219

11.12 Signal transduction pathways convert messages received at the cell surface to responses within the cell 220

11.13 Evolution Connection Cell-signaling systems appeared early in the evolution of life 220

Cloning of Plants and Animals 221
11.14 Plant cloning shows that differentiated cells may retain all of their genetic potential 221

11.15 Nuclear transplantation can be used to clone animals 222

11.16 Connection Reproductive cloning has valuable applications, but human reproductive cloning raises ethical issues 222

11.17 Connection Therapeutic cloning can produce stem cells with great medical potential 223

The Genetic Basis of Cancer 224
11.18 Cancer results from mutations in genes that control cell division 224

11.19 Multiple genetic changes underlie the development of cancer 225

11.20 Faulty proteins can interfere with normal signal transduction pathways 226

11.21 Connection Lifestyle choices can reduce the risk of cancer 227

Chapter Review 228

12 DNA Technology and Genomics 230

ESSAY DNA and Crime Scene Investigations 231

Gene Cloning 232

12.1 Genes can be cloned in recombinant plasmids 232

12.2 Enzymes are used to "cut and paste" DNA 234

12.3 Cloned genes can be stored in genomic libraries 235

12.4 Reverse transcriptase helps make genes for cloning 235

12.5 Nucleic acid probes identify clones carrying specific genes 236

Genetically Modified Organisms 236

12.6 Recombinant cells and organisms can mass-produce gene products 236

12.7 Connection DNA technology has changed the pharmaceutical industry and medicine 238

12.8 Connection Genetically modified organisms are transforming agriculture 239

12.9 Genetically modified organisms raise concerns about human and environmental health 240

12.10 Connection Gene therapy may someday help treat a variety of diseases 241

DNA Profiling 242

12.11 The analysis of genetic markers can produce a DNA profile 242

12.12 The PCR method is used to amplify DNA sequences 242

12.13 Gel electrophoresis sorts DNA molecules by size 243

12.14 STR analysis is commonly used for DNA profiling 244

12.15 Connection DNA profiling has provided evidence in many forensic investigations 245

12.16 RFLPs can be used to detect differences in DNA sequences 246

Genomics 247

12.17 Genomics is the scientific study of whole genomes 247

12.18 Connection The Human Genome Project revealed that most of the human genome does not consist of genes 248

12.19 The whole-genome shotgun method of sequencing a genome can provide a wealth of data quickly 249

12.20 Proteomics is the scientific study of the full set of proteins encoded by a genome 249

12.21 Evolution Connection Genomes hold clues to the evolutionary divergence of humans and chimps 250

Chapter Review 250

UNIT THREE Concepts of Evolution

13 How Populations Evolve 254

ESSAY Clown, Fool, or Simply Well Adapted? 255

Darwin's Theory of Evolution 256

13.1 A sea voyage helped Darwin frame his theory of evolution 256

13.2 Darwin proposed natural selection as the mechanism of evolution 258

13.3 Scientists can observe natural selection in action 259

13.4 The study of fossils provides strong evidence for evolution 260

13.5 A mass of other evidence reinforces the evolutionary view of life 262

13.6 Homologies indicate patterns of descent that can be shown on an evolutionary tree 263

The Evolution of Populations 264

13.7 Populations are the units of evolution 264

13.8 Mutation and sexual reproduction produce genetic variation, making evolution possible 264

13.9 The Hardy-Weinberg equation can be used to test whether a population is evolving 266

13.10 Connection The Hardy-Weinberg equation is useful in public health science 267

Mechanisms of Microevolution 268

13.11 Natural selection, genetic drift, and gene flow can alter allele frequencies in a population 268

13.12 Natural selection is the only mechanism that consistently leads to adaptive evolution 269

13.13 Natural selection can alter variation in a population in three ways 270

13.14 Sexual selection may lead to phenotypic differences between males and females 271

13.15 Evolution Connection The evolution of antibiotic resistance in bacteria is a serious public health concern 272

13.16 Diploidy and balancing selection preserve genetic variation 272

13.17 Natural selection cannot fashion perfect organisms 273

Chapter Review 274

UNIT FOUR The Evolution of Biological Diversity

16 The Origin and Evolution of Microbial Life: Prokaryotes and Protists 318

ESSAY How Ancient Bacteria Changed the World 318

Prokaryotes 320

16.1 Prokaryotes are diverse and widespread 320

16.2 Bacteria and archaea are the two main branches of prokaryotic evolution 320

16.3 Prokaryotes come in a variety of shapes 321

16.4 Various structural features contribute to the success of prokaryotes 322

16.5 Prokaryotes obtain nourishment in a variety of ways 324

16.6 Archaea thrive in extreme environments—and in other habitats 325

16.7 Bacteria include a diverse assemblage of prokaryotes 326

16.8 Connection Some bacteria cause disease 327

16.9 Connection Bacteria can be used as biological weapons 328

16.10 Connection Prokaryotes help recycle chemicals and clean up the environment 329

Protists 330

16.11 Protists are an extremely diverse assortment of eukaryotes 330

16.12 Evolution Connection Secondary endosymbiosis is the key to protist diversity 331

16.13 A tentative phylogeny of eukaryotes includes multiple clades of protists 332

16.14 Diplomonads and parabasalids have modified mitochondria 332

16.15 Euglenozoans have flagella with a unique internal structure 333

16.16 Alveolates have sacs beneath the plasma membrane 333

16.17 Stramenopiles have "hairy" and smooth flagella 334

16.18 Amoebozoans have lobe-shaped pseudopodia 334

16.19 Foraminiferans and radiolarians have threadlike pseudopodia 335

16.20 Red algae and green algae are the closest relatives of land plants 336

16.21 Evolution Connection Multicellularity evolved several times in eukaryotes 337

Chapter Review 338

Appendix 1 Metric Conversion Table A-1

Appendix 2 The Periodic Table A-2

Appendix 3 The Amino Acids of Proteins A-3

Appendix 4 Chapter Review Answers A-4

Appendix 5 Student Media Activities A-28

Appendix 6 Credits A-39

Glossary G-1

Index I-1

chapter

1

Biology:
Exploring Life

Themes in the Study of Biology

1.1   In life's hierarchy of organization, new properties emerge at each level

1.2   Living organisms interact with their environments, exchanging matter and energy

1.3   Cells are the structural and functional units of life

Evolution, the Core Theme of Biology

1.4   The unity of life: All forms of life have common features

1.5   The diversity of life can be arranged into three domains

1.6   Evolution explains the unity and diversity of life

The Process of Science

1.7   Scientists use two main approaches to learn about nature

1.8   With hypothesis-based science, we pose and test hypotheses

Biology and Everyday Life

1.9   Biology, technology, and society are connected in important ways

1.10   Evolution is connected to our everyday lives

Dining in the Trees

A female leopard (*Panthera pardus*) and her young daughter have just killed a duiker, a small antelope and a preferred leopard meal. The pair could start their feast on the spot. But the mother instinctively knows that eating in the open might allow other predators, such as lions or hyenas, to steal their kill. The duiker is best consumed up in a tree, out of reach of thieves. The older leopard has hauled the family's prey up into the branches many times before. But this afternoon, the cub follows her mother's example and carries the meal herself. The mother, featured on the cover of this book, looks up from below. She'll wait to eat, watching first to see how well her daughter has learned the lessons she'll need to survive.

Leopards are the strongest climbers among the big cats that make up the genus *Panthera*. Scientific evidence indicates that members of *Panthera,* which include leopards, lions, tigers, and jaguars, last shared a common ancestor about 6 million years ago. This linkage still shows in these cats' large size, hunting prowess, and unique ability to roar. The leopard species, which is found across Africa and Asia, has the widest distribution of these big cats and displays many adaptations that enhance its survival.

African leopards, for example, have features that help them thrive alongside Africa's regal lion. Leopards tend to be nocturnal hunters, whereas lions hunt during the day. And leopards take a much larger variety of prey items than lions. With average weights of about 58 kilograms (128 pounds) for males and 38 kilograms (84 pounds) for females, African leopards are only about a third the size of a typical lion. But leopards are slightly faster, with top running speeds of 64 kilometers (40 miles) per hour.[1] And with superior jumping skills that propel leopards to 6 meters (20 feet) through the air horizontally and about 3 meters vertically, the cat is an exceptional climber. Powerful jaw, neck, and shoulder muscles give the leopard the ability to pounce and kill prey with a quick bite and the additional strength needed to haul prey upward, sometimes dragging a carcass as high as 15 meters into a tree.

Other characteristics of the leopard contribute to their survival. With the exception of mothers rearing cubs, leopards are generally loners and maintain separate, nonoverlapping territories. Thus, they do not compete with each other for prey. Sensitive whiskers on the face and head help the cat navigate through dense vegetation while hunting at night. The leopard's signature spotted coat, often an array of black patches dappled across tawny or

[1]You can review metric measurements in Appendix 1.

ochre fur, provides excellent camouflage in the dry grasses of the African plains. Leopards also thrive in desert areas, hilly country, or jungle terrain, and their coat color can vary from pale cream to deep gold, enabling them to blend in with their surroundings.

This habitat flexibility of leopards is linked to their amazing diet flexibility. Leopards consume everything from beetles and birds to baboons, hares, and smaller cats. Antelopes such as the duiker or the larger impala are a frequent favorite among leopards living in the African savannah. Observers have noted leopards killing impala larger than themselves and still managing to drag the carcass high into tree branches.

So far, the African leopard has fared better in the modern era than its leopard cousins farther north. In Asia, the pressures of human population growth mean less land for leopards to roam, less prey, and more hunters after the cats' beautiful fur. In southern Africa, vast protected refuges, such as the Sabi Sands Reserve of South Africa, where the leopard on the cover was photographed, help maintain the cats' numbers. But the African leopard still faces threats from illegal hunting. Farmers and ranchers, enraged when leopards snatch their livestock, also target the cats.

With unique characteristics that let them thrive across a diversity of habitats, leopards offer wonderful examples of the adaptations of organisms that fit them to their environment. Traits such as coat camouflage, strong jaws, and climbing prowess make leopards successful hunters and enhance their ability to survive and reproduce. These adaptations are the result of evolution, the process of change that has transformed life on Earth from its earliest beginnings to the diversity of organisms living today. In this chapter, we begin our exploration of **biology,** the scientific study of life. We start by introducing some common themes in biology, which will help guide our study of life, its evolution, and all its diversity. ■ ■ ■

In life's hierarchy of organization, new properties emerge at each level

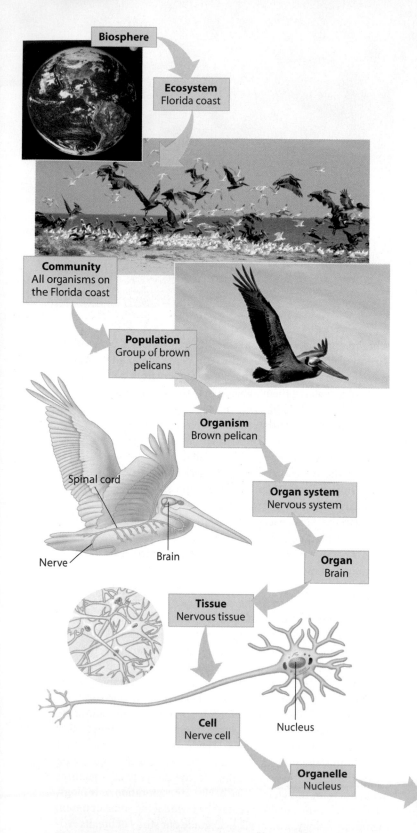

Biosphere

Ecosystem
Florida coast

Community
All organisms on
the Florida coast

Population
Group of brown
pelicans

Organism
Brown pelican

Spinal cord

Organ system
Nervous system

Nerve

Brain

Organ
Brain

Tissue
Nervous tissue

Cell
Nerve cell

Nucleus

Organelle
Nucleus

Molecule
DNA

Atom

Figure 1.1 Life's hierarchy of organization

The study of life extends from the microscopic scale of cells and molecules to the global scale of the biosphere. **Figure 1.1** takes you on a tour of these levels of biological organization, starting at the highest level. At the upper left we take a distant view of the **biosphere,** which consists of all the environments on Earth that support life—most regions of land, bodies of water, and the lower atmosphere. A closer look at one of these environments brings us to the level of an **ecosystem,** which consists of all the organisms living in a particular area, as well as all the nonliving, physical components of the environment with which the organisms interact, such as air, soil, water, and sunlight.

The entire array of organisms inhabiting a particular ecosystem is called a **community.** The community in the coastal ecosystem shown in Figure 1.1 includes the pelicans and the fish they eat, as well as seagulls; raccoons that eat pelican eggs; a huge diversity of insects, molluscs, and worms; many different kinds of plants and fungi; and enormous numbers of microscopic organisms, such as protists, algae, and bacteria. Each of these unique forms of life is called a species.

A **population** consists of all the individuals of a species living in a specified area, such as all the brown pelicans in the coastal community. Below the population level in the hierarchy is the **organism,** an individual living thing.

Within a complex organism such as a pelican, life's hierarchy continues to unfold. An **organ system,** such as a circulatory system, digestive system, or nervous system (shown here) consists of several **organs** that work together in performing specific functions. For instance, the main organs of the nervous system are the brain, the spinal cord, and the nerves that transmit messages between the spinal cord and other parts of the body. A bird's nervous system controls its ability to fly.

As we continue down through the hierarchy, each organ is made up of several different **tissues,** each with a specific function and made up of a group of similar cells. The nervous tissue in a pelican's brain has millions of nerve cells organized into a communication network of spectacular complexity. A **cell** is separated from its environment by a boundary called a membrane. In the nerve cell shown here, you can see several organelles, such as the nucleus. An **organelle** is a membrane-bound structure that performs a specific function in a cell.

Finally, we reach the level of molecules in the hierarchy. A **molecule** is a cluster of atoms held together by chemical bonds. We show as our example DNA (deoxyribonucleic acid). DNA molecules provide the blueprint for constructing the organism's other molecules and transmit this information from parents to offspring. In the computer graphic of a small section of DNA at the bottom of Figure 1.1, each of the spheres represents an atom, the smallest particle of ordinary matter.

Now work your way in the opposite direction in Figure 1.1, building life's hierarchy from molecules to the biosphere. It takes many molecules to build organelles and make a cell, many cells to make a tissue, several kinds of tissues to make an organ, and so on. At each new level, notice that there are novel properties that emerge, properties that were not part of the components of the preceding level. For example, life emerges at the level of the cell—a test tube full of organelles is not alive. Such properties illustrate an important theme of biology, called **emergent properties.** The familiar saying that "the whole is greater than the sum of its parts" captures this idea. The emergent properties of the whole result from the specific arrangement and interactions of the component parts.

In the next two modules, we look at more themes in the study of life: the interaction of organisms with the environment and the cell as the structural and functional unit of life.

Web Activity *The Levels of Life Card Game*

? Which of the following levels of biological organization includes all others in the list: cell, molecule, organ, tissue?

■ Organ

1.2 Living organisms interact with their environments, exchanging matter and energy

Organisms interact with both the living and nonliving components of their environment. **Figure 1.2** is a simplified diagram of these interactions in an African savannah. Plants and other photosynthetic organisms are the **producers** that provide the food for a typical ecosystem. A tree, for example, absorbs water (H_2O) and minerals from the soil, and its leaves take in carbon dioxide (CO_2) from the air. In photosynthesis, a tree's leaves use energy from sunlight to convert CO_2 and H_2O to sugar and oxygen (O_2). The tree releases O_2 to the air, and its roots help form soil by breaking up rocks. Thus, both organism and environment are affected by the interactions between them.

The **consumers** of the ecosystem eat plants and other animals. The giraffe in Figure 1.2 eats leaves; the leopard described in the chapter introduction eats meat. All animals take in oxygen from the air and release carbon dioxide. Their wastes return other chemicals to the environment.

Another vital part of the ecosystem includes the bacteria, fungi, and small animals in the soil that decompose wastes and the remains of dead organisms. These decomposers act as recyclers, changing complex matter into simpler mineral nutrients that plants can use.

The dynamics of ecosystems include two major processes—the recycling of chemical nutrients and the flow of energy. These processes are illustrated in Figure 1.2. The most basic chemicals necessary for life—carbon dioxide, oxygen, water, and various minerals—flow from the air and soil to plants, to animals and decomposers, and back to the air and soil. As shown by the blue arrows in the figure, chemical nutrients cycle within an ecosystem.

By contrast, an ecosystem gains and loses energy constantly. Energy flows into the ecosystem when plants and other photosynthesizers absorb light energy from the sun (yellow arrow) and convert it to the chemical energy of sugars and other complex molecules. Chemical energy (green arrow) is then passed through a series of consumers and, eventually, decomposers, powering each organism in turn. In the process of these energy conversions between and within organisms, some

Figure 1.2 The cycling of nutrients and flow of energy in an ecosystem

energy is converted to heat, which is then lost from the system (red arrows). In contrast to chemical nutrients, which recycle *within* an ecosystem, energy flows *through* an ecosystem, entering as light and exiting as heat.

? Explain how the photosynthesis of plants functions in both the cycling of chemical nutrients and the flow of energy in an ecosystem.

■ Photosynthesis uses light to convert carbon dioxide and water to energy-rich food, making it the pathway by which both chemical nutrients and energy become available to most organisms.

1.3   Cells are the structural and functional units of life

The cell has a special place in the hierarchy of biological organization. It is the level at which the properties of life emerge—the lowest level of structure that can perform all activities required for life. A cell can regulate its internal environment, take in and use energy, respond to its environment, and develop and maintain its complex organization. The ability of cells to give rise to new cells is the basis for all reproduction and for the growth and repair of multicellular organisms. Your every movement and thought are based on the activities of muscle cells and nerve cells. Even a global process such as the cycling of carbon is the result of cellular activities, including the photosynthesis of plant cells and the cellular respiration of nearly all cells, a process that breaks down sugar for energy and releases carbon dioxide.

Cells illustrate another theme of biology: *the correlation of structure and function*. Experience shows you that form generally fits function. A screwdriver tightens or loosens screws, a hammer pounds nails. Because of their form, these tools can't do each other's jobs. Applied to biology, this theme of form fitting function is a guide to the structure of life at all its organizational levels. As you can see in Figure 1.1, the long extension of the nerve cell enables it to transmit impulses throughout the body. Often, analyzing a biological structure gives us clues about what it does and how it works.

The properties of life emerge from the ordered interactions of the structures of a cell. Such a combination of components forms a more complex organization called a *system*. Cells are examples of biological systems, as are organisms and ecosystems. Systems and their emergent properties are not unique to life. Consider a box of bicycle parts. When all of the individual parts are properly assembled, the result is a mechanical system you can use for exercise or transportation.

The emergent properties of life, however, are particularly challenging to study because of the unrivaled complexity of biological systems. At the cutting edge of large-scale research today is an approach called **systems biology.** The goal of systems biology is to construct models for the dynamic behavior of whole biological systems, ranging from the functioning of the biosphere to the complex molecular machinery of a cell.

All cells share many characteristics. For example, every cell is enclosed by a membrane that regulates the passage of materials between the cell and its surroundings. And every cell uses DNA as its genetic information. There are two basic kinds of cells. Figure 1.3 shows artificially colored photographs of these cells taken with an electron microscope. A **prokaryotic cell** is much simpler and usually much smaller than a eukaryotic cell. The cells of the microorganisms we commonly call bacteria are prokaryotic. Forms of life such as plants, animals, and fungi are composed of eukaryotic cells. As you can see in Figure 1.3, a **eukaryotic cell** is subdivided by internal membranes into many different functional compartments, or organelles, including the nucleus that houses the cell's DNA.

In the next module, we see how DNA unifies all of life, as we begin to explore the core theme of life—evolution.

Prokaryotic cell

DNA (no nucleus)

Membrane

Eukaryotic cell

Nucleus (contains DNA)

Organelles

TEM 40,000×

Figure 1.3 Contrasting the size and complexity of prokaryotic and eukaryotic cells. (Cells are shown approximately 40,000 times their real size.)

?   Explain why cells are considered the basic units of life.

■ They are the lowest level in the hierarchy of biological organization at which the properties of life emerge.

Evolution, the Core Theme of Biology

1.4   The unity of life: All forms of life have common features

All cells have DNA, and the continuity of life is based on this genetic material. DNA is the substance of **genes,** the units of inheritance that transmit information from parents to offspring. The molecular structure of DNA accounts for this function. Let us explain: Each DNA molecule is made up of two long chains coiled together into what is called a double helix (see Figure 1.1). The chains are made up of four kinds of chemical building blocks.

Figure 1.4A on the next page diagrams a short section of one of the chains and indicates the four different building blocks, called bases, with different colors and letter abbreviations of their names.

The way DNA encodes a cell's information is analogous to the way we arrange letters of the alphabet into precise sequences with specific meanings. The word *rat,* for example, conjures up an image of a rodent; *tar* and *art,* which contain the same letters,

A
C
T
A
T
A
C
C
G
T
A
G
T
A

Figure 1.4A One chain of a DNA molecule, its message written in the order of its four bases

mean very different things. We can think of the four building blocks as the alphabet of inheritance. Specific sequential arrangements of these four chemical letters encode precise information in genes, which are typically hundreds or thousands of "letters" long. A bacterial gene may direct the cell to "Build a purple pigment." A particular human gene may mean "Make the hormone insulin." All forms of life use essentially the same genetic code, which has made it possible to engineer cells that produce proteins normally found only in some other organism. Thus, bacteria can be used to produce insulin by inserting a gene for human insulin into bacterial cells.

The diversity of life arises from differences in DNA sequences—in other words, from variations on the common theme of storing genetic information in DNA. Bacteria and humans are different because they have different genes. But both sets of instructions are written in the same language.

Figure 1.4B illustrates some of the other properties that are common to all organisms.

(1) *Order.* All living things exhibit complex organization, as seen in the highly ordered structure of this sunflower.

(2) *Regulation.* The environment outside an organism may change markedly, but mechanisms maintain an organism's internal environment within limits that sustain life. Regulation of the amount of blood flowing through the blood vessels in the large ears of this jackrabbit helps maintain a constant body temperature by adjusting heat exchange with the air.

(3) *Growth and development.* Inherited information carried by genes controls the pattern of growth and development of organisms such as this Nile crocodile.

(4) *Energy processing.* Organisms take in energy and transform it to perform all of life's activities. When this bear eats the fish, it will use the chemical energy stored in the fish to power its own activities and chemical reactions (metabolism).

(5) *Response to the environment.* All organisms respond to environmental stimuli. This Venus flytrap closed its trap rapidly in response to the stimulus of a damselfly landing on it.

(6) *Reproduction.* Organisms reproduce their own kind. This emperor penguin is protecting its baby.

(7) *Evolutionary adaptation.* The appearance of this pygmy seahorse camouflages it in its environment. Such adaptations evolve over many generations as individuals with traits best suited to their environment pass them to offspring.

The organisms in Figure 1.4B illustrate some of the amazing diversity of life. In the next module, we see how biologists attempt to organize this diversity.

? What is the chemical basis for all of life's kinship?

■ DNA as the genetic material

(1) Order

(2) Regulation

(3) Growth and development

(4) Energy processing

(5) Response to the environment

(6) Reproduction

(7) Evolutionary adaptation

Figure 1.4B Some important properties of life

The diversity of life can be arranged into three domains

We can think of biology's enormous scope as having two dimensions. The "vertical" dimension, which we examined in Module 1.1, is the size scale that stretches from molecules to the biosphere. But biology's scope also has a "horizontal" dimension, spanning across the great diversity of organisms existing now and over life's long history.

Grouping Species Diversity is a hallmark of life. Biologists have so far identified and named about 1.8 million **species,** the term used for a particular type of organism, such as *Panthera pardus,* the leopard. Researchers identify thousands of additional species each year. Estimates of the total number of species range from 10 million to over 400 million. As an example, Figure 1.5A shows a small sample of the diversity of moths and butterflies. How do we make sense of so much diversity?

There seems to be a human tendency to group diverse items according to similarities. We may speak of bears or butterflies, though we recognize that each group includes many different species. We may even sort groups into broader categories, such as mammals and insects. Taxonomy, the branch of biology that names and classifies species, arranges them into a hierarchy of broader and broader groups, from genus, family, order, class, and phylum, to kingdom.

The Three Domains of Life Until the last few decades, most biologists adopted a taxonomic scheme that divided all of the diversity of life into five kingdoms. But new methods, such as comparison of DNA sequences, have led to an ongoing reevaluation of the number and boundaries of kingdoms. New classification schemes have been proposed that range from six to dozens of kingdoms. As that debate continues, however, most biologists now agree that the kingdoms of life can be organized into three overarching groups called **domains.** The organisms in Figure 1.5B on the facing page are representatives of the three domains.

Domain **Bacteria** and domain **Archaea** both consist of prokaryotes, organisms with prokaryotic cells. Most prokaryotes are unicellular and microscopic. The photos of these prokaryotes in Figure 1.5B were made with a scanning electron microscope, and the number along the side indicates how many times these images were magnified. (We will discuss microscopy in Chapter 4.) In the five-kingdom system, bacteria and archaea were combined in a single kingdom. But newer evidence from comparisons of DNA and other molecules suggests that they represent two very distinct branches of life, as you'll learn in Chapters 15 and 16.

Bacteria are the most diverse and widespread prokaryotes and are now divided among several kingdoms. In the photo of bacteria in Figure 1.5B, each of the rod-shaped structures is a bacterial cell.

Many of the prokaryotes known as archaea live in Earth's extreme environments, such as salty lakes and boiling hot springs. Domain Archaea also includes multiple kingdoms. The photo of archaea in Figure 1.5B shows a colony composed of many cells.

Figure 1.5A   Drawers of diversity: some of the tens of thousands of species in the moth and butterfly collection at the National Museum of Natural History in Washington, D.C.

All the eukaryotes, organisms with eukaryotic cells, are now grouped into the various kingdoms of domain **Eukarya.** As you learned in Module 1.3, eukaryotic cells have a nucleus and other internal structures called organelles.

Most aquatic or moist habitats support members of domain Eukarya called protists. Protists are a diverse collection of mostly single-celled organisms. Some protists, including those commonly called algae, make their own food by photosynthesis. Another assortment of protists, commonly called protozoans, are animal-like in that they eat other organisms. The top center photo in Figure 1.5B shows a number of different protists in a drop of water viewed with a microscope (magnified 275 times). The large, irregular, bluish cell in the center is an amoeba, and the smaller cells are mostly single-celled algae. Also present are multicellular algae (the rodlike organisms). In the five-kingdom scheme, protists were classified in a single kingdom, but evidence from molecular studies now indicates that they include several different evolutionary lineages. The recent trend has been to split the protists into several kingdoms to accurately reflect their evolutionary relationships.

The three remaining kingdoms within Eukarya contain multicellular eukaryotes. These three kingdoms are distinguished partly by their modes of nutrition. Kingdom Plantae consists of plants, which produce their own food by photosynthesis and have cells with rigid walls made of cellulose. The photo representing kingdom Plantae in Figure 1.5B is a tropical bromeliad, a plant native to the Americas.

Kingdom Fungi, represented by the mushrooms in Figure 1.5B, is a diverse group that includes molds, yeasts, and mushrooms. Fungi are mostly decomposers. They break down the remains of dead organisms and organic wastes, such as leaf litter and animal feces, and absorb the nutrients into their cells.

Animals obtain food by ingestion, which means they eat other organisms. Most animals are motile and are made of cells that lack rigid walls. Representing the kingdom Animalia (animals), the sloth in Figure 1.5B resides in the trees of American rain forests. There are actually members of three groups in the sloth photo. The sloth is clinging to a tree (kingdom Plantae), and the greenish tinge in the animal's hair is a luxuriant growth of photosynthetic prokaryotes (domain Bacteria). This photograph exemplifies a theme reflected in our book's title: connections between living things. The sloth depends on trees for food and shelter; the tree uses nutrients from the decomposition of the sloth's feces; the prokaryotes gain access to the sunlight necessary for photosynthesis by living on the sloth; and the sloth is camouflaged from predators by its green coat.

Life's diversity and its interconnectedness are evident almost everywhere. We have looked at life's unity and surveyed its diversity. In the next module, we describe how evolution explains both the unity and the diversity of life.

Web Activity *Classification Schemes*

? To which of the three domains of life do we belong?

■ Eukarya

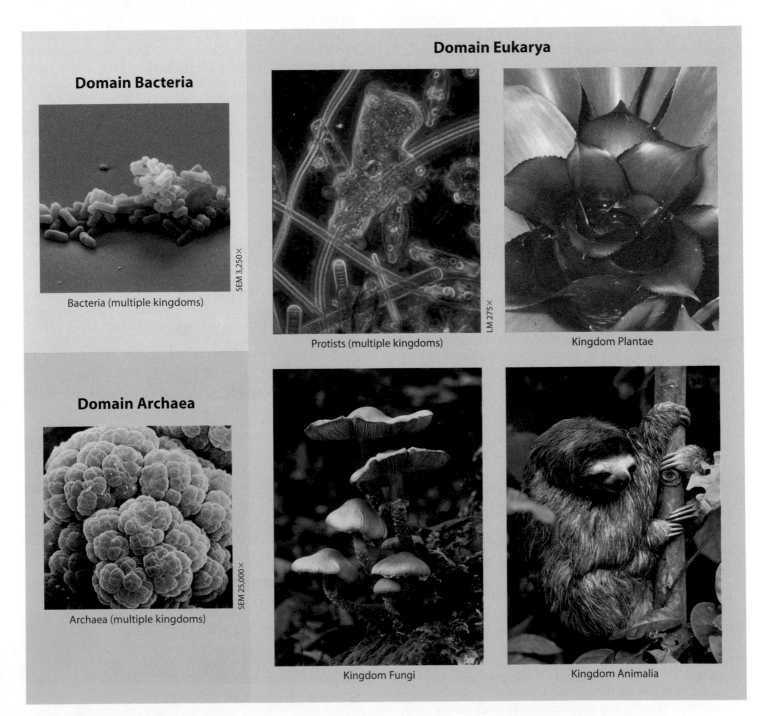

Domain Eukarya

Domain Bacteria

Bacteria (multiple kingdoms)

SEM 3,250×

Protists (multiple kingdoms)

LM 275×

Kingdom Plantae

Domain Archaea

Archaea (multiple kingdoms)

SEM 25,000×

Kingdom Fungi

Kingdom Animalia

Figure 1.5B   The three domains of life

Evolution explains the unity and diversity of life

Figure 1.6A
Charles Darwin
in 1859

In November 1859, Charles Darwin (Figure 1.6A) published one of the most important and influential books ever written. Entitled *On the Origin of Species by Means of Natural Selection,* Darwin's book was an immediate bestseller and soon made his name almost synonymous with the concept of evolution. Darwin stands out in history with people like Newton and Einstein, scientists who synthesized ideas with great explanatory power. Such comprehensive ideas are called theories.

The Origin of Species articulated two main points. First, Darwin presented evidence to support the idea of **evolution**—that species living today are descendants of ancestral species. Darwin called his evolutionary theory "descent with modification." It was an insightful phrase, as it captured both the unity of life (descent from a common ancestor) and the diversity of life (modification as species diverged from their ancestors).

Darwin's second point was to propose a mechanism for evolution, a mechanism he called **natural selection.** Darwin synthesized this idea from observations that by themselves were neither profound nor original. Others had the pieces of the puzzle, but Darwin saw how they fit together. He inferred natural selection by connecting two readily observable features of life:

OBSERVATION #1: **Individual variation.** Individuals in a population vary in many heritable traits.

OBSERVATION #2: **Overproduction of offspring.** A population of any species has the potential to produce far more offspring than will survive to produce offspring of their own.

INFERENCE #1: **Unequal reproductive success.** From these two observations, Darwin inferred that individuals are unequal in their likelihood of surviving and reproducing. Those individuals with heritable traits best suited to the environment will leave the greatest number of healthy, fertile offspring.

INFERENCE #2: **Over time, favorable traits accumulate in a population.** Over many generations, a higher and higher proportion of individuals will have the advantageous traits.

Unequal reproductive success is what Darwin called natural selection, because the natural environment "selects" for individuals with certain traits. And the product of natural selection is evolutionary adaptation, the accumulation of favorable traits in a population over time.

Figure 1.6B uses a simple example to show how natural selection works. ❶ An imaginary beetle population has colonized an area where the soil has been blackened by a recent brush fire. Initially, the population varies extensively in the inherited coloration of individuals, from very light gray to charcoal. ❷ A predatory bird eats the beetles it sees most easily, the light-colored ones. This selective predation favors the survival and reproductive success of the darker beetles compared to the lighter ones. ❸ The surviving beetles have reproduced. The population is now quite different from the original one, as natural selection has produced a change in the frequencies of the different-colored beetles.

Our example also illustrates that natural selection is not a creative process but an editing mechanism. It can only select among the variations that are present in the population.

We can summarize natural selection as follows: Natural selection occurs as heritable variations are exposed to environmental factors that favor the reproductive success of some individuals over others. In our example, birds are the "selecting" environmental factor.

Darwin realized that numerous small changes in populations caused by natural selection could eventually lead to major alterations of species. He proposed that new species could evolve as a result of the gradual accumulation of changes over long periods of time. We will explore evolution and natural selection in more detail in Chapters 13 and 14.

We see the exquisite results of natural selection in every kind of organism. Each species has its own set of evolutionary adaptations that evolved by means of natural selection. In Figure 1.6C, on the facing page, we see the pangolin, a mammal that lives in

❶ Population with varied inherited traits

❷ Elimination of individuals with certain traits

❸ Reproduction of survivors

Figure 1.6B An example of natural selection in action

East African rain forests. One of its main adaptations, its tough body armor of overlapping scales, protects it from most predators. The pangolin also has an unusually long tongue, which it uses to prod termites and ants out of their nests. Another mammal shown in Figure 1.6C, the killer whale (orca), is adapted for life at sea. It breathes air through nostrils on the top of its head and communicates with its companions by emitting clicking sounds. Orcas use sound echoes to detect obstacles and schools of fish or other prey. The pangolin's armor and the orca's echolocating ability arose over many, many generations as individuals with heritable traits that made them better adapted to their environment had the greatest reproductive success.

Evolution is biology's core theme—the one idea that makes sense of all we know about life.

Web Process of Science *How Do Environmental Changes Affect a Population?*

? How does natural selection adapt a population of organisms to its environment?

■ On average, those individuals with heritable traits best suited to the local environment produce the greatest number of offspring that survive and reproduce. This increases the frequency of those traits in the population.

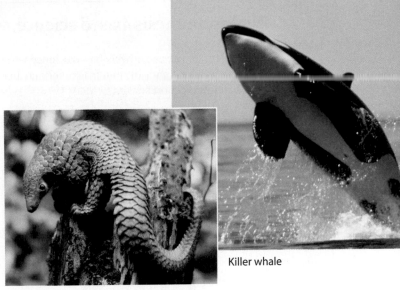

Figure 1.6C Examples of adaptations to different environments

Killer whale

Pangolin

The Process of Science

1.7 Scientists use two main approaches to learn about nature

The word *science* is derived from a Latin verb meaning "to know." Science is a way of knowing. It stems from our curiosity about ourselves and the world around us. Science seeks natural causes for natural phenomena. Thus the scope of science is limited to the study of structures and processes that we can observe and measure, either directly or with the help of tools such as microscopes that extend our senses. This dependence on direct observations that other people can confirm distinguishes science from belief in the supernatural. Science can neither prove nor disprove the existence of a God or supernatural power—for such questions are outside the bounds of science.

Biology blends two main scientific approaches: discovery science, which is mostly about *describing* nature, and hypothesis-based science, which is mostly about *explaining* nature. Most research combines these two forms of inquiry.

Discovery Science Verifiable observations and measurements are the data of discovery science. In biology, discovery science describes life at its many levels, from the biosphere down to cells and molecules. An example is the sequencing of the human genome. While this research involves complicated methods and instruments, it is essentially just a detailed dissection and description of human DNA.

Discovery science can lead to important conclusions based on a type of logic called *inductive reasoning*. This kind of reasoning derives general principles from a large number of specific observations. "All organisms are made of cells" is an inductive conclusion based on the discovery of cells in every microscopic biological specimen observed by biologists over two centuries of time. The careful observations of discovery science and the inductive conclusions they sometimes produce are fundamental to our understanding of nature.

Hypothesis-Based Science The observations of discovery science stimulate us to seek natural causes and explanations for those observations. Such inquiry usually involves the proposing and testing of hypotheses. A **hypothesis** is a proposed explanation for a set of observations. A good hypothesis leads to predictions that scientists can test by recording additional observations or by designing experiments.

Deductive reasoning is the logic used in hypothesis-based science to come up with ways to test hypotheses. In deduction, the reasoning flows from the general to the specific. From general premises, we extrapolate to the specific results we should expect if the premises are true. If all organisms are made of cells (premise 1), and humans are organisms (premise 2), then humans are composed of cells (deduction). This deduction is a prediction that can be tested by examining human tissues.

Theories in Science How is a theory different from a hypothesis? A **theory** in science is much broader in scope. It explains a great diversity of observations and is supported by a large and usually growing body of evidence. And theories continue to generate new hypotheses, which can be tested.

🎧 MP3 Tutor *The Process of Science*

? What is the difference between discovery science and hypothesis-based science?

■ In the first, scientists observe and describe objects and phenomena; in the second, they propose hypotheses, make deductions, and test predictions.

With hypothesis-based science, we pose and test hypotheses

We will explore the elements of hypothesis-based science with the help of two scientific investigations, one from everyday life and one from a research project on snakes.

A Case Study from Everyday Life   We all use hypotheses in solving everyday problems. Let's say, for example, that your flashlight fails during a campout. That's an observation. The question is obvious: Why doesn't the flashlight work? Two reasonable hypotheses based on past experience are that either the batteries in the flashlight are dead or the bulb is burned out. Figure 1.8A diagrams this campground inquiry.

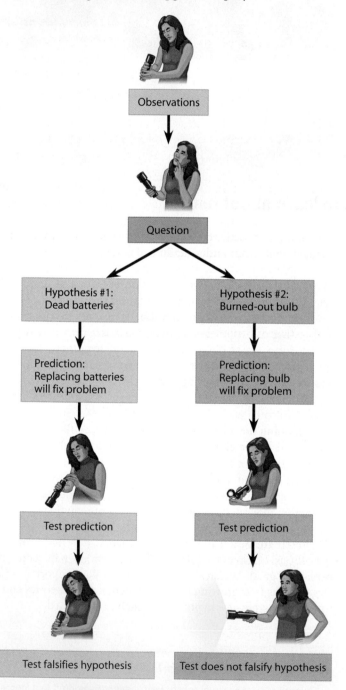

Observations

Question

| Hypothesis #1: Dead batteries | Hypothesis #2: Burned-out bulb |

| Prediction: Replacing batteries will fix problem | Prediction: Replacing bulb will fix problem |

| Test prediction | Test prediction |

| Test falsifies hypothesis | Test does not falsify hypothesis |

Figure 1.8A   An example of hypothesis-based science

Now let's use deductive reasoning. In the process of science, deduction usually takes the form of predictions of experimental results or observations we should expect *if* a particular hypothesis is correct. We then test our predictions by carrying out the appropriate experiments or observations to see whether or not the results are expected. This deductive testing uses "*If . . . then*" logic. For example, *if* the dead-batteries hypothesis is correct and I replace the batteries with new ones, *then* the flashlight should work. If the flashlight still does not work, we can test our other hypothesis by replacing the flashlight bulb.

The flashlight example illustrates two important points. First, a hypothesis must be *testable*—there must be some way to check its validity. Second, a hypothesis must be *falsifiable*—there must be some observation or experiment that could show that it is not true. As shown on the left in Figure 1.8A, the hypothesis that dead batteries are the sole cause of the problem was falsified by replacing the batteries with new ones. As shown on the right, the burned-out-bulb hypothesis is the more likely explanation. Notice that testing supports a hypothesis not by proving that it is correct but by not eliminating it through falsification. Perhaps the bulb was simply loose and the new bulb was inserted correctly. No amount of experimental testing can *prove* a hypothesis beyond a shadow of doubt, because it is impossible to exhaust all alternative hypotheses. A hypothesis gains credibility by surviving various attempts to falsify it.

A Case Study of Hypothesis-Based Science   One way to learn more about how hypothesis-based science works is to examine a case study from actual scientific research.

The story begins with a set of observations and generalizations from discovery science. Many poisonous animals are brightly colored, often with distinctive patterns. This so-called warning coloration apparently says "dangerous species" to potential predators. But there are also mimics. These imposters look like poisonous species but are actually harmless. A question that follows from these observations is: What is the function of such mimicry? A reasonable hypothesis is that such deception is an evolutionary adaptation that reduces the harmless animal's risk of being eaten.

In 2001, biologists David and Karin Pfennig, along with William Harcombe, one of their undergraduate students, designed an elegant set of field experiments to test the hypothesis that mimics benefit because predators confuse them with the harmful species. A poisonous snake called the eastern coral snake has warning coloration: bold, alternating rings of red, yellow, and black (Figure 1.8B). Predators rarely attack these snakes. The predators do not learn this avoidance behavior by trial and error; a first encounter with a coral snake would usually be deadly. A predator making that mistake will not pass its genes on to any more offspring. Natural selection has apparently increased the frequency of predators that inherit an instinctive avoidance of the coral snake's coloration.

The nonpoisonous scarlet king snake mimics the ringed coloration of the coral snake (Figure 1.8C). Both types of snakes live in North and South Carolina, but the king snakes'

Figure 1.8B   Eastern coral snake (poisonous)

Figure 1.8C   Scarlet king snake (nonpoisonous)

geographic range also extends into regions where no coral snakes are found.

The geographic distribution of these snakes made it possible for the researchers to test a key prediction of the mimicry hypothesis: Mimicry should help protect king snakes from predators, but only in regions where coral snakes also live. Avoiding snakes with warning coloration is an adaptation of predator populations that evolved in areas where the poisonous coral snakes are present. The mimicry hypothesis predicts that predators adapted to the warning coloration of coral snakes will attack king snakes less frequently than will predators in areas where coral snakes are absent.

To test this prediction, Harcombe made hundreds of artificial snakes out of wire covered with a claylike substance called plasticine. He made two versions of fake snakes: an *experimental group* with the red, black, and yellow ring pattern of king snakes and a *control group* of plain brown artificial snakes as a basis of comparison.

The researchers placed equal numbers of the two types of artificial snakes in field sites throughout North and South Carolina, including the region where coral snakes are absent. After four weeks, they retrieved the snakes and recorded how many had been attacked by looking for bite or claw marks. The most common predators were foxes, coyotes, and raccoons, but black bears also attacked some of the artificial snakes (Figure 1.8D).

The data fit the key prediction of the mimicry hypothesis. Compared to the brown artificial snakes, the ringed snakes were attacked by predators less frequently only in field sites within the geographic range of the poisonous coral snakes. The bar graph in Figure 1.8E summarizes the results.

This case study is an example of a **controlled experiment,** one that is designed to compare an experimental group (the artificial king snakes, in this case) with a control group (the artificial brown snakes). Ideally, the experimental and control groups differ only in the one factor the experiment is designed to test—in our example, the effect of the snakes' coloration on the behavior of predators. Without the control group, the researchers would not have been able to rule out the number of predators in the different test areas as the cause of the different number of attacks on the artificial king snakes. The experimental design left coloration as the only factor that could account for the low predation rate on the artificial king snakes placed within the range of coral snakes.

Both of these case studies illustrate the "scientific method," a process of inquiry that involves observations, questions, hypotheses, predictions, and tests of predictions. But there is no rule book that says science must follow rigid steps. As in all quests, science includes elements of challenge, adventure, and luck, along with careful planning, reasoning, creativity, cooperation, competition, patience, and persistence.

Web Process of Science *How Does Acid Precipitation Affect Trees?*

? Why is it difficult to draw a conclusion from an experiment that does not include a control group?

■ Without a control group, you don't know if the experimental outcome is due to the variable you are trying to test or to some other variable.

Figure 1.8D   Artificial king snake that was not attacked (left); artificial brown snake that was attacked by a bear (right)

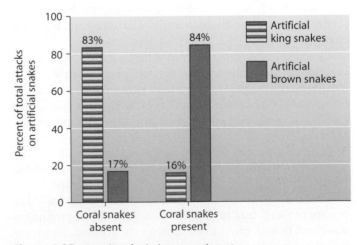

Figure 1.8E   Results of mimicry experiment

1.9 Biology, technology, and society are connected in important ways

Figure 1.9 Biology and technology in the news

Many issues facing society are related to biology (Figure 1.9). Most of these issues also involve our expanding technology. Science and technology are interdependent, but their basic goals differ. The goal of science is to understand natural phenomena. In contrast, the goal of **technology** is to apply scientific knowledge for some specific purpose. Scientists often speak of "discoveries," while engineers more often speak of "inventions." The beneficiaries of those inventions also include scientists, who use new technology in their research. And scientific discoveries often lead to the development of new technologies.

Technology depends less on the curiosity that drives basic science than it does on the needs and wants of people and on the social environment of the times. Debates about technology center more on "should we do it" than "can we do it." Should insurance companies have access to individuals' DNA information? Should we permit research with embryonic stem cells?

Technology has improved our standard of living in many ways, but not without adverse consequences. Technology that keeps people healthier has enabled Earth's population to grow more than tenfold in the past three centuries, to more than 6 billion. The environmental effects of this growth can be devastating. Global warming, toxic wastes, acid rain, deforestation, nuclear accidents, and extinction of species are just some of the repercussions of more and more people wielding more and more technology. Science can help us identify such problems and provide insight into what course of action may prevent further damage. But solutions to these problems have as much to do with politics, economics, and cultural values as with science and technology. Now that science and technology have become such powerful aspects of society, every citizen has a responsibility to develop a reasonable amount of scientific literacy. The crucial science-technology-society relationship is a theme that adds to the significance of any biology course.

? How do science and technology interact?

■ New scientific discoveries may lead to new technologies; new technologies may increase the ability of scientists to search for new knowledge.

1.10 Evolution is connected to our everyday lives

Evolution is the core theme of biology. To emphasize the centrality of evolution to biology, we have added an Evolution Connection module to each chapter in this book. But is evolution connected to our everyday lives? And if so, in what ways?

Evolution tells us that all living species are descendants of ancestral species that have become modified as natural selection adapts populations to their environments. As environments change, populations change. What accounts for these changes?

Biologists now recognize that differences in DNA among individuals, populations, and species reflect the pattern of evolutionary change. Scientists have determined the order of billions of DNA bases in thousands of different species. Comparisons of those sequences allow us to identify genes shared across many species, study their actions in other species, and, in some cases, search for new medical treatments. Identifying beneficial genes in relatives of our crop plants has permitted the breeding or genetic engineering of enhanced crops.

The recognition that DNA differs between people has led to the use of DNA tests to identify individuals. DNA profiling is now used to help convict or exonerate the accused, determine paternity, and identify remains.

Evolution teaches us that the environment matters because it is a powerful selective force for traits that best adapt populations to their environment. We are major agents of environmental change when we take drugs to combat infection or grow crops in pesticide-dependent monocultures or alter most of Earth's habitats. We have seen the effects of such environmental changes in antibiotic-resistant bacteria, pesticide-resistant pests, endangered species, and increasing rates of extinction.

How can evolutionary theory help? It can help us be more judicious in our use of antibiotics and pesticides, and develop strategies for conservation efforts. It can help us create flu vaccines and HIV drugs by tracing the evolution of these viruses.

We hope this book will help you develop an appreciation for evolution and for biology and help you apply that understanding to evaluating issues ranging from your personal health to the well-being of the whole world. Biology offers us a deeper understanding of ourselves and our planet and a chance to more fully appreciate life in all its diversity.

? How might an understanding of evolution contribute to the development of new drugs?

■ As one example, we can find organisms that share our genes and similar cellular processes and test the actions of potential drugs in these organisms.

Chapter Review

Reviewing the Concepts

Biology is the scientific study of life (**Introduction**).

Themes in the Study of Biology (1.1–1.3)

Life's hierarchy of organization unfolds as follows: biosphere > ecosystem > community > population > organism > organ system > organ > tissue > cell > organelle > molecule. Starting at the bottom of the hierarchy, with each step "upward," new properties emerge as a result of interactions among components of the lower levels (**1.1**).

Ecosystems are characterized by the cycling of chemical nutrients from the atmosphere and soil to producers to consumers to decomposers and back to the environment. Energy flows one way through an ecosystem from the sun to producers to consumers and exits as heat (**1.2**).

A **cell** is the basic unit of life, the lowest level of organization that can perform all activities required for life. Eukaryotic cells contain membrane-enclosed organelles, including a DNA-containing nucleus. Prokaryotic cells are smaller and lack such organelles (**1.3**).

Systems biology models the complex interactions of biological systems, such as the molecular interactions within a cell (**1.3**).

Evolution, the Core Theme of Biology (1.4–1.6)

DNA is the genetic information responsible for heredity and for programming the production of an organism's molecules. Each species' genes are coded in the sequences of the four building blocks (bases) making up DNA's two helically coiled chains. All organisms share a set of common features: ordered structures, regulation of internal conditions, growth and development, energy processing, response to environmental stimuli, the ability to reproduce, and evolutionary adaptations (**1.4**).

Three domains. Taxonomy names species and classifies them into a system of broader groups. Domain Bacteria and Archaea consist of prokaryotes. The eukaryotic domain Eukarya includes various protist kingdoms and the kingdoms Fungi, Plantae, and Animalia (**1.5**).

Evolution and natural selection. Evolution explains the unity and diversity of life. Charles Darwin synthesized the theory of evolution by natural selection. Natural selection is an editing mechanism that occurs when populations of organisms, having inherited variations, are exposed to environmental factors that favor the reproductive success of some individuals over others. All organisms have adaptations that have evolved by means of natural selection (**1.6**).

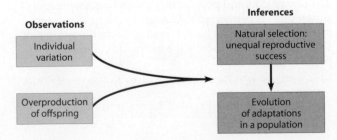

The Process of Science (1.7–1.8)

Scientific inquiry. In discovery science, scientists carefully observe and describe some aspect of the world and use inductive reasoning to draw general conclusions. In hypothesis-based science, they attempt to explain observations by testing hypotheses (**1.7**).

Hypothesis-based science involves observations, questions, hypotheses as tentative explanations, deductions leading to predictions, and then tests of the predictions to see if the hypotheses are falsifiable. Deductive reasoning is used: *If* a hypothesis is correct *and* we test one of its predictions (by performing an experiment or making observations), *then* a particular outcome will occur. In experiments designed to test hypotheses, the use of control groups and experimental groups helps to control variables (**1.8**).

Biology and Everyday Life (1.9–1.10)

Biology, technology, and society. Technological advances stem from scientific research, and research benefits from technology. The science-technology-society relationship is an important aspect of a biology course (**1.9**).

Evolution affects everyday life in medicine, agriculture, forensics, and conservation. Environmental changes are powerful selective pressures on the adaptive traits of many populations (**1.10**).

Connecting the Concepts

1. Biology can be described as having both a vertical scale and a horizontal scale. Explain what that means.

2. Complete the following map organizing some of biology's major concepts.

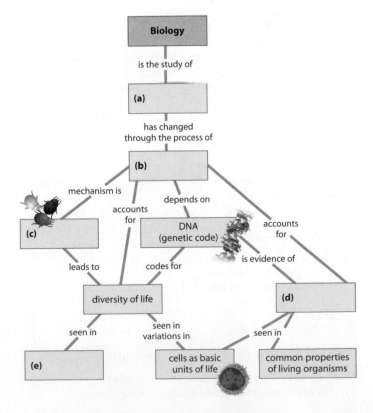

Testing Your Knowledge

Multiple Choice

3. Which of the following best describes the logic of the scientific process?
   a. If I generate a testable hypothesis, tests and observations will support it.
   b. If my prediction is correct, it will lead to a testable hypothesis.
   c. If my observations are accurate, they will support my hypothesis.
   d. If my hypothesis is correct, I can expect certain test results.
   e. If my tests are right, they will prove my hypothesis.

4. Amoebas and bacteria are grouped into different domains because
   a. amoebas eat bacteria.
   b. bacteria are not made of cells.
   c. bacterial cells lack a membrane-enclosed nucleus.
   d. bacteria decompose amoebas.
   e. amoebas are photosynthetic.

5. A biologist studying interactions among the protists in an ecosystem could *not* be working at which level in life's hierarchy? (*Choose carefully and explain your answer.*)
   a. the population level   d. the organism level
   b. the molecular level   e. the organ level
   c. the community level

6. Which of the following questions is outside the realm of science?
   a. Which organisms play the most important role in energy input to a savannah?
   b. What percentage of music majors take a biology course?
   c. What is the physical nature of the universe?
   d. What is the nature of the supernatural?
   e. What is the historical basis for the division of Earth's human population into ethnic groups?

7. Which of the following statements best distinguishes hypotheses from theories in science?
   a. Theories are hypotheses that have been proved.
   b. Hypotheses are tentative guesses; theories are correct answers to questions about nature.
   c. Hypotheses usually are narrow in scope; theories have broad explanatory power.
   d. Hypotheses and theories are different terms for essentially the same thing in science.
   e. Theories cannot be falsified; hypotheses are expected to be falsified.

8. Which of the following best demonstrates the unity among all living organisms?
   a. descent with modification   d. natural selection
   b. the structure and function of DNA e. the three domains
   c. emergent properties

9. The core idea that makes sense of all of biology is
   a. the process of science.
   b. the correlation of function with structure.
   c. systems biology.
   d. evolution.
   e. unity in diversity.

Describing, Comparing, and Explaining

10. In an ecosystem, how is the movement of energy similar to that of chemical nutrients, and how is it different?

11. Explain the role of heritable variations in Darwin's theory of natural selection.

12. Explain what is meant by this statement: The scientific process is not a rigid method.

13. Contrast technology with science. Give an example of each to illustrate the difference.

14. Explain what is meant by this statement: Natural selection is an editing mechanism rather than a creative process.

Applying the Concepts

15. The graph below shows the results of an experiment in which mice learned to run through a maze.

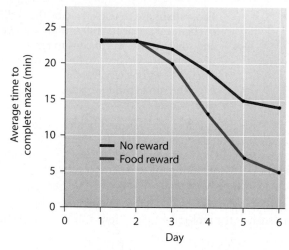

   a. State the hypothesis and prediction that you think this experiment tested.
   b. Which was the control group and which the experimental? Why was a control group needed?
   c. List some variables that must have been controlled so as not to affect the results.
   d. Do the data support your hypothesis? Explain.

16. In an experiment similar to the mimicry experiment described in Module 1.8, a researcher found that there were more predator attacks on artificial king snakes in areas with coral snakes than in areas outside the range of coral snakes. From this the researcher concluded that the mimicry hypothesis is false. Do you think this conclusion is justified? Why or why not?

17. The fruits of wild species of tomato are tiny compared to the giant beefsteak tomatoes available today. This difference in fruit size is almost entirely due to the larger number of cells in the domesticated fruits. Plant biologists have recently discovered genes that are responsible for controlling cell division in tomatoes. Why would such a discovery be important to producers of other kinds of fruits and vegetables? To the study of human development and disease? To our basic understanding of biology?

18. The news media and popular magazines frequently report stories that are connected to biology. In the next 24 hours, record all the ones you hear or read about in three different sources and briefly describe the biological connections you perceive in each story.

Answers to all questions can be found in Appendix 4.

For Practice Quizzes, BioFlix, MP3 Tutors, and Activities, go to www.mybiology.com.

The Life of
the Cell

UNITONE

2 The Chemical Basis of Life

3 The Molecules of Cells

4 A Tour of the Cell

5 The Working Cell

6 How Cells Harvest
Chemical Energy

7 Photosynthesis:
Using Light to Make Food

The Chemical Basis of Life

Elements, Atoms, and Molecules

2.1 Living organisms are composed of about 25 chemical elements

2.2 Trace elements are common additives to food and water

2.3 Elements can combine to form compounds

2.4 Atoms consist of protons, neutrons, and electrons

2.5 Radioactive isotopes can help or harm us

2.6 Electron arrangement determines the chemical properties of an atom

2.7 Ionic bonds are attractions between ions of opposite charge

2.8 Covalent bonds join atoms into molecules through electron sharing

2.9 Unequal electron sharing creates polar molecules

2.10 Hydrogen bonds are weak bonds important in the chemistry of life

Water's Life-Supporting Properties

2.11 Hydrogen bonds make liquid water cohesive

2.12 Water's hydrogen bonds moderate temperature

2.13 Ice is less dense than liquid water

2.14 Water is the solvent of life

2.15 The chemistry of life is sensitive to acidic and basic conditions

2.16 Acid precipitation and ocean acidification threaten the environment

2.17 The search for extraterrestrial life centers on the search for water

Chemical Reactions

2.18 Chemical reactions make and break bonds, changing the composition of matter

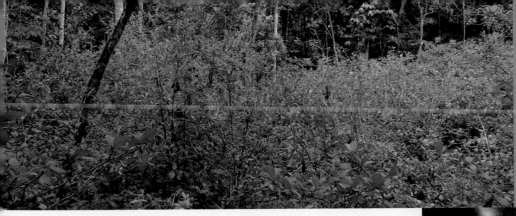

A researcher chiseling into a tree in Peru to find lemon ants (opposite)

A "Devil's Garden" in the Peruvian Amazon (left)

Who Tends This Garden?

The Amazonian rain forest in South America is a showcase for the diversity of life on Earth. Colorful birds, insects, and other animals live among a myriad of trees, shrubs, vines, and wildflowers, and an excursion along a waterway or a forest path typically reveals a lush variety of plant life. Visitors traveling near the Amazon's headwaters in Peru are therefore surprised to come across tracts of forest like that seen in the foreground of the photo at the top of this page. This patch is almost completely dominated by a single plant species—a willowy flowering tree called the lemon ant tree (*Duroia hirsute*). At first, it may appear that the garden is planted and maintained by local people. However, the indigenous people are as mystified as any visitors. They call these stands of trees "devil's gardens," from a legend attributing them to an evil forest spirit. Local legend is that the devil's gardens are home to a mythical dwarf who is half monkey and half human, with one hoof and one human foot. This creature is said to change his appearance into that of a friend or relative and then lead lone travelers in circles until they are lost.

Seeking a scientific explanation for the "devil's garden," a research team recently solved the mystery of these unusual forests. Graduate student Megan Frederickson, working with Deborah Gordon, a professor at Stanford University, showed that the "farmers" who create and maintain these gardens are actually ants that live in the hollow stems of the trees. Indeed, the common name for the trees comes from the lemon ant (*Myrmelachista schumanni*) usually found living there. The ants do not plant the trees, of course, but they prevent other kinds of plants from growing in the garden by injecting intruders with a poisonous chemical.

How was the mystery solved? To test the hypothesis that the ants were killing competing trees, Frederickson did field experiments in Peru. She planted saplings of another tree species inside and outside ten devil's gardens. At the base of some saplings, a sticky insect barrier was applied. The other saplings had no barrier to ant traffic. The researchers observed ants making injections from the tips of their abdomens into leaves of the unprotected saplings in their gardens (see photo). Within one day, these leaves developed dead areas. But the ants did not harm the saplings outside their gardens. These results and observations indicate that it is the ants who tend the gardens.

An ant injecting formic acid into a competitor's leaves

The chemical the ants use to weed their garden turns out to be formic acid. You may have experienced formic acid if you have ever been stung by a bee or wandered into a patch of stinging nettles. This substance is produced by many species of ants and, in fact, got its name from the Latin word for ant, *formica*. In many species, the formic acid probably serves as a disinfectant that protects the ants against microbial parasites. The lemon ant is the first ant species found to use formic acid as a herbicide. This use of a chemical is an important addition to the list of functions mediated by chemicals in the insect world. Scientists already know that chemicals play important roles in insect communication, attraction of mates, and defense against predators.

Research on devil's gardens is only one example of the relevance of chemistry to the study of life. Chemicals play many more roles in life than herbicides produced by ants, of course: They are the very stuff making up our bodies, those of other organisms, and the physical environment.

In this chapter, we make connections to the themes introduced in Chapter 1. One of these themes is the organization of life into a hierarchy of structural levels, with additional properties emerging at each successive level. The community formed of lemon ants and the garden of lemon ant trees they weed is one example. The interaction of these two species provides a home for colonies of ants and a habitat free of plant competitors for the trees.

Emergent properties are also apparent at the lowest levels of biological organization—such as the ordering of atoms into molecules and the interactions of those molecules. We begin our study of biology with the basic concepts of chemistry that will apply throughout our study of life. ■ ■ ■

2.1 Living organisms are composed of about 25 chemical elements

Why does a biology textbook begin with a chapter on chemistry? To learn about life, you will study the structures and functions of living organisms. In the process, you will travel through all the levels of the hierarchy of biological organization described in Module 1.1, from molecules to ecosystems. At the base of this hierarchy are atoms and molecules. You will see that the properties of life emerge from the arrangement of these chemical parts into higher and higher levels of structural organization.

Living organisms are composed of **matter,** which is anything that occupies space and has mass. (In everyday language, we can think of mass as an object's weight.) Matter, in forms as diverse as rock, water, gases, and living organisms, is composed of chemical elements. An **element** is a substance that cannot be broken down to other substances by ordinary chemical means. Today, chemists recognize 92 elements occurring in nature; gold, copper, carbon, and oxygen are some examples. (Chemists have also made dozens more.) Each element has a symbol, the first letter or two of its English, Latin, or German name. For instance, the symbol for sodium, Na, is from the Latin word *natrium;* the symbol O stands for the English word *oxygen.*

About 25 chemical elements are essential to life. As you can see in Table 2.1, four of these—oxygen (O), carbon (C), hydrogen (H), and nitrogen (N)—make up about 96% of the weight of the human body, as well as that of most other living organisms. These four elements are the main ingredients of biological molecules such as proteins, sugars, and fats. Calcium (Ca), phosphorus (P), potassium (K), sulfur (S), sodium (Na), chlorine (Cl), and magnesium (Mg) account for most of the remaining 4% of the human body. These elements are involved in such important functions as bone formation, nerve signaling, and DNA synthesis.

TABLE 2.1	ELEMENTS IN THE HUMAN BODY	
Element	Symbol	Percentage of Human Body Weight
Oxygen	O	65.0 ⎫
Carbon	C	18.5 ⎪
Hydrogen	H	9.56 ⎬ 96.3
Nitrogen	N	3.3 ⎭
Calcium	Ca	1.5
Phosphorus	P	1.0
Potassium	K	0.4
Sulfur	S	0.3
Sodium	Na	0.2
Chlorine	Cl	0.2
Magnesium	Mg	0.1

Trace elements (less than 0.01%): boron (B), chromium (Cr), cobalt (Co), copper (Cu), fluorine (F), iodine (I), iron (Fe), manganese (Mn), molybdenum (Mo), selenium (Se), silicon (Si), tin (Sn), vanadium (V), and zinc (Zn).

The **trace elements** listed at the bottom of the table are essential, but only in minute quantities. We explore the importance of trace elements to your health next.

Web Process of Science *Connection: How Are Space Rocks Analyzed for Signs of Life?*

? Which four chemical elements are most abundant in living matter?

■ Oxygen, carbon, hydrogen, and nitrogen

2.2 Trace elements are common additives to food and water

Some trace elements, such as iron (Fe), are needed by all forms of life. Iron makes up only 0.004% of your body mass but is vital for energy processing and for transporting oxygen in your blood. Other trace elements, such as iodine (I), are required only by certain species. The average human needs about 0.15 milligram (mg) of iodine each day. Iodine is an essential ingredient of a hormone produced by the thyroid gland, which is located in the neck. An iodine deficiency in the diet causes the thyroid gland to grow to abnormal size, a condition called goiter. The goiter of the woman shown in Figure 2.2A can probably be reversed by iodine supplements. Adding iodine to table salt has reduced the incidence of goiter in many countries. Indeed, the salt on your table is probably iodized; check

the label on the box. Unfortunately, iodized salt is not available or affordable everywhere, and goiter still affects many thousands of people in developing nations.

Iodine is just one example of a trace element added to food or water to improve health. For

Figure 2.2A Goiter in a Malaysian woman, a symptom of iodine deficiency

more than 50 years, the American Dental Association has supported fluoridation of community drinking water supplies as a public health measure. Fluoride is a form of fluorine (F), an element in Earth's crust that is found in small amounts in all water sources. In many areas, fluoride is added as part of the municipal water treatment process to raise levels to a concentration that can reduce tooth decay. If you mostly drink bottled water, your fluoride intake may be reduced, although some bottled water now contains added fluoride.

Chemicals are added to food to help preserve it, make it more nutritious, or simply make it look better. Look at the nutrition facts label from the side of the cereal box in Figure 2.2B to see a familiar example of how foods are fortified with mineral elements. Iron, for example, is a trace element commonly added to foods. (You can actually see the iron that has been added to a fortified cereal by crushing the cereal and then stirring a magnet through it.) Also note that the nutrition facts label lists numerous vitamins that are added to improve the nutritional value of the cereal. For instance, the cereal in this example supplies 10% of the recommended daily value for vitamin A. Vitamins consist of more than one element and are examples of compounds, which we consider next.

? In addition to iron, what other trace elements have been added to the cereal in Figure 2.2B? Does *Total* provide the "total" amount needed of these elements?

■ Zinc and copper: Total provides 100% of the zinc but only 4% of the copper needed in a day.

Figure 2.2B Nutrition facts from a fortified cereal

Nutrition Facts
Serving Size ¾ cup (30g)
Servings Per Container about 17

Amount Per Serving	Whole Grain Total	with ½ cup skim milk
Calories	100	140
Calories from Fat	5	10
	% Daily Value	
Total Fat 0.5g*	1%	1%
Saturated Fat 0g	0%	0%
Trans Fat 0g		
Polyunsaturated Fat 0g		
Monounsaturated Fat 0g		
Cholesterol 0mg	0%	1%
Sodium 190mg	8%	11%
Potassium 90mg	3%	8%
Total Carbohydrate 23g	8%	10%
Dietary Fiber 3g	10%	10%
Sugars 5g		
Other Carbohydrate 15g		
Protein 2g		
Vitamin A	10%	15%
Vitamin C	100%	100%
Calcium	100%	110%
Iron	100%	100%
Vitamin D	10%	25%
Vitamin E	100%	100%
Thiamin	100%	100%
Riboflavin	100%	110%
Niacin	100%	100%
Vitamin B₆	100%	100%
Folic Acid	100%	100%
Vitamin B₁₂	100%	110%
Pantothenic Acid	100%	100%
Phosphorus	8%	20%
Magnesium	6%	10%
Zinc	100%	100%
Copper	4%	4%

* Amount in cereal. A serving of cereal plus skim milk provides 1g total fat, less than 5mg cholesterol, 260mg sodium, 290mg potassium, 29g total carbohydrate (11g sugars) and 7g protein.
** Percent Daily Values are based on a 2,000 calorie diet. Your daily values may be higher or lower depending on your calorie needs:

		Calories	2,000	2,500
Total Fat	Less than		65g	80g
Sat Fat	Less than		20g	25g
Cholesterol	Less than		300mg	300mg
Sodium	Less than		2,400mg	2,400mg
Potassium			3,500mg	3,500mg
Total Carbohydrate			300g	375g
Dietary Fiber			25g	30g

2.3 Elements can combine to form compounds

A **compound** is a substance consisting of two or more different elements combined in a fixed ratio. Compounds are much more common than pure elements. In fact, few elements exist in a pure state in nature.

Many compounds consist of only two elements; for instance, table salt (sodium chloride, NaCl) has equal parts of the elements sodium and chlorine. Pure sodium is a metal and pure chlorine is a poisonous gas. Chemically combined, however, they form an edible compound (Figure 2.3). The elements hydrogen (H) and oxygen (O) exist as gases. Combined in a ratio of 2 : 1, they form the most abundant compound on Earth, water (H_2O). These are simple examples of organized matter having emergent properties: A compound has characteristics different from those of its elements.

Most of the compounds in living organisms contain at least three or four elements, mainly carbon, hydrogen, oxygen, and nitrogen. Sugar, for example, is formed of just carbon, hydrogen, and oxygen. The formic acid produced by ants (see chapter introduction) is also formed from those three elements. Proteins are compounds containing carbon, hydrogen, oxygen, nitrogen, and a small amount of sulfur. Different arrangements of the atoms of these elements determine unique properties for each compound.

Each element has its own kind of atom. In the next module we explore the structure of an atom and then see how this structure determines the chemical properties of elements.

Sodium + Chlorine → Sodium Chloride

Figure 2.3 The emergent properties of the edible compound sodium chloride

? Explain how table salt illustrates the theme of emergent properties.

■ We are able to eat table salt, showing that it has properties different from those of a metal and a poisonous gas.

Introduction to Organic Compounds

3.1 Life's molecular diversity is based on the properties of carbon

3.2 Characteristic chemical groups help determine the properties of organic compounds

3.3 Cells make a huge number of large molecules from a small set of small molecules

Carbohydrates

3.4 Monosaccharides are the simplest carbohydrates

3.5 Cells link two single sugars to form disaccharides

3.6 What is high-fructose corn syrup and is it to blame for obesity?

3.7 Polysaccharides are long chains of sugar units

Lipids

3.8 Fats are lipids that are mostly energy-storage molecules

3.9 Phospholipids and steroids are important lipids with a variety of functions

3.10 Anabolic steroids pose health risks

Proteins

3.11 Proteins are essential to the structures and functions of life

3.12 Proteins are made from amino acids linked by peptide bonds

3.13 A protein's specific shape determines its function

3.14 A protein's shape depends on four levels of structure

3.15 Linus Pauling contributed to our understanding of the chemistry of life

Nucleic Acids

3.16 Nucleic acids are information-rich polymers of nucleotides

3.17 Lactose tolerance is a recent event in human evolution

Model of a
milk-digesting enzyme

Got Lactose?

Is a big glass of milk a way to a healthy diet—or an upset stomach? For much of the world's population, the answer is often the latter. Most of the world's people cannot easily digest milk-based foods. Those who can happily devour ice cream and cheese, scientists have found, are in the minority, benefiting from a lucky connection between human evolution and the major molecules that shape life.

Milk and other dairy products have long been recognized as highly nutritious foods, rich in protein and minerals necessary for healthy teeth and strong bones. But for millions of people, those health benefits come with a heavy dose of digestive discomfort. Such people suffer from lactose intolerance, or the inability to properly break down lactose, the main sugar found in milk.

For those with lactose intolerance, the problem starts once lactose passes through the stomach and enters the small intestine. There, to absorb the sugar, digestive cells need to secrete an enzyme called lactase, which is necessary for the breakdown of lactose. (An enzyme, such as the one shown above, is a protein that speeds up a specific chemical reaction.) Those with lactose intolerance, however, produce insufficient amounts of the enzyme. Without enough lactase, lactose cannot be digested or absorbed properly, leading to uncomfortable symptoms that include nausea, cramps, and bloating.

Scientists who study the problem have known for many years that the condition is closely tied to age and heritage. When it comes to milk, most people are born equal. Nearly everyone produces enough lactase in infancy to digest the lactose in breast milk and dairy products. Thus, milk—high in protein, fats, and sugars—provides excellent nourishment for infants. But after the age of 2, lactase levels start to decline in most of the world's populations, as if the lactase-producing mechanism in the body is being slowly shut down. In the United States, researchers have noted, as many as 75% of African Americans and Native Americans and 90% of Asian Americans are lactase-deficient once they reach their teenage years. People of European descent make up one of the few groups with relatively low levels of lactose intolerance; only about 15% are believed to suffer from the problem.

Why would lactose intolerance be linked with ancestry? It appears that the majority of humans do not produce lactase as adults. Indeed, lactose-intolerance is the normal human condition. The ability to digest milk after childhood is due to a mutation that allows lactase production to continue into adulthood. About 9,000 years ago, this beneficial mutation spread among cultures in northern Europe as they began to raise dairy herds and consume greater quantities of dairy products. And the mutation was passed down to their descendants.

What works for this lactose-tolerant minority, however, can mean more complicated eating for the rest of the world. There is no treatment for the underlying genetic cause of lactase deficiency, and lactose is now used widely in everything from bottled salad dressings and lunch meat to prescription drugs. But the condition's uncomfortable symptoms can be controlled through diet. People with lactose intolerance must watch what they eat and how much milk-based food they consume. Some avoid foods that contain lactose altogether, and doctors and nutritionists advise such people to take calcium supplements and vitamins. Others turn to substitutes: In many Asian cultures, for example, beverages have long been made from soy or rice instead of milk. Other foods are prepared from milk that has been pre-treated with lactase. Lactase, in pill form, can also be taken along with food to ease digestion.

Lactose intolerance, with its interplay between genes and milk sugar, illustrates the importance of biological molecules to the functioning of living cells and to human health. In people who easily digest milk, lactose, a sugar, is broken down by lactase, a protein, which is produced by a gene, made of DNA, a nucleic acid. If the gene for lactase production is not active, lactase is not present. And the presence of lactase can mean the difference between delight and discomfort when someone contemplates an ice cream sundae. Such molecular interactions, repeated in countless variations, drive all biological processes. In this chapter, we explore the structure and function of sugars, proteins, fats, and nucleic acids—the biological molecules that are essential to life. We begin with a look at carbon, the versatile atom at the center of life's molecules. ■ ■ ■

Introduction to Organic Compounds

3.1 Life's molecular diversity is based on the properties of carbon

Almost all the molecules a cell makes are composed of carbon atoms bonded to one another and to atoms of other elements. Carbon is unparalleled in its ability to form large, diverse molecules. The diversity of carbon compounds is the foundation for the myriad of molecules and chemical processes required for life. This diversity has also made possible the great diversity of organisms that have evolved on Earth.

Carbon-based molecules are called **organic compounds.** As we discussed in Chapter 2, an element's chemical properties are determined by the electrons in the outermost shell of its atoms. A carbon atom has four outer electrons in a shell that holds eight. Carbon completes its outer shell by sharing electrons with other atoms in four covalent bonds (see Module 2.8). Thus, each carbon atom is a connecting point from which a molecule can branch in up to four directions.

Figure 3.1A illustrates three representations of methane (CH_4), one of the simplest organic molecules. The structural formula shows that covalent bonds link four hydrogen atoms to the carbon atom. Each of the four lines in the formula represents a pair of shared electrons. The two models show that methane is three-dimensional, with the space-filling version portraying its overall shape more accurately. The ball-and-stick model shows that carbon's four bonds (the gray "sticks") angle out toward the corners of an imaginary tetrahedron (an object with four triangular sides). The red lines trace this shape, with the four hydrogen atoms of methane at the corners of the tetrahedron. This tetrahedral shape occurs wherever a carbon atom participates in four single bonds. Different bond angles occur where carbon atoms form double bonds. Large organic molecules can have elaborate shapes. And, as we will see many times, the shape of a molecule often determines its function.

Methane and other compounds composed of only carbon and hydrogen are called **hydrocarbons.** Figure 3.1B illustrates some variations in hydrocarbon structure. Carbon atoms, with attached hydrogens, can bond together in chains of various lengths to form compounds such as ethane or propane, a gas used as household fuel. The chain of carbon atoms in an organic molecule is called a **carbon skeleton** (shaded in gray in Figure 3.1B). Carbon skeletons can be unbranched, as in butane, or

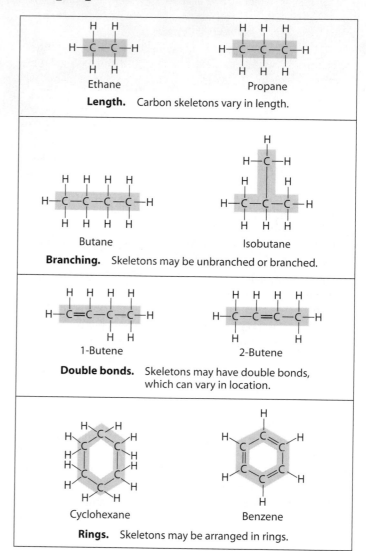

Length.   Carbon skeletons vary in length.

Branching.   Skeletons may be unbranched or branched.

Double bonds.   Skeletons may have double bonds, which can vary in location.

Rings.   Skeletons may be arranged in rings.

Figure 3.1B   Variations in carbon skeletons

branched, as in isobutane. Carbon skeletons may also include double bonds, as in 1-butene and 2-butene. These two compounds have the same molecular formula, C_4H_8, but differ in the position of their double bond. Compounds with the same formula but different structures are called **isomers.** Their different shapes result in unique properties. Cyclohexane and benzene, the only hydrocarbons in the figure that are liquids rather than gases, are examples of carbon skeletons arranged in rings.

A general characteristic of all hydrocarbons is that they are nonpolar molecules due to their nonpolar C—H bonds.

Web Activity *Diversity of Carbon-Based Molecules*

?   Why do isomers, which have the same formula (same number of atoms), have different properties?

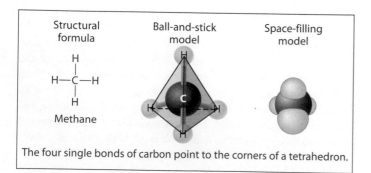

The four single bonds of carbon point to the corners of a tetrahedron.

Figure 3.1A   Three representations of methane (CH_4)

■ Isomers have different structures, or shapes, and the shape of a molecule usually helps determine the way it functions—how it interacts with other molecules.

3.2   Characteristic chemical groups help determine the properties of organic compounds

The unique properties of an organic compound depend on the size and shape of its carbon skeleton and on the groups of atoms that are attached to that skeleton.

Table 3.2 illustrates six chemical groups important in the chemistry of life. The first five chemical groups shown are **functional groups.** They affect a molecule's function by participating in chemical reactions in characteristic ways. These groups are polar, because their oxygen or nitrogen atoms exert a strong pull on shared electrons. This polarity tends to make the compounds containing these groups **hydrophilic** (water-loving) and therefore soluble in water—a necessary condition for their roles in water-based life. The methyl group is nonpolar and not reactive, but it affects molecular shape and thus function.

A **hydroxyl group** consists of a hydrogen atom bonded to an oxygen atom, which in turn is bonded to the carbon skeleton. Ethanol, shown in the table, and other organic compounds containing hydroxyl groups are called alcohols.

In a **carbonyl group** a carbon atom is linked by a double bond to an oxygen atom. If the carbon of the carbonyl group is at the end of a carbon skeleton, the compound is called an aldehyde; if it is within the chain, the compound is called a ketone. Sugars contain a carbonyl group and several hydroxyl groups.

A **carboxyl group** consists of a carbon double-bonded to an oxygen and also bonded to a hydroxyl group. The carboxyl group acts as an acid by contributing an H^+ to a solution (see Module 2.15) and becoming ionized. Compounds with carboxyl groups are called carboxylic acids. Acetic acid, shown in the table, gives vinegar its sour taste.

An **amino group** is composed of a nitrogen bonded to two hydrogen atoms and the carbon skeleton. It acts as a base by picking up an H^+ from a solution. Organic compounds with an amino group are called amines. Amino acids, the building blocks of proteins, contain a carboxyl and an amino group.

A **phosphate group** consists of a phophorus atom bonded to four oxygen atoms. It is usually ionized and attached to the carbon skeleton by one of its oxygen atoms. This structure is

TABLE 3.2	FUNCTIONAL GROUPS OF ORGANIC COMPOUNDS
Functional Group	**Examples**
Hydroxyl group —OH	*Alcohol*
Carbonyl group >C=O	*Aldehyde* *Ketone*
Carboxyl group —COOH	*Carboxylic acid* *Ionized*
Amino group —NH₂	*Amine* *Ionized*
Phosphate group —OPO₃²⁻	*Organic phosphate (ATP)*
Methyl group —CH₃	*Methylated compound*

abbreviated as Ⓟ in this text. Compounds with phosphate groups are called organic phosphates and are often involved in energy transfers, as is the energy compound ATP.

A **methyl group** consists of a carbon bonded to three hydrogens. Compounds with methyl groups are called methylated compounds. The addition of a methyl group to the component of DNA shown in the table affects the expression of genes.

Figure 3.2 compares female and male sex hormones. They differ only in the chemical groups, highlighted with colored boxes. These subtle differences result in the different actions of these molecules, which help produce the features of females and males in humans and other vertebrates.

Web Activity *Functional Groups*

❓ Identify the chemical groups that do *not* contain carbon.

■ The amino, hydroxyl, and phosphate groups

Figure 3.2   Differences in the chemical groups of sex hormones

3.3 Cells make a huge number of large molecules from a small set of small molecules

The four main classes of large biological molecules are carbohydrates, lipids, proteins, and nucleic acids. On a molecular scale, many of these molecules are gigantic; in fact, biologists call them **macromolecules.** Proteins, for example, may consist of thousands of covalently connected atoms.

Cells make most of their large molecules by joining smaller molecules into chains called **polymers** (from the Greek *polys,* many, and *meros,* part). A polymer is a long molecule consisting of many identical or similar building blocks strung together, much as a train consists of many individual cars. The building blocks of polymers are called **monomers.**

The Diversity of Polymers Living cells make a vast number of different polymers. For proteins alone, there are about a trillion different kinds in nature, and the variety is potentially endless. Remarkably, a cell makes all of its diverse macromolecules from a small list of ingredients—about 40 to 50 common components and a few others that are rare. Proteins, for example, are built from only 20 kinds of amino acids. DNA is built from just four kinds of monomers called nucleotides. As we will see, the key to the great diversity of protein and DNA molecules is arrangement—variation in the sequence in which their monomers are strung together.

The variety in polymers accounts for the uniqueness of each organism. The monomers used to make polymers, however, are essentially universal. Your proteins and those of a tree or ant are assembled from the same 20 amino acids; the amino acids are just arranged in different sequences. Life has a simple yet elegant molecular logic: Small molecules common to all organisms are ordered into large molecules, which vary from species to species and even from individual to individual.

Making Polymers Cells link monomers together to form polymers by a **dehydration reaction,** a reaction that removes a molecule of water. As you can see in Figure 3.3A, an unlinked monomer has a hydroxyl group (—OH) at one end and a hydrogen atom (—H) at the other. For each monomer added to a chain, a water molecule (H_2O) is removed. Notice that two monomers contribute to the H_2O molecule, one monomer (the one at the right end of the short polymer in this example) losing a hydroxyl group and the other monomer losing a hydrogen atom. As this occurs, a new covalent bond forms, linking the two monomers. Dehydration reactions are the same regardless of the type of polymer the cell is producing.

Breaking Polymers Cells not only make macromolecules but also have to break them down. For example, food that an organism ingests is often in the form of polymers that are much too large to enter its cells. To digest these polymers, a cell carries out **hydrolysis.** Essentially the reverse of a dehydration reaction, hydrolysis means to break (*lyse*) with water (*hydro-*), and cells break bonds between monomers by adding water to them, as Figure 3.3B shows. In the process, a hydroxyl group

Figure 3.3A Dehydration reactions build a polymer chain

Figure 3.3B Hydrolysis breaks a polymer chain

joins to one monomer, and a hydrogen joins to the adjacent monomer.

The lactose-intolerant individuals you learned about in the chapter introduction are unable to hydrolyze such a bond in lactose because they lack the enzyme lactase. Both dehydration reactions and hydrolysis require the help of enzymes to make and break bonds. **Enzymes** are specialized macromolecules that speed up chemical reactions in cells.

In the remainder of the chapter, we explore each of the four classes of large biological molecules. We will see that polysaccharides, proteins, and nucleic acids are polymers assembled by dehydration reactions from their monomers. Lipids are not true polymers. However, some lipids are formed by dehydration reactions from several smaller molecules.

Like water and simple organic molecules, large biological molecules have unique emergent properties arising from the orderly arrangement of their atoms. As you will see, for these molecules of life, structure and function are inseparable.

Web Activity *Making and Breaking Polymers*

? Suppose you eat some cheese. What reactions must occur for the amino acid monomers in the protein of the cheese to be converted to proteins in your body?

■ In digestion, the amino acids are released by hydrolysis. New proteins are formed in your body from these monomers in dehydration reactions.

3.4 Monosaccharides are the simplest carbohydrates

The name **carbohydrate** refers to a class of molecules ranging from the small sugar molecules dissolved in soft drinks to large polysaccharides, such as the starch molecules we consume in pasta and potatoes.

The carbohydrate monomers (single-unit sugars) are **monosaccharides** (from the Greek *monos-*, single, and *sacchar*, sugar). The honey shown in **Figure 3.4A** consists mainly of monosaccharides called glucose and fructose. These and other single-unit sugars can be hooked together by a dehydration reaction to form more complex sugars and polysaccharides.

Monosaccharides generally have molecular formulas that are some multiple of CH_2O. For example, the formula for glucose, a common monosaccharide of central importance in the chemistry of life, is $C_6H_{12}O_6$. **Figure 3.4B** illustrates the molecular structure of glucose; its carbons are numbered 1 to 6. This structure also shows the two trademarks of a sugar: a number of hydroxyl groups ($—OH$) and a carbonyl group ($>C=O$). The hydroxyl groups make a sugar an alcohol, and the carbonyl group, depending on its location, makes it either an aldose (an aldehyde sugar) or a ketose (a ketone sugar). As you see in Figure 3.4B, glucose is an aldose and fructose is a ketose. (Note that most names for sugars end in *-ose*.)

If you count the numbers of different atoms in the fructose molecule in Figure 3.4B, you will find that its molecular formula is $C_6H_{12}O_6$, identical to that of glucose. Thus, glucose and fructose are isomers; they differ only in the arrangement of their atoms (in this case, the positions of the carbonyl groups, highlighted in blue). Seemingly minor differences like this give isomers different properties, such as how they react with other molecules. In this case, the differences also make fructose taste considerably sweeter than glucose.

The carbon skeletons of both glucose and fructose are six carbon atoms long, whereas other monosaccharides have three to seven carbon atoms. The five-carbon sugars, called pentoses, and the six-carbon sugars, called hexoses, are among the most common.

It is convenient to draw sugars as if their carbon skeletons were linear, but in aqueous solutions, most monosaccharides form rings, as shown for glucose in **Figure 3.4C**. To form the glucose ring, carbon 1 bonds to the oxygen attached to carbon 5. As shown in the middle representation, the ring diagram of glucose and other sugars may be abbreviated by not showing the carbon atoms at the corners of the ring. Also, the bonds in the ring are often drawn with varied thickness, indicating that the ring is a relatively flat structure with atoms and functional groups, such as $—OH$, extending above and below it. The simplified ring symbol on the right is often used in this book to represent glucose.

Monosaccharides, particularly glucose, are the main fuel molecules for cellular work. Cells also use the carbon skeletons of monosaccharides as raw material for manufacturing other kinds of organic molecules, including amino acids. Monosaccharides that cells do not use immediately are usually incorporated into disaccharides and polysaccharides, as described next.

Web Activity *Models of Glucose*

? Write the formula for a monosaccharide that has three carbons.

∎ $C_3H_6O_3$

Figure 3.4A Bees with honey, a mixture of two monosaccharides

Glucose
(an aldose)

Fructose
(a ketose)

Figure 3.4B Structures of glucose and fructose

Structural formula

Abbreviated structure

Simplified structure

Figure 3.4C Three representations of the ring form of glucose

3.5 Cells link two single sugars to form disaccharides

Cells construct a **disaccharide** from two monosaccharides by a dehydration reaction. Figure 3.5 shows how maltose, also called malt sugar, forms from two glucose monomers. One monomer gives up a hydroxyl group and the other gives up a hydrogen atom from a hydroxyl group. As H_2O forms, an oxygen atom is left, linking the two monomers. Maltose, which is common in germinating seeds, is used in making beer, malted milk shakes, and malted milk candy.

The most common disaccharide is sucrose, which is made of a glucose monomer linked to a fructose monomer. The main carbohydrate in plant sap, sucrose nourishes all the parts of the plant. We extract it from the stems of sugarcane or the roots of sugar beets to use as table sugar.

? Lactose, as you read in the chapter introduction, is the disaccharide sugar in milk. It is formed from glucose and galactose. The formula for both these monosaccharides is $C_6H_{12}O_6$. What is the formula for lactose?

■ $C_{12}H_{22}O_{11}$

Figure 3.5 Disaccharide formation by a dehydration reaction

Connection

3.6 What is high-fructose corn syrup and is it to blame for obesity?

If you want to sweeten your coffee or tea, you probably reach for sugar—the disaccharide sucrose. But if you drink sodas or fruit drinks, you're probably consuming the monosaccharides of sucrose in the form of high-fructose corn syrup. In fact, if you look at the label of almost any processed food, you will see high-fructose corn syrup listed as one of the ingredients (Figure 3.6). And if you listen to news reports or read health-related articles, you have probably heard high-fructose corn syrup named as a likely culprit in the "obesity epidemic."

What is high-fructose corn syrup (HFCS)? Let's start with the corn syrup part. The main carbohydrate in corn is starch, a polysaccharide. Industrial processing hydrolyzes starch into its component monomers, glucose, producing corn syrup. Glucose, however, does not taste as sweet to us as sucrose. Fructose, on the other hand, tastes much sweeter than both glucose and sucrose. When a new process was developed in the 1970s that used an enzyme to rearrange the atoms of glucose into the sweeter isomer, fructose (see Figure 3.4B), the high-fructose corn syrup industry was born. (High-fructose corn syrup is a bit of a misnomer, however, because the fructose syrup produced is combined with regular corn syrup to produce a mixture of about 55% fructose and 45% glucose, not much different from the proportions in sucrose.)

Figure 3.6 HFCS, a main ingredient of soft drinks and processed foods

This clear, goopy liquid is cheaper than sugar and easier to mix into drinks and processed food. And it contains basically the same monosaccharides as sucrose, the disaccharide it is replacing. So is there a problem with HFCS? Some point to circumstantial evidence. From 1980 to 2000, the incidence of obesity doubled in the United States. In that same time period, the consumption of HFCS more than tripled, whereas the consumption of refined cane and beet sugar decreased 21%. The combined per capita consumption of HFCS and refined sugars was 33 kilograms (73 lb) in 1980 and 41.4 kg (91.3 lb) in 2000, a 25% increase. In 2005, that consumption was down somewhat to 39.7 kg: 19.2 kg of HFCS and 20.5 kg of sucrose. That still translates to about 26 teaspoons of added sweeteners a day.

So, is HFCS to blame for increases in obesity, type 2 diabetes, and other chronic diseases associated with increased weight? Scientific studies are ongoing, and the jury is still out. There is consensus, however, that overconsumption of either sweetener along with dietary fat and decreased physical activity contribute to weight gain. In addition, high sugar consumption also tends to replace eating more varied and nutritious foods. Sugars have been described as "empty calories" because they contain only neglibile amounts of other nutrients. For good health, we require proteins, fats, vitamins, and minerals, as well as complex carbohydrates, the topic of the next module.

? How is high-fructose corn syrup made from corn?

■ Corn starch is hydrolyzed to glucose, then enzymes convert glucose to fructose. This fructose is combined with corn syrup to produce HFCS.

3.7 Polysaccharides are long chains of sugar units

Polysaccharides are polymers of monosaccharides linked together by dehydration reactions. Polysaccharides may function as storage molecules or as structural compounds. Figure 3.7 illustrates three common types of polysaccharides.

Starch, a storage polysaccharide in plants, consists entirely of glucose monomers. Starch molecules coil into a helical shape because of the angles of the bonds joining their glucose units. A starch helix may be unbranched (as shown in the figure) or branched. Plant cells, like animal cells, need sugar for energy and as raw material for building other molecules. Plant cells often contain starch granules from which they can withdraw glucose by hydrolysis. Humans and most other animals also have enzymes that can hydrolyze plant starch to provide a source of glucose. Potatoes and grains, such as wheat, corn, and rice, are the major sources of starch in the human diet.

Animals store excess sugar in the form of another glucose polysaccharide, called **glycogen.** Glycogen is more highly branched than starch, as shown in the figure. Most of our glycogen is stored as granules in our liver and muscle cells, which hydrolyze the glycogen to release glucose when it is needed.

Cellulose, the most abundant organic compound on Earth, forms cablelike fibrils in the tough walls that enclose plant cells. Cellulose is also a polymer of glucose, but its glucose monomers are linked together in a different orientation. (Carefully compare the oxygen "bridges" highlighted in yellow between glucose monomers in starch, glycogen, and cellulose in the figure.) Arranged parallel to each other, cellulose molecules are joined by hydrogen bonds, forming part of a fibril. In wood, layers of cellulose fibrils combine with other polymers, making a material strong enough to support trees hundreds of feet high.

Most animals do not have enzymes that can hydrolyze the glucose linkages in cellulose. Therefore, cellulose is not a nutrient for humans, although it does contribute to digestive system health. The cellulose that passes unchanged through our digestive tract is commonly known as "insoluble fiber." Fresh fruits, vegetables, and grains are rich in fiber. Animals that do derive nutrition from cellulose, such as cows and termites, have cellulose-hydrolyzing prokaryotes inhabiting their digestive tracts.

Another structural polysaccharide, **chitin,** is used by insects and crustaceans to build their exoskeleton, the hard case enclosing the animal. Chitin is also found in the cell walls of fungi. Humans use chitin to make a strong and flexible surgical thread that decomposes after a wound or incision heals.

Almost all carbohydrates are hydrophilic owing to the many hydroxyl groups attached to their sugar monomers (see Figure 3.4B). Thus, cotton bath towels, which are mostly cellulose, are quite water absorbent. Next we look at a class of macromolecules that are not soluble in water.

Web Activity *Carbohydrates*

? Compare and contrast starch and cellulose, two plant polysaccharides.

■ Both are polymers of glucose, but the bonds between glucose monomers have different shapes. Starch functions mainly for sugar storage. Cellulose is a structural polysaccharide that is the main material of cell walls.

Figure 3.7
Polysaccharides

Starch granules in potato tuber cells

Glycogen granules in muscle tissue

Cellulose fibrils in a plant cell wall

Cellulose molecules

STARCH

Glucose monomer

GLYCOGEN

CELLULOSE

OH

Hydrogen bonds

OH

Lipids

3.8 Fats are lipids that are mostly energy-storage molecules

Lipids are diverse compounds that are grouped together because they share one trait: They mix poorly, if at all, with water. Lipids consist mainly of carbon and hydrogen atoms linked by nonpolar covalent bonds. In contrast to carbohydrates and most other biological molecules, lipids are **hydrophobic** (water-fearing). You can see the effect of this chemical difference in a bottle of salad dressing: The oil (a type of lipid) separates from the vinegar (which is mostly water). Other oils make the feathers in Figure 3.8A repel water, which you see as beads on the surface. By keeping feathers from absorbing water, oils help waterfowl such as ducks stay afloat.

Oils are a liquid fat. A **fat** is a large lipid made from two kinds of smaller molecules: glycerol and fatty acids. Shown at the top in Figure 3.8B, glycerol is an alcohol with three carbons, each bearing a hydroxyl group. A fatty acid consists of a carboxyl group (the functional group that gives these molecules the name fatty *acid*) and a hydrocarbon chain, usually 16 or 18 carbon atoms in length. The carbons in the chain are linked to each other and to hydrogen atoms by nonpolar covalent bonds, making the hydrocarbon chain hydrophobic.

The main function of fats is energy storage. A gram of fat stores more than twice as much energy as a gram of a polysaccharide such as starch. This compact energy storage enables a mobile animal, such as a duck or a human, to get around much better than if the animal had to lug its stored energy around in the bulkier form of a carbohydrate. In addition to storing energy, fatty tissue cushions vital organs and insulates the body.

Figure 3.8B shows how one fatty acid molecule can link to a glycerol molecule by a dehydration reaction. Linking three fatty acids to glycerol produces a fat, as illustrated in Figure 3.8C. A synonym for fat is *triglyceride*, a term you may see on food labels or on medical tests for fat in the blood. The three fatty acids in a fat are often of different kinds, as in our example.

As shown in the third fatty acid in Figure 3.8C, some fatty acids contain double bonds, which cause kinks (or bends) in the carbon chain. Double bonds prevent the maximum number

Figure 3.8B A dehydration reaction linking a fatty acid to glycerol

Figure 3.8C A fat molecule made from glycerol and three fatty acids

of hydrogen atoms from bonding to a carbon skeleton. Fatty acids and fats with double bonds in the carbon chain are said to be **unsaturated**—that is, having less than the maximum number of hydrogens. Fats with the maximum number of hydrogens are said to be **saturated.** The kinks in unsaturated fats prevent the molecules from packing tightly together and solidifying at room temperature. Corn oil, olive oil, and other vegetable oils are unsaturated fats. When you see "hydrogenated vegetable oils" on a margarine label, it means that unsaturated fats have been converted to saturated fats by adding hydrogen. Unfortunately, hydrogenation also creates trans fats, a form of fat that recent research associates with heart disease.

Most plant fats are unsaturated oils, whereas most animal fats are saturated. Their fatty acid chains pack closely together, which is why butter and beef fat are solid at room temperature. Diets rich in saturated fats and trans fats may contribute to cardiovascular disease by promoting atherosclerosis. In this condition, lipid-containing deposits called plaques build up within the walls of blood vessels, reducing blood flow.

? On a food package, what does "unsaturated fats" mean?

Figure 3.8A Water beading on the oily coating of feathers

■ Unsaturated fats are fats with some double bonds in the carbon chain of their fatty acids. These fats have fewer hydrogen atoms than they would without the double bonds.

3.9   Phospholipids and steroids are important lipids with a variety of functions

Cells could not exist without **phospholipids,** the major component of cell membranes. Phospholipids are structurally similar to fats, but they contain only two fatty acids attached to glycerol instead of three. In place of the third fatty acid is a negatively charged phosphate group. The structure of phospholipids provides a classic example of how form fits function, as we will explore further in Module 4.5. The hydrophilic and hydrophobic ends of multiple molecules assemble in a bilayer of phospholipids to form membranes (Figure 3.9A). The hydrophobic tails cluster in the center, and the hydrophilic phosphate heads face the watery environment on both sides of the membrane.

Steroids are lipids whose carbon skeleton contains four fused rings, as shown in the structural diagram of cholesterol in Figure 3.9B. (The diagram omits the carbons making up the rings and most of the chain and also the hydrogens attached to these carbons.) **Cholesterol** is a common component in animal cell membranes, and animal cells also use it as a starting material for making other steroids, including sex hormones. Different steroids vary in the chemical groups attached to the rings, as you saw in Figure 3.2. Too much cholesterol in the blood may contribute to atherosclerosis.

Web Activity *Lipids*

Figure 3.9A   Section of a phospholipid membrane

Figure 3.9B Cholesterol, a steroid

?   Why are human sex hormones considered lipids?

■ They are steroids, one of the hydrophobic compounds grouped as lipids.

3.10   Anabolic steroids pose health risks

Anabolic steroids are synthetic variants of the male hormone testosterone. Testosterone causes a general buildup of muscle and bone mass in males during puberty and maintains masculine traits throughout life. Because anabolic steroids structurally resemble testosterone, they also mimic some of its effects. (Anabolic comes from *anabolism,* the building of substances by the body.)

As prescription drugs, anabolic steroids are used to treat general anemia and diseases that destroy body muscle. However, some individuals abuse these drugs, with serious consequences. Overdosing may cause violent mood swings ("steroid rage") and deep depression. The liver may be damaged, leading to cancer. The use of anabolic steroids can also alter cholesterol levels and lead to high blood pressure, increasing the risk of cardiovascular problems. Use of these drugs often makes the body reduce its output of natural male sex hormones, which can cause shrunken testicles, reduced sex drive, infertility, and breast enlargement in men. Use in women has been linked to menstrual cycle disruption and development of masculine characteristics. A serious effect in teens is that bones may stop growing, stunting growth.

Despite the risks, some athletes use steroids to gain a competitive edge. Meanwhile, sports organizations ban their use, implement drug testing, and penalize violators in an effort to counter an environment in which athletes feel they have to take performance-enhancing drugs just to stay competitive.

In 2003, the discovery of a new designer steroid rocked the sports world. THG, short for tetrahydrogestrinone, is a chemically modified ("designer") steroid intended to avoid detection in ordinary drug testing. Once the U.S. Anti-Doping Agency received a sample of the drug, the agency was able to develop a test for it. This test revealed the substance's use among some high-profile track and field athletes as well as professional football players. The U.S. Food and Drug Administration declared THG an illegal steroid, and athletic governing bodies from the Olympics to swimming, soccer, football, and baseball organizations now prohibit its use.

Unscrupulous chemists, as well as dishonest trainers, coaches, and athletes, will continue to try to find ways to best the system, while the U.S. Congress, professional sports authorities, and most high school and college athletic programs struggle to keep the competition fair and protect the health of athletes.

?   What kind of carbon ring structure would you find in an anabolic steroid?

■ Four fused carbon rings: three six-sided and one five-sided, as in all steroids

3.11 Proteins are essential to the structures and functions of life

The name *protein*, from the Greek word *proteios*, meaning "first place," suggests the importance of this class of macromolecules. A **protein** is a polymer constructed from amino acid monomers. Each of our many thousands of different proteins has a unique three-dimensional structure that corresponds to a specific function. Proteins are important to the structures of cells and organisms and participate in everything they do.

Probably the most important role for proteins is as *enzymes*, the chemical catalysts that speed and regulate virtually all chemical reactions in cells. Lactase, which you read about in the chapter introduction, is just one of the thousands of different enzymes produced by body cells.

In Figure 3.11, you can see examples of two other types of proteins. *Structural proteins* are found in hair and the fibers that make up connective tissues such as tendons and ligaments. Muscles contain *contractile proteins*.

Other types of proteins include *defensive proteins,* such as the antibodies of the immune system, and *signal proteins,* such as many of the hormones and other messengers that help co-ordinate body activities by communicating between cells. *Receptor proteins* may be built into cell membranes and transmit signals into cells. Hemoglobin in red blood cells is a *transport protein* that delivers O_2 to working muscles. Different transport proteins move sugar molecules into cells for energy. Other proteins are *storage proteins,* such as ovalbumin, the protein of egg white, which serves as a source of amino acids for developing embryos. Milk proteins provide amino acids for baby mammals, and plants have storage proteins for the developing embryos in seeds.

As we see next, this huge diversity of proteins is based on just 20 building blocks.

Web Activity *Protein Functions*

? Which of the following is not a protein: hemoglobin, cholesterol, ovalbumin, an enzyme, an antibody?

■ Cholesterol

Figure 3.11 Structural proteins of hair, tendons, and ligaments; and contractile proteins of muscles

3.12 Proteins are made from amino acids linked by peptide bonds

Of all of life's molecules, proteins are the most elaborate and the most diverse in structure and function. Protein diversity is based on differing arrangements of a common set of just 20 amino acids. **Amino acids** all have an amino group and a carboxyl group (which makes it an acid, hence the name *amino acid*). As you can see in the general structure shown in Figure 3.12A, both of these functional groups are covalently bonded to a central carbon atom, called the alpha carbon. Also bonded to the alpha carbon is a hydrogen atom and a chemical group symbolized by the letter R. The R group, also called the side chain, differs with each amino acid. In the simplest amino acid (glycine), the R group is just a hydrogen atom. In others, such as those in Figure 3.12B, the R group consists of one or more carbon atoms with various chemical groups attached. The structure of the R group determines the specific properties of each of the 20 amino acids that are found in proteins (see Appendix 3).

The amino acids in Figure 3.12B represent two main types, hydrophobic and hydrophilic. Leucine (abbreviated Leu) is an example of an amino acid whose R group is nonpolar and hydrophobic. Serine (Ser), with a hydroxyl group in its R group,

Amino group   Carboxyl group

Figure 3.12A General structure of an amino acid

Leucine (Leu)   Serine (Ser)   Aspartic acid (Asp)

Hydrophobic   **Hydrophilic**

Figure 3.12B Examples of amino acids with hydrophobic and hydrophilic R groups.

is an example of an amino acid with a polar, hydrophilic R group. Aspartic acid (Asp) is acidic and negatively charged at the pH of a cell. (Indeed, the amino and carboxyl groups of amino acids are usually ionized at cellular pH, as shown in Table 3.2.) Other amino acids have basic R groups and are positively charged. Amino acids with polar and charged R groups help proteins dissolve in the aqueous solutions inside cells.

Now that we have examined amino acids, let's see how they are linked to form polymers. Cells join amino acids together in a dehydration reaction that links the carboxyl group of one amino acid to the amino group of the next amino acid as a water molecule is removed (Figure 3.12C). The resulting covalent linkage is called a **peptide bond.** The product of the reaction shown in the figure is called a *di*peptide, because it was made from *two* amino acids. Additional amino acids can be added by the same process to form a chain of amino acids, a **polypeptide.** To release amino acids from the polypeptide by hydrolysis, a molecule of H_2O must be added back to each peptide bond.

How is it possible to make thousands of different kinds of proteins from just 20 amino acids? The answer has to do with sequence. You know that thousands of English words can be made by varying the sequence of 26 letters. Although the protein alphabet is slightly smaller (just 20 "letters"), the "words" are much longer. Most polypeptides are at least 100 amino acids in length; some are a thousand or more. Each polypeptide has a unique sequence of amino acids. But a long polypeptide chain of specific sequence is not the same as a protein, any more than a long strand of yarn is the same as a sweater. A functioning protein is one or more polypeptide chains precisely coiled, twisted, and folded into a unique three-dimensional shape.

? In what way is the production of a dipeptide similar to the production of a disaccharide?

■ In both cases, the monomers are joined by a dehydration reaction.

Figure 3.12C
Peptide bond formation

Carboxyl group

Amino group

Amino acid + Amino acid

Dehydration reaction

H_2O

Peptide bond

Dipeptide

3.13 A protein's specific shape determines its function

Figure 3.13A shows a ribbon model of lysozyme, an enzyme found in our tears and white blood cells. Lysozyme consists of one long polypeptide, represented by the purple ribbon. Lysozyme's general shape is called globular. This overall shape is more apparent in **Figure 3.13B**, a space-filling model of lysozyme. (The colors represent different atoms: gray for carbon, red for oxygen, blue for nitrogen. The barely visible yellow balls are sulfur atoms that form the stabilizing bonds shown as yellow lines in the ribbon model.) Most enzymes and other proteins are globular. Structural proteins, such as those making up hair and tendons, are typically long and thin—fibrous.

General shape is one thing; specific shape is another. The coils and twists of lysozyme's polypeptide ribbon appear haphazard, but they represent the molecule's specific, three-dimensional shape, and this shape is what determines its specific function. Nearly all proteins must recognize and bind to some other molecule to function. Lysozyme, for example, can destroy bacterial cells, but first it must bind to specific molecules on the bacterial cell surface. Lysozyme's specific shape enables it to recognize and attach to its molecular target, which fits into the groove you see on the right in the figures.

The dependence of protein function on a protein's specific shape becomes clear when proteins are altered. In a process called **denaturation,** polypeptide chains unravel, losing their specific shape and, as a result, their function. Changes in salt concentration and pH can denature many proteins, as can excessive heat. For example, visualize what happens when you fry an egg. Heat quickly denatures the clear proteins surrounding the yolk, making them solid, white, and opaque. One of the reasons why extremely high fevers are so dangerous is that some proteins in the body become denatured and cannot function.

Given the proper cellular environment, a newly synthesized polypeptide chain spontaneously folds into its functional shape. We examine the four levels of a protein's structure next.

MP3 Tutor *Protein Structures and Function*

? Why does a denatured protein no longer function normally?

■ The function of each protein is a consequence of its specific shape, which is lost when a protein denatures.

Figure 3.13A
Ribbon model of the protein lysozyme

Groove

Figure 3.13B
Space-filling model of lysozyme

Groove

A protein's shape depends on four levels of structure

Primary Structure The **primary structure** of a protein is its unique sequence of amino acids. As an example, let's consider transthyretin, an important transport protein found in our blood. It is a globular molecule whose specific shape enables it to transport two key chemicals throughout the body, vitamin A and a hormone from the thyroid gland. A complete molecule of transthyretin has four polypeptide chains, each made up of 127 amino acids. Figure 3.14A on the next page shows part of one of these chains partially unraveled for a closer look at its primary structure. The three-letter abbreviations represent amino acids. One of the 20 amino acids occupies each of the 127 positions along the chain.

For this or any other protein to perform its specific function, it must have the correct amino acids arranged in a precise order. The primary structure of a protein is determined by inherited genetic information. Even a slight change in a protein's primary structure may affect its overall shape and its ability to function. For instance, a single amino acid change in hemoglobin, the oxygen-carrying blood protein, causes sickle-cell disease, a serious blood disorder.

Secondary Structure In the second level of protein structure, parts of the polypeptide coil or fold into local patterns called **secondary structure.** Coiling of a polypeptide chain results in a secondary structure called an **alpha helix;** a certain kind of folding leads to a **pleated sheet.** Both of these patterns are maintained by regularly spaced hydrogen bonds between the hydrogens of the $>$N—H groups and the oxygens of the $>$C$=$O groups of neighboring peptide bonds along the polypeptide chain. The hydrogen bonds are represented in Figure 3.14B by a row of dots. Because the R groups of the amino acids are not involved in the hydrogen bonds forming these secondary structures, they are omitted from the diagrams.

Transthyretin has only one alpha-helix region (see Figure 3.14C). In contrast, many fibrous proteins, such as the structural protein of hair, have the alpha-helix structure over most of their length. Pleated sheets make up the core of many globular proteins, as is the case for transthyretin. Pleated sheets also dominate some fibrous proteins, including the silk protein of a spider's web, shown to the left. The teamwork of so many hydrogen bonds makes each silk fiber of a web as strong as steel. Potential uses of spider silk proteins include surgical thread, fishing line, and bulletproof vests.

Tertiary Structure The term **tertiary structure** refers to the overall three-dimensional shape of a polypeptide. As already mentioned, most tertiary structures can be roughly described as either globular or fibrous. As you can see in Figure 3.14C, a transthyretin polypeptide has a generally globular shape, which results from the compact combination of an alpha helix and several pleated-sheet regions. The indentations and bulges arising from its particular arrangement of coils and folds give the polypeptide the specific shape that fits it to its function.

Tertiary structure generally results from interactions among the R groups of the amino acids making up the polypeptide. For example, globular proteins found in aqueous solutions such as transthyretin are folded so that the hydrophobic R groups are on the inside of the molecule and the hydrophilic groups on the outside, exposed to water. In addition to the clustering of hydrophobic groups, hydrogen bonding between polar side chains and ionic bonding of some of the charged R groups help maintain the tertiary structure. A protein's shape may be reinforced further by covalent bonds called disulfide bridges. The yellow lines in Figure 3.13A represent disulfide bridges.

Quaternary Structure Many proteins consist of two or more polypeptide chains, or subunits. Such proteins have a **quaternary structure,** resulting from the association of the subunits. Figure 3.14D shows a complete transthyretin molecule with its four identical globular subunits.

Another example of a protein with quaternary structure is collagen, shown to the right. Collagen is a fibrous protein with helical subunits intertwined into a larger triple helix. This arrangement gives the long fibers great strength, suited to their function as the girders of connective tissue in skin, bone, tendons, and ligaments. (Collagen accounts for 40% of the protein in a human body.)

Polypeptide chain

Collagen

Many other proteins have subunits that are different from one another. For example, the oxygen-transporting molecule hemoglobin has four subunits of two distinct types (see Figure 22.11). Each subunit also has a nonprotein component, called a heme, with an iron atom that binds oxygen.

What happens if a protein folds incorrectly? Many diseases, such as Alzheimer's and Parkinson's, involve an accumulation of misfolded proteins. Prions are infectious mishapened proteins that are associated with serious degenerative brain diseases such as mad cow disease (see Module 10.21). Such diseases reinforce the theme that structure fits function: A protein's unique three-dimensional shape determines its proper functioning.

Web Activity *Protein Structure*

? If a genetic mutation changes the primary structure of a protein, how might this destroy the protein's function?

■ Primary structure, the amino acid sequence, affects the secondary structure, which affects the tertiary structure, which affects the quaternary structure (if any). Thus primary structure affects the shape of the protein, and the function of a protein depends on its shape.

Four Levels of Protein Structure

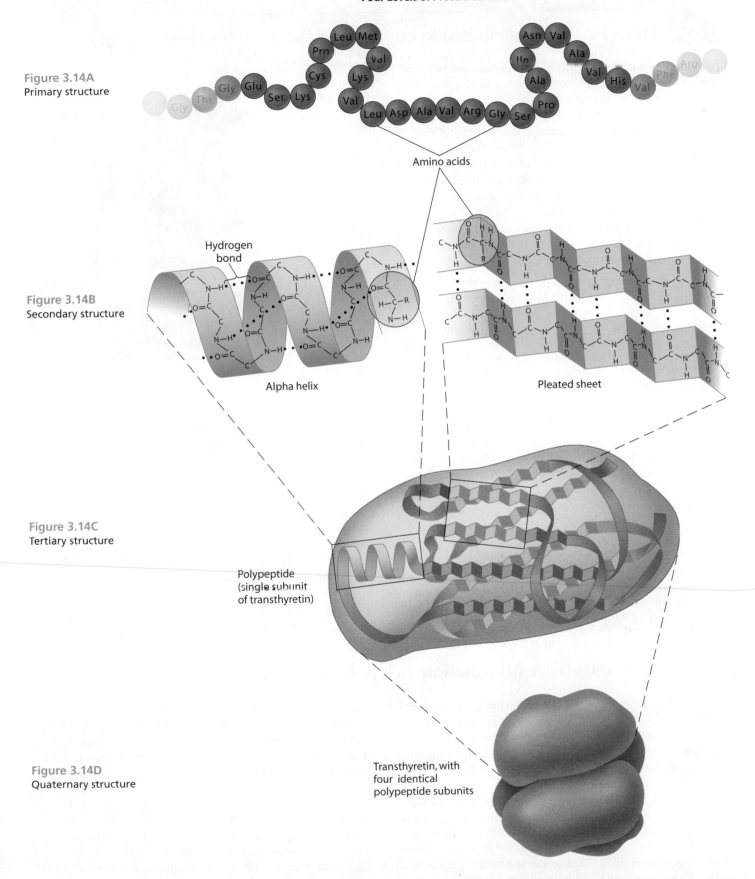

Figure 3.14A
Primary structure

Amino acids

Hydrogen
bond

Figure 3.14B
Secondary structure

Alpha helix

Pleated sheet

Figure 3.14C
Tertiary structure

Polypeptide
(single subunit
of transthyretin)

Figure 3.14D
Quaternary structure

Transthyretin, with
four identical
polypeptide subunits

3.15 Linus Pauling contributed to our understanding of the chemistry of life

Linus Pauling, one of the giants of 20th-century science, made extraordinary contributions to both science and human affairs. Driven by the desire "to understand the world," Pauling started out in chemistry and physics. He published a series of papers on chemical bonding that eventually led to a Nobel Prize in Chemistry in 1954. By that time, Pauling was also studying biological molecules. In 1935, he and a colleague discovered how oxygen molecules attach to the iron atoms of hemoglobin. He also discovered how an abnormal hemoglobin molecule causes sickle-cell disease. And it was Pauling who first described the two fundamental secondary structures of proteins, the alpha helix and the pleated sheet (Figure 3.15). In an interview a number of years ago, he recounted that work:

> I began trying to find the structure of proteins in 1937, and didn't succeed. So I began working with my collaborators to determine the three-dimensional structures of amino acids and simple peptides. In 1937, no one had yet determined such structures. . . . And then in 1948 I found the alpha-helix and pleated-sheet structures in proteins. . . . I'm surprised that nobody else had done this job in the 11 years that intervened—in a sense, surprised that I hadn't done it in '37, when my ideas were all the right ones. I just hadn't worked hard enough.

Pauling's efforts were not limited to science. He also became the scientific community's leading advocate for halting the testing of nuclear weapons. As a result of his politics, the U.S. State Department viewed him as a threat and revoked his passport. Nevertheless, in 1963 he received the Nobel Peace Prize for helping produce a ban on nuclear testing. Pauling is the only person to receive two unshared Nobel Prizes.

The cancellation of Pauling's passport in 1952 kept him from working directly with scientists in Europe. This may have

Figure 3.15
Linus Pauling with a model of the alpha helix in 1948

prevented Pauling from earning a third Nobel Prize, for at that time he was hot on the trail of the structure of DNA. But his triple-helix model was wrong, and it was James Watson and Francis Crick, working in England, who came up with the correct solution—a double helix, which we describe in the next module.

? **What contribution did Pauling make to our understanding of protein structure?**

■ He identified the alpha helix and pleated sheet of secondary structure.

Nucleic Acids

3.16 Nucleic acids are information-rich polymers of nucleotides

The primary structure of polypeptides determines the shape of a protein. But what determines the primary structure? The amino acid sequence of a polypeptide is programmed by a discrete unit of inheritance known as a **gene.** Genes consist of **DNA (deoxyribonucleic acid),** one of the two types of polymers known as **nucleic acids.**

A gene does not put its genetic DNA information to work directly. It works through an intermediary—the second type of nucleic acid known as **ribonucleic acid (RNA).** DNA is transcribed into RNA, which is then translated into the primary structure of polypeptides. We return to this chain of command and the functions of DNA and RNA later in the book.

The monomers that make up nucleic acids are **nucleotides.** As indicated in Figure 3.16A, each nucleotide has three parts.

One part is a five-carbon sugar (blue); DNA has deoxyribose (shown in Figure 3.16A), whereas RNA has a slightly different sugar called ribose. Linked to one side of the sugar in both types of nucleic acid is a phosphate group (yellow). Linked to the sugar's other side is a nitrogenous base (green), a molecular structure containing carbon and nitrogen. (The nitrogen atoms tend to take up H^+ from solution, which is why it is called a nitrogenous *base.*) DNA has the nitrogenous bases adenine (A), thymine (T), cytosine (C), and guanine (G). RNA also has A, C, and G, but instead of thymine, it has uracil (U).

Like polysaccharides and polypeptides, a nucleic acid polymer—a polynucleotide—forms from its monomers by dehydration reactions. In this process, the phosphate group of one nucleotide bonds to the sugar of the next monomer. The result

Figure 3.16A A nucleotide, consisting of a phosphate group, sugar, and a nitrogenous base

Phosphate group

Nitrogenous base (adenine)

Sugar

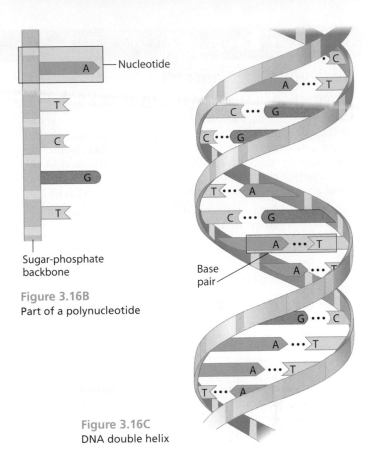

Nucleotide

Sugar-phosphate backbone

Figure 3.16B
Part of a polynucleotide

Base pair

Figure 3.16C
DNA double helix

is a repeating sugar-phosphate backbone in the polymer, as represented by the blue and yellow ribbon in Figure 3.16B.

RNA usually consists of a single polynucleotide strand, but DNA is a **double helix,** in which two polynucleotides wrap around each other (Figure 3.16C). The nitrogenous bases protrude from the two sugar-phosphate backbones into the center of the helix. There they always pair up as shown: A pairs with T, and C pairs with G. The two DNA chains are held in a double helix by hydrogen bonds (dotted lines) between their paired bases. Most DNA molecules have thousands or even millions of base pairs.

An organism's genes determine the proteins and thus the structures and functions of its body. Let's return to the subject of the chapter introduction—lactose intolerance—to conclude our study of biological molecules. In the next chapter, we move up in the biological hierarchy to the level of the cell.

🎧 **MP3 Tutor** *DNA Structure*

Web Activity *Nucleic Acid Structure*

Web Process of Science *Connection: What Factors Determine the Effectiveness of Drugs?*

? How are the two types of nucleic acids functionally related?

■ The hereditary material of DNA contains the instructions for the primary structure of polypeptides. RNA is the intermediary that translates those instructions into the order of amino acids.

Evolution Connection

3.17   Lactose tolerance is a recent event in human evolution

As you'll recall from the chapter introduction, the majority of people stop producing the enzyme lactase in early childhood and thus do not easily digest the milk sugar lactose. Researchers suspected that there must be a genetic link to explain the regional distribution of lactose tolerance and intolerance. In 2002, American and Finnish scientists completed a study of the genes of 196 lactose-intolerant adults of African, Asian, and European descent. They determined that lactose intolerance is actually the human norm. It is "lactose tolerance" that represents a relatively recent mutation in the human genome.

The ability to make lactase into adulthood is concentrated in people of northern European descent, and the researchers speculated that lactose tolerance became widespread among this group because it offered a survival advantage. In northern Europe's relatively cold climate, only one harvest a year is possible. For earlier humans, that meant nonplant sources of food often had to be found. Cattle were first domesticated in northern Europe about 9,000 years ago. With milk and other dairy products at hand year-round, natural selection would have favored anyone with a mutation that kept the lactase gene switched on.

Researchers wondered whether the lactose tolerance mutation found in Europeans might be present in other cultures who kept dairy herds. Indeed, a 2006 study compared the genetic makeup and lactose tolerance of 43 ethnic groups in East Africa. The researchers identified three mutations, all different from each other and from the European mutation, that keep the lactase gene permanently turned on. The mutations appear to have occurred beginning around 7,000 years ago, around the time that archaeological evidence shows the domestication of cattle in these African regions.

Mutations that confer a selective advantage, such as surviving cold winters or withstanding drought by drinking milk, spread rapidly in these early pastoral peoples. Their evolutionary and cultural history is thus recorded in their genes and in their continuing ability to digest milk.

? Explain how lactose intolerance involves three of the four major classes of biological macromolecules.

■ Lactose, milk sugar, is a carbohydrate that is hydrolyzed by the enzyme lactase, a protein. The ability to make this enzyme and the regulation of when it is made is coded for in DNA, a nucleic acid.

Chapter Review

Reviewing the Concepts

Introduction to Organic Compounds (3.1–3.3)

Carbon. Carbon's ability to bond with four other atoms is the basis for building large and diverse organic compounds. Hydrocarbons are composed of only carbon and hydrogen. Isomers have the same molecular formula but different structures (**3.1**). Characteristic chemical groups, such as the hydrophilic functional groups, give organic molecules specific properties (**3.2**).

Polymers. A huge number of different polymers are built from a small number of monomers (**3.3**).

Carbohydrates (3.4–3.7)

Monosaccharides. A monosaccharide has a formula that is a multiple of (CH_2O) and contains hydroxyl groups and a carbonyl group. Two monosaccharides join to form a disaccharide (**3.4–3.5**). High-fructose corn syrup is commonly added to drinks and processed foods (**3.6**).

Polysaccharides are polymers of monosaccharides, such as glucose. Starch and glycogen are storage polysaccharides; cellulose is structural, found in plant cell walls. Chitin is a component of insect exoskeletons and fungal cell walls (**3.7**).

Lipids (3.8–3.10)

Lipids, diverse compounds composed largely of carbon and hydrogen, are grouped together because they are hydrophobic. Fats, also called triglycerides, are energy-storage molecules consisting of glycerol linked to three fatty acids (**3.8**). Other lipids include phospholipids (found in cell membranes), and steroids such as cholesterol (**3.9**). Use of anabolic steroids by athletes can cause serious health problems (**3.10**).

Proteins (3.11–3.15)

Proteins are involved in almost all of a cell's activities; as enzymes, they regulate chemical reactions (**3.11**).

Amino acids. Protein diversity is based on different sequences of amino acids, monomers that contain an amino group, a carboxyl group, an H, and an R group, all attached to a central carbon. The R groups distinguish 20 amino acids, each with specific properties. Amino acids are linked together by peptide bonds to form polypeptides (**3.12**).

Protein structure. A protein consists of one or more polypeptide chains folded into a unique shape that determines the protein's function (**3.13**). A protein's primary structure is the sequence of amino acids forming its polypeptide chains. Its secondary structure is the coiling or folding of the chain, stabilized by hydrogen bonds. Tertiary structure is the overall three-dimensional shape of a polypeptide, resulting from interactions among R groups. Proteins made of more than one polypeptide have quaternary structure (**3.14**). Linus Pauling made important contributions to our understanding of proteins (**3.15**)

Nucleic Acids (3.16–3.17)

Nucleic acids. DNA and RNA serve as the blueprints for proteins and thus control the life of a cell. The monomers of nucleic acids are nucleotides, composed of a sugar, a phosphate group, and a nitrogenous base. DNA is a double helix; RNA is a single-stranded polynucleotide (**3.16**). Mutations in DNA have led to lactose tolerance in several human groups whose ancestors raised dairy cattle (**3.17**).

Connecting the Concepts

1. The diversity of life is staggering. Yet the molecular logic of life is simple and elegant: Small molecules common to all organisms are ordered into unique macromolecules. Explain why carbon is central to this diversity of organic molecules. How do carbon skeletons, chemical groups, monomers, and polymers relate to this molecular logic of life?

2. There are four classes of organic molecules that are essential to all living organisms. Complete the following table to help review the structures and functions of these macromolecules.

Classes of macromolecules and their components		Functions	Examples
Carbohydrates Monosaccharides		Energy for cell, raw material	a. _____
		b. _____	Starch, glycogen
		Plant cell support	c. _____
Lipids (don't form polymers) Glycerol Fatty acid Components of a fat molecule		Energy storage	d. _____
		e. _____	Phospholipids
		Hormones	f. _____
Proteins g. ____ h. ____ i. ____ Amino acid		j. _____	Lactase
		k. _____	Hair, tendons
		l. _____	Muscles
		Transport	m. _____
		Communication	Signal proteins
		n. _____	Antibodies
		Storage	Egg albumin
		Receive signals	Receptor protein
Nucleic Acids o. ____ p. ____ q. ____ Nucleotide		Heredity	r. _____
		s. _____	DNA and RNA

Testing Your Knowledge

Multiple Choice

3. A glucose molecule is to starch as (*Explain your answer.*)
   a. a steroid is to a lipid.
   b. a protein is to an amino acid.
   c. a nucleic acid is to a polypeptide.
   d. a nucleotide is to a nucleic acid.
   e. an amino acid is to a nucleic acid.

4. What makes a fatty acid an acid?
   a. It does not dissolve in water.
   b. It is capable of bonding with other molecules to form a fat.
   c. It has a carboxyl group that donates an H^+ ion to a solution.
   d. It contains only two oxygen atoms.
   e. It is a polymer made of many smaller subunits.

5. Where in the tertiary structure of a water-soluble protein would you most likely find an amino acid with a hydrophobic R group?
   a. at both ends of the polypeptide chain
   b. on the outside, next to the water
   c. covalently bonded to another R group
   d. on the inside, away from water
   e. hydrogen-bonded to nearby amino acids

6. Cows can derive nutrients from cellulose because
   a. they produce enzymes that recognize the shape of the glucose-glucose bonds and hydrolyze them.
   b. they rechew their cud to break down cellulose fibers.
   c. one of their stomachs contains prokaryotes that can hydrolyze the bonds of cellulose.
   d. their intestinal tract contains termites, which produce enzymes to hydrolyze cellulose.
   e. they convert cellulose to starch and can digest starch.

7. A shortage of phosphorus in the soil would make it especially difficult for a plant to manufacture
   a. DNA.   d. fatty acids.
   b. proteins.   e. sucrose.
   c. cellulose.

8. Lipids differ from other macromolecules in that they
   a. are much larger.
   b. are not truly polymers.
   c. do not have specific shapes.
   d. are nonpolar and therefore hydrophilic.
   e. contain nitrogen atoms.

9. Which functional group (or groups) is polar and tends to make organic compounds hydrophilic?
   a. carbonyl   d. carboxyl
   b. amino   e. all of the above
   c. hydroxyl

10. Unsaturated fats
    a. are more common in animals than in plants.
    b. have fewer fatty acid molecules per fat molecule.
    c. are associated with greater health risks than are saturated fats.
    d. have double bonds in their fatty acid chains.
    e. are usually solid at room temperature.

Describing, Comparing, and Explaining

11. List three different kinds of lipids and describe their functions.

12. Explain why heat, pH changes, and other environmental changes can interfere with a protein's function.

13. How can a cell make many different kinds of protein out of only 20 amino acids? Of the myriad possibilities, how does the cell "know" which proteins to make?

14. Briefly describe the various functions performed by proteins in a cell.

15. Explain how DNA controls the functions of a cell.

16. Sucrose is broken down in your intestine to the monosaccharides glucose and fructose, which are then absorbed into your blood. What is the name of this type of reaction? Using this diagram of sucrose, show how this would occur.

Sucrose

17. Circle and name the functional groups in this organic molecule. What type of compound is this? For which class of macromolecules is it a monomer?

Applying the Concepts

18. Toward the end of his 93 years, Pauling was most often associated with his controversial belief that large doses of vitamin C can help prevent the common cold, cancer, and other diseases. Imagine you are applying for a research grant from the National Institutes of Health to evaluate Pauling's claims. How would you go about setting up an experimental study to determine whether vitamin C can prevent colds? How would you evaluate your results?

19. Enzymes usually function best at an optimal pH and temperature. The following graph shows the effectiveness of two enzymes at various temperatures.

   a. At which temperature does enzyme A perform best? Enzyme B?
   b. One of these enzymes is found in humans and the other in thermophilic (heat-loving) bacteria. Which enzyme would you predict comes from which organism?
   c. From what you know about enzyme structure, explain why the rate of the reaction catalyzed by enzyme A slows down at temperatures above 40 °C.

20. Some scientists hypothesize that life elsewhere in the universe might be based on the element silicon rather than on carbon. Look at the electron shell diagrams in Figure 2.6. What properties does silicon share with carbon that would make silicon-based life more likely than, for example, neon-based or sulfur-based life?

Answers to all questions can be found in Appendix 4.

For Practice Quizzes, BioFlix, MP3 Tutors, and Activities, go to www.mybiology.com.

chapter

4

A Tour of the Cell

Introduction to the Cell

4.1 Microscopes reveal the world of the cell
4.2 Most cells are microscopic
4.3 Prokaryotic cells are structurally simpler than eukaryotic cells
4.4 Eukaryotic cells are partitioned into functional compartments
4.5 The structure of membranes correlates with their functions

Cell Structures Involved in Manufacturing and Breakdown

4.6 The nucleus is the cell's genetic control center
4.7 Ribosomes make proteins for use in the cell and export
4.8 Overview: Many cell organelles are connected through the endomembrane system
4.9 The endoplasmic reticulum is a biosynthetic factory
4.10 The Golgi apparatus finishes, sorts, and ships cell products
4.11 Lysosomes are digestive compartments within a cell
4.12 Vacuoles function in the general maintenance of the cell
4.13 A review of the structures involved in manufacturing and breakdown

Energy-Converting Organelles

4.14 Mitochondria harvest chemical energy from food
4.15 Chloroplasts convert solar energy to chemical energy
4.16 Mitochondria and chloroplasts evolved by endosymbiosis

Internal and External Support: The Cytoskeleton and Cell Surfaces

4.17 The cell's internal skeleton helps organize its structure and activities
4.18 Cilia and flagella move when microtubules bend
4.19 Problems with sperm motility may be environmental or genetic
4.20 The extracellular matrix of animal cells functions in support, movement, and regulation
4.21 Three types of cell junctions are found in animal tissues
4.22 Cell walls enclose and support plant cells

Functional Categories of Cell Structures

4.23 Review: Eukaryotic cell structures can be grouped on the basis of four basic functions

Cells on the Move

Movement might seem like a characteristic of life—at least animal life and the lives of some single-celled organisms. For example, any biology student who has tried to chase a *Paramecium* under a microscope knows that some protists move quite fast. When you think about cells of the human body, you probably know that sperm cells swim and white blood cells creep about, engulfing bacteria and debris from injury sites. You may also realize that, unfortunately, cancer cells move, letting go of connections with neighboring cells and migrating to other tissues, where their rapid cell divisions establish secondary tumors. The **micrograph** (photo taken through a microscope) on the facing page shows beautiful but deadly cancer cells in the midst of dividing. (Part of their beauty comes from the fluorescently colored stains that selectively attach to certain components of the cells.)

But what about plant cells? Or bacteria? Do they move? In 1665 Robert Hooke used a crude microscope to examine a piece of bark (cork). Hooke compared these structures to "little rooms"—*cellulae* in Latin—and the term *cells* stuck. These cells certainly did not move, because they were merely the outer cell walls of former plant cells.

But some of the cells viewed by Hooke's contemporary, Antoni van Leeuwenhoek, did move. Working in the late 1600s with refined lenses that he crafted, Leeuwenhoek examined numerous subjects, from human blood and sperm to pond water. His reports to the Royal Society of London included drawings and descriptions of his discoveries. About what he found in the scrapings from his teeth he wrote, "I then most always saw, with great wonder, that in the said matter there were many very little living animalcules, very prettily a-moving. The biggest sort . . . shot through the spittle like a pike does through the water. The second sort . . . oft-times spun round like a top." Indeed, Leeuwenhoek was the first to observe and describe bacteria.

Leeuwenhoek established that some bacterial cells move. In fact, we now know that some move at incredible speeds. For example, *Bdellovibrio bacteriophorus* is a bacterium that attacks other bacteria. It can charge its prey at up to 100 µm/sec,* comparable to a human running 600 km/hr (about 375 mi/hr). It

*Metric measurements are described in Table 4.1 on the following page.

then bores into its hapless victim by spinning at 100 revolutions per second. Most bacteria aren't quite that fast, but they can locomote with whipping flagella or by spiraling through their environment.

But can plant cells move as well? If you look through a microscope at a thin piece of the common aquarium plant *Elodea*, you may see green chloroplasts marching in an orderly procession around the perimeter of the cells. The micrograph pictured above shows what such plant cells would look like, minus the movement. The fact is that all living cells have movement inside, even if they are anchored within a leaf or attached to other cells in your body. Whereas some cells are motile and move from place to place, all cells have internal structures that move about and interact.

Since the days of Leeuwenhoek and Hooke, improved microscopes have vastly expanded our view of the intricate structures within a cell. Photography and electronic imaging now enable biologists to capture microscope images directly. But just as Hooke and Leeuwenhoek illustrated what they saw, drawings and diagrams are still important in helping us understand the microscopic world. You will see in this chapter, for example, that the use of different colors in drawings makes it easier to distinguish between the various cellular structures, most of which are actually colorless. You will also notice that drawings are often paired with micrographs of cell structures. This pairing provides the best of both worlds: The micrograph shows a structure as a biologist sees it, and the drawing helps you understand the microgaph by emphasizing specific details.

But neither drawings nor micrographs allow you to see the movement that is characteristic of all living cells. For that you need to look for yourself through a microscope or view videos in lecture or on websites, such as the one associated with this book. As you study the still images in this textbook, remind yourself that these cellular parts aren't static—they move.

This chapter focuses on the cellular structures that microscopes have revealed and describes their functions in a living cell. Cells are dynamic, moving, living systems. As you learn about their parts, remember that the phenomenon we call life emerges from the arrangement and interactions of the components of a cell. ■ ■ ■

4.1 Microscopes reveal the world of the cell

Our understanding of nature often parallels the invention and refinement of instruments that extend human senses to new limits. Before microscopes were first used in the 17th century, no one knew that living organisms were composed of cells. The first microscopes were light microscopes, like the ones you may use in a biology laboratory. A **light microscope (LM),** such as the one shown in Figure 4.1A, works by passing visible light through a specimen, such as a microorganism or a thin slice of animal or plant tissue. Glass lenses in the microscope bend the light to magnify the image of the specimen and project the image into the viewer's eye or onto photographic film or a video screen.

Magnification is the increase in the apparent size of an object. Figure 4.1B shows a protist called *Paramecium*. The notation "LM 230×" printed along the right edge of this micrograph is one we use throughout this book. It tells you that the photograph was taken through a light microscope and that this image is about 230 times the actual size of the organism. This *Paramecium* is about 0.33 mm in length. Table 4.1 gives the most common units of length that biologists use. (As you can see, the units are metric, so conversions are easy.) Although this image could be magnified further, additional magnification would not allow us to see more detail. Indeed, at higher magnification, the image would become blurrier. Light microscopes can effectively magnify objects only about 1,000 times.

Thus, another important factor in microscopy (the use of a microscope) is *resolution,* a measure of the clarity of an image. Resolution is the ability of an optical instrument to show two close objects as separate. For example, what looks to your unaided eye like a single star in the sky may be resolved as two separate stars with the help of a telescope.

Any optical device—be it an eye, a telescope, or a microscope—has a limit to its resolution. The human eye cannot resolve details finer than 0.1 mm. The light microscope can resolve objects as small as 0.2 micrometer, about the size of the smallest bacterium. (As you can see in the table, a micrometer (μm) is one-thousandth of a millimeter. The μ in the abbreviation for micrometer is the Greek letter mu.) But no matter how many times its image of such a bacterium is magnified, the light microscope cannot show the details of this small cell's structure.

Enlarges image formed by objective lens { Eyepiece — Ocular lens —

Magnifies specimen, forming primary image — Objective lens —

Specimen —

Focuses light through specimen

Condenser lens —

Light source —

Figure 4.1A Light microscope (LM)

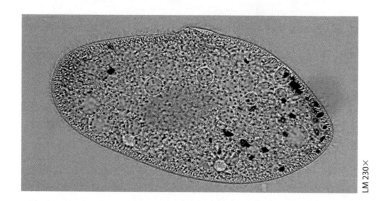

LM 230×

Figure 4.1B Light micrograph of a protist, *Paramecium*

From the year 1665, when Robert Hooke discovered cells, until the middle of the 20th century, biologists had only light microscopes for viewing cells. With these microscopes, they discovered a great deal, including microorganisms, the cells composing animal and plant tissues, and also some of the structures within cells. By the mid-1800s, these discoveries led to the **cell theory,** which states that all living things are composed of cells and that all cells come from other cells.

Our knowledge of cell structure took a giant leap forward as scientists began using the electron microscope in the 1950s. Instead of light, the **electron microscope (EM)** uses a beam of electrons. The EM has a much greater resolution than the light microscope. It can distinguish biological structures as small as about 2 nanometers (nm), a hundredfold improvement over the light microscope. This high resolution has allowed biologists to explore cellular *ultrastructure,* the complex internal anatomy of a cell. The highest power electron micrographs you will see in this book have magnifications of about 100,000 times.

Figures 4.1C and 4.1D on the next page show images produced by two kinds of electron microscopes. Biologists use the **scanning electron microscope (SEM)** to study the detailed architecture of cell surfaces. The SEM uses an electron beam to

TABLE 4.1	MEASUREMENT EQUIVALENTS
1 meter (m) = 10^0 m = 39.37 inches	
1 millimeter (mm) = 10^{-3} m (1/1,000 m) = 0.04 inch	
1 micrometer (μm) = 10^{-3} mm = 10^{-6} m (1/1,000,000 m)	
1 nanometer (nm) = 10^{-3} μm = 10^{-9} m (1/1,000,000,000 m)	
1 meter = 10^3 mm = 10^6 μm = 10^9 nm	

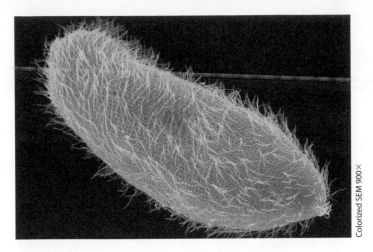

Figure 4.1C Scanning electron micrograph of *Paramecium*

Figure 4.1D Transmission electron micrograph of *Paramecium*

Figure 4.1E Micrograph produced by differential interference-contrast microscopy of *Paramecium*

scan the surface of a cell or group of cells that has been coated with a thin film of metal. When the surface is hit by the beam, it emits electrons. The electrons are detected by a device that then translates their pattern into an image projected onto a video screen. The scanning electron micrograph in Figure 4.1C highlights the numerous cilia on a *Paramecium,* projections it uses for movement. Many structural details of cell surfaces have been discovered using the SEM. As you can see, the SEM produces images that look three-dimensional.

The **transmission electron microscope (TEM)** (Figure 4.1D) is used to study the details of internal cell structure. Specimens are cut into extremely thin sections and stained with atoms of heavy metals, which attach to certain cellular structures more than others. The TEM aims an electron beam through the thin section, just as a light microscope aims a beam of light through a specimen. The image is created by the pattern of transmitted electrons. Instead of using glass lenses, the TEM uses electromagnets as lenses to bend the paths of the electrons, magnifying and focusing an image onto a viewing screen or photographic film. The micrograph in Figure 4.1D shows internal details of *Paramecium* as seen with the TEM. SEMs and TEMs are initially black and white but are often artificially colorized to highlight or clarify structural features.

Electron microscopes have truly revolutionized the study of cells and their structures. Nonetheless, they have not replaced the light microscope. One problem is that electron microscopes cannot be used to study living specimens because the methods used to prepare the specimen kill the cells. For a biologist studying a living process, such as the movement of *Paramecium,* a light microscope equipped with a video camera is more suitable than either an SEM or a TEM.

There are different types of light microscopy, each using different techniques to enhance contrast and selectively highlight cellular components. Figure 4.1E shows a *Paramecium,* as seen using differential interference-contrast microscopy. This optical technique amplifies differences in density while still allowing living cells to be examined. Figure 4.1F is a striking example of fluorescence and confocal microscopy. In this technique, specific molecules are tagged with fluorescent dyes, which selectively bind to various cellular molecules. A type of "optical sectioning" technique then brings a very thin section of

Figure 4.1F Micrograph produced by fluorescence confocal microscopy, showing nerve cells growing in tissue culture

the cell into focus. By capturing sharp, in-focus images at many different planes, a three-dimensional reconstruction of the sample can be created. You will see many beautiful examples of fluorescence microscopy in this textbook.

Web Activity *Metric System Review*

? Which type of microscope would you use to study (a) the changes in shape of a living human white blood cell; (b) the finest details of surface texture of a human hair; (c) the detailed structure of an organelle in a human liver cell?

■ (a) light microscope; (b) scanning electron microscope; (c) transmission electron microscope

4.2 Most cells are microscopic

There is a reason that our knowledge of cells depended on the development of microscopes: Most cells cannot be seen with the unaided eye. **Figure 4.2A** shows the size range of cells compared with objects both larger and smaller. The smallest cells are bacteria called mycoplasmas, with diameters as small as 0.2 μm (see Table 4.1). Some of the bulkiest cells are bird eggs, and the longest human cells are certain muscle and nerve cells. Most cells lie between these extremes, in the range indicated by the yellow area in the figure below. The scale is logarithmic, with the length labels on the left ascending in powers of ten, to accommodate the range of sizes shown. Thus, most plant and

Surface area of one large cube = 5,400 μm²

Total surface area of 27 small cubes = 16,200 μm²

Figure 4.2B Effect of cell size on surface area

animal cells, with diameters ranging from 10 to 100 μm, are ten times larger than most bacteria.

The logistics of carrying out a cell's functions sets limits on cell size. At minimum, a cell must be able to house enough DNA, protein molecules, and internal structures to survive and reproduce. The maximum size of a cell is influenced by its requirement for enough surface area to obtain adequate nutrients and oxygen from the environment and dispose of wastes. Size is also limited by the distance these materials must diffuse within a cell.

Large cells have more surface area than small cells, but large cells have much less surface area *relative to their volume* than small cells of the same shape. **Figure 4.2B** illustrates the relationship of surface area to volume using cubes to represent cells. The figure shows one large cube and 27 small ones. The total volume is the same in both cases:

$$\text{Volume} = 30 \ \mu m \times 30 \ \mu m \times 30 \ \mu m = 27{,}000 \ \mu m^3$$

In contrast to the total volume, the total surface areas are very different. A cube has six sides, thus its surface area is six times the area of one side. The surface areas are as follows:

$$\text{Area of large cube} = 6 \times (30 \ \mu m \times 30 \ \mu m) = 5{,}400 \ \mu m^2$$

$$\text{Area of one small cube} = 6 \times (10 \ \mu m \times 10 \ \mu m) = 600 \ \mu m^2$$

Combining all 27 of the small cubes, the total surface area is 27 × 600 μm², which equals 16,200 μm², three times the surface area of the large cube. Thus, we see that a large cell has a much smaller surface area relative to its volume than smaller cells have. The need for a surface area large enough to service a cell's volume helps explain the microscopic size of most cells.

In the next module, we look briefly at the smallest cells, the prokaryotic cells of domains Bacteria and Archaea.

Web Process of Science *Connection: What Is the Size and Scale of Our World?*

? To convince yourself of the larger surface area to volume of small cells, compare the ratio of surface area to volume of the large cube and one small cube.

10 m — Human height

1 m — Length of some nerve and muscle cells

100 mm (10 cm) — Chicken egg

10 mm (1 cm)

— Frog egg

1 mm

Unaided eye

Light microscope

Electron microscope

100 μm — Most plant and animal cells

10 μm — Nucleus — Most bacteria — Mitochondrion

1 μm

Mycoplasmas (smallest bacteria)

100 nm — Viruses

— Ribosome

10 nm — Proteins

— Lipids

1 nm — Small molecules

0.1 nm — Atoms

Figure 4.2A The sizes of cells and related objects

■ large cube: 5,400/27,000 = 1/5; small cube: 600/1,000 = 3/5 (volume is 10 μm × 10 μm × 10 μm = 1,000 μm³)

Prokaryotic cells are structurally simpler than eukaryotic cells

Two kinds of structurally different cells have evolved over time. Bacteria and archaea consist of **prokaryotic cells,** whereas all other forms of life (protists, fungi, plants, and animals) are composed of **eukaryotic cells.**

All cells have several basic features in common. They are all bounded by a membrane, called a **plasma membrane.** All cells have **chromosomes** carrying genes made of DNA. And all cells contain **ribosomes,** tiny structures that make proteins according to instructions from the genes. Eukaryotic cells are distinguished by having a membrane-enclosed nucleus, which houses most of their DNA. The entire region betweeen the nucleus and the plasma membrane is called the **cytoplasm.** The term *cytoplasm* is also used for the interior of a prokaryotic cell. Eukaryotic cells contain many membrane-enclosed organelles, another key difference from prokaryotic cells.

It takes an electron microscope to see clearly the structural details of any cell, and this is especially true of prokaryotic cells (**Figure 4.3**). Most prokaryotic cells range from 1 to 10 μm in length, about one-tenth the size of a typical eukaryotic cell. A prokaryotic cell lacks a nucleus (its name comes from the Greek *pro,* before, and *karyon,* kernel, referring to the nucleus).

The cutaway diagram in Figure 4.3 reveals the structure of a generalized prokaryotic cell. The DNA of a prokaryotic cell is coiled into a region called the **nucleoid** (nucleus-like), but in contrast to the nucleus of eukaryotic cells, no membrane surrounds the DNA. The ribosomes of prokaryotes are smaller and differ somewhat from those of eukaryotes.

These molecular differences are the basis for the action of some antibiotics, which specifically target prokaryotic ribosomes, interrupting protein synthesis for the bacterium but not for the eukaryote taking the drug.

Outside the plasma membrane (shown here in gray) of most prokaryotes is a fairly rigid, chemically complex cell wall (orange). The wall protects the cell and helps maintain its shape. In some prokaryotes, another layer, a sticky outer coat called a capsule (shown here in yellow), surrounds the cell wall and further protects the cell surface. Capsules also help glue prokaryotes to surfaces, such as sticks and rocks in fast-flowing streams or tissues within the human body. In addition to capsules, some prokaryotes have surface projections. Short projections called pili (singular, *pilus*) help attach prokaryotes to surfaces. Longer projections called **flagella** (singular, *flagellum*) may propel the prokaryotic cell through its liquid environment.

Prokaryotes will be described in more detail in Chapter 16. Eukaryotic cells are the main focus of this chapter.

Web Activity *Prokaryotic Cell Structure and Function*

? List three features that are common to prokaryotic and eukaryotic cells. List three features that differ.

■ Both types of cells have plasma membranes, chromosomes containing DNA, and ribosomes. Prokaryotic cells are smaller, do not have a nucleus that houses their DNA or other membrane-enclosed organelles, and have smaller, somewhat different ribosomes.

Pili: attachment structures on the surface of some prokaryotes

Nucleoid: region where the cell's DNA is located (not enclosed by a membrane)

Ribosomes: structures that synthesize proteins

Plasma membrane: membrane enclosing the cytoplasm

Cell wall: rigid structure outside the plasma membrane

Capsule: jellylike outer coating of many prokaryotes

Bacterial chromosome

Flagella: locomotion organelles of some bacteria

A typical rod-shaped bacterium

A thin section through the bacterium *Bacillus coagulans* **(TEM)**

TEM 35,500×

Figure 4.3   A structural diagram (left) and electron micrograph (right) of a typical prokaryotic cell

4.4 Eukaryotic cells are partitioned into functional compartments

All eukaryotic cells (Greek *eu,* true, and *karyon,* kernel)—whether from animals, plants, protists, or fungi—are fundamentally similar to one another and profoundly different from prokaryotic cells. Let's look at an animal cell and a plant cell as representatives of the eukaryotes.

Figure 4.4A is a diagram of an idealized animal cell. No cell would look exactly like what this diagram depicts. In this text, we color-code the various organelles and other structures for easier identification. And recall from the chapter introduction that in living cells these structures are moving and interacting.

The nucleus, with its nuclear membrane, multiple chromosomes, and nucleolus, is the most obvious difference between a prokaryotic and eukaryotic cell. A eukaryotic cell also has various **organelles** ("little organs") in the cytoplasm. These membrane-bounded structures perform specific functions in the cell.

The structures and organelles of eukaryotic cells can be organized into four basic functional groups as follows. (1) The nucleus, ribosomes, endoplasmic reticulum, and Golgi apparatus function in manufacturing. (2) Organelles involved in

breakdown or hydrolysis of molecules include lysosomes, vacuoles, and peroxisomes. (3) Mitochondria in all cells and chloroplasts in plant cells are involved in energy processing. (4) Structural support, movement, and communication among cells are the functions of components of the cytoskeleton, plasma membrane, and cell wall. These cellular components are identified in the figures that follow and will be examined in detail in the chapter.

In essence, the internal membranes of a eukaryotic cell partition it into compartments. Many of the chemical activities of cells—activities known collectively as **cellular metabolism**—occur within organelles. In fact, many enzymatic proteins essential for metabolic processes are built into the membranes of organelles. The fluid-filled spaces within organelles are important as sites where specific chemical conditions are maintained, conditions that vary from one organelle to another and that favor the metabolic processes occurring in each kind of organelle. For example, while a part of the endoplasmic reticulum is engaged in making steroid hormones, neighboring peroxisomes may be detoxifying harmful compounds and making

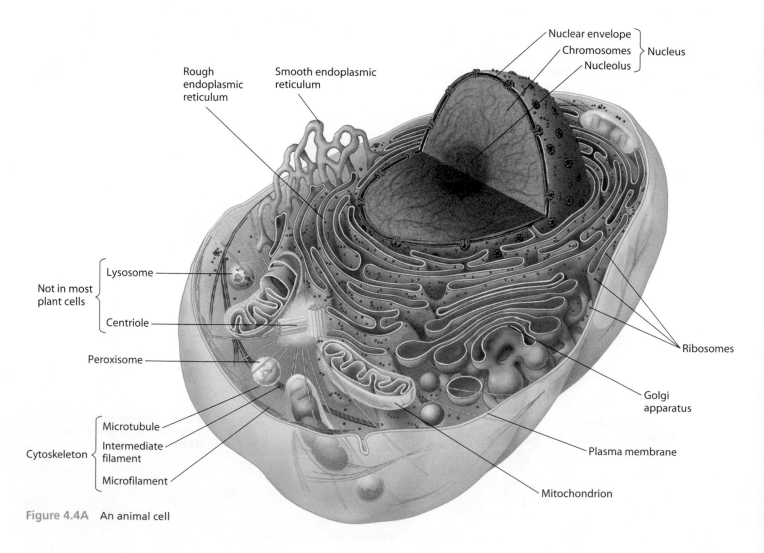

Figure 4.4A An animal cell

hydrogen peroxide (H_2O_2) as a poisonous by-product of their activities. But because the H_2O_2 is confined within peroxisomes, where it is quickly converted to H_2O by resident enzymes, the rest of the cell is protected from destruction.

Almost all of the organelles and other structures appearing in Figure 4.4A are also present in plant cells. As you can see in Figure 4.4A, there are a few exceptions: Lysosomes and centrioles are not found in plant cells. Some animal cells have flagella or cilia (not shown in Figure 4.4A). Among plants, only the sperm cells of a few plant species have flagella. (The eukaryotic and prokaryotic flagella differ in both structure and function.)

A plant cell (Figure 4.4B) has some structures that an animal cell lacks. For example, a plant cell has a rigid, rather thick cell wall (as do the cells of fungi and many protists). Cell walls protect cells and help maintain their shape. Chemically different from prokaryotic cell walls, plant cell walls contain the polysaccharide cellulose. Plasmodesmata are channels through cell walls that connect adjacent cells. An important organelle found in plant cells is the chloroplast, where photosynthesis occurs. (Chloroplasts are also found in algae and some other protists.) Unique to plant cells is a large central vacuole, a compartment that stores water and a variety of chemicals.

Although we have emphasized organelles, eukaryotic cells contain nonmembranous structures as well. Among them are the cytoskeleton, which consists of protein tubes called microtubules and other protein filaments, and ribosomes. You can see by the many brown dots in both figures that ribosomes, the sites of protein synthesis, occur throughout the cytoplasm, as they do in prokaryotic cells. In addition to ribosomes in the cytoplasmic fluid, eukaryotic cells have many ribosomes attached to parts of the endoplasmic reticulum (making it "rough") and to the outer membrane of the nucleus.

Before we begin our in-depth tour of the cell, let's explore the structure of membranes—those all-important components that enclose and partition cells into functional compartments.

(Bio Flix) **BioFlix** *Tour of an Animal Cell*

(Bio Flix) **BioFlix** *Tour of a Plant Cell*

(🎧) **MP3 Tutor** *Cell Organelles*

[?] Which of the following organelles does not belong in the list: mitochondrion, chloroplast, ribosome, lysosome, peroxisome? Why?

■ Ribosome, because it is the only organelle in the list that is not bounded by a membrane

Figure 4.4B A plant cell

4.5 The structure of membranes correlates with their functions

For all cells, the plasma membrane forms a boundary between the living cell and its surroundings and controls the traffic of materials into and out of the cell. For a structure that separates life from nonlife, the plasma membrane is amazingly thin. It would take a stack of more than 8,000 membranes to equal the thickness of this page. The plasma membrane and the internal membranes of a eukaryotic cell perform diverse functions—functions that depend on the structure of these membranes.

Phospholipids are the main components of biological membranes. As you learned in Module 3.9, a phospholipid has two distinct regions: a negatively charged and thus hydrophilic phosphate group (head) and two nonpolar, hydrophobic fatty acid tails. The structural formula of a phospholipid in Figure 4.5A highlights these two parts. The phospholipid symbol shown in the figure is used in this book in depicting membranes.

The structure of phospholipid molecules is well suited to their role in membranes. Phospholipids form a two-layer sheet called a phospholipid bilayer. Their hydrophilic heads face outward, exposed to the aqueous solution on both sides of a membrane, and their hydrophobic tails point inward, mingling together and shielded from water (Figure 4.5B). Embedded in this lipid bilayer or attached to its

Figure 4.5A Phospholipid molecule

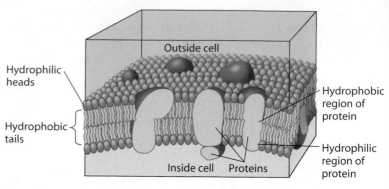

Figure 4.5B Phospholipid bilayer with associated proteins

surfaces are diverse proteins. The interior portions of membrane proteins are hydrophobic. The exterior parts of these proteins and the proteins attached to the membrane are hydrophilic.

The permeability of a membrane to various substances relates to the properties of the lipid bilayer. Nonpolar molecules such as O_2 and CO_2 can easily pass through its hydrophobic interior. Other functions of a membrane depend largely on the kinds of proteins associated with the membrane. Some of these proteins form channels that allow specific ions and other hydrophilic molecules to cross the membrane.

We will return to a more detailed look at the structure and function of biological membranes in Chapter 5. Now we begin a more detailed tour of the cell.

? Describe the structure of a biological membrane.

A membrane is a phospholipid bilayer with associated proteins. The hydrophilic heads of the phospholipids face the water on both sides of the membrane; the hydrophobic tails mingle in the center.

Cell Structures Involved in Manufacturing and Breakdown

4.6 The nucleus is the cell's genetic control center

The **nucleus** contains most of the cell's DNA and controls the cell's activities by directing protein synthesis. Eukaryotic chromosomes are made up of a material called **chromatin,** which is a complex of proteins and DNA. Chromatin appears as a diffuse mass, as shown in the TEM (left) and diagram (right) of a nucleus in Figure 4.6. As a cell prepares to divide, the DNA is copied and the thin chromatin fibers coil up, becoming thick enough to be visible with a light microscope as the familiar separate structures we know as chromosomes.

Enclosing the nucleus is a **nuclear envelope,** a double membrane perforated with protein-lined

Figure 4.6 TEM (left) and diagram (right) of the nucleus

pores that control the flow of materials into and out of the nucleus. As you can see in the diagram in Figure 4.6, the nuclear envelope connects with the cell's network of membranes called the endoplasmic reticulum.

The **nucleolus,** a prominent structure in the nucleus, is the site where a special type of RNA called ribosomal RNA (rRNA) is synthesized according to instructions in the DNA. Proteins brought in through the nuclear pores from the cytoplasm are assembled with this rRNA to form the subunits of ribosomes. These subunits then exit through the pores to the cytoplasm, where they will join to form functional ribosomes.

The nucleus directs protein synthesis by making another type of RNA, messenger RNA (mRNA) according to instructions in the DNA. The messenger RNA moves through the pores to the cytoplasm and is translated there by ribosomes into the amino acid sequences of proteins. Protein synthesis will be explored in more detail in Chapter 10.

? What are the main functions of the nucleus?

■ To contain DNA and pass it on to daughter cells in cell division, to build ribosomes, to copy DNA instructions into RNA

4.7   Ribosomes make proteins for use in the cell and export

Ribosomes are the cellular components that carry out protein synthesis. Cells that have high rates of protein synthesis have a particularly large number of ribosomes. For example, a human pancreas cell producing digestive enzymes may contain a few million ribosomes. Not surprisingly, cells active in protein synthesis also have prominent nucleoli, which, as you just learned, function in ribosome synthesis.

Ribosomes are found in two locations in the cell (Figure 4.7). *Free ribosomes* are suspended in the fluid of the cytoplasm, while *bound ribosomes* are attached to the outside of the endoplasmic reticulum or nuclear envelope. Free and bound ribosomes are structurally identical, and ribosomes can alternate between the two locations (free or bound to the ER). As shown in the diagram, ribosomes are composed of a large and small subunit.

Most of the proteins made on free ribosomes function within the cytoplasm; examples are enzymes that catalyze the first steps of sugar breakdown. In Module 4.9, you will see how bound ribosomes make proteins that will be inserted into membranes, packaged in certain organelles, or exported from the cell. Cells that specialize in protein secretion—for instance, the cells of the pancreas that secrete digestive enzymes—have a

TEM 50,500×

TEM showing ER and ribosomes

Diagram of a ribosome

Figure 4.7   Ribosomes

high proportion of bound ribosomes that produce proteins for export.

? What role do ribosomes play in carrying out the genetic instructions of a cell?

■ Ribosomes synthesize proteins according to the instructions carried by messenger RNA from the DNA in the nucleus.

4.8   Overview: Many cell organelles are connected through the endomembrane system

Many of the membranes of the eukaryotic cell are part of an **endomembrane system.** Some of these membranes are physically connected and some are related by the transfer of membrane segments by tiny **vesicles** (sacs made of membrane). The endomembrane system includes the nuclear envelope, endoplasmic reticulum, Golgi apparatus, lysosomes, vacuoles, and the plasma membrane. Many of these organelles work together in the synthesis, storage, and export of molecules. We focus on these interrelated membranes in Modules 4.9–4.12.

An extensive network of flattened sacs and tubules called the **endoplasmic reticulum (ER)** is the prime example of the direct interrelatedness of parts of the endomembrane system. (The term *endoplasmic* means "within the cytoplasm," and

reticulum is Latin for "little net.") As illustrated in Figure 4.6, membranes of the ER are continuous with the nuclear envelope. As we discuss next, there are two regions of ER, smooth ER and rough ER, which differ in structure and function. The membranes that form them, however, are connected.

The tubules and sacs of the ER enclose an interior space that is separate from the cytoplasmic fluid. Dividing the cell into separate compartments is a major function of the endomembrane system.

? Which structure includes all others in the list: rough ER, smooth ER, endomembrane system, nuclear envelope?

■ Endomembrane system

The endoplasmic reticulum is a biosynthetic factory

The diagram in **Figure 4.9A** shows a cutaway view of the interconnecting membranes of the smooth and rough ER. These two types of ER can be distinguished in the electron micrograph. **Smooth endoplasmic reticulum** is called *smooth* because it lacks attached ribosomes. **Rough endoplasmic reticulum** has ribosomes that stud the outer surface of the membrane, and thus it appears *rough* in the electron micrograph.

Smooth ER   The smooth ER of various cell types functions in diverse metabolic processes. Enzymes of the smooth ER are important in the synthesis of lipids, including oils, phospholipids, and steroids. In vertebrates, for example, cells of the ovaries and testes synthesize the steroid sex hormones. These cells are rich in smooth ER, a structural feature that fits their function by providing ample space for steroid synthesis.

Our liver cells also have large amounts of smooth ER, with additional kinds of functions. Certain enzymes in the smooth ER of liver cells help process drugs and other potentially harmful substances. The sedative phenobarbital and other barbiturates are examples of the drugs detoxified by these enzymes. Undesirable complications can result when liver cells respond to drugs. As the cells are exposed to such chemicals, the amount of smooth ER and its detoxifying enzymes increase, thereby increasing the rate of detoxification and thus the body's tolerance to the drugs. This means that higher and higher doses of a drug are required to achieve a particular effect, such as sedation. Another complication is that detoxifying enzymes often cannot distinguish among related chemicals. As a result, the growth of smooth ER in response to one drug can increase tolerance to other drugs, including important medicines. Barbiturate use, for example, can decrease the effectiveness of certain antibiotics.

Smooth ER has yet another function, the storage of calcium ions. In muscle cells, for example, a specialized smooth ER membrane pumps calcium ions into the interior of the ER. When a nerve signal stimulates a muscle cell, calcium ions rush from the smooth ER into the cytoplasmic fluid and trigger contraction of the cell.

Rough ER   One of the functions of rough ER is to make more membrane. Phospholipids made by enzymes of the ER are inserted into the membrane. As a result, the rough ER membrane enlarges, and some of this membrane is transferred to other components of the endomembrane system in vesicles.

The bound ribosomes that attach to rough ER produce proteins that will be inserted into the ER membrane, transported to other organelles, or secreted by the cell. An example of a secretory protein is insulin, a hormone secreted by certain cells in the pancreas.

Figure 4.9B shows the synthesis, modification, and packaging of a secretory protein. ❶ As the polypeptide is synthesized by a bound ribosome, it is threaded into the cavity of

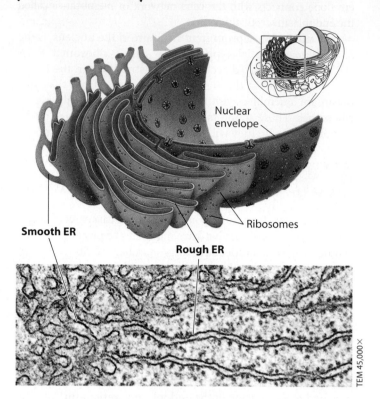

Figure 4.9A   Smooth and rough endoplasmic reticulum

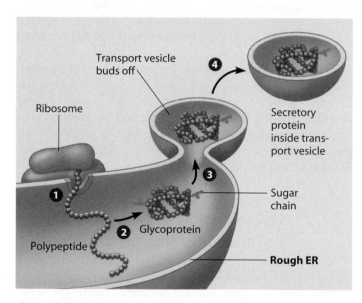

Figure 4.9B   Synthesis and packaging of a secretory protein by the rough ER

the rough ER through a pore formed by a protein complex. As it enters, the new protein folds into its three-dimensional shape. ❷ Short chains of sugars are often linked to the polypeptide, making the molecule a **glycoprotein** (*glyco-* means "sugar"). ❸ When the molecule is ready for export from the ER, it is packaged in a **transport vesicle,** a vesicle that is in transit from one part of the cell to another. ❹ This vesicle buds off from the ER membrane. The protein now travels to the Golgi apparatus (described in the next module) for further processing. From there, a transport vesicle containing the finished molecule will make its way to the plasma membrane and release its contents from the cell.

Web Activity *Overview of Protein Synthesis*

> **?** Contrast the form and functions of smooth ER and rough ER.

■ *Smooth ER:* no bound ribosomes. Functions include lipid synthesis; destruction of toxic substances; regulation of muscle contraction by release of calcium. *Rough ER:* ribosomes attach to surface; functions include production of membrane by adding proteins and phospholipids; bound ribosomes produce proteins that are modified and packaged in transport vesicles

4.10 The Golgi apparatus finishes, sorts, and ships cell products

After leaving the ER, many transport vesicles travel to the **Golgi apparatus.** The Golgi apparatus was named after Italian biologist and physician Camillo Golgi, whose career spanned the turn of the 20th century. Using the light microscope, Golgi and his contemporaries discovered this membranous organelle and a number of others in animal and plant cells. The electron microscope confirmed Golgi's discovery. Electron micrographs reveal that the Golgi apparatus consists of flattened sacs stacked on top of each other. As you can see in Figure 4.10, the sacs are not interconnected like ER sacs. A cell may contain only a few Golgi stacks or hundreds. The number of Golgi stacks correlates with how active the cell is in secreting proteins—a multistep process that, as we have just seen, is initiated in the rough ER.

The Golgi apparatus performs several functions in close partnership with the ER. Serving as a molecular warehouse and finishing factory, a Golgi apparatus receives and modifies products manufactured by the ER. One side of a Golgi stack serves as a receiving dock for transport vesicles produced by the ER. These vesicles join and form a new Golgi sac. The other side of the Golgi, the shipping side, gives rise to vesicles, which bud off and travel to other sites.

Products of the ER are usually modified during their transit from the receiving to the shipping side of the Golgi. For example, various Golgi enzymes modify the carbohydrate portions of glycoproteins. Molecular identification tags, such as phosphate groups, may be added that serve to mark and sort molecules into different batches for different destinations.

Until recently, the Golgi was viewed as a static structure, with products in various stages of processing moved from sac to sac by transport vesicles. Recent research has given rise to a new *maturation model* in which entire sacs "mature" as they move from the receiving to the shipping side, carrying and modifying their cargo as they go. The shipping side of the Golgi stack serves as a depot from which finished secretory products, packaged in transport vesicles, move to the plasma membrane for export from the cell. Alternatively, finished products may become part of the plasma membrane itself or part of another organelle, such as a lysosome, which we discuss next.

> **?** What is the relationship of the Golgi apparatus to the ER in a protein-secreting cell?

■ The Golgi receives transport vesicles that bud from the ER and that contain proteins synthesized by ribosomes attached to the ER. The Golgi finishes processing the proteins and then dispatches transport vesicles that secrete the proteins to the outside of the cell.

Golgi apparatus

Golgi apparatus

"Receiving" side of Golgi apparatus

Transport vesicle from ER

New vesicle forming

"Shipping" side of Golgi apparatus

Transport vesicle from the Golgi

Figure 4.10 The Golgi apparatus

TEM 130,000×

4.11 Lysosomes are digestive compartments within a cell

A **lysosome** consists of digestive enzymes enclosed in a membranous sac. The name *lysosome* is derived from two Greek words meaning "breakdown body." The enzymes and membranes of lysosomes are made by rough ER and then transferred to the Golgi apparatus for further processing. Lysosomes illustrate the main theme of eukaryotic cell structure—compartmentalization. The lysosomal membrane encloses a compartment in which digestive enzymes are provided with an acidic environment and are safely isolated from the rest of the cell.

Lysosomes have several types of digestive functions. Many protists engulf food particles into cytoplasmic sacs called food vacuoles. As **Figure 4.11A** shows, lysosomes fuse with the food vacuoles and then break down the food, releasing nutrients to the cell. Our white blood cells ingest bacteria into vacuoles, and lysosomal enzymes emptied into these vacuoles rupture the bacterial cell walls. Lysosomes also serve as recycling centers for animal cells. Damaged organelles or small amounts of cell fluid become enclosed in a membrane vesicle. A lysosome fuses with such a vesicle (**Figure 4.11B**) and dismantles its contents, making organic molecules available for reuse. With the help of lysosomes, a cell continually renews itself.

The cells of people with inherited lysosomal storage diseases lack one or more lysosomal enzymes. The lysosomes become engorged with undigested material, eventually interfering with cellular function. In Tay-Sachs disease, for example, a lipid-digesting enzyme is missing, and brain cells become impaired by an accumulation of lipids. A child with Tay-Sachs disease will die within a few years.

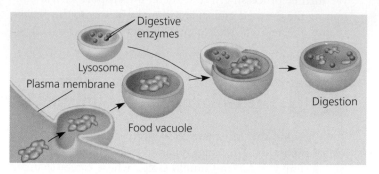

Figure 4.11A Lysosome fusing with a food vacuole and digesting food

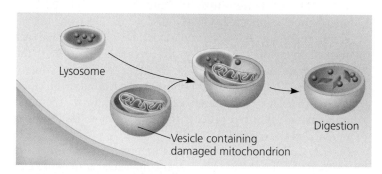

Figure 4.11B Lysosome fusing with vesicle containing damaged organelle and digesting and recyling its contents

? How is a lysosome like a recycling center?

■ It breaks down damaged organelles and recycles their molecules.

4.12 Vacuoles function in the general maintenance of the cell

Vacuoles are membranous sacs that have a variety of functions. In Module 4.11, we saw that the food vacuole functions in collaboration with a lysosome. **Figure 4.12A** shows a plant cell's **central vacuole,** which has hydrolytic functions like a lysosome. The central vacuole also helps the cell grow in size by absorbing water and enlarging, and it can store vital chemicals or waste products. Vacuoles in flower petals contain pigments that attract pollinating insects. Central vacuoles may also contain poisons that protect the plant against predators.

Figure 4.12B shows a very different kind of vacuole in the protist *Paramecium*. Notice the two contractile vacuoles, looking somewhat like wheel hubs with radiating spokes. The "spokes" collect excess water from the cell, and the hub expels it to the outside. Freshwater protists constantly take in water from their environment. Without a way to get rid of the excess water, the cell fluid would become too dilute to support life, and eventually the cell would swell and burst.

? Is a food vacuole part of the endomembrane system?

■ Yes, it forms by pinching in from the plasma membrane, which is part of the endomembrane system.

Figure 4.12A Central vacuole in a plant cell

Figure 4.12B Contractile vacuoles in *Paramecium*, a single-celled organism

A review of the structures involved in manufacturing and breakdown

Figure 4.13 summarizes the relationships among the major organelles of the endomembrane system. You can see the direct *structural* connections between the nuclear envelope, rough ER, and smooth ER. The red arrows show their *functional* connections, as membranes and proteins produced by the ER travel in transport vesicles to the Golgi and from there to other destinations. Some vesicles develop into lysosomes or vacuoles.

Transport vesicles carry secretory proteins or other products to the plasma membrane. When vesicles fuse with the membrane, the products are secreted from the cell and the vesicle membrane is added to the plasma membrane.

A **peroxisome** is an organelle that is not part of the endomembrane system but is involved in various metabolic functions, including the breakdown of fatty acids to be used as fuel and the detoxification of alcohol and other harmful substances.

Next we consider two organelles that are also not part of the endomembrane system—mitochondria and chloroplasts. Both are involved in energy processing.

Web Activity *The Endomembrane System*

? How do transport vesicles help tie together the endomembrane system?

■ Transport vesicles move membranes and substances they enclose between components of the endomembrane system.

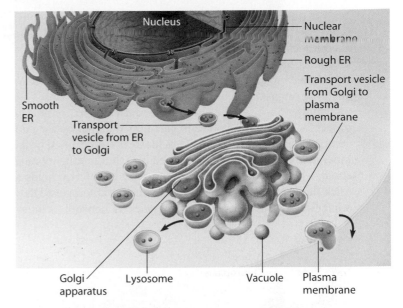

Figure 4.13 Connections among the organelles of the endomembrane system

Energy-Converting Organelles

Mitochondria harvest chemical energy from food

Mitochondria (singular, *mitochondrion*) are organelles that carry out cellular respiration in nearly all eukaryotic cells, converting the chemical energy of foods such as sugars to the chemical energy of a molecule called ATP (adenosine triphosphate). ATP is the main energy source for cellular work.

The mitochondrion's structure suits its function. It is enclosed by two membranes, each a phospholipid bilayer with a unique collection of embedded proteins (**Figure 4.14**). The mitochondrion has two internal compartments. The first is the **intermembrane space,** the narrow region between the inner and outer membranes. The inner membrane encloses the second compartment, the **mitochondrial matrix,** which contains the mitochondrial DNA and ribosomes, as well as many enzymes that catalyze some of the reactions of cellular respiration. The inner membrane is highly folded, with protein molecules that make ATP embedded in it. The folds, called cristae, increase the membrane's surface area, enhancing the mitochondrion's ability to produce ATP. We discuss the role of mitochondria in cellular respiration in more detail in Chapter 6.

? What is cellular respiration?

■ A process that converts the chemical energy of sugars and other molecules to chemical energy in the form of ATP

Figure 4.14 The mitochondrion

4.15　Chloroplasts convert solar energy to chemical energy

Most of the living world runs on the energy provided by photosynthesis, the conversion of light energy from the sun to the chemical energy of sugar molecules. **Chloroplasts** are the photosynthesizing organelles of all photosynthetic eukaryotes. The chloroplast's solar power system is much more successful than anything yet produced by human ingenuity.

Befitting an organelle that carries out complex, multistep processes, internal membranes partition the chloroplast into compartments (Figure 4.15). The chloroplast is enclosed by an inner and outer membrane separated by a thin intermembrane space. The compartment inside the inner membrane holds a thick fluid called **stroma,** which contains the chloroplast DNA and ribosomes as well as many enzymes. A network of inter-

connected sacs called **thylakoids** is inside the chloroplast. The compartment inside these sacs is called the thylakoid space. In some regions, thylakoids are stacked like poker chips; each stack is called a **granum** (plural, *grana*). The grana are the chloroplast's solar power packs—the sites where the green chlorophyll molecules embedded in their membranes trap solar energy. In Chapter 7, we discuss the role of each part of a chloroplast in converting solar energy to chemical energy.

Web Activity *Build a Chloroplast and a Mitochondrion*

? Which membrane in a chloroplast appears to be the most extensive? Why might this be so?

■ The thylakoid membranes are most extensive, providing a large area of membrane that contains chlorophyll for photosynthesis.

Figure 4.15　The chloroplast

Stroma

Inner and outer membranes

Granum

Intermembrane space

Chloroplast

TEM 9,750×

Evolution Connection

4.16　Mitochondria and chloroplasts evolved by endosymbiosis

Did it seem unusual to you that mitochondria and chloroplasts contain DNA and ribosomes? They have a single circular DNA molecule, similar in structure to the chromosome of prokaryotes. Their ribosomes are more similar to prokaryotic ribosomes than to eukaryotic ribosomes. Mitochondria and chloroplasts reproduce by a splitting process that is similar to that of certain prokaryotes. Both organelles are surrounded by a

double membrane, and the inner membrane has many similarities to the plasma membranes of living prokaryotes.

The hypothesis of **endosymbiosis** proposes that mitochondria and chloroplasts were formerly small prokaryotes that began living within larger cells. The term *endosymbiont* refers to a cell that lives within another cell, called the host cell. These small prokaryotes may have gained entry to the larger cell as undigested prey or internal parasites (Figure 4.16).

By whatever means the relationships began, we can hypothesize how the symbiosis could have become beneficial. A host could use nutrients released from photosynthetic endosymbionts. And in a world that was becoming increasingly aerobic from the photosynthesis of prokaryotes, a host would have benefited from endosymbionts that were able to use oxygen to release large amounts of energy in cellular respiration. Over time, the host and endosymbionts would have become increasingly interdependent, eventually becoming a single organism.

All eukaryotes have mitochondria, but not all eukaryotes have chloroplasts. The hypothesis of serial endosymbiosis proposes that mitochondria evolved before chloroplasts.

? Can you see in Figure 4.16 how the outer membrane of mitochondria and chloroplasts may have originated?

■ The outer membrane would have been part of the host plasma membrane that enclosed the prokaryote as it was engulfed by the host cell.

Mitochondrion

Engulfing of aerobic prokaryote

Host cell

Some cells

Engulfing of photosynthetic prokaryote

Chloroplast

Mitochondrion

Host cell

Figure 4.16　Endosymbiotic origin of mitochondria and chloroplasts

4.17 The cell's internal skeleton helps organize its structure and activities

Biologists once thought that organelles floated freely in the cell. But improvements in both light microscopy and electron microscopy have allowed scientists to uncover a network of protein fibers, collectively called the **cytoskeleton,** extending throughout the cytoplasm of a cell. These fibers function like a skeleton in providing for both structural support and cell motility. As discussed in the chapter introduction, cell movement includes both internal movement and the locomotion of a cell. These movements generally require the interaction of the cytoskeleton with proteins called motor proteins. Mounting evidence also suggests that the cytoskeleton helps regulate activities by transmitting signals from the cell's surface to its interior.

Three main kinds of fibers make up the cytoskeleton: microfilaments, the thinnest fiber; microtubules, the thickest; and intermediate filaments, in between in thickness. **Figure 4.17** shows micrographs of three cells of the same type, each stained with a different fluorescent dye that selectively highlights one of these types of fibers.

Microfilaments, also called actin filaments, are solid rods composed mainly of globular proteins called actin, arranged in a twisted double chain (bottom left of Figure 4.17). Microfilaments form a three-dimensional network just inside the plasma membrane that helps support the cell's shape.

Microfilaments are also involved in cell movements. As we will see in Chapter 30, actin filaments and thicker filaments made of the motor protein myosin interact to cause contraction of muscle cells. Localized contractions brought about by actin and myosin are involved in the amoeboid (crawling) movement of the protist *Amoeba* and certain of our white blood cells.

Intermediate filaments are made of various fibrous proteins and have a ropelike structure. Intermediate filaments serve mainly to reinforce cell shape and to anchor certain organelles. The nucleus is held in place by a cage of intermediate filaments. While microfilaments may be disassembled and reassembled elsewhere, intermediate filaments are often more permanent fixtures in the cell. The outer layer of our skin consists of dead skin cells full of intermediate filaments made of keratin proteins.

Microtubules are straight, hollow tubes composed of globular proteins called tubulins. As shown in the bottom right of Figure 4.17, microtubules elongate by adding subunits consisting of tubulin pairs. They are readily disassembled in a reverse manner, and the tubulin subunits can then be reused elsewhere in the cell. In many animal cells, microtubules grow out from a "microtubule-organizing center" called a centrosome. Within the centrosome is a pair of **centrioles** (see Figure 4.4A). We will return to centrioles when we discuss cell division in Chapter 8.

Microtubules shape and support the cell and also act as tracks along which organelles equipped with motor proteins can move. For example, a lysosome might "walk" along a microtubule to reach a food vacuole. Microtubules also guide the movement of chromosomes when cells divide, and as we see next, they are the main components of cilia and flagella.

? Which component of the cytoskeleton is most important in (a) holding the nucleus in place within the cell; (b) guiding transport vesicles from the Golgi to the plasma membrane; (c) contracting muscle cells?

■ (a) intermediate filaments; (b) microtubules; (c) microfilaments

Figure 4.17 Fibers of the cytoskeleton: microfilaments are stained red (left), intermediate filaments are stained yellow-green (center), and microtubules are stained green (right)

5.1   Membranes are a fluid mosaic of phospholipids and proteins

Recall from Chapter 4 that biological membranes are composed of phospholipids and proteins. Figure 5.1A reviews the structure of the plasma membrane of an animal cell. Like other membranes, it is commonly described as a **fluid mosaic.** The word *mosaic* denotes a surface made of small pieces. A membrane is a "mosaic" in having diverse protein molecules embedded in a framework of phospholipids. The membrane is "fluid" in that most of these molecules can drift about in the membrane.

Double bonds in the unsaturated fatty acid tails of many phospholipids produce kinks that prevent phospholipids from packing tightly together, keeping the membrane fluid. In animal cells, the steroid cholesterol (see Module 3.9), wedged into the bilayer, helps stabilize the membrane at warm temperatures but also helps keep the membrane fluid at lower temperatures. In a cell, the phospholipid bilayer remains about as fluid as salad oil.

The word *mosaic* can refer not only to the position of proteins in the phospholipid bilayer but also to the varied functions of these proteins. More than 50 kinds of proteins have been found in the plasma membrane of red blood cells. Different types of cells contain different membrane proteins, and the various membranes within a cell each have unique proteins.

Two of the functions of membrane proteins are illustrated in Figure 5.1A. Some proteins give the membrane a stronger *framework*. These proteins called integrins, span the membrane and attach to the cytoskeleton on the inside and the extracellular matrix (ECM) on the outside (see Module 4.20). Glycoproteins are involved in *cell–cell recognition,* a second function of plasma membrane proteins. The outside surface of the membrane has carbohydrates (chains of sugars, blue in Figure 5.1A) bonded to proteins or lipids in the membrane. The carbohydrates vary among species, among individuals, and even among cell types. Many function as identification tags that are recognized by other cells. This cell–cell recognition allows cells in an embryo to sort themselves into tissues and organs. It also enables cells of the immune system to recognize and reject foreign cells, such as infectious bacteria. A third function specific to plasma membrane proteins is forming *junctions* between cells (see Module 4.21).

Many membrane proteins are *enzymes.* Figure 5.1B shows how enzymes may work as a team to carry out sequential steps in a pathway. Other proteins function as *receptors* for chemical messengers from other cells (Figure 5.1C). A receptor protein has a shape that fits a specific messenger, such as a hormone. Often the binding of the messenger to the receptor triggers a chain reaction involving other proteins, which relay the message to molecules that perform specific functions inside the cell. This message-transfer process is called *signal transduction* and will be described in more detail in Chapter 11.

A final important function of membrane proteins is in *transport* (Figure 5.1D). Membranes exhibit **selective permeability;** that is, they allow some substances to cross more easily than others. Their hydrophobic interior is one reason for this selective permeability. Nonpolar, hydrophobic molecules can easily pass through membranes. In contrast, polar molecules and ions are not soluble in lipids. Many essential molecules, such as glucose and ions, require transport proteins to enter or leave the cell.

Web Activity   *Membrane Structure*

Web Activity   *Selective Permeability of Membranes*

Web Activity   *Signal Transduction*

Web Process of Science   *How Do Cells Communicate with Each Other?*

?   Review the six different types of functions that membrane proteins can perform.

■ Support by attaching to the cytoskeleton and ECM, cell–cell recognition, intercellular junctions , enzymes, signal transduction, and transport.

Figure 5.1B
Enzyme activity

Figure 5.1C
Signal transduction

Figure 5.1D
Transport

Figure 5.1A   The plasma membrane and extracellular matrix of an animal cell

5.2   Membranes form spontaneously, a critical step in the origin of life

Phospholipids, the key ingredients of biological membranes, were probably among the first organic molecules that formed from chemical reactions on early Earth (see Module 15.2). These lipids could spontaneously self-assemble into simple membranes, as we can demonstrate in a test tube. When a mixture of phospholipids and water is shaken, the phospholipids organize into bilayers surrounding water-filled bubbles (Figure 5.2). This assembly requires neither genes nor other information beyond the properties of the phospholipids themselves.

The formation of membrane-enclosed collections of molecules was a critical step in the evolution of the first cells. A membrane can enclose a solution that is different in composition from its surroundings. A plasma membrane that allows cells to regulate their chemical exchanges with the environment is a basic requirement for life. Indeed, all cells are enclosed by a plasma membrane that is similar in structure and function—one of the features that illustrates the evolutionary unity of life.

Water-filled bubble made of phospholipids

Figure 5.2 Artificial membrane-bound sacs

? To the right is a diagram of a section of one of the membrane sacs shown in the photo above. Describe its structure.

Water

Water

■ The phospholipids form a bilayer. The hydrophobic fatty acid tails cluster in the center and the hydrophilic phosphate heads face the water on both sides.

5.3   Passive transport is diffusion across a membrane with no energy investment

Diffusion is the tendency for particles of any kind to spread out evenly in an available space, moving from where they are more concentrated to regions where they are less concentrated. Molecules vibrate and move randomly as a result of a type of energy called thermal motion (heat). Diffusion requires no work; it results from the thermal motion of atoms and molecules.

The figures to the right will help you to visualize diffusion across a membrane. Figure 5.3A shows a solution of green dye separated from pure water by a membrane. Assume that this membrane has microscopic pores through which dye molecules can move. Thus, it is permeable to the dye. Although each molecule moves randomly, there will be a *net* movement from the side of the membrane where dye molecules are more concentrated to the side where they are less concentrated. Put another way, the dye diffuses down its **concentration gradient.** Eventually, the solutions on both sides have equal concentrations of dye. At this dynamic equilibrium, molecules still move back and forth, but there is no *net* change in concentration on either side of the membrane. Figure 5.3B illustrates the important point that two or more substances diffuse independently of each other; that is, each diffuses down its own concentration gradient.

Because a cell does not perform work when molecules diffuse across its membrane, the diffusion of a substance across a biological membrane is called **passive transport.** Much of the traffic across cell membranes occurs by diffusion. In our lungs, diffusion down concentration gradients is the sole means by which oxygen (O_2), essential for metabolism, enters red blood cells and carbon dioxide (CO_2), a metabolic waste, passes out of them.

Both O_2 and CO_2 are small, nonpolar molecules that diffuse easily across the phospholipid bilayer of a membrane. But can ions and polar molecules also move by passive transport into or

Molecules of dye   Membrane   Equilibrium

Figure 5.3A Passive transport of one type of molecule

Equilibrium

Figure 5.3B Passive transport of two types of molecules

out of a cell? They can if they are moving down their concentration gradients and if they have transport proteins to provide a pathway across the membrane.

Web Activity *Diffusion*

? Why is diffusion across a membrane called passive transport?

■ The cell does not expend energy to transport substances that are diffusing down their concentration gradients.

5.4 Osmosis is the diffusion of water across a membrane

One of the most important substances that crosses membranes by passive transport is water. In the next module, we consider the critical balance of water between a cell and its environment. But first let's explore a physical model of the diffusion of water molecules across a selectively permeable membrane, a process called **osmosis.** Remember that a selectively permeable membrane allows some substances to cross more easily than others.

The top of Figure 5.4 shows what happens if a membrane permeable to water but not to a solute (such as glucose) separates two solutions with different concentrations of solute. (A solute is a substance that dissolves in a liquid solvent, producing a solution.) The solution on the right side initially has a higher concentration of solute than that on the left. As you can see, water crosses the membrane until the solute concentrations (molecules per milliliter of solution) are equal on both sides.

In the close-up view at the bottom of Figure 5.4, you can see what happens at the molecular level. Clusters of polar water molecules form weak bonds with solute molecules, so that fewer water molecules are free to diffuse across the membrane. The less concentrated solution on the left, with fewer solute molecules, has more free water molecules. There is a net movement of water down its own concentration gradient, from the solution with the lower solute concentration and more free water molecules to that with the higher solute concentration and fewer free water molecules. The result is the difference in water levels you see at the top of Figure 5.4.

Here we show only one type of solute, but the same net movement of water would occur no matter how many kinds of solutes were present. The direction of osmosis is determined by the difference in *total* solute concentration, not by the nature of the solutes. Let's now apply to living cells what we have learned about osmosis in artificial systems.

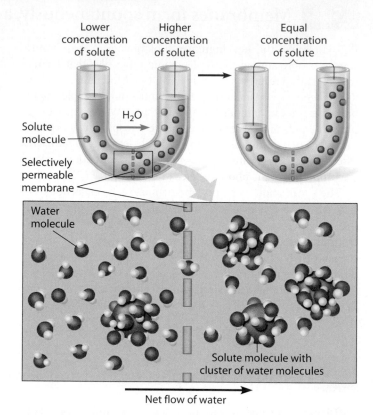

Figure 5.4 Osmosis, the diffusion of water across a membrane

? Indicate the direction of net water movement between two solutions—a 0.5% sucrose solution and a 2% sucrose solution—separated by a membrane not permeable to sucrose.

■ From the 0.5% sucrose solution (lower solute concentration) to the 2% sucrose solution (higher solute concentration)

5.5 Water balance between cells and their surroundings is crucial to organisms

Biologists use a special vocabulary to describe the relationship between a cell and its surroundings with regard to the movement of water. The term **tonicity** describes the ability of a solution to cause a cell to gain or lose water. The tonicity of a solution mainly depends on its concentration of solutes that cannot cross the plasma membrane relative to the concentrations of solutes in the cell.

Figure 5.5 on the facing page illustrates how the principles of osmosis and tonicity apply to cells. The effects of solutions of various tonicities on an animal cell are shown at the top of the illustration; the effect of the same solutions on a plant cell are shown at the bottom of the figure. When an animal cell, such as the red blood cell shown in part A of the figure, is immersed in a solution that is **isotonic** to the cell (*iso,* same, and *tonos,* tension), the cell's volume remains constant. The solute concentration of a cell and its isotonic environment are essentially equal, and the cell gains water at the same rate that it loses it. Red blood

cells are transported in the isotonic plasma of the blood, and intravenous (IV) fluids administered in hospitals must also be isotonic to blood cells. The cells of most animals are bathed in an extracellular fluid that is isotonic to the cells. Many marine animals, such as sea stars and crabs, are isotonic to seawater.

Part B of the figure shows what can happen to an animal cell in a **hypotonic** solution (*hypo,* below), a solution with a solute concentration lower than that of the cell. The cell gains water, swells, and may burst (lyse) like an overfilled balloon. Part C shows the opposite case—an animal cell in a **hypertonic** solution (*hyper,* above), a solution with a higher solute concentration. The cell shrivels and can die from water loss.

For an animal to survive in a hypotonic or hypertonic environment, it must have a way to prevent excessive uptake or excessive loss of water. The control of water balance is called **osmoregulation.** For example, a freshwater fish, which lives in a hypotonic environment, has kidneys and gills that work constantly to prevent an excessive buildup of water in the body. (We discuss osmoregulation further in Chapter 25.)

Water balance issues are somewhat different for the cells of plants, prokaryotes, and fungi because of their cell walls. As shown in **part D**, a plant cell immersed in an isotonic solution is flaccid (limp). In contrast, a plant cell is turgid (very firm), which is the healthy state for most plant cells, in a hypotonic environment (**part E**). To become turgid, a plant cell needs a net inflow of water. Although the somewhat elastic cell wall expands a bit, the pressure it exerts prevents the cell from taking in too much water and bursting, as an animal cell would in a hypotonic environment. Some plants, including most houseplants, depend on their turgid cells for mechanical suppport.

Part F shows that in a hypertonic environment, a plant cell is no better off than an animal cell. As a plant cell loses water, it shrivels, and its plasma membrane pulls away from the cell wall. This process, called plasmolysis, causes the plant to wilt and can be lethal to the cell and the plant.

Web Activity *Osmosis and Water Balance in Cells*

Web Process of Science *How Does Osmosis Affect Cells?*

Figure 5.5   How animal and plant cells behave in different solutions

? Explain the function of the contractile vacuoles in the freshwater *Paramecium* shown in Figure 4.12B in terms of what you have just learned about water balance in cells.

■ The pond water in which *Paramecium* lives is hypotonic to the cell, and thus there is a constant net osmosis of water into the cell. The contractile vacuoles expel this excess water, preventing the cell from bursting.

5.6   Transport proteins may facilitate diffusion across membranes

Recall that nonpolar, hydrophobic molecules can dissolve in the lipid bilayer of a membrane and cross it with ease. Numerous substances that do not diffuse freely across membranes because of their polarity or charge can move across a membrane with the help of specific transport proteins. When one of these proteins makes it possible for a substance to move down its concentration gradient, the process is called **facilitated diffusion.** Without the protein, the substance does not cross the membrane or it diffuses across it too slowly to be useful to the cell. Facilitated diffusion is a type of passive transport because it does not require energy. As in all passive transport, the driving force is the concentration gradient.

Figure 5.6 shows a common type of transport protein, which provides a hydrophilic channel that some molecules or ions use as a tunnel through the membrane. Another type of transport protein binds its passenger, changes shape, and releases its passenger on the other side. In both cases, the transport protein is specific for the substance it helps move across the membrane. The greater the number of transport proteins for a particular solute present in a membrane, the faster the solute's rate of diffusion across the membrane.

Substances that use facilitated diffusion for crossing cell membranes include a number of sugars, amino acids, ions—and even water. The water molecule is very small, but because it

is polar (see Module 2.9), its diffusion through a membrane's hydrophobic interior is relatively slow. The very rapid diffusion of water into and out of certain cells, such as plant cells, kidney cells, and red blood cells, is made possible by transport proteins called **aquaporins.** In the next module, we meet the scientist who discovered these water channels and received the 2003 Nobel Prize in Chemistry for his work.

Web Activity *Facilitated Diffusion*

? How do transport proteins contribute to a membrane's selective permeability?

■ Transport proteins are specific for the solutes they transport. Thus, the numbers and kinds of different transport protein molecules embedded in the membrane affect its permeability to various solutes.

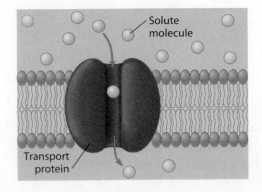

Figure 5.6
Transport protein providing a channel for the diffusion of a specific solute across a membrane

5.7 Peter Agre talks about aquaporins, water-channel proteins found in some cells

Figure 5.7   Peter Agre

An aquaporin is an hourglass-shaped protein that spans the membrane and allows entry or exit of up to 3 billion water molecules per second. The presence of aquaporins in cells that require the rapid diffusion of water illustrates the correlation between structure and function in biological membranes.

In a recent interview, Dr. Peter Agre (Figure 5.7), who is a medical doctor and a professor at the Johns Hopkins University School of Medicine, described his research that led to the discovery of aquaporins:

I'm a blood specialist (hematologist), and my particular interest has been proteins found in the plasma membrane of red blood cells. When I joined the faculty at Hopkins, I began to study the Rh blood antigens. Rh is of medical importance because of Rh incompatibility, which occurs when Rh-negative mothers have Rh-positive babies. Membrane-spanning proteins like the Rh-protein are really messy to work with. But we worked out a method to isolate and partially purify the Rh protein. Our sample seemed to consist of two proteins,

but we were sure that the smaller one was just a breakdown product of the larger one. We were completely wrong.

Using antibodies we made to the protein, we showed it to be one of the most abundant proteins in red cell membranes (200,000 copies per cell!) and even more abundant in certain kidney cells.

We asked Dr. Agre why cells have water-channel proteins.

Not all cells do. Before our discovery, however, many physiologists thought that diffusion through the phospholipid bilayer was enough for getting water into and out of *all* cells. Others said this couldn't be enough, especially for cells whose water permeability needs to be very high or regulated. For example, our kidneys must filter and reabsorb many liters of water every day.... People whose kidney cells have defective aquaporin molecules need to drink 20 liters of water a day to prevent dehydration. In addition, some patients make too much aquaporin, causing them to retain too much fluid. Fluid retention in pregnant women is caused by the synthesis of too much aquaporin. Knowledge of aquaporins may in the future contribute to the solution of medical problems.

? Why are aquaporins important in kidney cells?

■ Kidney cells must reabsorb a large amount of water from the urine before it is excreted.

5.8 Cells expend energy in the active transport of a solute against its concentration gradient

In **active transport** a cell must expend energy to move a solute *against* its concentration gradient—that is, across a membrane toward the side where the solute is more concentrated. The cell's energy molecule ATP (described in more detail in Module 5.13) supplies the energy for most active transport.

Figure 5.8 shows a simple model of an active transport system that moves a solute out of the cell against its concentration gradient. ❶ The process begins when solute on the cytoplasmic side of the plasma membrane attaches to a specific binding site on the transport protein. ❷ ATP then transfers one of its phosphate groups to the transport protein, ❸ causing it to change shape in such a way that the solute is released on the other side of the membrane. ❹ Then, the phosphate group detaches, and the transport protein returns to its original shape, ready for a new round of active transport. (As indicated in the figure, two solute ions or molecules are often transported together.)

Active transport allows a cell to maintain concentrations of small molecules that are different from concentrations in its surroundings. For example, the inside of an animal cell has a higher concentration of potassium ions (K^+) and a lower

concentration of sodium ions (Na^+) than the solution outside the cell. The generation of nerve signals depends on these concentration differences. A transport protein called the sodium-potassium pump helps cells maintain these steep gradients by shuttling Na^+ and K^+ across the membrane against their concentration gradients.

Web Activity *Active Transport*

? Cells actively transport Ca^{2+} out of the cell. Is calcium more concentrated inside or outside the cell? Explain.

■ Outside the cell. If the cell uses active transport, it is moving calcium against its concentration gradient.

Transport protein

Solute

ATP → ADP

P

Protein changes shape

P

Phosphate detaches

P

❶ Solute binding   ❷ Phosphorylation   ❸ Transport   ❹ Protein reversion

Figure 5.8   Active transport of a solute across a membrane

So far, we've focused on how water and small solutes enter and leave cells. The story is different for large molecules.

A cell uses the process of **exocytosis** (from the Greek *exo*, outside, and *kytos*, cell) to export bulky materials such as proteins or polysaccharides. As shown in Figure 4.13, a transport vesicle filled with macromolecules buds from the Gogli apparatus and moves to the plasma membrane. Once there, the vesicle fuses with the plasma membrane, and the vesicle's contents spill out of the cell while the vesicle membrane becomes part of the plasma membrane. When we weep, for instance, cells in our tear glands use exocytosis to export a salty solution containing proteins. In another example, certain cells in the pancreas manufacture the hormone insulin and secrete it into the bloodstream by exocytosis.

Endocytosis (*endo*, inside) is a transport process that is the opposite of exocytosis. In endocytosis, a cell takes in substances. A depression in the plasma membrane pinches in and forms a vesicle enclosing material that had been outside the cell.

Figure 5.9 shows three kinds of endocytosis. The top diagram illustrates **phagocytosis**, or "cellular eating." A cell engulfs a particle by wrapping extensions called pseudopodia around it and packaging it within a membrane-enclosed sac large enough to be called a vacuole. As Module 4.11 described, the vacuole then fuses with a lysosome, whose hydrolytic enzymes digest the contents of the vacuole. The micrograph on the top right shows an amoeba taking in a food particle via phagocytosis.

The center diagram shows **pinocytosis**, or "cellular drinking." The cell "gulps" droplets of fluid into tiny vesicles. Pinocytosis is not specific; it takes in any and all solutes dissolved in the droplets. The micrograph in the middle shows pinocytosis vesicles forming (arrows) in a cell lining a small blood vessel.

Receptor-mediated endocytosis is highly specific, in contrast to pinocytosis. Receptor proteins for specific molecules are embedded in regions of the membrane that are lined by a layer of coat proteins. The bottom diagram shows that the plasma membrane has indented to form a coated pit, whose receptor proteins have picked up particular molecules from the surroundings. The coated pit then pinches closed to form a vesicle that carries the molecules into the cytoplasm. The micrograph shows material bound to receptor proteins inside a coated pit.

Our cells use receptor-mediated endocytosis to take in cholesterol from the blood for synthesis of membranes and as a pre-cursor for other steroids. Cholesterol circulates in the blood in particles called low-density lipoproteins (LDLs). LDLs bind to receptor proteins and then enter cells by endocytosis. In humans with the inherited disease hypercholesterolemia, LDL receptor proteins are defective and cholesterol accumulates to high levels in the blood, leading to atherosclerosis (see Modules 9.12 and 23.6).

Web Activity *Exocytosis and Endocytosis*

? As a cell grows, its plasma membrane expands. Does this involve endocytosis or exocytosis? Explain.

■ Exocytosis. When a transport vesicle fuses with the plasma membrane, the vesicle membrane becomes part of the plasma membrane.

Phagocytosis

Pinocytosis

Receptor-mediated endocytosis

Figure 5.9 Three kinds of endocytosis

5.10   Cells transform energy as they perform work

The title of this chapter is "The Working Cell." But just what type of work does a cell do? You just learned that a cell actively transports substances across membranes. The cell also builds those membranes and the transport proteins embedded in them. A cell is a miniature chemical factory in which thousands of reactions occur within a microscopic space. Some of these reactions break down sugars and other fuels to release energy. The cell uses this energy in other reactions to manufacture cellular parts and products and to move cellular structures or even the whole cell. Bioluminescent organisms use energy in chemical reactions to produce light (see chapter introduction). Life requires energy, and cells are energy transformers. To understand how the cell works, you must have a basic knowledge of energy.

Energy is defined as the capacity to perform work. Work is performed when an object is moved against an opposing force, such as gravity or friction. Put another way, energy is the capacity to rearrange matter. There are two basic forms of energy: kinetic energy and potential energy.

Kinetic energy is the energy of motion. Moving objects can perform work by transferring motion to other matter. A pool player uses the motion of the cue stick to push the cue ball, which in turn moves the other balls. The contraction of leg muscles pushes bicycle pedals, turning the wheels and moving the bike and its rider up a hill (Figure 5.10A). **Heat,** or thermal energy, is a form of kinetic energy associated with the random movement of atoms or molecules. Light is another kind of kinetic energy that can be harnessed to perform work, such as powering photosynthesis in green plants.

Potential energy, the second form of energy, is stored energy that an object possesses as a result of its location or structure. Water behind a dam, for instance, possesses energy because of its altitude above sea level. A cyclist at the top of a hill has potential energy as a result of elevation (Figure 5.10B).

Likewise, molecules possess potential energy because of the arrangement of their atoms. **Chemical energy** is a term that refers to the potential energy available for release in a chemical reaction. Chemical energy is the most important type of energy for living organisms—it is the energy that is available to do the work of the cell. And just as the potential energy of the cyclist can be converted to kinetic energy in the speedy ride downhill (Figure 5.10C), the chemical energy of molecules can be released to power the work of the cell. Life depends on the fact that energy can be converted from one form to another. Next we consider some basic principles of energy transformation.

🎧 MP3 Tutor *Basic Energy Concepts*

Web Activity *Energy Transformations*

? How can an object at rest have energy?

■ It can have potential energy as a result of its location.

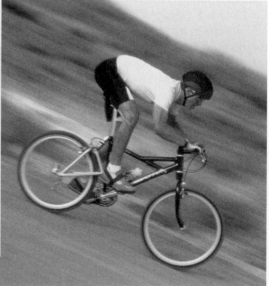

Figure 5.10A Kinetic energy, the energy of motion

Figure 5.10B Potential energy, stored energy as a result of location or structure

Figure 5.10C Potential energy being converted to kinetic energy

5.11 Two laws govern energy transformations

Thermodynamics is the study of energy transformations that occur in a collection of matter. Scientists use the word *system* for the matter under study and refer to the rest of the universe—everything outside the system—as the *surroundings*. A system can be an electric power plant, a single cell, or the entire planet. An organism is an open system; that is, it exchanges both energy and matter with its surroundings.

The First Law of Thermodynamics According to the **first law of thermodynamics,** also known as the law of energy conservation, the energy in the universe is constant. Energy can be transferred and transformed, but it cannot be created or destroyed. A power plant does not create energy; it merely converts it from one form (such as the energy stored in coal) to the more convenient form of electricity. A light bulb does not make light; it converts electricity to light energy. By converting sunlight to chemical energy, a green plant acts as an energy transformer, not an energy producer.

The Second Law of Thermodynamics If energy cannot be destroyed, then why can't organisms simply recycle their energy? It turns out that during every energy transfer or transformation, some energy becomes unusable—unavailable to do work. In most energy transformations, some energy is converted to heat, the energy associated with random molecular motion. Heat is a disordered form of energy, and its release makes the universe more random. Scientists use a quantity called **entropy** as a measure of disorder, or randomness. The more randomly arranged a collection of matter is, the greater its entropy. According to the **second law of thermodynamics,** energy conversions increase the entropy (disorder) of the universe.

Figure 5.11 compares a car and a cell to show how energy is transformed and transferred and how entropy increases as a result. Automobile engines and living cells use the same basic process to make the chemical energy stored in their fuel available for work. The engine of an automobile mixes oxygen with gasoline in an explosive chemical reaction that pushes the pistons, which eventually move the wheels. The waste products emitted from the exhaust pipe are mostly carbon dioxide and water, energy-poor, simple molecules. Only about 25% of the chemical energy stored in gasoline is converted to the kinetic energy of the car's movement; the rest is lost as heat energy.

Cells also use oxygen in the process of cellular respiration, which harvests chemical energy from food molecules. Just like the car, the waste products are mostly carbon dioxide and water. Cells are more efficient than car engines, however, converting about 40% of the chemical energy stored in foods to energy for cellular work. The other 60% generates heat, which explains why vigorous exercise makes you hot. For the bicyclist pumping his way up the hill in Figure 5.10A, sweating and evaporative cooling help release this excess heat to the surroundings.

According to the second law of thermodynamics, energy transformations result in the universe becoming more disordered. How, then, can we account for biological order? A cell creates its structures from less organized materials. For example, amino acids are ordered into the specific sequences of polypeptides. Although this increase in order corresponds to a decrease in entropy, it is accomplished at the expense of ordered forms of energy taken in from the surroundings. As shown in Figure 5.11, cells extract the chemical energy of glucose and return disordered heat and the lower-energy molecules of carbon dioxide and water to their surroundings. In a thermodynamic sense, a cell or an organism is an island of low entropy in an increasingly random universe.

? How does the second law of thermodynamics help explain the diffusion of a solute across a membrane?

■ Diffusion across a membrane results in equal concentrations of solute molecules, which is a more disordered arrangement (higher entropy) than a high concentration on one side and a low concentration on the other.

Fuel	Energy conversion	Waste products
Gasoline + Oxygen	Heat energy — **Combustion** Kinetic energy of movement — Energy conversion in a car	Carbon dioxide + Water
Glucose + Oxygen	Heat — **Cellular respiration** ATP ATP — Energy for cellular work — Energy conversion in a cell	Carbon dioxide + Water

Figure 5.11 Energy transformations (with an increase in entropy) in a car and a cell

Chemical reactions either release or store energy

Chemical reactions are of two types: They either release energy, or they require an input of energy and store energy.

An **exergonic reaction** is a chemical reaction that releases energy (exergonic means "energy outward"). As shown in Figure 5.12A, an exergonic reaction begins with reactants whose covalent bonds contain more energy than those in the products. The reaction releases to the surroundings an amount of energy equal to the difference in potential energy between the reactants and the products.

As an example of an exergonic reaction, consider what happens when wood burns. One of the major components of wood is cellulose, a large carbohydrate composed of many glucose monomers. Each glucose is rich in potential energy. The burning of wood releases the energy of glucose as heat and light. Carbon dioxide and water are the products of the reaction.

Burning is one way to release energy from chemicals. Cells release energy by means of a different exergonic process, called cellular respiration. **Cellular respiration** is a chemical process that uses oxygen to convert the chemical energy stored in fuel molecules to a form of chemical energy that the cell can use to perform work. Burning and cellular respiration are alike in being exergonic. They differ in that burning is essentially a one-step process that releases all of a substance's energy at once. Cellular respiration, on the other hand, involves many steps, each a separate chemical reaction; you can think of it as a "slow burn." As you saw in Figure 5.11, some of the energy released from glucose by cellular respiration escapes as heat, but a substantial amount of released energy is converted to the chemical energy of ATP. Cells use ATP as an immediate source of energy. We explore ATP in more detail in the next module.

The other type of chemical reaction requires a net input of energy. **Endergonic reactions** yield products that are rich in potential energy (endergonic means "energy inward"). As you can see in Figure 5.12B, on the bottom right of this page, an endergonic reaction starts out with reactant molecules that contain relatively little potential energy. Energy is absorbed from the surroundings as the reaction occurs, so the products of an endergonic reaction store more energy than the reactants did. The energy is potential energy stored in the covalent bonds of the product molecules. And as the graph shows, the amount of additional energy stored in the products equals the difference in potential energy between the reactants and the products.

Photosynthesis, the process by which plant cells make sugar, is an example of an endergonic process. Photosynthesis starts with energy-poor reactants (carbon dioxide and water molecules) and, using energy absorbed from sunlight, produces energy-rich sugar molecules.

All cells use endergonic reactions in the process of building the macromolecules that form the structure and perform the functions of the cell.

Every working cell in every organism carries out thousands of exergonic and endergonic reactions. The total of an organism's chemical reactions is called **metabolism** (from the Greek *metabole*, change). We can picture a cell's metabolism as a road map of thousands of chemical reactions, arranged as intersecting metabolic pathways. A **metabolic pathway** is a series of chemical reactions that either builds a complex molecule or breaks down a complex molecule into simpler compounds. The "slow burn" of cellular respiration is an example of a metabolic pathway in which a sequence of reactions slowly releases the potential energy stored in sugar.

All of an organism's activities require energy, which is obtained from sugar and other molecules by the exergonic reactions of cellular respiration. Cells then use that energy in endergonic reactions to make molecules and do the work of the cell. **Energy coupling**—the use of energy released from exergonic reactions to drive essential endergonic reactions—is a crucial ability of all cells. ATP molecules are the key to energy coupling. In the next module, we explore the structure and function of ATP.

Web Activity *Chemical Reactions and ATP*

? Cellular respiration is an exergonic process. Remembering that energy must be conserved, what becomes of the energy extracted from food during cellular respiration?

■ Some of it is stored in ATP molecules; the rest is released as heat.

Figure 5.12A   Exergonic reaction, energy released

Figure 5.12B   Endergonic reaction, energy required

5.13 ATP shuttles chemical energy and drives cellular work

ATP powers nearly all forms of cellular work. The structure of ATP, or adenosine triphosphate, is shown in **Figure 5.13A**. The adenosine part of ATP consists of adenine, a nitrogenous base (see Module 3.16), and ribose, a five-carbon sugar. The triphosphate part is a chain of three phosphate groups (each symbolized by (P)). All three phosphate groups are negatively charged (see Table 3.2). These like charges are crowded together, and their mutual repulsion makes the triphosphate chain of ATP the chemical equivalent of a compressed spring.

As a result, the bonds connecting the phosphate groups are unstable and can readily be broken by hydrolysis (the addition of water). Notice in Figure 5.13A, below, that when the bond to the third group breaks, a phosphate group leaves ATP—which becomes ADP (adenosine diphosphate)—and energy is released.

Thus, the hydrolysis of ATP is an exergonic reaction—it releases energy. How does the cell couple this reaction to an endergonic one? It usually does so by transferring the third phosphate group from ATP to some other molecule. This transfer is called **phosphorylation,** and most cellular work depends on ATP energizing molecules by phosphorylating them.

There are three main types of cellular work: chemical, mechanical, and transport. As shown in **Figure 5.13B**, to the right, ATP drives all three types of work. In chemical work, the phosphorylation of reactants provides energy to drive the endergonic synthesis of products. In an example of mechanical work, the transfer of phosphate groups to special motor proteins in muscle cells causes the proteins to change shape and pull on actin filaments, in turn causing the cells to contract. In transport work, as discussed in Module 5.8, ATP drives the active transport of solutes across a membrane against their concentration gradient by phosphorylating certain membrane proteins.

Figure 5.13B How ATP powers cellular work

Work can be sustained because ATP is a renewable resource that cells regenerate. Figure 5.13C, below, shows the ATP cycle. Energy released in exergonic reactions, such as the breakdown of glucose during cellular respiration, is used to regenerate ATP from ADP. In this endergonic (energy-storing) process, a phosphate group is bonded to ADP. A cell at work uses ATP continuously, and the ATP cycle runs at an astonishing pace. In fact, a working muscle cell may consume and regenerate 10 million ATP molecules each second.

But even with a constant supply of energy, few metabolic reactions would occur without the assistance of enzymes. We explore these biological catalysts next.

Web Activity *The Structure of ATP*

? Explain how ATP transfers energy from exergonic to endergonic processes in the cell.

■ Exergonic processes phosphorylate ADP to form ATP. ATP transfers energy to endergonic processes by phosphorylating other molecules.

Figure 5.13A The structure and hydrolysis of ATP. The reaction of ATP and water yields ADP, a phosphate group, and energy.

Figure 5.13C The ATP cycle

5.14 Enzymes speed up the cell's chemical reactions by lowering energy barriers

Proteins, DNA, carbohydrates, phospholipids—most of the cell's molecules are rich in potential energy. Why don't these molecules spontaneously break down into simpler, less energetic molecules? For the same reason that wood doesn't normally burst into flames. There is an energy barrier that must be overcome before a chemical reaction can begin. Energy must be absorbed to contort or weaken bonds in reactant molecules so that they can break and new bonds can form. We call this the **energy of activation (E_A),** and we can think of it as the amount of energy needed to push the reactants over an energy barrier, or "hill," so that the "downhill" part of the reaction can begin.

Now we have a dilemma. Most of the essential reactions of metabolism must occur quickly and precisely for a cell to survive. How can the specific reactions that a cell requires get over that energy barrier? One way to speed reactions is to add heat. Certainly, adding a match to kindling will start a fire. But heating a cell would speed up all reactions, not just the necessary ones, and too much heat would obviously kill a cell.

The solution lies in **enzymes**—proteins that function as biological catalysts, increasing the rate of a reaction without being consumed by the reaction. (Some RNA molecules also function as enzymes.) An enzyme speeds up a reaction by lowering the E_A barrier. In Figure 5.14, a graph shows the effect of an enzyme on the reaction it catalyzes. The black curve represents the course of the reaction without an enzyme; the E_A barrier is higher than in the reaction with an enzyme (red curve). Notice that the net change in energy from reactants to products, however, is the same for both curves.

? Explain why an enzyme cannot change an endergonic reaction into an exergonic one.

■ Although an enzyme speeds a reaction by lowering the energy of activation, it does not change the difference in energy between reactants and products. An endergonic reaction would still require an input of energy.

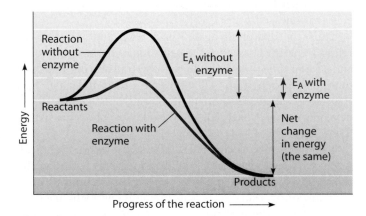

Figure 5.14 The effect of an enzyme is to lower E_A

5.15 A specific enzyme catalyzes each cellular reaction

As a protein, an enzyme has a unique three-dimensional shape, and that shape determines which chemical reaction the enzyme catalyzes. A specific reactant that an enzyme acts on is called the enzyme's **substrate.** A substrate fits into a region of the enzyme called an **active site.** An active site is typically a pocket or groove on the surface of the enzyme formed by only a few of the enzyme's amino acids. The rest of the protein maintains the shape of the active site. Enzymes are specific because their active sites fit only specific substrate molecules.

Figure 5.15 illustrates the catalytic cycle of an enzyme. Our example is the enzyme sucrase, which catalyzes the hydrolysis of sucrose (table sugar) to glucose and fructose. (Most enzymes have names that end in -ase, and many are named for their substrate.) ❶ Sucrase starts with an empty active site. ❷ Sucrose enters the active site, attaching by weak bonds. The active site changes shape slightly so that it embraces the substrate more snugly, like a firm handshake. This **induced fit** may strain substrate bonds or place chemical groups of the amino acids making up the active site in position to catalyze the reaction. (In reactions involving two or more reactants, the active site may hold the substrates in the proper orientation for a reaction to occur.) ❸ The strained bond reacts with water, and the

Figure 5.15 The catalytic cycle of an enzyme

substrate is converted (hydrolyzed) to the products glucose and fructose. ❹ The enzyme releases the products and emerges unchanged from the reaction. Its active site is now available for another substrate molecule, and another round of the cycle can begin. A single enzyme molecule may act on thousands or even millions of substrate molecules per second.

Optimal Conditions for Enzymes As with all proteins, an enzyme's shape is central to its function, and this three-dimensional shape is affected by the environment. For every enzyme, there are conditions under which it is most effective. Temperature, for instance, affects molecular motion, and an enzyme's optimal temperature produces the highest rate of contact between reactant molecules and the enzyme's active site. Higher temperatures denature the enzyme, altering its specific shape and destroying its function. Most human enzymes work best at 35–40°C (95–104°F), close to our normal body temperature of 37°C. Prokaryotes that live in hot springs, however, contain enzymes with optimal temperatures of 70°C (158°F) or higher.

The optimal pH for most enzymes is near neutrality, in the range of 6–8. Outside this range, enzyme action may be impaired. Buffers (see Module 2.15) regulate cellular pH, helping to maintain the normal chemical functioning of cells.

Cofactors Many enzymes require nonprotein helpers called **cofactors.** The cofactors of some enzymes are inorganic, such as the ions of zinc, iron, or copper. If the cofactor is an organic molecule, it is called a **coenzyme.** Most vitamins are important in nutrition because they function as coenzymes.

Web Activity *How Enzymes Function*

Web Process of Science *How Is the Rate of Enzyme Catalysis Measured?*

? Explain how an enzyme speeds up a specific reaction.

■ An enzyme lowers the energy of activation needed for a reaction to proceed by the specific binding of its substrate in its active site. With an induced fit, the enzyme strains bonds that need to break or orients substrates so that reactants are converted to products.

5.16 Enzyme inhibitors block enzyme action and can regulate enzyme activity in a cell

A chemical that interferes with an enzyme's activity is called an inhibitor. If an inhibitor attaches to the enzyme by covalent bonds, the inhibition is usually irreversible. Inhibition is reversible when weak interactions bind inhibitor and enzyme.

Some inhibitors resemble the enzyme's normal substrate and compete for the active site. As shown in the lower left of **Figure 5.16**, such a **competitive inhibitor** reduces an enzyme's productivity by blocking substrates from entering the active site. Competitive inhibition can be overcome by increasing the concentration of substrate, making it more likely that a substrate molecule will be nearby when an active site becomes vacant.

In contrast, a **noncompetitive inhibitor** does not enter the active site. Instead, it binds to the enzyme somewhere else, and its binding changes the shape of the enzyme so that the active site no longer fits the substrate (lower right of figure).

Humans have developed and used enzyme inhibitors as beneficial drugs and pesticides, but also as deadly poisons for use in warfare. Many antibiotics work by inhibiting enzymes of disease-causing bacteria. Penicillin, for example, inhibits an enzyme that bacteria use in making cell walls. Protease inhibitors are HIV drugs that target a key viral enzyme. And many cancer drugs are inhibitors of enzymes that promote cell division.

Toxins and poisons are often irreversible inhibitors. Nerve gases bind in the active site of an enzyme vital to the transmission of nerve impulses. The inhibition of this enzyme leads to rapid paralysis of vital functions and death. Pesticides such as malathion and parathion are toxic to insects because they also irreversibly inhibit this enzyme.

Although such inhibitors are deadly and enzyme inhibition itself sounds harmful, in fact, cells use inhibitors as important regulators of cell metabolism. As discussed in Module 5.12, most chemical reactions are organized into metabolic pathways

Normal binding of substrate

Competitive inhibitor

Noncompetitive inhibitor

Enzyme inhibition

Figure 5.16 How inhibitors interfere with substrate binding

in which a molecule is altered in a series of steps, each catalyzed by a specific enzyme, to form a final product. If a cell is producing more of that product than it needs, the product may act as an inhibitor of one of the enzymes early in the pathway. This sort of inhibition, whereby a metabolic reaction is blocked by its products, is called **feedback inhibition** and is one of the most important mechanisms that regulate metabolism. In the next chapter, we will see how feedback inhibition helps regulate ATP production in cellular respiration.

? What is the advantage of feedback inhibition to a cell?

■ It prevents the cell from wasting valuable resources by synthesizing more of a particular product than is necessary.

Reviewing the Concepts

Membrane Structure and Function (5.1–5.9)

Membranes are a fluid mosaic, with protein molecules embedded in a phospholipid bilayer. Functions of membrane proteins include attachment to the cytoskeleton and extracellular matrix, cell-cell recognition, intercellular junctions, enzymatic activity, signal transduction, and transport. Phospholipids spontaneously form membranes, a necessary step in the evolution of life (**5.1–5.2**).

Diffusion, Passive Transport, Active Transport (5.3–5.8).

Tonicity. Cells shrink in a hypertonic solution and swell in a hypotonic solution. In isotonic solutions, animal cells are normal, but plant cells are limp. The control of water balance is called osmoregulation (**5.5**). Aquaporins are water channels in cells with high water-transport needs (**5.7**).

Exocytosis and Endocytosis. In moving large molecules across a membrane, a vesicle may fuse with the membrane and expel its contents (exocytosis), or the membrane may fold inward, enclosing material from the outside (**5.9**).

Energy and the Cell (5.10–5.13)

Energy is the capacity to perform work. Kinetic energy is the energy of motion. Potential energy is energy stored in the location or structure of matter. Chemical energy is potential energy stored in chemical bonds (**5.10**). According to the laws of thermodynamics, energy can change form but cannot be created or destroyed. Energy transformations increase disorder, or entropy, and some energy is lost as heat (**5.11**).

Chemical Reactions. Exergonic reactions release energy. Endergonic reactions require energy and yield products rich in potential energy. Metabolism includes all of a cell's chemical reactions. Energy coupling uses exergonic reactions to drive endergonic ones (**5.12**). ATP performs cellular work by phosphorylation, transferring a phosphate group to make molecules more reactive (**5.13**).

How Enzymes Function (5.14–5.16)

Enzymes are protein catalysts that decrease the energy of activation (E_A) needed to begin a reaction (**5.14**). Each type of enzyme has a unique active site that binds specifically with its substrate. Temperature and pH influence enzyme activity. Some enzymes require cofactors, such as metal ions or organic coenzymes (**5.15**).

Inhibitors. A competitive inhibitor competes with the substrate for the active site. A noncompetitive inhibitor alters an enzyme's function by changing its shape. Poisons, pesticides, and drugs may inhibit enzymes. Feedback inhibition helps regulate metabolism (**5.16**).

Connecting the Concepts

1. Fill in the following concept map to review the processes by which molecules move across membranes.

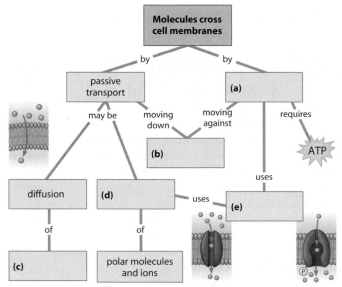

2. Label the parts of this diagram illustrating the catalytic cycle of an enzyme.

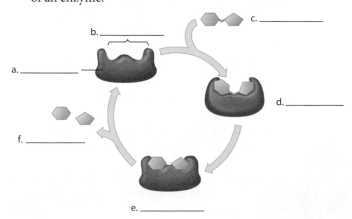

Testing Your Knowledge

Multiple Choice

3. Which best describes the structure of a cell membrane?
   a. proteins between two bilayers of phospholipids
   b. proteins embedded in a bilayer of phospholipids
   c. a bilayer of protein coating a layer of phospholipids

d. phospholipids between two layers of protein
e. cholesterol embedded in a bilayer of phospholipids

4. Consider the following: chemical bonds in the gasoline in a car's gas tank and the movement of the car along the road; a climber at the top of a hill and the hike she took to get there. The first parts of these situations illustrate _____, and the second parts illustrate _____.
a. the first law of thermodynamics . . . the second law
b. kinetic energy . . . potential energy
c. an exergonic reaction . . . an endergonic reaction
d. potential energy . . . kinetic energy
e. the second law of thermodynamics . . . the first law

5. A plant cell placed in distilled water will _____; an animal cell placed in distilled water will _____.
a. burst . . . burst
b. become flaccid . . . shrivel
c. become flaccid . . . be normal in shape
d. become turgid . . . be normal in shape
e. become turgid . . . burst

6. The sodium concentration in a cell is ten times less than the concentration in the surrounding fluid. How can the cell move sodium out of the cell? (*Explain.*)
a. passive transport   d. osmosis
b. diffusion   e. any of these processes
c. active transport

7. The synthesis of ATP from ADP and ℗
a. is an exergonic process.
b. involves the hydrolysis of a phosphate bond.
c. transfers a phosphate, priming a protein to do work.
d. stores energy in a form that can drive cellular work.
e. releases energy.

8. Facilitated diffusion across a membrane requires _____ and moves a solute _____ its concentration gradient.
a. transport proteins . . . up (against)
b. transport proteins . . . down
c. energy . . . up
d. energy and transport proteins . . . up
e. energy and transport proteins . . . down

Describing, Comparing, and Explaining

9. What are aquaporins? Where would you expect to find these structures?

10. How do the two laws of thermodynamics apply to living organisms?

11. What are the main types of cellular work? How does ATP provide the energy for this work?

12. Why is the barrier of the energy of activation beneficial for organic molecules? Explain how enzymes lower E_A.

13. How do the components and structure of cell membranes relate to the functions of membranes?

14. Sometimes inhibitors can be harmful to a cell; often they are beneficial. Explain.

Applying the Concepts

15. Explain how each of the following food preservation methods would interfere with a microbe's enzyme activity and ability to break down food: canning (heating), freezing, pickling (soaking in acetic acid), salting.

16. A biologist performed two series of experiments on lactase, the enzyme that hydrolyzes lactose to glucose and galactose. First, she made up 10% lactose solutions containing different concentrations of enzyme and measured the rate at which galactose was produced (grams of galactose per minute). Results of these experiments are shown in Table A below. In the second series of experiments (Table B), she prepared 2% enzyme solutions containing different concentrations of lactose and again measured the rate of galactose production.

Table A: Rate and Enzyme Concentration

Lactose concentration	10%	10%	10%	10%	10%
Enzyme concentration	0%	1%	2%	4%	8%
Reaction rate	0	25	50	100	200

Table B: Rate and Substrate Concentration

Lactose concentration	0%	5%	10%	20%	30%
Enzyme concentration	2%	2%	2%	2%	2%
Reaction rate	0	25	50	65	65

a. Graph and explain the relationship between the reaction rate and the enzyme concentration.
b. Graph and explain the relationship between the reaction rate and the substrate concentration. How and why did the results of the two experiments differ?

17. The following graph shows the rate of reaction for two different enzymes: One is pepsin, a digestive enzyme found in the stomach; the other is trypsin, a digestive enzyme found in the intestine. As you may know, the stomach secretes digestive juices containing hydrochloric acid. Which curve belongs to which enzyme?

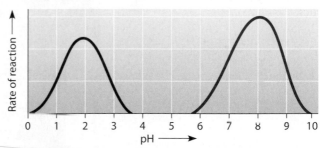

A lysosome, a digestive organelle in a cell, has an internal pH of around 4.5. Draw a curve on the graph that you would predict for a lysosomal enzyme, labeling its optimal pH.

18. Lead acts as an enzyme inhibitor and can interfere with the development of the nervous system. One manufacturer of lead-acid batteries instituted a "fetal protection policy" that banned female employees of childbearing age from working in areas where they might be exposed to high levels of lead. Women were involuntarily transferred to lower-paying jobs in lower-risk areas. A group of employees challenged the policy, claiming that it deprived women of job opportunities available to men. The U.S. Supreme Court ruled the policy illegal. What rights and responsibilities of employers, employees, and government agencies are in conflict in this situation? Who should determine what makes a safe environment?

Answers to all questions can be found in Appendix 4.

For Practice Quizzes, BioFlix, MP3 Tutors, and Activities, go to www.mybiology.com.

chapter

6

How Cells Harvest Chemical Energy

Introduction to Cellular Respiration

6.1 Photosynthesis and cellular respiration provide energy for life

6.2 Breathing supplies oxygen to our cells for use in cellular respiration and removes carbon dioxide

6.3 Cellular respiration banks energy in ATP molecules

6.4 The human body uses energy from ATP for all its activities

6.5 Cells tap energy from electrons "falling" from organic fuels to oxygen

Stages of Cellular Respiration and Fermentation

 6.6 Overview: Cellular respiration occurs in three main stages

 6.7 Glycolysis harvests chemical energy by oxidizing glucose to pyruvate

6.8 Pyruvate is chemically groomed for the citric acid cycle

6.9 The citric acid cycle completes the oxidation of organic molecules, generating many NADH and $FADH_2$ molecules

6.10 Most ATP production occurs by oxidative phosphorylation

6.11 Certain poisons interrupt critical events in cellular respiration

6.12 Review: Each molecule of glucose yields many molecules of ATP

6.13 Fermentation enables cells to produce ATP without oxygen

6.14 Glycolysis evolved early in the history of life on Earth

Interconnections Between Molecular Breakdown and Synthesis

6.15 Cells use many kinds of organic molecules as fuel for cellular respiration

6.16 Food molecules provide raw materials for biosynthesis

How Is a Marathoner Different from a Sprinter?

Athletes who participate in track competitions usually have a favorite event in which they excel. For some runners, this event may be a sprint, a short race of only 100 or 200 m. For others, it may be a race of 1,500, 5,000, or even 10,000 m. It is unusual to find a runner who competes equally well in both 100-m and 10,000-m races; runners just seem to feel more comfortable running races of particular lengths. But why?

Could it be that runners' bodies "tell" them which races are best for them? There are indications that this is indeed the case. The muscles that move our legs contain two main types of muscle fibers, called slow and fast muscle fibers. Slow muscle fibers (also called "slow-twitch" fibers) are muscle cells that can sustain repeated contractions but don't generate a lot of quick power for the body. They perform better in endurance exercises, like long-distance running, which require slow, steady muscle activity. Fast muscle fibers ("fast-twitch" fibers) are cells that can contract more quickly and powerfully than slow fibers but fatigue much more easily; they function best for short bursts of intense activity, like weight lifting or sprinting.

All human muscles contain both slow and fast fibers, but muscles differ in the percentage of each. The percentage of each fiber type in a particular muscle also varies from person to person. For example, in the quadriceps muscles of the thigh, most marathon runners have about 80% slow fibers, whereas sprinters have half as many slow fibers and about 60% fast fibers. These differences, which are genetically determined, undoubtedly help account for our differing athletic capabilities. No amount of training will turn a marathoner into a sprinter or vice versa!

What makes these two types of muscle fibers perform so differently? An important part of the answer is that they use different processes for making ATP (see Module 5.13), the molecule that supplies the energy for muscle contraction. While both types of muscle cells break down sugar (chiefly glucose) to make chemical energy available for ATP production, slow fibers do it *aerobically,* using oxygen (O_2), while fast fibers can work *anaerobically,* without oxygen.

The structures of these two kinds of muscle cells correlate with their differing functions. Slow fibers have many mitochondria, the organelles where aerobic ATP production occurs. And slow fibers contain many molecules of myoglobin, a red protein related to hemoglobin that, like hemoglobin, is a carrier of O_2 molecules. Myoglobin helps supply mitochondria with oxygen. The aerobic harvesting of energy from sugar by muscle cells (or other cells) is called **cellular respiration.** This process yields carbon dioxide (CO_2), water (H_2O), and a large amount of ATP—perfect for sustaining muscle contractions over a long period of time.

Fast muscle fibers, on the other hand, are thicker than slow ones, have fewer mitochondria, and have much less myoglobin. The thickness of fast fibers enhances their power. But they rapidly deplete their oxygen supply and switch to an energy-harvesting process that produces much less ATP per glucose molecule. Thus, they can't completely break down glucose to CO_2. Instead, they produce lactic acid, which lowers the pH in muscles, making them ache and fatigue. Fast muscle fibers are best at supplying short bursts of power. Anaerobic ATP production in our muscles is only effective for a minute or so.

Muscle cells are not the only cells in our body that break down sugars and other food molecules for ATP production. All our cells harvest chemical energy from food, as do the cells of all other organisms, eukaryotic and prokaryotic alike. Cells of most eukaryotic organisms—protists, fungi, plants, and animals— function like slow muscle fibers in that they carry out the aerobic process of cellular respiration. Before learning more about how cellular respiration powers the work of cells, let's take a step back and consider the bigger picture of energy flow through an ecosystem. In other words, where does the energy for cellular work originate? ■ ■ ■

6.1   Photosynthesis and cellular respiration provide energy for life

Life requires energy. A cell uses energy to build and maintain its structure, transport materials, manufacture products, move, grow, and reproduce. This energy ultimately comes from the sun. Through the process of photosynthesis, green plants, algae, and photosynthetic protists and bacteria convert light energy into chemical energy. Photosynthesis is the topic of Chapter 7. But a brief overview here of the relationship between cellular respiration and photosynthesis will illustrate how these two processes provide energy for life. As **Figure 6.1** shows, in photosynthesis the energy of sunlight is used to rearrange the atoms of CO_2 and H_2O to produce glucose and O_2. In cellular respiration, O_2 is consumed as glucose is broken down to CO_2 and H_2O; the cell captures the energy released in ATP.

This figure also shows that in these energy conversions some energy is lost as heat. Life on Earth is solar powered, and energy makes a one-way trip through an ecosystem. Chemicals, however, are recycled. For example, the CO_2 and H_2O released by cellular respiration are converted through photosynthesis to glucose and O_2, which are then used in respiration.

Before we take a closer look at how our cells harvest energy through cellular respiration, let's consider the connection between breathing and respiration.

Web Activity *Build a Chemical Recycling System*

Figure 6.1 The connection between photosynthesis and cellular respiration

? What is misleading about the following statement? "Plants perform photosynthesis and animals perform cellular respiration."

■ The statement implies that cellular respiration does not occur in plants. In fact, almost all eukaryotic cells use cellular respiration to obtain energy.

6.2   Breathing supplies oxygen to our cells for use in cellular respiration and removes carbon dioxide

We often use the word *respiration* as a synonym for "breathing," the meaning of its Latin root. In this sense, respiration refers to an exchange of gases: An organism obtains O_2 from its environment and releases CO_2 as a waste product. Biologists also define respiration as the aerobic harvesting of energy from food molecules by cells. This process is called cellular respiration to distinguish it from breathing.

Breathing and cellular respiration are closely related. As the runner in **Figure 6.2** breathes in air, her lungs take up O_2 and pass it to her bloodstream. The bloodstream carries the O_2 to her muscle cells. Mitochondria in the muscle cells use the O_2 in cellular respiration, harvesting energy from glucose and other organic molecules to generate ATP, which the cells then use to contract. The runner's bloodstream and lungs also perform the vital function of disposing of the CO_2 waste produced by cellular respiration.

? How is your breathing related to your cellular respiration?

■ In breathing, CO_2 and O_2 are exchanged between your lungs and the air. In cellular respiration, cells use O_2 to break down fuel, releasing CO_2 as a waste product.

Figure 6.2 The connection between breathing and cellular respiration

6.3 Cellular respiration banks energy in ATP molecules

As the runner example in Figure 6.2 implies, oxygen usage is only a means to an end. Generating ATP for cellular work is the fundamental function of cellular respiration.

The balanced chemical equation in Figure 6.3 summarizes cellular respiration as carried out by cells that use O_2 in harvesting energy from glucose. Throughout this chapter, we use glucose as a representative food molecule, although cells also "burn" many other organic molecules in cellular respiration. The equation tells us that the atoms of the starting (reactant) molecules glucose and O_2 regroup to form the products CO_2 and H_2O. In this exergonic process, the chemical energy of the bonds in glucose is transferred and stored (or "banked") in the chemical bonds of ATP (see Modules 5.11–5.13). The series of arrows in Figure 6.3 indicates that cellular respiration consists of many steps, not just a single reaction.

Cellular respiration can produce up to 38 ATP molecules for each glucose molecule, representing about 40% of the energy in glucose. The rest of the energy is released as heat (see Module 5.11). This may seem inefficient, but it compares

Figure 6.3 Summary equation for cellular respiration:
$C_6H_{12}O_6 + 6\ O_2 \rightarrow 6\ CO_2 + 6\ H_2O + \text{energy}$

very well with the efficiency of most energy-conversion systems. The average automobile engine is able to convert only about 25% of the energy in gasoline to the kinetic energy of movement.

How great are the energy needs of a cell? If ATP could not be regenerated through cellular respiration, humans would use up nearly their body weight in ATP each day. Let's consider the energy requirements for various human activities next.

? Why are sweating and other body-cooling mechanisms necessary during vigorous exercise?

■ The demand for ATP is supported by an increased rate of cellular respiration, but about 60% of the energy from food produces body heat instead of ATP.

6.4 The human body uses energy from ATP for all its activities

Your body requires a continuous supply of energy just to stay alive—to keep the heart pumping, to breathe, and to maintain body temperature. Your brain requires a huge amount of energy—its cells burn about 120 g (1/4 lb) of glucose a day and account for about 15% of total oxygen consumption. Maintaining brain cells and other life-sustaining activities uses as much as 75% of the energy a person takes in as food during a typical day.

Above and beyond the energy we need for body maintenance, cellular respiration provides energy for voluntary activities. Table 6.4 shows the amount of energy it takes to perform some

of these activities. The energy units are **kilocalories (kcal),** the quantity of heat required to raise the temperature of 1 kilogram (kg) of water by 1°C. (The "calories" listed on food packages are actually kilocalories.) The values shown do not include the energy the body consumes for its basic life-sustaining activities. Thus, sleeping or lying quietly does not consume any energy above the energy used in maintenance.

The U.S. National Academy of Sciences estimates that the average adult human needs to take in food that provides about 2,200 kcal of energy per day. This includes the energy expended in both maintenance and voluntary activity.

Obviously, the human diet includes more than just glucose. But taking glucose as our example, how much would it take to provide that 2,200 kcal? Burning a mole* of glucose (about 180 g) releases 686 kcal of heat. Thus, 3.2 moles of glucose (about 577 g or 1.25 lb) is needed to fuel the production of ATP equal to 2,200 kcal.

? Walking at 3 mph, how far would you have to travel to "burn off" the equivalent of an extra slice of pizza, which has about 475 kcal? How long would that take?

■ About 6 miles; about 2 hours (Now you understand why it is said that the most effective exercise for losing weight is pushing away from the table!)

TABLE 6.4	ENERGY CONSUMED BY VARIOUS ACTIVITIES (IN KCAL)
Activity	**Kcal Consumed per Hour by a 67.5-kg (150-lb) Person***
Running (7 min/mi)	979
Dancing (fast)	510
Bicycling (10 mph)	490
Swimming (2 mph)	408
Walking (3 mph)	245
Dancing (slow)	204
Sitting (writing)	28

*Not including kcal needed for body maintenance

*A mole is the molecular mass of a molecule (sum of the masses of all its atoms) in grams and represents 6.02×10^{23} molecules (Avogadro's number). The molecular mass of glucose ($C_6H_{12}O_6$) is 180; thus, a mole of glucose = 180 g.

Cells tap energy from electrons "falling" from organic fuels to oxygen

Just how do our cells extract energy from organic molecules? The energy available to a cell is contained in the arrangement of electrons in the chemical bonds that hold an organic molecule like glucose together. During cellular respiration, electrons are transferred to oxygen as the carbon-hydrogen bonds of glucose are broken and the hydrogen-oxygen bonds of water form. Oxygen very strongly attracts electrons, and an electron loses potential energy when it "falls" to oxygen. If you burn a cube of sugar, this electron fall happens very rapidly, releasing energy in the form of heat and light. Cellular respiration is a more controlled descent of electrons—more like stepping down an energy staircase, with energy released in small amounts that can be stored in the chemical bonds of ATP.

In the cellular respiration equation in Figure 6.5A, you cannot see any electron transfers. What you do see are changes in hydrogen atom distribution. Glucose loses hydrogen atoms as it is converted to carbon dioxide; simultaneously, oxygen (O_2) gains hydrogen atoms in being converted to water. These hydrogen movements represent electron transfers because, as we saw in Chapter 2, each hydrogen atom consists of an electron and a proton.

The movement of electrons from one molecule to another is an oxidation-reduction reaction, or **redox reaction** for short. In a redox reaction, the loss of electrons from one substance is called **oxidation,** and the addition of electrons to another substance is called **reduction.** A molecule is said to become oxidized when it loses one or more electrons and reduced when it gains one or more electrons. Because an electron transfer requires both a donor and an acceptor, oxidation and reduction always go together. You can see the overall results of the redox reactions of cellular respiration in Figure 6.5A: Glucose loses electrons (in H atoms) and becomes oxidized, while O_2 gains electrons (in H atoms) and becomes reduced. The electrons lose potential energy along the way, and energy is released.

Two key players in the process of oxidizing glucose are an enzyme called **dehydrogenase** and a coenzyme called NAD^+. NAD^+ (nicotinamide adenine dinucleotide) is an organic molecule that cells make from the vitamin niacin and use to shuttle electrons in redox reactions. The top equation in Figure 6.5B at the top of the next column depicts the oxidation of an organic molecule. We show only its three carbons (⬤) and a few of its other atoms. Dehydrogenase strips two hydrogen atoms from this molecule. Simultaneously, as shown in the lower equation, NAD^+ picks up the two electrons (one of which neutralizes its positive charge) and becomes reduced to NADH. One proton

Figure 6.5B A pair of redox reactions, occuring simultaneously

(H^+) is released. (Reduced NADH is represented throughout this chapter as a light brown box carrying two blue electrons.)

Using the energy staircase analogy of electrons falling from glucose to oxygen, the transfer of electrons from an organic molecule to NADH represents the first step. Figure 6.5C shows NADH delivering these electrons to the rest of the staircase—an **electron transport chain.** The steps in the chain are electron carrier molecules, shown here as purple ovals, built into the inner membrane of a mitochondrion. At the bottom of the staircase is O_2, the final electron acceptor.

The electron transport chain involves a series of redox reactions in which electrons pass from carrier to carrier down to oxygen. The redox steps in the staircase release energy in amounts small enough to be used by the cell to make ATP.

With an understanding of this basic mechanism of electron transfer and energy release, we can now explore cellular respiration in more detail.

? What chemical characteristic of the element oxygen accounts for its function in cellular respiration?

■ Oxygen is very electronegative (see Module 2.9), meaning that it is very powerful in pulling electrons from other elements.

$$C_6H_{12}O_6 + 6 O_2 \longrightarrow 6 CO_2 + 6 H_2O + Energy$$
Glucose   (ATP)

Loss of hydrogen atoms (oxidation)

Gain of hydrogen atoms (reduction)

Figure 6.5A Rearrangement of hydrogen atoms (with their electrons) in the redox reactions of cellular respiration

Figure 6.5C In cellular respiration, electrons fall down an energy staircase and finally reduce O_2.

6.6   Overview: Cellular respiration occurs in three main stages

Cellular respiration consists of a sequence of steps that can be divided into three main stages. **Figure 6.6** below gives an overview of the three stages and shows where they occur in a eukaryotic cell. (In prokaryotic cells that use aerobic respiration, these steps occur in the cytoplasm, and the electron transport chain is built into the plasma membrane.)

Stage 1: Glycolysis (shown with an aqua background throughout) occurs in the cytoplasmic fluid of the cell, that is, outside the organelles. Glycolysis begins respiration by breaking glucose into two molecules of a three-carbon compound called pyruvate.

Stage 2: The **citric acid cycle** (shown in this chapter with a light salmon color) takes place within the mitochondria. It completes the breakdown of glucose by decomposing a derivative of pyruvate to carbon dioxide. As suggested by the smaller ATP symbols in the diagram, the cell makes a small amount of ATP during these first two stages. The main function of glycolysis and the citric acid cycle, however, is to supply the third stage of respiration with electrons (shown with gold arrows).

Stage 3: Oxidative phosphorylation (a purple background) involves the electron transport chain (see Module 6.5) and a process known as chemiosmosis. NADH and a related electron carrier, $FADH_2$ (flavin adenine dinucleotide), shuttle electrons to the electron transport chain embedded in the inner mitochondrion membrane. Most of the ATP produced by cellular respiration is generated by oxidative phosphorylation, which uses the energy released by the downhill fall of electrons from NADH and $FADH_2$ to O_2 to phosphorylate ADP. (Recall from Module 5.13 that cells generate ATP by adding a phosphate group to ADP.)

What couples the electron transport chain to ATP synthesis? As the electron transport chain passes electrons down the energy staircase, it also pumps hydrogen ions (H^+) across the inner mitochondrial membrane into the narrow intermembrane space. The result is a concentration gradient of H^+ across the membrane. In **chemiosmosis,** the potential energy of this concentration gradient is used to make ATP. The concentration gradient drives the diffusion of H^+ through **ATP synthases,** protein complexes built into the inner membrane that synthesize ATP. The details of this process are explored in Module 6.10. In 1978, British biochemist Peter Mitchell was awarded the Nobel Prize for developing the theory of chemiosmosis.

The small amount of ATP produced in glycolysis and the citric acid cycle is made by substrate-level phosphorylation, a process we discuss in more detail in the next module. In the next several modules, we look more closely at the three stages of cellular respiration and the two mechanisms of ATP synthesis.

Bio Flix **BioFlix** *Cellular Respiration*

Web Activity *Overview of Cellular Respiration*

? Of the three main stages of cellular respiration represented in Figure 6.6, which one uses oxygen to extract chemical energy from organic compounds?

■ Oxidative phosphorylation, using the electron transport chain, which eventually transfers electrons to oxygen

Figure 6.6
An overview of cellular respiration

6.7 Glycolysis harvests chemical energy by oxidizing glucose to pyruvate

Now that we have introduced the major players and processes, it's time to focus on the individual stages of cellular respiration. The term for the first stage, *glycolysis,* means "splitting of sugar" (*glyco,* sweet, and *lysis,* split), and that's exactly what happens during this phase.

Figure 6.7A below gives an overview of glycolysis in terms of input and output. Glycolysis begins with a single molecule of glucose and concludes with two molecules of pyruvate. (Pyruvate is the ionized form of pyruvic acid.) The gray balls represent the carbon atoms in each molecule; glucose has six, and these same six end up in the two molecules of pyruvate (three in each). The straight arrow from glucose to pyruvate represents nine chemical steps, each catalyzed by its own enzyme. As these reactions occur, the cell reduces two molecules of NAD^+, forming two molecules of NADH, and produces two molecules of ATP by substrate-level phosphorylation.

In **substrate-level phosphorylation** (see Figure 6.7B, next column) an enzyme transfers a phosphate group from a substrate molecule directly to ADP, forming ATP. This process produces a small amount of ATP in both glycolysis and the citric acid cycle.

Thus, the energy extracted from glucose during glycolysis is banked in a combination of ATP and NADH. The cell can use the energy in ATP immediately, but for it to use the energy in NADH, electrons from NADH must pass down the electron transport chain located in the inner mitochondrial membrane. And the pyruvate still holds most of the energy of glucose; these molecules will be oxidized in the citric acid cycle.

Let's take a closer look at glycolysis. **Figure 6.7C** (next page) shows all the organic compounds that form in the nine chemical reactions of glycolysis. Commentary on the left highlights the main features of the reactions. The gray balls represent the carbon atoms in each of the compounds named on the right.

Figure 6.7B Substrate-level phosphorylation: transfer of a phosphate group (P) from a substrate to ADP, producing ATP

The compounds that form between the initial reactant, glucose, and the final product, pyruvate, are known as **intermediates.** Glycolysis is an example of a metabolic pathway in which each chemical step leads to the next one. For instance, the intermediate glucose-6-phosphate is the product of step 1 and the reactant for step 2. Similarly, fructose-6-phosphate is the product of step 2 and the reactant for step 3. Also essential are the specific enzymes that catalyze each of the chemical steps; however, to keep the figures simple, we have not included enzymes in the diagrams.

As indicated in Figure 6.7C, the steps of glycolysis can be grouped into two main phases. Steps ❶–❹, the energy investment phase, actually *consume* energy. In this phase, ATP is used to energize a glucose molecule, which is then split into two small sugars that are now primed to release energy. The figure follows both of these three-carbon sugars through the second phase.

Steps ❺–❾, the energy payoff phase, *yield* energy for the cell. In this phase, two NADH molecules are produced for each initial glucose molecule, and four ATP molecules are generated. Since the first phase uses two molecules of ATP, *the net gain to the cell is two ATP molecules for each glucose molecule that enters glycolysis.*

These two ATP molecules from glycolysis account for only 5% of the energy that a cell can harvest from a glucose molecule. The two NADH molecules generated during step 5 account for another 16%, but their stored energy is not available for use in the absence of O_2. Some organisms—yeasts and certain bacteria, for instance—can satisfy their energy needs with the ATP produced by glycolysis alone. And the fast-twitch muscle fibers described in the chapter introduction may use this anaerobic production of ATP for short periods. Most cells and organisms, however, have far higher energy demands. The stages of cellular respiration that follow glycolysis release much more energy. In the next two modules, we see what happens in most organisms after glycolysis forms pyruvate.

🎧 MP3 Tutor *Cellular Respiration Part 1: Glycolysis*

Web Activity *Glycolysis*

? For each glucose molecule processed, what are the net molecular products of glycolysis?

Figure 6.7A
An overview
of glycolysis

■ Two molecules of pyruvate, two molecules of ATP, and two molecules of NADH

Steps ❶–❸ A fuel molecule is energized, using ATP. A sequence of three chemical reactions converts glucose to a molecule of the intermediate fructose-1,6-bisphosphate. The coupled arrows indicate the transfer of a phosphate group from ATP to another molecule. In these preparatory steps, the cell invests two ATP molecules, one at step 1 and one at step 3, to energize a fuel molecule. In becoming energized, the molecule becomes more reactive.

Step ❹ A six-carbon intermediate splits into two three-carbon intermediates. Fructose-1,6-bisphosphate is highly reactive and breaks into two three-carbon intermediates. Two molecules of glyceraldehyde-3-phosphate (G3P) emerge from each glucose molecule that enters glycolysis. The two G3P molecules enter step 5.

Step ❺ A redox reaction generates NADH. The coupled arrows indicate the transfer of two hydrogen atoms (containing two electrons) as G3P is oxidized and NAD⁺ is reduced to NADH. This oxidation releases enough energy to attach a phosphate group to the substrate.

Steps ❻–❾ ATP and pyruvate are produced. This series of four chemical reactions completes glycolysis, producing two molecules of pyruvate for each initial molecule of glucose. During steps 6–9, specific enzymes make four molecules of ATP by substrate-level phosphorylation. (Step 6 is diagrammed in Figure 6.7B.) Water is produced at step 8 as a by-product. ——

Glucose

Step ❶

Glucose-6-phosphate

❷

Fructose-6-phosphate

❸

Fructose-1,6-bisphosphate

❹

Glyceraldehyde-3-phosphate (G3P)

ENERGY PAYOFF PHASE

❺

1,3-Bisphosphoglycerate

❻

3-Phosphoglycerate

❼

2-Phosphoglycerate

❽

Phosphoenolpyruvate (PEP)

❾

Pyruvate

Figure 6.7C Details of glycolysis

6.8 Pyruvate is chemically groomed for the citric acid cycle

As pyruvate forms at the end of glycolysis, it is transported from the cytoplasm into a mitochondrion, the site of the citric acid cycle. Pyruvate itself does not enter the citric acid cycle. As shown in **Figure 6.8**, it first undergoes some major chemical "grooming." A large, multienzyme complex catalyzes three reactions: ❶ A carboxyl group ($-COO^-$) is removed from pyruvate and given off as a molecule of CO_2 (this is the first step in which CO_2 is released during respiration); ❷ the two-carbon compound remaining is oxidized while a molecule of NAD^+ is reduced to NADH; and ❸ a compound called coenzyme A, derived from a B vitamin, joins with the two-carbon group to form a molecule called acetyl coenzyme A.

These grooming steps—a chemical "haircut and conditioning" of pyruvate—set up the second major stage of cellular respiration. Acetyl coenzyme A, abbreviated **acetyl CoA,** is a high-energy fuel molecule for the citric acid cycle. For each molecule of glucose that entered glycolysis, two molecules of acetyl CoA are produced and enter the citric acid cycle.

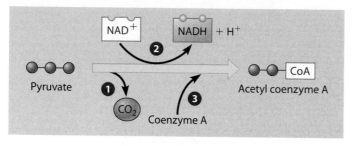

Figure 6.8   The conversion of pyruvate to acetyl CoA

❓ Which molecule in Figure 6.8 has been reduced?

■ NAD^+ is reduced to NADH.

6.9 The citric acid cycle completes the oxidation of organic molecules, generating many NADH and FADH₂ molecules

The citric acid cycle is often called the Krebs cycle in honor of Hans Krebs, the German-British researcher who worked out much of this cyclic phase of cellular respiration in the 1930s. We present an overview figure first, followed by a more detailed look at this cycle.

Figure 6.9A   An overview of the citric acid cycle: Two carbons enter the cycle through acetyl CoA, and 2 CO_2, 3 NADH, 1 FADH₂, and 1 ATP exit the cycle.

As shown in **Figure 6.9A**, only the two-carbon acetyl part of the acetyl CoA molecule actually participates in the citric acid cycle. Coenzyme A helps the acetyl group enter the cycle and then splits off and is recycled. Not shown in this figure are the multiple steps that follow, each catalyzed by a specific enzyme located in the mitochondrial matrix or embedded in the inner membrane. The acetyl group joins a four-carbon molecule. The resulting six-carbon molecule is processed through a series of redox reactions, two carbon atoms are removed as CO_2, and the four-carbon molecule is regenerated. This regeneration accounts for the word *cycle;* the six-carbon compound first formed in the cycle is citrate, the ionized (negatively charged) form of citric acid. Hence the name *citric acid cycle.*

Compared with glycolysis, the citric acid cycle pays big energy dividends to the cell. Each turn of the cycle makes one ATP molecule by substrate-level phosphorylation (shown at the bottom of Figure 6.9A). It also produces four other energy-rich molecules: three NADH molecules and one molecule of the electron carrier, FADH₂. Since the citric acid cycle processes two molecules of acetyl CoA for each initial molecule of glucose, the overall yield per molecule of glucose is 2 ATP, 6 NADH, and 2 FADH₂. This yield is considerably more than the 2 ATP plus 2 NADH produced by glycolysis alone.

Overall, how many energy-rich molecules has the cell gained by processing one molecule of glucose through glycolysis and the citric acid cycle? Up to this point, the cell has gained a total of 4 ATP (from substrate-level phosphorylation), 10 NADH, and 2 FADH₂. Still, for the cell to be able to put to use the energy banked in NADH and FADH₂, these molecules must shuttle their high-energy electrons to the electron transport chain. There the energy from the oxidation of organic molecules can be used for the oxidative phosphorylation of ADP to ATP. Before we look at how oxidative phosphorylation works, you may want to examine the inner workings of the citric acid cycle in Figure 6.9B, below.

🎧 MP3 Tutor *Cellular Respiration Part 2: Citric Acid Cycle and Electron Transport Chain*

Web Activity *The Citric Acid (Krebs) Cycle*

❓ What is the total number of NADH molecules generated during the complete breakdown of one glucose molecule to six carbon dioxide molecules? (*Hint:* Combine the outputs of Modules 6.7–6.9.)

■ 10 NADH: 2 from glycolysis; 2 from the grooming of pyruvate; 6 from the citric acid cycle. (Did you remember to double the output due to the sugar-splitting step of glycolysis?)

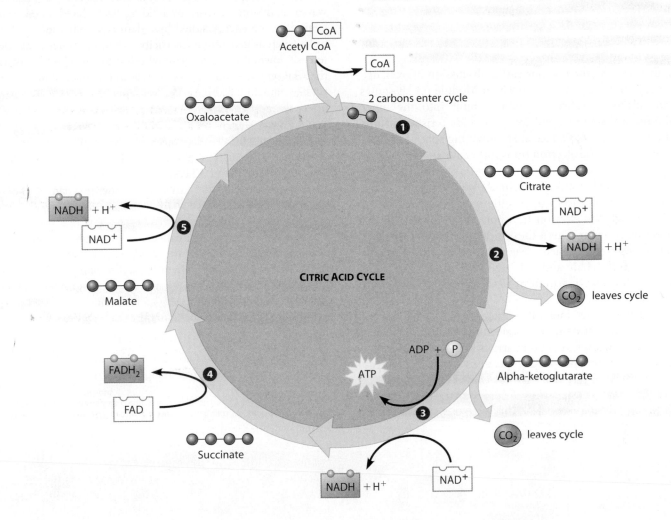

Step ❶
Acetyl CoA stokes the furnace.

A turn of the citric acid cycle begins (top center) as enzymes strip the CoA portion from acetyl CoA and combine the remaining two-carbon acetyl group with the four-carbon molecule oxaloacetate (top left) already present in the mitochondrion. The product of this reaction is the six-carbon molecule citrate. Citrate is the ionized form of citric acid. All the acid compounds in this cycle exist in the cell in their ionized form, hence the suffix -ate.

Steps ❷–❸
NADH, ATP, and CO_2 are generated during redox reactions.

Successive redox reactions harvest some of the energy of the acetyl group by stripping hydrogen atoms from organic acid intermediates (such as alpha-ketoglutarate) and producing energy-laden NADH molecules. In two places, an intermediate compound loses a CO_2 molecule. Energy is harvested by substrate-level phosphorylation of ADP to produce ATP. A four-carbon compound called succinate emerges at the end of step 3.

Steps ❹–❺
Redox reactions generate FADH₂ and NADH.

Enzymes rearrange chemical bonds, eventually completing the citric acid cycle by regenerating oxaloacetate. Redox reactions reduce the electron carriers FAD and NAD^+ to FADH₂ and NADH, respectively. One turn of the citric acid cycle is completed with the conversion of a molecule of malate to oxaloacetate. This compound is then ready to start the next turn of the cycle by accepting another acetyl group from acetyl CoA.

Figure 6.9B Details of the citric acid cycle

6.10 Most ATP production occurs by oxidative phosphorylation

The final stage of cellular respiration is oxidative phosphorylation, which involves the electron transport chain and chemiosmosis. Oxidative phosphorylation is a clear illustration of structure fitting function: The spatial arrangement of electron carriers built into a membrane makes it possible for the mitochondrion to use the chemical energy released by redox reactions to create a hydrogen ion (H^+) gradient and then, through the process called chemiosmosis, use the energy stored in that gradient to drive ATP synthesis.

Figure 6.10 expands on our earlier discussion of oxidative phosphorylation and chemiosmosis in Module 6.6. It shows that the electron transport chain is built into the inner membrane of the mitochondrion. The folds (cristae) of this membrane enlarge its surface area, providing space for thousands of copies of the electron transport chain and many ATP synthase complexes.

Starting on the left in Figure 6.10, the gold arrow traces the path of electron flow from the shuttle molecules NADH and $FADH_2$ through the electron transport chain to oxygen, the final electron acceptor. This is the critical role that oxygen plays in cellular respiration. Each oxygen atom ($\frac{1}{2}O_2$) accepts two electrons from the chain and picks up two hydrogen ions from the surrounding solution to form H_2O, one of the final products of cellular respiration.

Most of the carrier molecules reside in four main protein complexes, while two mobile carriers transport electrons between the complexes. All of the carriers bind and release electrons in redox reactions, passing electrons down the "energy staircase." Three of the protein complexes use the energy released from these electron transfers to actively transport H^+ across the membrane, from where H^+ is less concentrated to

where it is more concentrated. The green vertical arrows indicate that the hydrogen ions are transported from the matrix of the mitochondrion (its innermost compartment) into the mitochondrion's narrow intermembrane space.

The resulting H^+ gradient stores potential energy, much the way a dam stores energy by holding back the elevated water behind it. The energy stored by a dam can be harnessed to do work (such as generating electricity) when the water is allowed to rush downhill, turning giant wheels called turbines. Similarly, the ATP synthases built into the inner mitochondrial membrane act like miniature turbines. The hydrogen ions tend to be driven across the membrane by the energy of their concentration gradient. However, the membrane is not permeable to hydrogen ions, and they can only cross through a channel in the ATP synthase, as shown on the far right of the figure. Hydrogen ions rush back "downhill" through an ATP synthase, spinning a component of the complex, just as water turns the turbines in a dam. The rotation activates catalytic sites in the synthase that attach phosphate groups to ADP molecules to generate ATP.

So why is this process called oxidative phosphorylation? The energy derived from the *oxidation*-reduction reactions of the electron transport chain is used to *phosphorylate* ADP. The exergonic reactions of electron transport produce an H^+ gradient. Through chemiosmosis, the energy stored in this H^+ gradient drives the endergonic synthesis of ATP.

Web Activity *Electron Transport and Chemiosmosis*

? What effect would an absence of oxygen (O_2) have on the process illustrated in Figure 6.10?

■ There would be no ATP produced. Without oxygen to "pull" electrons down the electron transport chain, the energy stored in NADH cannot be harnessed for ATP synthesis.

Figure 6.10 Oxidative phosphorylation, using electron transport and chemiosmosis in the mitochondrion

6.11 Certain poisons interrupt critical events in cellular respiration

A number of poisons produce their deadly effects by interfering with some of the events we have just discussed. Figure 6.11 shows the places where three different categories of poisons obstruct cellular respiration.

Poisons in one category block the electron transport chain. A substance called rotenone, for instance, binds tightly with one of the electron carrier molecules in the first protein complex, preventing electrons from passing to the next carrier molecule. Rotenone is often used to kill pest insects and fish. By blocking the electron transport chain near its start and thus preventing ATP synthesis, rotenone literally starves an organism's cells of energy.

Two other electron transport blockers, cyanide and carbon monoxide, bind with an electron carrier in the fourth protein complex. Here they block the passage of electrons to oxygen. This blockage is like turning off a faucet; electrons cease to flow through the "pipe." The result is the same as that of rotenone: No H$^+$ gradient is generated, and no ATP is made. Cyanide was the lethal agent in the Tylenol murders of 1982. Seven people in the Chicago area died after ingesting Tylenol capsules that had been laced with cyanide. The perpetrator of that crime was never caught.

A second kind of respiratory poison inhibits ATP synthase. On the right side of the figure, the antibiotic oligomycin blocks the passage of H$^+$ through the channel in ATP synthase. Oligomycin is used on the skin to combat fungal infections. It kills fungal cells by preventing them from using the potential energy of the H$^+$ gradient to make ATP. (Because the drug cannot get past the outer layer of dead cells into the living skin cells, they are protected from its effects.)

A third kind of poison, collectively called uncouplers, makes the membrane of the mitochondrion leaky to hydrogen ions. Electron transport continues, but ATP cannot be made because leakage of H$^+$ through the membrane abolishes the H$^+$ gradient. Cells continue to consume oxygen, often at a higher than normal rate, but to no avail, for they cannot make any ATP through chemiosmosis because no H$^+$ gradient exists.

A highly toxic uncoupler called dinitrophenol (DNP) is shown in the figure. DNP poisoning produces an enormous increase in metabolic rate, profuse sweating as the body attempts to dissipate excess heat, collapse, and then death. For a short time in the 1940s, some physicians prescribed DNP in low doses as weight loss pills, but fatalities soon made it clear that there were far safer ways to lose weight. When DNP is present, all steps of cellular respiration except chemiosmosis continue to run, consuming fuel molecules, even though almost all the energy is lost as heat.

Poisons do serve some productive purposes. In addition to being useful as pesticides or antibiotics, toxins may be used in biochemical research. Discovering exactly what these substances do to the cell's respiratory machinery has, in many cases, helped biochemists understand how that machinery works. The effects of uncouplers, for example, made it clear that ATP synthesis is a complicated activity involving the distinct, but related, processes of electron transport and generation of a membrane H$^+$ gradient.

The function of cellular respiration is to generate ATP for cellular work. Without energy, a cell cannot live. We review cellular respiration and the essential production of ATP in the next module.

Figure 6.11 The effects of five poisons on the electron transport chain and chemiosmosis

? The poison DNP causes what one biochemist calls "mitochondrial wheel-spinning." Explain this metaphor.

■ Like an automobile wasting fuel by spinning its wheels and going nowhere, a mitochondrion poisoned with DNP consumes fuel and powers electron transport but makes no ATP. The DNP destroys the H$^+$ gradient required for the chemiosmotic synthesis of ATP.

Review: Each molecule of glucose yields many molecules of ATP

Now that we have looked at all stages of cellular respiration, let's review what the cell accomplishes by oxidizing a molecule of glucose. Figure 6.12 shows all the stages and indicates where they occur in a eukaryotic cell. At the bottom of the figure is a tally of ATP molecules, showing the potential energy payoff for a typical cell. If you wish to refer back to earlier modules, this diagram summarizes glycolysis (Module 6.7), the chemical grooming of pyruvate (Module 6.8), the citric acid cycle (Module 6.9), and oxidative phosphorylation (Module 6.10).

Starting on the left, glycolysis, occurring in the cytoplasmic fluid, and the citric acid cycle, occurring in the mitochondrial matrix, contribute a net total of 4 ATP per glucose molecule by substrate-level phosphorylation. The cell harvests much more energy than this from the carrier molecules NADH and FADH$_2$, which are produced by glycolysis, the grooming of pyruvate, and the citric acid cycle. The energy of the electrons they carry is used to make an estimated 34 molecules of ATP using the electron transport chain and chemiosmosis in oxidative phosphorylation.

Let's see where the numbers in the diagram come from. Our model assumes that each NADH that transfers a pair of high-energy electrons from a food molecule to the electron transport chain contributes enough to the mitochondrion's H$^+$ gradient to generate 3 ATP. Another assumption is that each FADH$_2$ molecule yields only 2 ATP because it contributes its electrons later in the electron transport chain (see Figure 6.10). These numbers are maximums; the actual amounts may vary. For instance, some of the energy of the H$^+$ gradient may be used for transport work instead of ATP production. Also, as shown in the diagram, a shuttle mechanism passes the electrons from NADH produced in glycolysis into the mitochondrion. Depending on the type of shuttle, either NAD$^+$ or FAD picks up the electrons (so the yield of oxidative phosphorylation may be 32 or 34 ATP). The total net yield of ATP molecules per glucose molecule has a theoretical maximum of about 38.

More important than the actual numbers of ATP molecules is the point that a cell can harvest a great deal of energy from glucose—up to about 40% of the molecule's potential energy. Because most of the ATP generated by cellular respiration results from oxidative phosphorylation, the ATP yield depends heavily on an adequate supply of oxygen to the cell. Without oxygen to function as the final electron acceptor in the electron transport chain, chemiosmosis ceases, and cells die from energy starvation. However, as we discussed in the chapter introduction, muscle cells may continue to function for a while without oxygen. We look at how some cells and organisms can oxidize organic fuel and generate ATP *without* oxygen next.

Web Process of Science *How Is the Rate of Cellular Respiration Measured?*

? What would a cell's net ATP yield per glucose be in the presence of the poison DNP? (See Module 6.11.)

■ 4 ATP, all from substrate-level phosphorylation. The uncoupler would destroy the H$^+$ concentration gradient necessary for chemiosmosis.

Figure 6.12 An estimated tally of the ATP produced by substrate-level and oxidative phosphorylation in cellular respiration

Fermentation enables cells to produce ATP without oxygen

The metabolic pathway that generates ATP during fermentation is glycolysis, the same pathway that functions in the first stage of cellular respiration. Remember that glycolysis uses no O_2; it simply generates a net gain of 2 ATP while oxidizing glucose to two molecules of pyruvate and reducing NAD^+ to NADH. The yield of 2 ATP is certainly a lot less than the possible 38 ATP per glucose generated during aerobic respiration, but it is enough to keep your muscles contracting for a short while when the need for ATP outpaces the delivery of O_2 via the bloodstream. And many microorganisms supply all their energy needs with the 2 ATP/glucose yield of glycolysis.

There is more to fermentation, however, than just glycolysis. To oxidize glucose in glycolysis, NAD^+ must be present as an electron acceptor. This is no problem under aerobic conditions, because the cell regenerates its pool of NAD^+ when NADH passes its electrons into the mitochondrion to be transported to the electron transport chain. Fermentation provides an anaerobic path for recycling NADH back to NAD^+.

Lactic Acid Fermentation Your muscle cells, a few other cell types, and certain bacteria can regenerate NAD^+ by a process called **lactic acid fermentation,** illustrated in **Figure 6.13A.** You can see that NADH is oxidized to NAD^+ as pyruvate is reduced to lactate (the ionized form of lactic acid). The lactate that builds up in muscle cells during strenuous exercise is carried in the blood to the liver, where it is converted back to pyruvate. (Panting after heavy exercise provides extra O_2 that repays the "oxygen debt," returning muscles to aerobic respiration and converting lactate back to pyruvate.)

The dairy industry uses lactic acid fermentation by bacteria to make cheese and yogurt. Other types of microbial fermentation turn soybeans into soy sauce and cabbage into sauerkraut.

Alcohol Fermentation For thousands of years people have used **alcohol fermentation** in brewing, winemaking, and baking. Yeasts are single-celled fungi that normally use aerobic respiration to process their food. But they are also able to survive in anaerobic environments. Yeasts and certain bacteria recycle their NADH back to NAD^+ while converting pyruvate to CO_2 and ethanol (**Figure 6.13B**). The CO_2 provides the bubbles in beer and champagne. Bubbles of CO_2 generated by baker's yeast cause bread dough to rise. Ethanol (ethyl alcohol), the two-carbon product, is toxic to the organisms that produce it. Yeasts release their alcohol wastes to their surroundings, where it usually diffuses away. When yeasts are confined in a wine vat, they die when the alcohol concentration reaches 14%.

Unlike muscle cells and yeasts, many prokaryotes that live in stagnant ponds and deep in the soil are **obligate anaerobes,** meaning they require anaerobic conditions and are poisoned by oxygen. Yeasts and many other bacteria are facultative anaerobes. A **facultative anaerobe** can make ATP either by fermentation or by oxidative phosphorylation, depending on whether O_2 is available. On the cellular level, our muscle cells behave as facultative anaerobes.

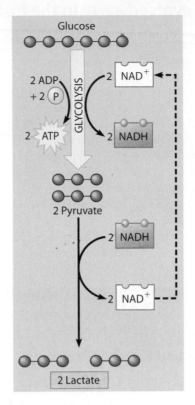

Figure 6.13A Lactic acid fermentation oxidizes NADH to NAD^+ and produces lactate.

Figure 6.13B Alcohol fermentation oxidizes NADH to NAD^+ and produces ethanol and CO_2.

Figure 6.13C Fermentation vats for wine

For a facultative anaerobe, pyruvate is a fork in the metabolic road. If oxygen is available, the organism will always use the more productive aerobic respiration. Thus, to make wine and beer, yeasts must be grown anaerobically so that they will ferment sugars and produce ethanol. For this reason, the large fermentation vats in **Figure 6.13C** are equipped with one-way gas valves that vent off excess CO_2 but keep air out.

Web Activity *Fermentation*

? A glucose-fed yeast cell is moved from an aerobic environment to an anaerobic one. For the cell to continue generating ATP at the same rate, how would its rate of glucose consumption need to change?

■ The cell must consume glucose at a rate about 19 times the consumption rate in the aerobic environment (2 ATP by fermentation versus 38 ATP by cellular respiration).

6.14 Glycolysis evolved early in the history of life on Earth

Glycolysis is the universal energy-harvesting process of life. If we looked inside a bacterial cell, inside one of our own body cells, or inside virtually any other living cell, we would find the metabolic machinery of glycolysis. The role of glycolysis in both fermentation and respiration has an evolutionary basis. Ancient prokaryotes probably used glycolysis to make ATP long before oxygen was present in Earth's atmosphere. The oldest known fossils of bacteria date back over 3.5 billion years, but significant levels of O_2 did not accumulate in the atmosphere until about 2.7 billion years ago. For almost a billion years, prokaryotes must have generated ATP exclusively from glycolysis, which does not require oxygen.

The fact that glycolysis occurs in almost all organisms suggests that it evolved very early in ancestors common to all the domains of life. The location of glycolysis within the cell also implies great antiquity; the pathway does not require any of the membrane-bounded organelles of the eukaryotic cell, which evolved more than a billion years after the prokaryotic cell. Glycolysis is a metabolic heirloom from early cells that continues to function in fermentation and as the first stage in the breakdown of organic molecules by cellular respiration.

? List some of the characteristics of glycolysis that indicate that it is an ancient metabolic system.

■ Glycolysis occurs universally (functioning in both fermentation and respiration), does not require oxygen, and does not occur in a membrane-bounded organelle.

Interconnections Between Molecular Breakdown and Synthesis

6.15 Cells use many kinds of organic molecules as fuel for cellular respiration

Throughout this chapter, we have spoken of glucose as the fuel for cellular respiration. But free glucose molecules are not common in our diet. We obtain most of our calories as fats, proteins, sucrose and other disaccharide sugars, and starch (a polysaccharide). You consume all these types of molecules when you eat a bag of peanuts, for instance.

Figure 6.15 illustrates how a cell uses three kinds of molecules to make ATP. A wide range of carbohydrates (polysaccharides and sugars) can be funneled into glycolysis, as shown by the blue arrows in the diagram. For example, enzymes in our digestive tract hydrolyze starch to glucose, which is then broken down by glycolysis and the citric acid cycle. Similarly, glycogen, the polysaccharide stored in our liver and muscle cells, can be hydrolyzed to glucose to serve as fuel between meals.

Proteins (purple arrows) can be used for fuel, but first they must be digested to their constituent amino acids. Typically, a cell will use most of the amino acids to make its own proteins. Enzymes will convert excess amino acids to intermediates of glycolysis or the citric acid cycle, and their energy is then harvested by cellular respiration. During the conversion, the amino groups are stripped off and later disposed of in urine.

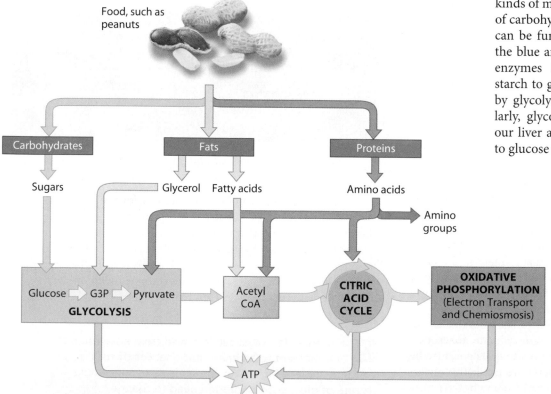

Figure 6.15 Pathways that break down various food molecules

Fats make excellent cellular fuel because they contain many hydrogen atoms and thus many energy-rich electrons. As the diagram on the previous page shows (tan arrows), the cell first hydrolyzes fats to glycerol and fatty acids. It then converts the glycerol to glyceraldehyde-3-phosphate (G3P), one of the intermediates in glycolysis. The fatty acids are broken into two-carbon fragments that enter the citric acid cycle as acetyl CoA. Processed this way, a gram of fat yields more than twice as much ATP as a gram of starch. Because so many calories are stockpiled in each gram of fat, a person must expend a large amount of energy to burn fat stored in the body. This explains why it is so difficult for a dieter to lose excess fat.

? Animals store most of their energy reserves as fats, not as polysaccharides. What is the advantage of this mode of storage for an animal?

■ Most animals are mobile and benefit from a compact and concentrated form of energy storage. Because fats are hydrophobic, they can be stored without extra water associated with them, as is the case with hydrophilic carbohydrates (see Module 3.8).

6.16 Food molecules provide raw materials for biosynthesis

Not all food molecules are destined to be oxidized as fuel for making ATP. Food also provides the raw materials a cell uses for biosynthesis—the production of organic molecules using energy-requiring metabolic pathways. A cell must be able to make its own molecules to build its structures and perform its functions. Some raw materials, such as amino acids, can be incorporated directly into an organism's macromolecules. However, cells also make molecules that are not present in food by using some of the intermediate compounds of glycolysis and the citric acid cycle.

Figure 6.16 outlines the pathways by which cells make three classes of organic molecules using some of the intermediate molecules of glycolysis and the citric acid cycle. By comparing Figures 6.15 and 6.16, we see clear connections between the energy-harvesting process of cellular respiration and the biosynthetic pathways used to construct all parts of the cell.

Basic principles of supply and demand regulate these pathways. If there is an excess of a certain amino acid, for example, the pathway that synthesizes it is switched off. The most common mechanism for this control is feedback inhibition: The end product inhibits an enzyme that catalyzes an early step in the pathway (see Module 5.16). Feedback inhibition also controls cellular respiration. If ATP accumulates in a cell, it inhibits an early enzyme in glycolysis, slowing down respiration and conserving resources. On the other hand, the same enzyme is activated by a buildup of ADP in the cell, signaling the need for more energy.

The cells of all living organisms—including those of the panda shown in Figure 6.16 and the bamboo plants it eats—have the ability to harvest energy from the breakdown of organic molecules. When the process is cellular respiration, the atoms of the starting materials end up in CO_2 and H_2O. In contrast, the ability to make organic molecules from CO_2 and H_2O is not universal. Animal cells lack this ability, but plant cells can actually produce organic molecules from inorganic ones using the energy of sunlight. This process, photosynthesis, is the subject of Chapter 7.

Figure 6.16 Biosynthesis of large organic molecules from intermediates of cellular respiration

? Explain how one can gain weight and store fat even when on a low-fat diet. (Hint: Look for G3P and acetyl CoA in Figures 6.15 and 6.16.)

■ If caloric intake is excessive, body cells use metabolic pathways to convert the excess to fat. The glycerol and fatty acids of fats are made from G3P and acetyl CoA, respectively, both produced from the oxidation of carbohydrates.

Photosynthesis:
Using Light to Make Food

An Overview of Photosynthesis

7.1 Autotrophs are the producers of the biosphere

Bio Flix 7.2 Photosynthesis occurs in chloroplasts in plant cells

7.3 Plants produce O_2 gas by splitting water

7.4 Photosynthesis is a redox process, as is cellular respiration

🎧 7.5 Overview: The two stages of photosynthesis are linked by ATP and NADPH

The Light Reactions: Converting Solar Energy to Chemical Energy

7.6 Visible radiation drives the light reactions

7.7 Photosystems capture solar power

7.8 Two photosystems connected by an electron transport chain generate ATP and NADPH

7.9 Chemiosmosis powers ATP synthesis in the light reactions

The Calvin Cycle: Converting CO_2 to Sugars

7.10 ATP and NADPH power sugar synthesis in the Calvin cycle

Photosynthesis Reviewed and Extended

7.11 Review: Photosynthesis uses light energy, CO_2, and H_2O to make food molecules

7.12 Adaptations that save water in hot, dry climates evolved in C_4 and CAM plants

Photosynthesis, Solar Radiation, and Earth's Atmosphere

7.13 Photosynthesis moderates global warming

7.14 Mario Molina talks about Earth's protective ozone layer

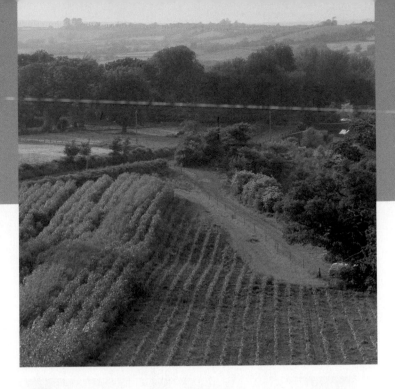

Plant Power

With every new car, MP3 player, and cell phone, the world's demand for energy grows. In an era when most energy is generated from pollution-laden fossil fuels, more power often means more air pollution, more acid precipitation, and more of the "greenhouse gases" that contribute to global warming. Is there a better energy solution, one that could somehow produce power without harming our atmosphere? Some scientists believe they've found such a solution—and if you can see green through a nearby window, their answer might literally be in sight.

Energy researchers from Brazil to upstate New York have seized on the potential of plant power, turning to trees and other green vegetation to create "energy plantations" as a promising fuel source. In many ways, this solution draws from an ancient one, relying on one of the oldest energy pathways on the planet—**photosynthesis.** In this process, green plants, algae, and certain bacteria transform light energy to chemical energy stored in the bonds of the sugar they make from carbon dioxide and water. During the process, they also produce the oxygen we and all other aerobic organisms (including the plants themselves) need for cellular respiration. And they store an energy source that could help solve the human power problem.

As you learned in Chapter 6, both carbon dioxide and water are waste products of cellular respiration. Plants take in this cellular "exhaust," bringing in CO_2 through their leaves and pulling up water through their roots. Their leaves also absorb the solar energy of sunlight. In a sort of molecular shuffling driven by this energy, carbon dioxide and water are converted to a simple sugar and oxygen gas is released. One way to summarize this process is shown in the following equation.

$$6\ CO_2 + 6\ H_2O \xrightarrow[\text{Photosynthesis}]{\text{Light energy}} C_6H_{12}O_6 + 6\ O_2$$

Carbon dioxide   Water   Glucose   Oxygen gas

Photosynthesis happens on a microscopic level, but carried out repeatedly in plants around the world, it is responsible for an enormous amount of product. Earth's plants and other photosynthetic organisms make about 160 billion metric tons (176 billion tons) of carbohydrate each year. Almost all food can be traced back to plants—either eaten directly or fed to animals that are then consumed. And for most of human history, burning plant material has been a major source of heat, light, and cooking fuel. Its replacement by fossil fuels is relatively recent and centered in the developed world.

Now, as fossil fuel supplies dwindle and pollution accumulates, scientists are once again looking to plants and researching ways to make them a more efficient energy source. Certain types of fast-growing trees have shown promise as fuel to grow and burn in power generation facilities. Willows, for example, grow quickly and resprout once they are cut, limiting the amount of new planting, herbicides, and pesticides required to produce each generation of trees. They also grow much faster than most trees: Willow crops should be able to produce about 5–8 dry tons of wood per acre each year, according to researchers in New York. In comparison, natural forests produce only about 0.5–1.0 ton of wood per acre. Other fast-growing tree species, including sycamore, poplar, eucalyptus, and black locust, are also being tested as fuel sources.

Fuel from energy plantations is not only a renewable energy source; it can also be environmentally safer than fossil fuels. The products of burned wood do not include the sulfur contaminants released by fossil fuels, which contribute to acid rain. To be sure, burning wood fuel releases carbon dioxide into the air. But as energy plantation crops are quickly regrown, their photosynthesizing removes carbon dioxide from the atmosphere even as recently harvested trees release the gas through a power plant's smokestack. In contrast, the burning of fossil fuels, which come from the remains of ancient organisms, releases back carbon dioxide that was removed from the atmosphere through photosynthesis hundreds of millions of years ago.

Today, this "biomass energy" accounts for only about 4% of all energy consumed in the United States. But the idea has drawn enough support to be studied or tried in many countries and may play a role in meeting future energy needs.

In this chapter, you will learn how photosynthesis works. Because photosynthesis can seem like a complex process, we begin with some basic concepts. Then we look at the two stages of photosynthesis: the light reactions, in which solar energy is captured and transformed into chemical energy, and the Calvin cycle, in which the chemical energy is used to make organic molecules. Finally, we explore ways in which photosynthesis affects our global environment. ■ ■ ■

7.1   Autotrophs are the producers of the biosphere

Figure 7.1A   Forest plants

Figure 7.1B   Wheat field

Figure 7.1C   Kelp, a large alga

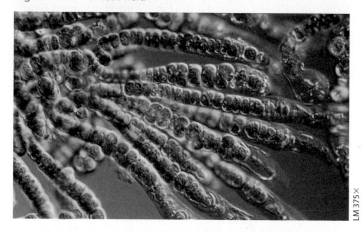

Figure 7.1D   Micrograph of cyanobacteria (photosynthetic bacteria)

Plants are **autotrophs** (meaning "self-feeders" in Greek) in that they make their own food and thus sustain themselves without consuming organic molecules derived from any other organisms. Plant cells capture light energy that has traveled 150 million kilometers from the sun and convert it to chemical energy. Using this energy, plants make their own organic molecules and are the ultimate source of organic molecules for almost all other organisms. They are often referred to as the **producers** of the biosphere because they produce its food supply. Actually, plants are not the only producers; algae, certain other protists, and some prokaryotes also make food molecules from carbon dioxide, water, and other inorganic materials. All organisms that produce organic molecules from inorganic molecules using the energy of light are called **photoautotrophs.**

The photographs on this page illustrate some of the diversity among photoautotrophs. On land, plants, such as those in the forest scene in Figure 7.1A and the wheat field in Figure 7.1B, are the predominant producers. In aquatic environments, algae and photosynthetic bacteria are the main food producers. Figure 7.1C shows kelp, a large alga that forms extensive underwater "forests" off the coast of California. Figure 7.1D is

a micrograph of prokaryotic cyanobacteria, abundant and important producers in freshwater and marine ecosystems.

In this chapter, we focus on photosynthesis in plants, which takes place in chloroplasts. The remarkable ability to harness light energy and use it to drive the synthesis of organic compounds emerges from the structural organization of these organelles: Photosynthetic pigments, enzymes, and other molecules are grouped together in membranes, enabling the sequences of reactions to be carried out efficiently. The process of photosynthesis most likely originated in a group of bacteria that had infolded regions of the plasma membrane containing such clusters of enzymes and molecules. In fact, chloroplasts appear to have originated from a photosynthetic prokaryote that lived inside a eukaryotic cell (see Module 4.16). Let's begin with an overview of the location and structure of plant chloroplasts.

? What do "self-feeding" autotrophs require from the environment in order to make their own food?

■ Light, carbon dioxide, and water. (Plants also require inorganic minerals, as you'll learn in Chapter 32.)

Photosynthesis occurs in chloroplasts in plant cells

All green parts of a plant have chloroplasts in their cells and can carry out photosynthesis. In most plants, however, the leaves have the most chloroplasts (about half a million per square millimeter of leaf surface) and are the major sites of photosynthesis. Their green color is from **chlorophyll,** a light-absorbing pigment in the chloroplasts that plays a central role in converting solar energy to chemical energy.

Figure 7.2 zooms in on a leaf to show the actual sites of photosynthesis. At the top is a cross section (slice) of a leaf as it would look under a light microscope. Chloroplasts are concentrated in the cells of the **mesophyll,** the green tissue in the interior of the leaf. Carbon dioxide enters the leaf, and oxygen exits, by way of tiny pores called **stomata** (singular, *stoma,* meaning "mouth"). Water absorbed by the roots is delivered to the leaves in veins.

As you can see in the light micrograph of a single cell (second panel down), each mesophyll cell has numerous chloroplasts. The bottom drawing and electron micrograph show the structures in a single chloroplast. Membranes in the chloroplast form the framework where many of the reactions of photosynthesis occur, just as mitochondrial membranes do for the energy-harvesting machinery we discussed in Chapter 6. An envelope of two membranes encloses an inner compartment in the chloroplast, which is filled with a thick fluid called **stroma.** Suspended in the stroma is a system of interconnected membranous sacs, called **thylakoids,** which enclose another compartment, called the thylakoid space. (As you will see later, this thylakoid space plays a role analogous to the intermembrane space of a mitochondrion.) In some places, thylakoids are concentrated in stacks called **grana** (singular, *granum*). Built into the thylakoid membranes are the chlorophyll molecules that capture light energy. The thylakoid membranes also house much of the machinery that converts light energy to chemical energy, which is used in the stroma to make sugar.

Later in the chapter, we examine the function of these structures in more detail. But first, let's look more closely at the general process of photosynthesis.

(Bio Flix) **BioFlix** *Photosynthesis*

Web Activity *The Sites of Photosynthesis*

? How do the reactant molecules of photosynthesis reach the chloroplasts in leaves?

■ CO_2 enters leaves through stomata, and H_2O enters the roots and is carried to leaves through veins.

Leaf Cross Section

Leaf

Mesophyll

Vein

CO_2 O_2 Stoma

Mesophyll Cell

LM 2,600×

Chloroplast

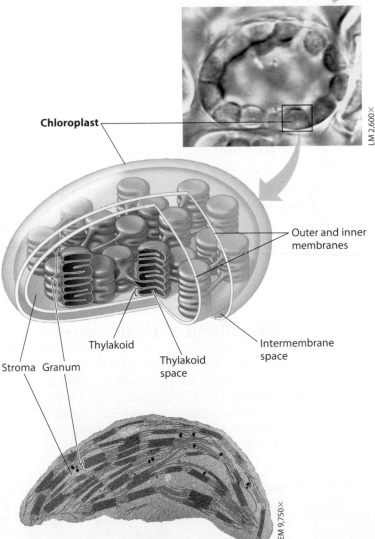

Outer and inner membranes

Intermembrane space

Thylakoid

Thylakoid space

Stroma Granum

TEM 9,750×

Figure 7.2 The location and structure of chloroplasts

7.3   Plants produce O_2 gas by splitting water

The leaves of plants that live in lakes and ponds are often covered with bubbles like the ones shown in Figure 7.3A. The bubbles are oxygen gas (O_2) produced during photosynthesis.

The basic equation for photosynthesis was determined in the 1800s, and most scientists assumed that plants produce O_2 by extracting it from CO_2. In the 1950s, scientists tested this hypothesis by using a heavy isotope of oxygen, ^{18}O, to follow the fate of oxygen atoms during photosynthesis. (This was one of the first uses of isotopes as tracers in biological research. To review isotopes and their use as tracers, see Module 2.5.) In the photosynthesis equations in Figure 7.3B, the orange type denotes ^{18}O. The equations here are written in a slightly more detailed form than the summary photosynthesis equation you often see. These show that water is actually both a reactant and a product in the reaction. (As is often done, glucose is shown as a product, although the direct product of photosynthesis is a three-carbon sugar, which can be used to make glucose.)

In experiment 1, a plant given carbon dioxide containing ^{18}O gave off no labeled (^{18}O-containing) oxygen gas. But in experiment 2, a plant given water containing ^{18}O did produce labeled O_2. These experiments showed that the O_2 produced during photosynthesis comes from water and not from CO_2. It takes two water (H_2O) molecules to make each molecule of O_2.

Knowing where the O_2 comes from gives us a hint of what else happens during photosynthesis. Additional experiments have revealed that the oxygen atoms in CO_2 and the hydrogens in the reactant H_2O molecules end up in the sugar molecule and in water that is formed anew. Figure 7.3C summarizes the fates of all the atoms that start out in the reactant molecules of photosynthesis.

> **?** Photosynthesis produces 160 billion metric tons of carbohydrate a year. Where does most of the mass of this huge amount of organic matter come from?

■ Mostly from CO_2 in the air, which provides both the carbon and oxygen in carbohydrate. Water supplies only the hydrogen.

Figure 7.3A Oxygen bubbles on the leaves of an aquatic plant

Figure 7.3B Experiments tracking the oxygen atoms in photosynthesis

Figure 7.3C Fates of all the atoms in photosynthesis

7.4   Photosynthesis is a redox process, as is cellular respiration

What actually happens when photosynthesis converts CO_2 and water into sugar and O_2? Photosynthesis is a redox (oxidation-reduction) process, just as cellular respiration is (see Module 6.5). As indicated in the summary photosynthesis equation (Figure 7.4A), when water molecules are split apart, yielding O_2, they are actually oxidized; that is, they lose electrons, along

with hydrogen ions (H^+). Meanwhile, CO_2 is reduced to sugar as electrons and hydrogen ions are added to it. Oxidation and reduction go hand in hand.

Now move from the food-producing equation for photosynthesis to the energy-releasing equation for cellular respiration (Figure 7.4B). Overall, cellular respiration harvests energy

Figure 7.4A Photosynthesis (uses light energy)

Figure 7.4B Cellular respiration (releases chemical energy)

stored in a glucose molecule by oxidizing the sugar and reducing O_2 to H_2O. This process involves a number of energy-releasing redox reactions, with electrons losing potential energy as they travel down an energy "hill" from sugar to O_2. Along the way, the mitochondrion uses some of the energy to synthesize ATP, as we saw in Chapter 6.

In contrast, the food-producing redox reactions of photosynthesis involve an uphill climb. As water is oxidized and CO_2 is reduced during photosynthesis, electrons gain energy by being boosted up an energy hill. The light energy captured by chlorophyll molecules in the chloroplast provides the boost for the electrons. Photosynthesis converts light energy to chemical energy and stores it in the chemical bonds of sugar molecules, which can provide energy for later use or raw materials for biosynthesis.

? Which redox process, photosynthesis or cellular respiration, is endergonic? (*Hint:* See Module 5.12.)

■ Photosynthesis

7.5 Overview: The two stages of photosynthesis are linked by ATP and NADPH

The equation for photosynthesis is a simple summary of a very complex process. Actually, photosynthesis occurs in two stages, each with multiple steps. Figure 7.5 shows the inputs and outputs of the two stages and how the stages are related.

The **light reactions** (left in figure) include the steps that convert light energy to chemical energy and produce O_2. The light reactions occur in the thylakoid membranes. Water is split, providing a source of electrons and giving off O_2 gas as a by-product. Light energy absorbed by chlorophyll molecules built into the membranes is used to drive the transfer of electrons and H^+ from water to $NADP^+$, reducing it to NADPH. NADPH is an electron carrier similar to the NADH that transports electrons in cellular respiration. NADPH temporarily stores the electrons and provides "reducing power" to the Calvin cycle. The light reactions also generate ATP from ADP and a phosphate group.

In summary, the light reactions of photosynthesis are the steps that absorb solar energy and convert it to chemical energy stored in ATP and NADPH. Notice that these reactions produce no sugar; sugar is not made until the Calvin cycle, the second stage of photosynthesis.

The **Calvin cycle** occurs in the stroma of the chloroplast (Figure 7.5). It is a cyclic series of reactions that assembles sugar molecules using CO_2 and the energy-containing products of the light reactions. This second stage of photosynthesis is named for American biochemist and Nobel laureate Melvin Calvin. In the 1940s, Calvin and his colleagues traced the path of carbon in the cycle, using the radioactive isotope ^{14}C to label the carbon in CO_2. The incorporation of carbon from CO_2 into organic compounds, shown in the figure as CO_2 entering the Calvin cycle, is called **carbon fixation.** After carbon fixation, enzymes of the cycle make sugars by further reducing the carbon compounds.

As the figure suggests, it is NADPH produced by the light reactions that provides the electrons for reducing carbon in the Calvin cycle. And ATP from the light reactions provides chemical energy that powers several of the steps of the Calvin cycle. The Calvin cycle is sometimes referred to as the dark reactions, or light-independent reactions, because none of the steps

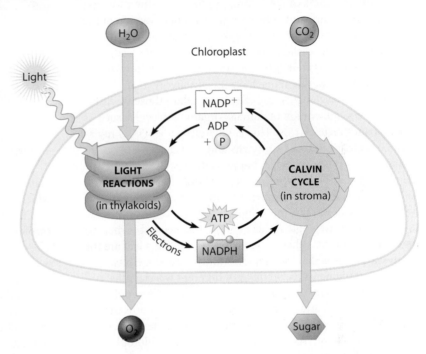

Figure 7.5 An overview of the two stages of photosynthesis that take place in a chloroplast

requires light directly. However, in most plants, the Calvin cycle runs during daytime, when the light reactions power the cycle's sugar assembly line by supplying it with NADPH and ATP.

The word *photosynthesis* encapsulates the two stages. *Photo-*, from the Greek word for light, refers to the light reactions; *synthesis*, meaning "putting together," refers to sugar construction by the Calvin cycle. In the next several modules, we look at these two stages in more detail. But first, let's consider some of the properties of light, the energy source that powers photosynthesis.

🎧 MP3 Tutor *Photosynthesis*

Web Activity *Overview of Photosynthesis*

? For chloroplasts to produce sugar from carbon dioxide in the dark, they would need to be supplied with _____ and _____.

■ ATP . . . NADPH

7.6   Visible radiation drives the light reactions

What exactly do we mean when we say that photosynthesis is powered by light energy from the sun? Sunlight is a type of energy called electromagnetic energy or radiation.

Electromagnetic energy travels in space as rhythmic waves analogous to those made by a pebble dropped in a puddle of water. Figure 7.6A shows the **electromagnetic spectrum,** the full range of electromagnetic wavelengths from the very short gamma rays to the very long-wavelength radio waves. As you can see in the center of the figure, visible light—the radiation your eyes see as different colors—is only a small fraction of the spectrum. It consists of wavelengths from about 380 nm to about 750 nm. The distance between the crests of two adjacent waves is called a **wavelength** (illustrated at the bottom of the figure). Shorter wavelengths have more energy than longer ones. In fact, wavelengths that are shorter than those of visible light have enough energy to damage organic molecules such as proteins and nucleic acids. This is why ultraviolet (UV) radiation in sunlight can cause sunburns and skin cancer.

Figure 7.6B shows what happens to visible light in the chloroplast. Light-absorbing molecules called pigments, built into the thylakoid membranes, absorb some wavelengths of light and reflect or transmit other wavelengths. We do not see the absorbed wavelengths; their energy has been absorbed by pigment molecules. What we see when we look at a leaf are the green wavelengths that the pigment transmits and reflects.

Different pigments absorb light of different wavelengths, and chloroplasts contain several kinds of pigments. Chlorophyll *a,* which participates directly in the light reactions, absorbs mainly blue-violet and red light. It looks grass-green because it reflects mainly green light. A very similar molecule, chlorophyll *b,* absorbs mainly blue and orange light and reflects (appears) yellow-green. Chlorophyll *b* broadens the range of light that a

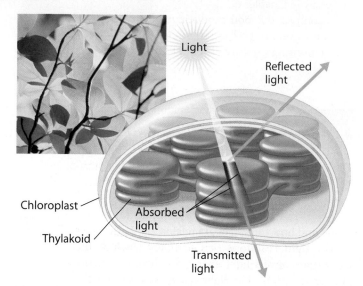

Figure 7.6B   The interaction of light with a chloroplast

plant can use by conveying absorbed energy to chlorophyll *a,* which then puts the energy to work in the light reactions.

Chloroplasts also contain a family of pigments called carotenoids, which are various shades of yellow and orange. The spectacular colors of fall foliage in certain parts of the world are due partly to the yellow-orange hues of longer lasting carotenoids that show through once the green chlorophyll breaks down. Carotenoids broaden the spectrum of colors that can drive photosynthesis by passing energy to chlorophyll *a,* as chlorophyll *b* does. However, a more important function of at least some carotenoids seems to be *photoprotection*: They absorb and dissipate excessive light energy that would otherwise damage chlorophyll or interact with oxygen to form reactive oxidative molecules that can damage cell molecules. Similar carotenoids, which we obtain from carrots and some other plants, have a photoprotective role in our eyes.

The theory of light as waves explains most of light's properties. However, light also behaves as discrete packets of energy called photons. A **photon** is a fixed quantity of light energy, and, as you have just learned, the shorter the wavelength, the greater the energy. Each type of pigment absorbs certain wavelengths of light because it is able to absorb the specific amounts of energy in those photons. Next we see what happens when a pigment molecule such as chlorophyll absorbs a photon of light.

Web Activity *Light Energy and Pigments*

Web Process of Science *How Does Paper Chromatography Separate Plant Pigments?*

? You may hear about the proposed health benefits of "phytochemicals" found in deep orange or red fruits and vegetables. How might such chemicals benefit a cell?

Figure 7.6A   The electromagnetic spectrum and the wavelengths of visible light. (A wavelength of 650 nm is illustrated.)

■ As antioxidants that protect from reactive forms of oxidative molecules

When a pigment molecule absorbs a photon, one of the pigment's electrons jumps to an energy level farther from the nucleus. In this location, the electron has more potential energy, and we say that the electron has been raised from a ground state to an excited state. The excited state is very unstable. Generally, when isolated pigment molecules absorb light, their excited electrons drop back down to the ground state in a billionth of a second, releasing their excess energy as heat. This conversion of light energy to heat is what makes a black car so hot on a sunny day (black pigments absorb all wavelengths of light).

Some isolated pigments, including chlorophyll, emit light as well as heat after absorbing photons. We can demonstrate this phenomenon in the laboratory with a chlorophyll solution, as shown on the left in Figure 7.7A. When illuminated, the chlorophyll emits photons that produce a reddish afterglow called fluorescence. The right side of Figure 7.7A illustrates what happens in fluorescence: An absorbed photon boosts an electron to an excited state, from which it falls back to the ground state, emitting its energy as heat and light.

But chlorophyll behaves very differently in isolation than it does in an intact chloroplast. In its native habitat of the thylakoid membrane, chlorophyll passes off its excited electron to a neighboring molecule before it has a chance to drop back to the ground state.

In the thylakoid membrane, chlorophyll molecules are organized along with other pigments and proteins into clusters called photosystems (Figure 7.7B). A **photosystem** consists of a number of light-harvesting complexes surrounding a reaction center complex. The light-harvesting complexes consist of pigment molecules (which may include chlorophyll *a*,

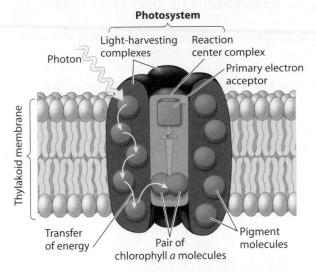

Figure 7.7B Light-excited chlorophyll embedded in a photosystem: Its electron is transferred to a primary electron acceptor before it returns to ground state

chlorophyll *b*, and carotenoids) bound to proteins. Collectively, the light-harvesting complexes function as a light-gathering antenna. The pigments absorb photons and pass the energy from molecule to molecule (thin yellow arrows) until it reaches the reaction center. The **reaction center complex** contains a pair of chlorophyll *a* molecules and a molecule called the primary electron acceptor, which is capable of accepting electrons and becoming reduced. The solar-powered transfer of an electron from the reaction center chlorophyll *a* to the primary electron acceptor is the first step of the light reactions.

Two types of photosystems have been identified, and they cooperate in the light reactions. They are referred to as photosystem I and photosystem II, in order of their discovery, although photosystem II actually functions first in the sequence of steps that make up the light reactions. Each photosystem has a characteristic reaction center. In photosystem II, the chlorophyll *a* of the reaction center is called P680 because the light it absorbs best is red light with a wavelength of 680 nm. The reaction center chlorophyll of photosystem I is called P700 because the wavelength of light it absorbs best is 700 nm (in the far-red part of the spectrum). Let's now see how the two photosystems work together in the light reactions to generate ATP and NADPH.

? Compared to a solution of isolated chlorophyll, why do intact chloroplasts release less heat and fluorescence when illuminated?

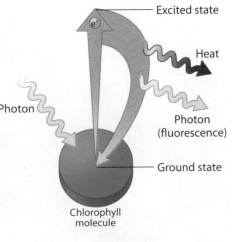

Figure 7.7A   A solution of chlorophyll glowing red when illuminated (left); a diagram of an isolated, light-excited chlorophyll molecule that releases a photon of red light (right)

■ In the chloroplasts, the light-excited electrons are trapped by a primary electron acceptor rather than immediately giving up all their energy as heat and light.

7.8 Two photosystems connected by an electron transport chain generate ATP and NADPH

In the light reactions, light energy is transformed into the chemical energy of ATP and NADPH. In this process, electrons removed from water molecules pass from photosystem II to photosystem I to NADP⁺. Between the two photosystems, the electrons move down an electron transport chain (similar to the one in cellular respiration) and provide energy for the synthesis of ATP.

Let's follow the flow of electrons (represented by gold arrows) in **Figure 7.8A** below, which shows the two photosystems embedded in a thylakoid membrane. ❶ A pigment molecule in a light-harvesting complex absorbs a photon of light. The energy is passed to other pigment molecules and finally to the reaction center of photosystem II, where it excites an electron of chlorophyll P680 to a higher energy state. ❷ This electron is captured by the primary electron acceptor. ❸ Water is split, and its electrons are supplied one by one to P680, each replacing an electron lost to the primary electron acceptor. The oxygen atom combines with an oxygen from another split water molecule to form a molecule of O_2.

❹ Each photoexcited electron passes from photosystem II to photosystem I via an electron transport chain. The exergonic "fall" of electrons provides energy for the synthesis of ATP by pumping H^+ across the membrane. ❺ Meanwhile, light energy excites an electron of chlorophyll P700 in the reaction center of photosystem I. The primary electron acceptor captures the electron, and an electron from the bottom of the electron transport chain replaces the lost electron in P700. ❻ The excited electron of photosystem I is passed through a short electron transport chain to NADP⁺, reducing it to NADPH.

Figure 7.8B, right, provides a mechanical analogy to help you review how the two photosystems cooperate in generating ATP and NADPH. The input of light energy, represented by the large

Figure 7.8B   A mechanical analogy of the light reactions

yellow mallets, boosts electrons in both photosystems up to the excited state. The electrons are caught by the primary electron acceptor on top of the platform in each photosystem. Photosystem II passes the electrons through an ATP mill. Photosystem I hands its electrons off to reduce NADP⁺ to NADPH.

NADPH, ATP, and O_2 are the products of the light reactions. Next we look in more detail at how ATP is formed.

? Tracing the light reactions in Figure 7.8A, there is a flow of electrons from _____ molecules to _____, which is reduced to _____, the source of electrons for sugar synthesis in the _____ cycle.

■ water . . . NADP⁺ . . . NADPH . . . Calvin

Figure 7.8A   Electron flow in the light reactions of photosynthesis: Both photosystems and the electron transport chain that connects them are located in the thylakoid membrane. The energy from light drives electrons from water to NADPH.

Chemiosmosis powers ATP synthesis in the light reactions

You first encountered chemiosmosis in Modules 6.6 and 6.10 as the mechanism of oxidative phosphorylation (ATP formation) in a mitochondrion. Chemiosmosis is also the mechanism that generates ATP in a chloroplast. Recall that the process of chemiosmosis drives ATP synthesis using the potential energy of a concentration gradient of hydrogen ions (H^+) across a membrane. The gradient is created when an electron transport chain uses the energy released as it passes electrons down the chain to pump hydrogen ions across a membrane.

Figure 7.9 illustrates the relationship between chloroplast structure and function in the light reactions of photosynthesis. As in Figure 7.8A, we show the two photosystems and electron transport chains, all located within the thylakoid membrane of a chloroplast. Here you can see that as photoexcited electrons are passed down the electron transport chain connecting the two photosystems, hydrogen ions are pumped across the membrane from the stroma into the thylakoid space (inside the thylakoid sacs). This generates a concentration gradient across the membrane.

The flask-shaped structure in the figure represents an ATP synthase complex, which is like the one we saw in the mitochon-

drion. The energy of the concentration gradient drives H^+ across the membrane through ATP synthase. As you learned in Module 6.10, ATP synthase couples the flow of H^+ to the phosphorylation of ADP. In photosynthesis, this chemiosmotic production of ATP is called **photophosphorylation** because the initial energy input is light energy.

How does photophosphorylation compare with oxidative phosphorylation? In cellular respiration, the high-energy electrons passed down the electron transport chain come from the oxidation of food molecules. In photosynthesis, light energy is used to drive electrons to the top of the transport chain. Mitochondria transfer chemical energy from food to ATP; chloroplasts transform light energy into the chemical energy of ATP.

Notice that in the light-driven flow of electrons through the two photosystems, the final electron acceptor is $NADP^+$, not O_2 as in cellular respiration. Electrons do not end up at a low energy level in H_2O, as they do in respiration. Instead, they are stored at a high state of potential energy in NADPH.

In summary, the light reactions provide the chemical energy (ATP) and reducing power (NADPH) for the next stage of photosynthesis, the Calvin cycle. Module 7.10 describes how that cycle makes sugar.

Web Activity *The Light Reactions*

❓ What is the advantage of the light reactions producing NADPH and ATP on the stroma side of the thylakoid membrane?

■ The Calvin cycle, which consumes the NADPH and ATP, occurs in the stroma.

Figure 7.9 The production of ATP by chemiosmosis in photosynthesis: The small diagram on the upper left illustrates the location of the components of the light reactions in a thylakoid membrane. Numerous copies of these components are present in each thylakoid.

7.10   ATP and NADPH power sugar synthesis in the Calvin cycle

Input $\begin{cases} CO_2 \\ ATP \\ NADPH \end{cases}$

Output: G3P

Figure 7.10A   An overview of the Calvin cycle

The Calvin cycle functions like a sugar factory within a chloroplast. As Figure 7.10A shows, inputs to this all-important food-making process are CO$_2$ (from the air) and ATP and NADPH (both generated by the light reactions). Using carbon from CO$_2$, energy from ATP, and high-energy electrons from NADPH, the Calvin cycle constructs an energy-rich, three carbon sugar, glyceraldehyde-3-phosphate (G3P). A plant cell can use G3P to make glucose and other organic molecules as needed. (You already met G3P in glycolysis: It is the three-carbon sugar formed by the splitting of glucose.)

Figure 7.10B presents the details of the Calvin cycle. It is called a cycle because, like the citric acid cycle in cellular respiration, the starting material is regenerated as the process occurs. In this case, the starting material is a five-carbon sugar named ribulose bisphosphate (RuBP). ❶ In the carbon fixation step, the enzyme rubisco attaches CO$_2$ to RuBP. ❷ In the next step, a reduction, NADPH reduces the organic acid 3-PGA to G3P with the assistance of ATP. To make a molecule of G3P, the cycle must incorporate the carbon atoms from three molecules of CO$_2$. The cycle actually incorporates one carbon at a time, but we show it starting with three CO$_2$ molecules so that we end up with a complete G3P molecule.

For this to be a cycle, RuBP must be regenerated. ❸ For every three CO$_2$ molecules fixed, one G3P molecule leaves the cycle as product, and the remaining five G3P molecules are rearranged, ❹ using energy from ATP to regenerate three molecules of RuBP. Review the steps of the Calvin cycle below.

Note that for the net synthesis of one G3P molecule, the Calvin cycle consumes nine ATP and six NADPH molecules, which were provided by the light reactions.

Web Activity *The Calvin Cycle*

? To synthesize one glucose molecule, the Calvin cycle must turn six times, using 6 CO$_2$, 18 ATP, and 12 NADPH. Explain why this high number of ATP and NADPH molecules is consistent with the value of glucose as an energy source.

■ Glucose is a valuable energy source because it is highly reduced, storing lots of potential energy in its electrons. The more energy a molecule stores, the more energy and reducing power required to produce that molecule.

Step ❶ Carbon fixation. An enzyme called rubisco combines CO$_2$ with a five-carbon sugar called ribulose bisphosphate (abbreviated RuBP). The unstable product splits into two molecules of the three-carbon organic acid, 3-phosphoglyceric acid (3-PGA). For three CO$_2$ entering, six 3-PGA result.

Step ❷ Reduction. Two chemical reactions (indicated by the two blue arrows) consume energy from six molecules of ATP and oxidize six molecules of NADPH. Six molecules of 3-PGA are reduced, producing six molecules of the energy-rich three-carbon sugar, G3P.

Step ❸ Release of one molecule of G3P. Five of the G3Ps from step 2 remain in the cycle. The single molecule of G3P you see leaving the cycle is the net product of photosynthesis. A plant cell uses G3P to make glucose and other organic compounds.

Step ❹ Regeneration of RuBP. A series of chemical reactions uses energy from ATP to rearrange the atoms in the five G3P molecules (15 carbons total), forming three RuBP molecules (15 carbons). These can start another turn of the cycle.

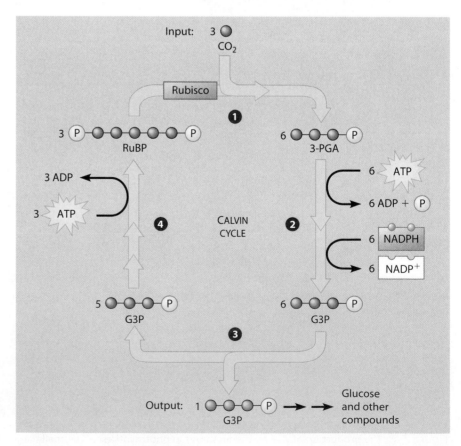

Figure 7.10B   Details of the Calvin cycle, which takes place in the stroma of a chloroplast

7.11 Review: Photosynthesis uses light energy, CO$_2$, and H$_2$O to make food molecules

Life on Earth is solar powered. As we have discussed, most of the living world depends on the food-making machinery of photosynthesis. Figure 7.11 summarizes the two stages of this vital process and reviews where they occur in the chloroplast. The production of sugar from CO$_2$ is an emergent property of the structural arrangement of a chloroplast, which integrates the two stages of photosynthesis.

Starting on the left in the diagram, you see a summary of the light reactions, which occur in the thylakoid membranes (green). Two photosystems in the membranes capture solar energy, using it to energize electrons. Simultaneously, water is split, and O$_2$ is released. The photosystems transfer photo-excited electrons through electron transport chains, where energy is harvested to make ATP, and to NADP$^+$, where electrons are stored in the high-energy compound NADPH.

The chloroplast's sugar factory is the Calvin cycle, the second stage of photosynthesis. In the stroma, the enzyme rubisco combines CO$_2$ with RuBP, and ATP and NADPH are used to reduce 3-PGA to G3P. Sugar molecules made from G3P serve as a plant's own food supply. Plants use about 50% of the carbohydrate they make as fuel for cellular respiration. Sugars also serve as starting material for making other organic molecules, such as the structural molecule cellulose. Most plants make considerably more food each day than they need. They stockpile the excess sugar as starch, storing it in roots, tubers, and fruits.

Plants (and other photosynthesizers) not only feed themselves but are also the ultimate source of food for virtually all other organisms. Humans and other animals make none of their own food and are totally dependent on the organic matter made by photosynthesizers. Even the energy we acquire when we eat meat was originally captured by photosynthesis. The energy in a hamburger, for instance, came from sunlight that was originally converted to a chemical form in chloroplasts in the cells of the grasses eaten by cattle. Photosynthesis is the ultimate source of the food we eat and the oxygen we breathe.

This review of photosynthesis is an appropriate place to reflect on the metabolic ground we have covered in this chapter and the previous one. In Chapter 6, we saw that virtually all organisms, plants included, use cellular respiration to obtain the energy they need from fuel molecules such as glucose. We followed the chemical pathways of glycolysis and the citric acid cycle, which break glucose down and release energy from it. We have now come full circle, seeing how plants trap sunlight energy and use it to make glucose from the raw materials carbon dioxide and water.

In tracing glucose synthesis and its breakdown, we have also seen that cells use several of the same mechanisms—electron transport, redox reactions, and chemiosmosis—in energy storage (photosynthesis) and energy harvest (cellular respiration).

Web Process of Science *How Is the Rate of Photosynthesis Measured?*

? Explain why a poison that inhibits an enzyme of the Calvin cycle will also inhibit the light reactions.

■ The light reactions require ADP and NADP$^+$, which are not recycled from ATP and NADPH when the Calvin cycle stops.

Figure 7.11
A summary of the chemical processes of photosynthesis

7.12   Adaptations that save water in hot, dry climates evolved in C_4 and CAM plants

The algal ancestors of plants lived in water. Since plants first moved onto land about 475 million years ago, they have been adapting to the challenges of terrestrial life, particularly the problem of dehydration. Some solutions involve trade-offs, such as the compromise between the requirements for photosynthesis and preventing excessive water loss. Closing stomata on a hot, dry day is an adaptation that reduces water loss, but it also prevents CO_2 from entering the leaf and O_2 from leaving. As a result, CO_2 levels get very low in the leaf, while O_2 from the light reactions builds up. These conditions reduce photosynthesis and favor an apparently wasteful process called photorespiration.

In most plants, initial fixation of carbon occurs when the enzyme rubisco adds CO_2 to RuBP (see Figure 7.10B). Such plants are called C_3 **plants** because the first organic compound produced is the three-carbon compound 3-PGA. C_3 plants are common and widely distributed; they include soybeans, oats, wheat, and rice. One of the problems that farmers face in growing C_3 plants is that hot, dry weather can decrease crop yield. When stomata close to reduce water loss and O_2 builds up in a leaf, rubisco adds O_2 instead of CO_2 to RuBP. A two-carbon product of this reaction is then broken down by the cell to CO_2 and H_2O. This process is called **photorespiration.** Unlike photosynthesis, photorespiration yields no sugar, and unlike cellular respiration, it produces no ATP. It can, however, drain away as much as 50% of the carbon fixed by the Calvin cycle.

According to one hypothesis, photorespiration is an evolutionary relic from when the atmosphere had less O_2 than it does today. In the ancient atmosphere that prevailed when rubisco first evolved, the inability of the enzyme's active site to exclude O_2 would have made little difference. It is only after O_2 became so concentrated in the atmosphere that the "sloppiness" of rubisco presented a problem. There are also alternative hypotheses for photorespiration, including that it plays a protective role in plants when the products of the light reactions build up in a cell (as occurs when the Calvin cycle has slowed due to a lack of CO_2).

C_4 Plants   In certain plant species, alternate modes of carbon fixation have evolved that save water without shutting down photosynthesis. **C_4 plants** are so named because they precede the Calvin cycle by first fixing CO_2 into a four-carbon compound. When the weather is hot and dry, a C_4 plant keeps its stomata mostly closed, thus conserving water. At the same time, it continues making sugars by photosynthesis, using the pathway and the two types of cells shown in the left side of Figure 7.12. An enzyme in the mesophyll cells has a high affinity for CO_2 and can continue to fix carbon even when the CO_2 concentration in the leaf is low. The resulting four-carbon compound then acts as a carbon shuttle; it moves into bundle-sheath cells, which are packed around the veins of the leaf, and releases CO_2. Thus, the CO_2 concentration in these cells remains high enough for the Calvin cycle to make sugars and avoid photorespiration. Corn and sugarcane are examples of agriculturally important C_4 plants. C_4 photosynthesis is advantageous in hot, dry climates, which is where C_4 plants evolved and thrive today.

CAM Plants   A second photosynthetic adaptation to arid conditions has evolved in pineapples, many cacti, and succulent (water-storing) plants, such as aloe and jade plants. Collectively called **CAM plants,** these species are adapted to very dry climates. A CAM plant (right side of Figure 7.12) conserves water by opening its stomata and admitting CO_2 only at night. When CO_2 enters the leaves, it is fixed into a four-carbon compound, as in C_4 plants. The four-carbon compound in a CAM plant banks CO_2 at night and releases it to the Calvin cycle during the day. This keeps photosynthesis operating during the day, even though the leaf's stomata remain closed. CAM stands for crassulacean acid metabolism, after the plant family Crassulaceae, in which this water-saving adaptation was first discovered.

In C_4 plants, carbon fixation and the Calvin cycle occur in different types of cells. In CAM plants, these processes occur in the same cells, but at different times. Keep in mind that CAM, C_4, and C_3 plants all eventually use the Calvin cycle to make sugar from CO_2. The C_4 and CAM pathways are two evolutionary solutions to the problem of maintaining photosynthesis with stomata partially or completely closed on hot, dry days.

Web Activity *Photosynthesis in Dry Climates*

? How would you expect the relative abundance of C_3 versus C_4 and CAM species to change in a geographic region where the climate becomes much hotter and drier?

Figure 7.12   Comparison of photosynthesis in C_4 and CAM plants: In both pathways, CO_2 is first incorporated into a four-carbon compound, which then provides CO_2 to the Calvin cycle.

■ C_4 and CAM species would replace many of the C_3 species.

7.13 Photosynthesis moderates global warming

The greenhouse in **Figure 7.13A** is used to grow plants where the weather outside is too cold. The glass or plastic walls of a greenhouse allow solar radiation to pass through. The sunlight heats the soil, which in turn warms the air. The walls trap the warm air, raising the temperature inside.

An analogous process, called the **greenhouse effect,** operates on a global scale (**Figure 7.13B**). Solar radiation reaching Earth's atmosphere includes ultraviolet radiation and visible light. As we discuss in the next module, the ozone layer filters out most of the damaging UV radiation. Visible light passes through and is absorbed by the planet's surface, warming it. Heat is radiated by the warmed planet, and these longer, infrared wavelengths are absorbed by gases in the atmosphere, which then reflect some of the heat back to Earth. This natural heating effect is highly beneficial. Without it, Earth would be much colder and much less hospitable to life.

The gases in the atmosphere that absorb heat radiation are called greenhouse gases. Some occur naturally, such as water vapor, carbon dioxide (CO_2), and methane (CH_4), while others are synthetic, such as chlorofluorocarbons (CFCs). Human activities are adding to the levels of these greenhouse gases.

Carbon dioxide is one of the most important greenhouse gases. You have just learned that CO_2 is a raw material for photosynthesis and a waste product of cellular respiration. These two processes, taking place in microscopic chloroplasts and mitochondria, keep carbon cycling between inorganic and organic compounds on a global scale. Photosynthetic organisms absorb billions of tons of CO_2 each year. Most of that fixed carbon returns to the atmosphere via cellular respiration, the action of decomposers, and fires. But much of it remains locked in large tracts of forests and undecomposed organisms. And large amounts of carbon are in long-term storage in fossil fuels buried deep under Earth's surface.

Before 1850, carbon dioxide was estimated to make up less than 0.03% of the air we breathe. Since the start of the Industrial Revolution, the atmospheric concentration of CO_2 has increased about 40%, mostly due to the combustion of carbon-based fossil fuels, such as coal, oil, and gasoline.

Increasing concentrations of greenhouse gases have been linked to **global warming,** a slow but steady rise in Earth's surface temperature. Predicted changes of just a few degrees over the next 50 years may have dramatic and wide-ranging consequences. These would likely include melting of polar ice, rising sea levels, extreme weather patterns, droughts, and the spread of tropical diseases.

Unfortunately, the rise in atmospheric CO_2 levels during the last century coincided with widespread deforestation, which aggravated the global warming problem by reducing an effective CO_2 sink. As forests are cleared for lumber or agriculture, and as population growth increases the demand for fossil fuels,

Figure 7.13A   Plants growing in a greenhouse

Figure 7.13B CO_2 in the atmosphere and global warming

CO_2 levels will continue to rise. We discuss global warming in more detail in Module 38.5.

Can photosynthesis help mitigate this increase in atmospheric CO_2? As you read in the chapter introduction, "energy plantations" hold out the promise of a cleaner, renewable fuel source. Recent studies show that increasing CO_2 levels will increase plant production somewhat, but far less than predicted even a decade ago. Slowing the destruction of forests will sustain their photosynthetic and carbon-storing contributions. Taking a lesson from plants, we can explore technologies that utilize solar energy for some of our energy needs. Almost all life on Earth depends on the ability of plants and other photosynthetic organisms to convert light energy to the chemical energy of food molecules. Their contribution to life on Earth may also come to include increased removal of CO_2 from the atmosphere.

? Explain the greenhouse effect.

■ Sunlight warms Earth's surface, which radiates heat to the atmosphere. CO_2 and other greenhouse gases absorb and radiate some heat back to Earth.

7.14 Mario Molina talks about Earth's protective ozone layer

Figure 7.14A   Mario Molina

As the process of photosynthesis consumes CO_2, it produces the O_2 on which plants, animals, and most other organisms depend for cellular respiration. This O_2 has another benefit: High in the atmosphere it is converted to ozone (O_3), which plays a protective role for life on Earth. Among the scientists who study the ozone layer is Mario Molina of the University of California, San Diego (Figure 7.14A), who in 1995 shared a Nobel Prize for his research on how certain pollutants are damaging that layer. In an interview, Dr. Molina explained why the ozone layer is important:

> The ozone layer shields the Earth's surface from powerful ultraviolet radiation that comes from the sun. This UV radiation is harmful to organisms, including humans. For example, UV radiation causes sunburn, and skin cancer can be a cumulative result of exposure. There is also evidence that UV can damage crops. Certain developing animals, such as the larvae of fish, seem to be particularly sensitive.

He described how ozone forms and how it is destroyed:

> The ozone forms when high-energy solar radiation breaks apart O_2 molecules and frees oxygen atoms. These then react with unbroken O_2 molecules. The result is ozone, which has three oxygen atoms (O_3). So ozone is continuously forming by the action of sunlight on the atmosphere. This is balanced by continuous destruction of the ozone molecules when they react with other chemical compounds that are naturally present in the atmosphere. Humans have disrupted that balance by releasing certain industrial chemicals that hasten this destruction.

The research that won Dr. Molina the Nobel Prize dealt with the destruction of ozone by one particular class of industrial chemicals, called chlorofluorocarbons, or CFCs (mentioned as greenhouse gases in Module 7.13). In 1974, when Dr. Molina and his colleagues first published their CFC-ozone depletion hypothesis, CFCs were used in large amounts as refrigerants, as propellants in spray cans, as solvents, and in the process for making plastic foams:

> We predicted that the continuous release of CFCs would damage the protective ozone layer. CFCs are very stable compounds, and this stability allows them to make it up to the ozone layer, which is about 15 miles above the surface of the Earth. There solar radiation converts them to very reactive chemicals called free radicals, which then destroy the ozone.

How did scientists and the general public react to the alarming possibility that the ozone layer was thinning?

> At first, there was very little reaction because not many people were aware of the importance of invisible things like the ozone layer and

Southern tip of South America

Antarctica

Figure 7.14B   The ozone hole in the Southern Hemisphere, spring 2006

> UV radiation. Experts in our field quickly realized that the prediction of the CFC-ozone depletion theory was something to worry about, but many other scientists were skeptical, which is natural for scientists. Then, as we and others began doing experiments to test the idea, the evidence became strong, and more and more people, including politicians, became concerned about ozone depletion. Then, in 1985, scientists documented a drastic depletion of the ozone layer over Antarctica—an ozone hole.

Figure 7.14B shows an image produced from atmospheric data from 2006 of the "ozone hole" over Antarctica. Greens and yellows are where there is more ozone; blue and purple colors are where there is the least. This thinning of the ozone layer appears every spring. What is being done to correct this problem?

> The Montreal Protocol was an international agreement that required a complete phasing out of CFC production by developed countries by 1996. So that's already happened. These countries now use other refrigerants, which are destroyed in the atmosphere before they reach the ozone layer. Because CFCs are so stable, however, we predict that the ozone layer won't recover until the middle of the twenty-first century.

We asked Dr. Molina what he has learned since 1974 about the interface between science and politics:

> One lesson is that science is not always something that politicians care very much about. Often, supporting science is considered a luxury, though actually it is a good investment. Another challenge is that many issues related to science and technology are long-term issues that require patience and long-term commitment.

Whether an environmental problem involves CFCs or carbon dioxide emissions, the scientific research is often complicated, and solutions are often complex and expensive. The connections between science, technology, and society, so clearly exemplified by the work of Mario Molina, are a major theme of this book. This theme will come up again in the next unit, on cellular reproduction and genetics.

? **Where does the ozone layer in Earth's atmosphere come from?**

■ Photosynthesis releases O_2. High in the atmosphere, radiation from the sun converts some of the O_2 to ozone, O_3.

Chapter Review

Reviewing the Concepts

An Overview of Photosynthesis (Introduction–7.5)

Photosynthesis is summarized by the following equation:

$$6\,CO_2 + 6\,H_2O + \text{Light energy} \rightarrow C_6H_{12}O_6 + 6\,O_2$$

Plants, algae, and some bacteria are photoautotrophs, the producers of food consumed by virtually all organisms. Chloroplasts appear to have evolved from an endosymbiotic photosynthetic prokaryote (**Introduction–7.1**). In plants, photosynthesis occurs primarily in the leaves, within chloroplasts, which contain stroma and stacks of thylakoids called grana (**7.2**).

The Two Stages of Photosynthesis. The O_2 liberated by photosynthesis comes from H_2O (**7.3**). In photosynthesis, H_2O is oxidized and CO_2 is reduced (**7.4**). The light reactions convert light energy to chemical energy and produce O_2. The Calvin cycle assembles sugar molecules from CO_2 using ATP and NADPH from the light reactions (**7.5**).

The Light Reactions: Converting Solar Energy to Chemical Energy (7.6–7.9)

Photosystems. Certain wavelengths of visible light, absorbed by pigments such as chlorophyll and carotenoids, drive photosynthesis (**7.6**). Thylakoid membranes contain multiple photosystems, each consisting of light-harvesting complexes of pigments and a reaction center complex with a primary electron acceptor that receives excited electrons from a reaction center chlorophyll *a* (**7.7**).

The Light Reactions. Two photosystems absorb photons and transfer energy to chlorophyll P680 and P700. Their excited electrons are passed from primary electron acceptors to electron transport chains. Electrons shuttle from photosystem II to I, providing energy to make ATP. Electrons from photosystem I reduce $NADP^+$ to NADPH. Photosystem II regains electrons by splitting water, releasing O_2 (**7.8**).

Photophosphorylation. ATP is synthesized by chemiosmosis. The electron transport chain pumps H^+ into the thylakoid space. The concentration gradient drives H^+ back across the membrane through ATP synthase and powers the phosphorylation of ADP to produce ATP (**7.9**).

The Calvin Cycle: Converting CO₂ to Sugars (7.10)

The Calvin cycle, occurring in the stroma, consists of carbon fixation, reduction, release of G3P, and regeneration of RuBP. Using carbon from CO_2, electrons from NADPH, and energy from ATP, the cycle constructs G3P, which is used to build glucose and other organic molecules (**7.10**).

Photosynthesis Reviewed and Extended (7.11–7.12)

A summary diagram of the two stages of photosynthesis is shown at the top of the next column (**7.11**).

C₃, C₄, and CAM plants. In C_3 plants, a drop in CO_2 and rise in O_2 when stomata close on hot, dry days divert the Calvin cycle to photorespiration. C_4 plants first fix CO_2 into a four-carbon compound that provides CO_2 to the Calvin cycle. CAM plants open stomata at night, making a four-carbon compound used as a CO_2 source during the day (**7.12**).

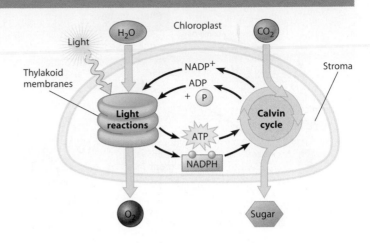

Photosynthesis, Solar Radiation, and Earth's Atmosphere (7.13–7.14)

Excess CO_2 is contributing to global warming. Photosynthesis, which removes CO_2 from the atmosphere, moderates this warming (**7.13**). Solar radiation converts O_2 high in the atmosphere to ozone (O_3), which shields organisms from damaging UV radiation. Industrial chemicals called CFCs have caused dangerous thinning of the ozone layer, but international restrictions on CFC use is allowing recovery (**7.14**).

Connecting the Concepts

1. This diagram compares the chemiosmotic synthesis of ATP in mitochondria and chloroplasts. In both cases, label the structures involved and indicate which side of the membrane has the higher H^+ concentration. Then label on the right the locations within the chloroplast.

2. Continue your comparison of chemiosmosis and electron transport in mitochondria and chloroplasts. In each case,
   a. where do the electrons come from?
   b. where do the electrons get their energy?
   c. what picks up the electrons at the end of the chain?
   d. how is the energy given up by the electrons used?

3. Complete this summary map of photosynthesis.

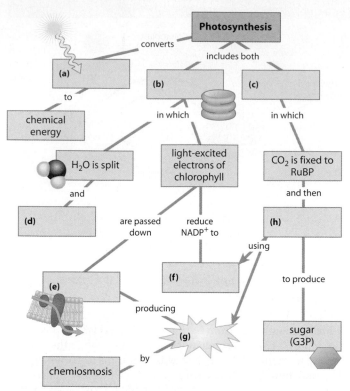

Testing Your Knowledge

Multiple Choice

4. Photosynthesis consumes _____ and produces _____.
   a. O_2 . . . H_2O
   b. H_2O . . . CO_2
   c. CO_2 . . . chlorophyll
   d. H_2O . . . O_2
   e. glucose . . . O_2

5. Which of the following are produced by reactions that take place in the thylakoids and consumed by reactions in the stroma?
   a. CO_2 and H_2O
   b. $NADP^+$ and ADP
   c. ATP and NADPH
   d. ATP, NADPH, and O_2
   e. CO_2 and ATP

6. In photosynthesis, _____ is oxidized and _____ is reduced.
   a. glucose . . . oxygen
   b. carbon dioxide . . . water
   c. water . . . carbon dioxide
   d. glucose . . . carbon dioxide
   e. water . . . oxygen

7. Why is it difficult for most plants to carry out photosynthesis in very hot, dry environments such as deserts?
   a. The light is too intense and overpowers the pigment molecules.
   b. The closing of stomata keeps CO_2 from entering and O_2 from leaving the plant.
   c. They must rely on photorespiration to make ATP.
   d. Global warming is intensified in a desert environment.
   e. CO_2 builds up in the leaves, blocking carbon fixation.

8. When light strikes chlorophyll molecules, they lose electrons, which are ultimately replaced by
   a. splitting water.
   b. breaking down ATP.
   c. oxidizing NADPH.
   d. fixing carbon.
   e. oxidizing glucose.

9. What is the role of $NADP^+$ in photosynthesis?
   a. It assists chlorophyll in capturing light.
   b. It acts as the primary electron acceptor for the photosystems.
   c. As part of the electron transport chain, it helps to synthesize ATP.
   d. It assists photosystem II in the splitting of water.
   e. It accepts electrons and carries them to the Calvin cycle.

10. The reactions of the Calvin cycle are not directly dependent on light, but they usually do not occur at night. Why? (*Explain your answer.*)
    a. It is often too cold at night for these reactions to take place.
    b. Carbon dioxide concentrations decrease at night.
    c. The Calvin cycle depends on products of the light reactions.
    d. Plants usually close their stomata at night.
    e. Most plants do not make four-carbon compounds, which they would need for the Calvin cycle at night.

11. How many "turns" of the Calvin cycle are required to produce one molecule of glucose? (Assume one CO_2 is fixed in each turn of the cycle.)
    a. 1   b. 2   c. 3   d. 6   e. 12

12. Which of the following does *not* occur during the Calvin cycle?
    a. carbon fixation
    b. oxidation of NADPH
    c. consumption of ATP
    d. regeneration of RuBP, the CO_2 acceptor
    e. release of oxygen

Describing, Comparing, and Explaining

13. What are the major inputs and outputs of the two stages of photosynthesis?

14. What do plants do with the sugar they produce in photosynthesis?

Applying the Concepts

15. Most experts now agree that global warming is occurring, and in response to its potential threat, a number of countries have made a commitment to reduce CO_2 emissions significantly. However, some countries oppose taking strong action at this time. Several reasons are cited: First, a few experts think that the apparent warming trend may be just a random fluctuation in temperature. Second, if the temperature increase is real, it has yet to be shown that it is caused by increased CO_2. Some people also believe that it would be difficult to cut CO_2 emissions without sacrificing economic growth. Do you think we should have more evidence before taking action? Or is it better to play it safe and act now to reduce CO_2 emissions? What are the possible costs and benefits of each of these two strategies?

16. The use of biomass energy (see chapter introduction) avoids many of the problems associated with gathering, refining, transporting, and burning fossil fuels. Yet biomass energy is not without its own set of problems. What challenges do you think would arise from a large-scale conversion to biomass energy? How do these challenges compare with those encountered with fossil fuels? Which set of challenges do you think is more likely to be overcome eventually? Do you think any one type of energy has more benefits and fewer costs than the others? Which one, and why?

Answers to all questions can be found in Appendix 4.

For Practice Quizzes, BioFlix, MP3 Tutors, and Activities, go to www.mybiology.com.

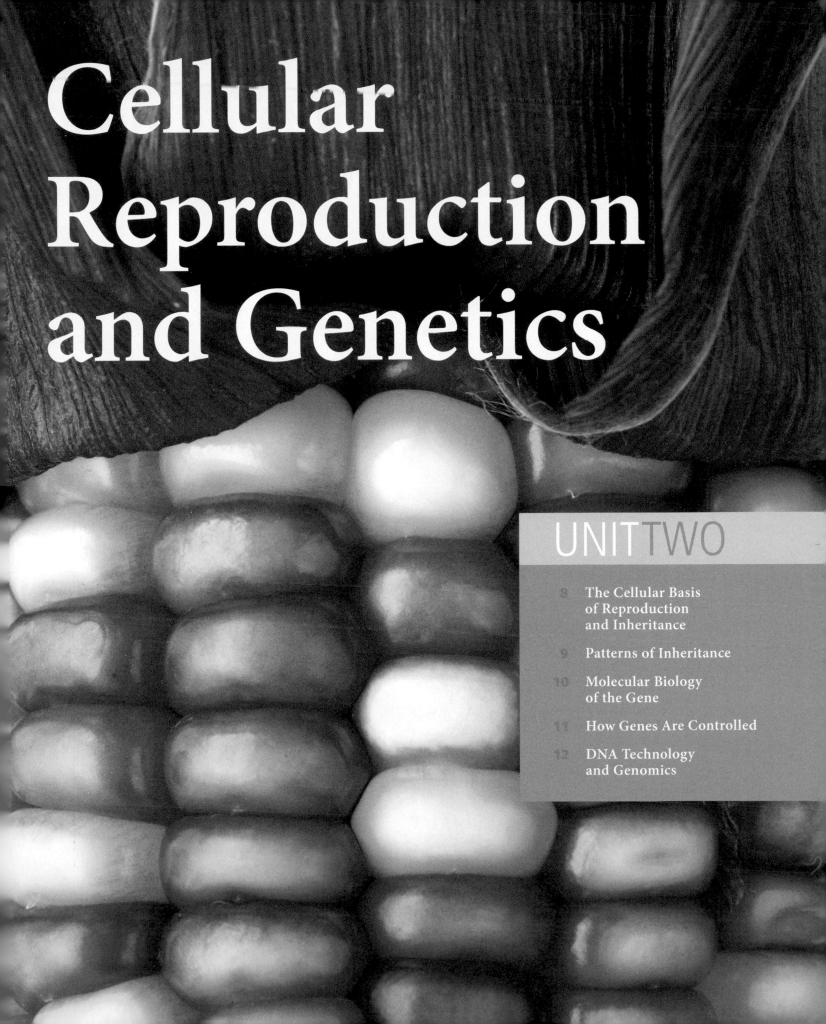

Cellular Reproduction and Genetics

UNIT TWO

8   The Cellular Basis of Reproduction and Inheritance

9   Patterns of Inheritance

10   Molecular Biology of the Gene

11   How Genes Are Controlled

12   DNA Technology and Genomics

Connections Between Cell Division and Reproduction

8.1   Like begets like, more or less
8.2   Cells arise only from preexisting cells
8.3   Prokaryotes reproduce by binary fission

The Eukaryotic Cell Cycle and Mitosis

8.4   The large, complex chromosomes of eukaryotes duplicate with each cell division
Bio Flix 🎧 8.5   The cell cycle multiplies cells
8.6   Cell division is a continuum of dynamic changes
8.7   Cytokinesis differs for plant and animal cells
8.8   Anchorage, cell density, and chemical growth factors affect cell division
8.9   Growth factors signal the cell cycle control system
8.10 Growing out of control, cancer cells produce malignant tumors
8.11 Review: Mitosis provides for growth, cell replacement, and asexual reproduction

Meiosis and Crossing Over

8.12 Chromosomes are matched in homologous pairs
8.13 Gametes have a single set of chromosomes
Bio Flix 🎧 8.14 Meiosis reduces the chromosome number from diploid to haploid
🎧 8.15 Mitosis and meiosis have important similarities and differences
8.16 Independent orientation of chromosomes in meiosis and random fertilization lead to varied offspring
8.17 Homologous chromosomes may carry different versions of genes
8.18 Crossing over further increases genetic variability

Alterations of Chromosome Number and Structure

8.19 A karyotype is a photographic inventory of an individual's chromosomes
8.20 An extra copy of chromosome 21 causes Down syndrome
8.21 Accidents during meiosis can alter chromosome number
8.22 Abnormal numbers of sex chromosomes do not usually affect survival
8.23 New species can arise from errors in cell division
8.24 Alterations of chromosome structure can cause birth defects and cancer

Rain Forest Rescue

Deep in a Hawaiian rain forest, the thrumming of a helicopter cuts through the dense tropical air. After touching down in a clearing, a pair of rescuers jump out, one of them carrying a precious bundle. A 20-minute hike through dense foliage brings them to their "patient": the last known wild *Cyanea kuhihewa* plant, a member of the bellflower family (pictured at right). The rescuers now stand in the middle of a life-or-death battle, armed with the pollen of a species on the very brink of extinction.

Despite its tiny size, Hawaii is home to over 300 endangered or threatened species, including more endangered plants than any other state in the United States. Of these, 11 plant species have fewer than five representatives growing anywhere in the wild. At the time of this rescue attempt in 2002, the small bellflower was among the rarest of the rare, with only a single surviving member in the forest.

So when this lone wild bellflower bloomed, scientists from the National Tropical Botanical Garden on Kauai saw an opportunity. Their goal was to promote sexual reproduction, the reproductive process that involves fertilization, the union of a sperm and an egg. Using a fine brush, the botanical rescuers transferred sperm-carrying pollen from a garden-grown plant onto the egg-containing wild bloom. If sperm and egg join, the fertilized egg may divide and eventually form an embryo and then a seed. Upon germination of the seed, the embryo may further develop into a juvenile and later into an adult plant.

Development from a fertilized egg to a new adult organism is one phase of a multicellular organism's **life cycle,** the sequence of stages leading from the adults of one generation to the adults of the next. The other phase of the life cycle is reproduction, the formation of new individuals from preexisting ones. The reproductive phase of the life cycle entails the creation of offspring carrying genetic information, as DNA, from their parents. Sperm and egg each carry one set of genetic information—one copy of the organism's **genome.** Thus, the offspring of sexual reproduction inherit traits from two parents. In the case of *C. kuhihewa*, sexual reproduction could provide desperately needed genetic diversity.

Unfortunately, the bellflower fertilization attempt failed. Even worse, the last remaining wild specimen died in 2003. But hope remains for *C. kuhihewa.* The garden's botanists are now trying asexual reproduction, the production of offspring by a single parent. Many plants that normally reproduce sexually can be induced to reproduce asexually in the laboratory. Indeed, work at Kauai's botanical garden has produced several new bellflower plants through asexual reproduction, using stem tissue snipped from wild plants in the 1990s.

These examples of sexual and asexual reproduction illustrate the main point of this chapter: Cell division is at the heart of organismal reproduction. Plants created from cuttings result from repeated cell divisions, as does the more familiar development of a multicellular organism from a fertilized egg. And eggs and sperm themselves result from cell division of a special kind. In this chapter, we discuss the two main types of cell division and their functions in organisms. ■ ■ ■

8.1 Like begets like, more or less

The ability of organisms to reproduce their own kind is the one characteristic that best distinguishes living things from nonliving matter (see Module 1.4 to review the characteristics of life). Only amoebas produce more amoebas, only people make more people, and only maple trees produce more maple trees. These simple facts of life have been recognized for thousands of years and are summarized by the age-old saying "Like begets like."

In a strict sense, the adage "Like begets like" applies only to **asexual reproduction,** the creation of genetically identical offspring by a single parent, without the participation of sperm and egg. For example, the amoeba in **Figure 8.1A** has duplicated its **chromosomes,** the structures that contain most of the organism's DNA. After doubling, identical chromosomes were allocated to opposite sides of the parent cell. When the parent cell divides, the resulting two daughter amoebas will be genetically identical to each other and to the original parent. (Biologists traditionally use the word "daughter" in this context only to indicate offspring, not to imply gender.) In asexual reproduction, there is one simple principle of inheritance: The lone parent and each of its offspring have identical genes.

The photograph of the family in **Figure 8.1B** makes the point that in a *sexually* reproducing species, like does not precisely beget like. Offspring produced by **sexual reproduction** generally resemble their parents more closely than they resemble unrelated individuals of the same species, but they are not identical to their parents or to each other. Each offspring inherits a unique combination of genes from its two parents, and this one-and-only set of genes programs a unique combination of traits. As a result, sexual reproduction can produce great variation among offspring. Notice in the photo that despite the family resemblances, each family member has a unique appearance. You probably resemble your parents more closely than a

Figure 8.1B Sexual reproduction produces offspring with unique combinations of genes.

stranger, but you do not look exactly like either parent or any of your siblings (unless you are an identical twin).

Long before anyone knew about genes, chromosomes, or the underlying principles of inheritance, people recognized that individuals of sexually reproducing species are highly varied. Furthermore, people learned to develop domestic breeds of plants and animals by controlling sexual reproduction. A domestic breed displays particular traits from among the great variety of traits found in the species as a whole. For example, though all domestic dogs belong to a single species, each breed of dog exhibits much less variability than the species as a whole. In producing each kind of domestic dog, breeders selected from a varied population of dogs certain individuals with specific traits and allowed these individuals to mate and produce offspring. The ancestry of a dog breed such as the German shepherd can be traced back many generations, during which breeders reduced variability in the breed by rigidly selecting for mating only those dogs with specific traits. In a sense, selective breeding is an attempt to make like beget like more than it does in nature.

LM 340×

Figure 8.1A A single-celled amoeba producing a genetically identical offspring cell through asexual reproduction

? In terms of the "like begets like" adage, contrast asexual with sexual reproduction.

■ Asexual reproduction produces genetically identical offspring that inherit all their DNA from a single parent. The offspring of sexual reproduction show a family resemblance, but siblings vary because they inherit different combinations of genes from the two parents.

Cells arise only from preexisting cells

In 1858, German physician Rudolf Virchow stated an important biological principle: "Where a cell exists, there must have been a preexisting cell." Like many significant ideas now taken for granted, Virchow's principle (which he summarized as "Every cell from a cell") is both simple and profound. It tells us that the perpetuation of life, including all aspects of reproduction and inheritance, is based on the reproduction of cells, or **cell division.**

Cell division plays several important roles in the lives of organisms. In unicellular organisms, cell division can reproduce an entire organism. Cell division on a larger scale allows some multicellular organisms to reproduce asexually (such as plants that grow from cuttings). Among sexually reproducing organisms, cell division is the basis of sperm and egg formation. Cell division also enables sexually reproducing organisms to

develop from a single cell—the fertilized egg, or zygote—into an adult organism. After an organism is fully grown, cell division continues to function in renewal and repair, replacing cells that die from normal wear and tear or accidents.

So far, we have discussed only the division of eukaryotic cells, and we will emphasize them in this chapter. Prokaryotes, however, also illustrate Virchow's principle, and in the next module, we look briefly at prokaryotic cell division.

? What function does cell division play in an amoeba? What functions does it play in your body?

■ Reproduction; development, growth, and repair

Prokaryotes reproduce by binary fission

Prokaryotes (bacteria and archaea) reproduce by a type of cell division called **binary fission** ("dividing in half"). In typical prokaryotes, most genes are carried on a circular DNA molecule that, with associated proteins, constitutes the organism's single chromosome. Although prokaryotic chromosomes are

Prokaryotic chromosomes

Colorized TEM 32,500×

Figure 8.3B Electron micrograph of a dividing bacterium

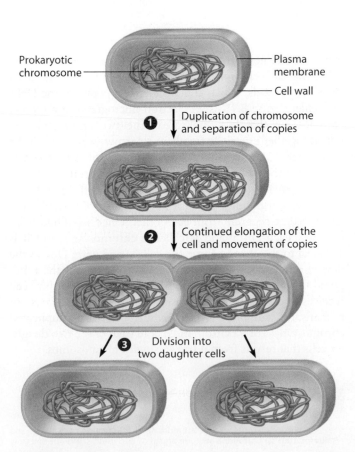

Prokaryotic chromosome

Plasma membrane

Cell wall

❶ Duplication of chromosome and separation of copies

❷ Continued elongation of the cell and movement of copies

❸ Division into two daughter cells

Figure 8.3A Binary fission of a prokaryotic cell

much smaller than those of eukaryotes, duplicating them in an orderly fashion and distributing the copies equally to two daughter bacteria is still a formidable task. Consider, for example, that when stretched out, the chromosome of the bacterium *Escherichia coli* is about 500 times longer than the cell itself. Accurately replicating this molecule when it is coiled and packed inside the cell is no small achievement.

Figure 8.3A illustrates binary fission in a prokaryote. ❶ As the chromosome is duplicating, one copy moves toward the opposite end of the cell. ❷ Meanwhile, as chromosome duplication progresses, the cell elongates. ❸ When chromosome duplication is complete and the bacterium has reached about twice its initial size, the plasma membrane grows inward, dividing the parent cell into two daughter cells. **Figure 8.3B** is an electron micrograph of a dividing bacterium at a stage similar to step 3 in Figure 8.3A.

? Why is binary fission classified as asexual reproduction?

■ Because the genetically identical offspring inherit their DNA from a single parent

8.4 The large, complex chromosomes of eukaryotes duplicate with each cell division

Eukaryotic cells are more complex and generally much larger than prokaryotic cells, and they have many more genes. Human cells, for example, carry about 25,000 genes, versus about 3,000 for a typical bacterium. Almost all the genes in the cells of humans, and in all other eukaryotes, are found in the cell nucleus, grouped into multiple chromosomes. (The exceptions include genes on the small DNA molecules of mitochondria and, in plants, of chloroplasts.)

Most of the time, chromosomes exist as a diffuse mass of long, thin fibers. This material, called **chromatin,** is a combination of DNA and protein molecules. As a cell prepares to divide, its chromatin coils up, forming compact, distinct chromosomes. In this state, the chromosomes become visible under the light microscope. Figure 8.4A is a micrograph of a plant cell that is about to divide; each dark thread is an individual chromosome. In fact, chromosomes (from the Greek *chromo,* colored, and *somes,* bodies) get their name from the fact that they are colored by certain stains used in microscopy.

Like a prokaryotic chromosome, each eukaryotic chromosome contains one long DNA molecule bearing hundreds or thousands of genes and, attached to the DNA, a number of protein molecules. However, the eukaryotic chromosome has a much more complex structure than the prokaryotic chromosome. The eukaryotic chromosome includes many more protein molecules, which help maintain the chromosome structure and control the activity of its genes. The number of chromosomes in a eukaryotic cell depends on the species. For example, human body cells generally have 46 chromosomes, while the body cells of a dog have 78.

Well before a eukaryotic cell begins to divide, it duplicates all of its chromosomes. The DNA molecule of each chromosome

Sister chromatids

Centromere

Chromosome duplication

Sister chromatids

Chromosome distribution to daughter cells

TEM 36,600×

Figure 8.4B Electron micrograph of a duplicated chromosome

Figure 8.4C Chromosome duplication and distribution

is copied, and new protein molecules attach as needed. The result is that each chromosome now consists of two copies called **sister chromatids,** which contain identical copies of the DNA molecule. Figure 8.4B is an electron micrograph of a human chromosome that has duplicated. The two chromatids are joined together especially tightly at a narrow "waist" called the **centromere.** The fuzzy appearance of the chromosome comes from the intricate twists and folds of its two chromatin fibers.

Figure 8.4C is a simple diagram making the point that when the cell divides, the sister chromatids of a duplicated chromosome separate from each other. Once separated from its sister, each chromatid is called a chromosome, and it is identical to the chromosome the cell started with. One of the new chromosomes goes to one daughter cell, and the other goes to the other daughter cell. In this way, each daughter cell receives a complete and identical set of chromosomes. In humans, for example, a typical dividing cell has 46 duplicated chromosomes (or 92 chromatids), and each of the two daughter cells that results from it has 46 single chromosomes.

? When does a chromosome consist of two identical chromatids?

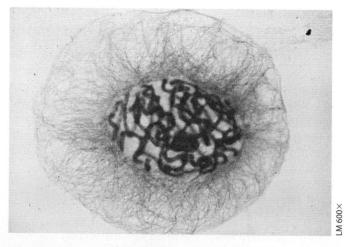

LM 600×

Figure 8.4A A plant cell (from an African blood lily) just before division

■ When the cell is preparing to divide and has duplicated its chromosomes, but before the duplicates actually separate

The cell cycle multiplies cells

How do chromosome duplication and cell division fit into the life of a cell—and the life of an organism? As you already know, cell division is essential to life. Cell division is the basis of reproduction for every organism. It enables a multicellular organism to grow to adult size. It also replaces worn-out or damaged cells, keeping the total cell number in a mature individual relatively constant. In your own body, for example, millions of cells must divide every second to maintain the total number of about 100 trillion cells. Some cells divide once a day, others less often, and highly specialized cells, such as our mature muscle cells, not at all.

The process of cell division is a key component of the **cell cycle,** an ordered sequence of events that extends from the time a cell is first formed from a dividing parent cell until its own division into two cells. The cell cycle consists of two broad stages: a growing stage (called interphase), during which the cell roughly doubles everything in its cytoplasm and precisely replicates its chromosomal DNA, and the actual cell division (called the mitotic phase).

As Figure 8.5 indicates, most of the cell cycle is spent in **interphase.** This is a time when a cell's metabolic activity is very high and the cell performs its various functions within the organism. Moreover, a cell in interphase increases its supply of proteins, creates more cytoplasmic organelles (such as mitochondria and ribosomes), and grows in size. Additionally, the chromosomes duplicate during this period. Typically, interphase lasts for at least 90% of the total time required for the cell cycle.

Interphase can be divided into three subphases: the G_1 phase ("first gap"), the S phase, and the G_2 phase ("second gap"). During all three subphases, the cell grows. However, chromosomes are duplicated only during the S phase. S stands for synthesis of DNA—also known as DNA replication—a process that will be discussed in Chapter 10. At the beginning of the S phase, each chromosome is single. At the end of this phase, after DNA replication, the chromosomes are double, each consisting of two sister chromatids. To summarize interphase, a cell grows (G_1), continues to grow as it copies its chromosomes (S), and then grows more as it completes preparations for cell division (G_2).

The **mitotic phase (M phase),** the part of the cell cycle when the cell actually divides, accounts for only about 10% of the total time required for the cell cycle. The mitotic phase is divided into two stages, called mitosis and cytokinesis, although the second stage begins before the first one ends. In **mitosis** (light yellow area in the figure), the nucleus and its contents, including the duplicated chromosomes, divide and are evenly distributed to form two daughter nuclei. During **cytokinesis,** the cytoplasm is divided in two. The combina-

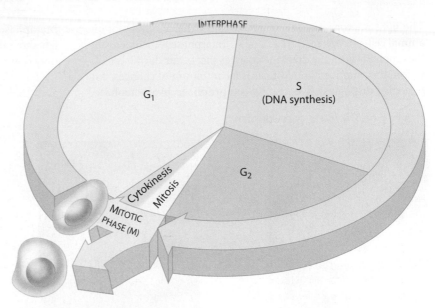

Figure 8.5 The eukaryotic cell cycle

tion of mitosis and cytokinesis produces two genetically identical daughter cells, each with a single nucleus, surrounding cytoplasm, and plasma membrane. Each newly produced daughter cell may then proceed through G_1 and repeat the cycle.

Mitosis is unique to eukaryotes and may be an evolutionary solution to the problem of allocating identical copies of a large amount of genetic material in a number of separate chromosomes to two daughter cells. Mitosis is a remarkably accurate mechanism. Experiments with yeast, for example, indicate that an error in chromosome distribution occurs only once in about 100,000 cell divisions.

A living cell viewed through a light microscope undergoes dramatic changes in appearance during the mitotic phase. During interphase, the cell's individual chromosomes are not distinguishable because they are in the form of loosely packed chromatin fibers. With the onset of mitosis, however, striking changes are visible in the chromosomes and other structures, as we see in the next module.

BioFlix *Mitosis*

MP3 Tutor *Mitosis*

Web Activity *The Cell Cycle*

? A researcher treats cells with a chemical that prevents DNA synthesis from starting. This treatment would trap the cells in which part of the cell cycle?

G_1

Cell division is a continuum of dynamic changes

The light micrographs in **Figure 8.6** show the cell cycle for an animal cell—in this case, from a newt. Interphase is included, but the emphasis is on the dramatic changes that occur during cell division, the mitotic phase. Mitosis is a continuum of changes, but biologists distinguish five main stages: **prophase, prometaphase,** **metaphase, anaphase,** and **telophase.** The drawings in Figure 8.6 show details not visible in the micrographs. For simplicity, only four chromosomes are drawn.

The chromosomes are the stars of the mitotic drama, and their movements depend on the **mitotic spindle,** a

Figure 8.6   The stages of cell division

Interphase Interphase is the period of cell growth when the cell synthesizes new molecules and organelles. At the point shown here, late interphase (G₂), the cell looks much the same as it does throughout interphase. Nonetheless, by the G_2 stage the cell has doubled much of its earlier contents and the cytoplasm contains two centrosomes. Within the nucleus, the chromosomes are duplicated, but they cannot be distinguished individually because they are still in the form of loosely packed chromatin. The nucleus also contains one or more nucleoli, an indication that the cell is actively making proteins. Nucleoli are where the parts of ribosomes are assembled before export to the cytoplasm (see Chapter 10).

Prophase During prophase, changes occur in both the nucleus and the cytoplasm. Within the nucleus, the chromatin fibers become more tightly coiled and folded, forming discrete chromosomes that can be seen with the light microscope. The nucleoli disappear. Each duplicated chromosome appears as two identical sister chromatids joined together, with a narrow "waist" at the centromere. In the cytoplasm, the mitotic spindle begins to form as microtubules rapidly grow out from the centrosomes, which begin to move away from each other.

Prometaphase The nuclear envelope breaks into fragments and disappears. Microtubules emerging from the centrosomes at the poles (ends) of the spindle reach the chromosomes, now highly condensed. At the centromere region, each sister chromatid has a protein structure called a kinetochore (shown as a black dot). Some of the spindle microtubules attach to the kinetochores, throwing the chromosomes into agitated motion. Other spindle microtubules make contact with microtubules coming from the opposite pole. Forces exerted by protein "motors" associated with spindle microtubules move the chromosomes toward the center of the cell.

football-shaped structure of microtubules that guides the separation of the two sets of daughter chromosomes. The spindle microtubules emerge from two **centrosomes,** clouds of cytoplasmic material that in animal cells contain centrioles (see Figure 4.4A). (Centrosomes are also known as *microtubule-organizing centers,* a term describing their function.) The role of centrioles in cell division is a mystery; destroying them experimentally does not interfere with normal spindle formation, and plant cells lack them entirely.

Web Process of Science *How Much Time Do Cells Spend in Each Phase of Mitosis?*

? An organism called a plasmodial slime mold is one large cytoplasmic mass with many nuclei. Explain how such a "megacell" could form.

■ Mitosis occurs repeatedly without cytokinesis.

METAPHASE

ANAPHASE

TELOPHASE AND CYTOKINESIS

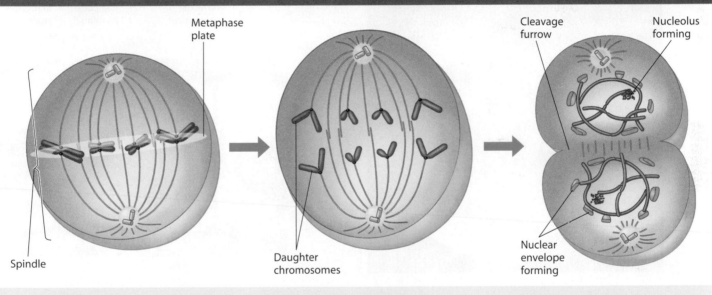

Metaphase plate

Spindle

Daughter chromosomes

Cleavage furrow

Nucleolus forming

Nuclear envelope forming

Metaphase At metaphase, the mitotic spindle is fully formed, with its poles at opposite ends of the cell. The chromosomes convene on the metaphase plate, an imaginary plane equidistant between the two poles of the spindle. The centromeres of all the chromosomes are lined up on the metaphase plate. For each chromosome, the kinetochores of the two sister chromatids face opposite poles of the spindle. The microtubules attached to a particular chromatid all come from one pole of the spindle, and those attached to its sister chromatid come from the opposite pole.

Anaphase Anaphase begins when the two centromeres of each chromosome come apart, separating the sister chromatids. Once separate, each sister chromatid is considered a full-fledged (daughter) chromosome. Motor proteins of the kinetochores, powered by ATP, "walk" the daughter chromosomes centromere-first along the microtubules toward opposite poles of the cell. As this happens, the spindle microtubules attached to the kinetochores shorten. However, the spindle microtubules not attached to chromosomes lengthen. The poles are moved farther apart, elongating the cell. Anaphase is over when equivalent—and complete—collections of chromosomes have reached the two poles of the cell.

Telophase Telophase is roughly the reverse of prophase. The cell elongation that started in anaphase continues. Daughter nuclei appear at the two poles of the cell as nuclear envelopes form around the chromosomes. Meanwhile, the chromatin fiber of each chromosome uncoils, and nucleoli reappear. At the end of telophase, the mitotic spindle disappears. Mitosis, the equal division of one nucleus into two genetically identical daughter nuclei, is now finished.

Cytokinesis Cytokinesis, the division of the cytoplasm, usually occurs along with telophase, with two daughter cells completely separating soon after the end of mitosis. In animal cells, cytokinesis involves a cleavage furrow, which pinches the cell in two.

Cytokinesis, or division of one cell into two, typically begins during telophase, although it may begin in late anaphase. In animal cells, cytokinesis occurs by a process known as cleavage. As shown in **Figure 8.7A**, the first sign of cleavage is the appearance of a **cleavage furrow,** a shallow groove in the cell surface. At the site of the furrow, the cytoplasm has a ring of microfilaments made of actin, associated with molecules of the protein myosin. (Actin and myosin are the same proteins responsible for muscle contraction—see Module 30.8.) When the actin microfilaments interact with the myosin, the ring contracts, like the pulling of drawstrings. The cleavage furrow deepens and eventually pinches the parent cell in two, producing two completely separate cells, each with its own nucleus and share of cytoplasm.

Cytokinesis is markedly different in plant cells, which possess cell walls **(Figure 8.7B)**. During telophase, vesicles containing cell wall material (tan in figure) collect at the middle of the parent cell. The vesicles fuse, forming a membranous **cell plate.** The cell plate grows outward, accumulating more cell wall materials as more vesicles fuse with it. Eventually, the outer edges of the cell plate fuse with the plasma membrane, and the cell plate's contents join the parental cell wall. The result is two daughter cells, each bounded by its own plasma membrane and cell wall.

Web Activity *Mitosis and Cytokinesis Video*

? Contrast cytokinesis in animals with cytokinesis in plants.

■ In animals, cytokinesis involves a cleavage furrow in which contracting microfilaments pinch the cell in two. In plants, it involves formation of a cell plate, a fusion of vesicles that forms new membrane and walls between the cells.

Cleavage furrow

SEM 140×

Wall of parent cell   Cell plate forming   Daughter nucleus

LM 1,050×

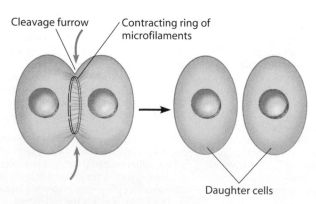

Cleavage furrow   Contracting ring of microfilaments

Daughter cells

Figure 8.7A   Cleavage of an animal cell

Cell wall   New cell wall

Vesicles containing cell wall material   Cell plate   Daughter cells

Figure 8.7B   Cell plate formation in a plant cell

Anchorage, cell density, and chemical growth factors affect cell division

For a plant or an animal to grow and develop normally and to maintain its tissues once full grown, it must be able to control the timing of cell division in different parts of its body. For example, in the adult human, skin cells and the cells lining the digestive tract divide frequently throughout life, replacing cells that are constantly being abraded and sloughed off. In contrast, cells in the human liver usually do not divide unless the liver is damaged. Cell division in this case repairs wounds.

By growing animal cells in culture, researchers have been able to identify many factors, both physical and chemical, that can influence cell division. For example, cells fail to divide if an essential nutrient is left out of the culture medium. And most types of mammalian cells divide in culture only if certain specific growth factors are included. A **growth factor** is a protein secreted by certain body cells that stimulates other cells to divide (Figure 8.8A). Researchers have discovered at least 50 different growth factors that can trigger cell division. Different cell types respond specifically to certain growth factors or a combination of growth factors. For example, injury to the skin causes blood platelets to release a protein called platelet-derived growth factor. This protein promotes the rapid growth of connective tissue cells that help seal the wound.

The effect of a physical factor on cell division is clearly seen in **density-dependent inhibition,** a phenomenon in which crowded cells stop dividing. For example, animal cells growing on the surface of a dish multiply to form a single layer and usually stop dividing when they touch one another (Figure 8.8B). If some cells are removed, those bordering the open space begin dividing again and continue until the vacancy is filled. What actually causes the cessation of growth? Studies of cultured cells suggest that physical contact of cell-surface proteins between adjacent cells is responsible for inhibiting cell division.

Most animal cells also exhibit **anchorage dependence;** they must be in contact with a solid surface—such as the inside of a culture dish or the extracellular matrix of a tissue—to divide. But density-dependent inhibition mediated by the availability of growth factors is probably the most important regulatory mechanism controlling the division of the body's cells. How exactly do growth factors work? We pursue answers to this question in the next module.

? Compared to a control culture, the cells in an experimental culture are fewer but much larger when they cover the dish surface and stop growing. What is a reasonable hypothesis for this difference?

■ The experimental culture is deficient in one or more growth factors.

Figure 8.8A An experiment demonstrating the effect of growth factors on the division of cultured animal cells

Culture of cells

Addition of growth factor

Cells anchor to dish surface and divide.

When cells have formed a complete single layer, they stop dividing (density-dependent inhibition).

If some cells are scraped away, the remaining cells divide to fill the dish with a single layer and then stop (density-dependent inhibition).

Figure 8.8B An experiment demonstrating density-dependent inhibition, using animal cells grown in culture

8.9 Growth factors signal the cell cycle control system

In a living animal, most cells are anchored in a fixed position and bathed in a solution of nutrients supplied by the blood, yet they usually do not divide unless they are signaled by other cells to do so. Growth factors are the main signals, and their role in promoting cell division leads us back to our earlier discussion of the cell cycle.

The sequential events of the cell cycle, represented by the circle of flat blocks in **Figure 8.9A**, are directed by a distinct cell cycle control system, represented by the knob in the center. Analogous to the control device of an automatic washing machine, the **cell cycle control system** is a cyclically operating set of molecules in the cell that both triggers and coordinates key events in the cell cycle. The cell cycle is *not* like a row of falling dominoes, with each event causing the next one in line. Within the M phase, for example, metaphase does not automatically lead to anaphase. Instead, proteins of the cell cycle control system must trigger the separation of sister chromatids that marks the start of anaphase.

A checkpoint in the cell cycle is a critical control point where stop and go-ahead signals can regulate the cycle. (The signals are transmitted within the cell by signal transduction pathways—see Figure 5.1C.) Animal cells generally have built-in stop signals that halt the cell cycle at checkpoints until overridden by go-ahead signals.

The red barriers in Figure 8.9A represent three major checkpoints in the cell cycle: during the G_1 and G_2 subphases of interphase and in the M phase. Intracellular signals detected by the control system tell it whether key cellular processes up to each point have been completed and thus whether or not the cell cycle should proceed past that point. The control system also receives messages from outside the cell, indicating both general environmental conditions and the presence of specific signal molecules from other cells. When the cell cycle control system gets a go-ahead signal at the G_1 checkpoint, for example, the cell soon enters the S phase of the cell cycle.

For many cells, the G_1 checkpoint seems to be the most important. If a cell receives a go-ahead signal—for example, from a growth factor—at the G_1 checkpoint, it will usually complete its cycle and divide. But if it does not receive a go-ahead signal at G_1, it will exit the cell cycle, switching into a nondividing state called the G_0 phase. For instance, nondividing nerve cells and muscle cells in your body are in the G_0 phase.

Figure 8.9B shows a simplified model for how a growth factor might affect the cell cycle control system at the G_1 checkpoint. A cell that responds to a growth factor (▼) has molecules of a specific receptor protein in its plasma membrane. Binding of the growth factor to the receptor triggers a signal transduction pathway in the cell, a pathway that in this case leads to cell division. The "signals" are changes that a molecule induces in the next molecule in the pathway. Via a series of relay molecules, a signal finally reaches the cell cycle control system and overrides the brakes that otherwise prevent progress of the cell cycle. In Figure 8.9B, the cell cycle is set off from the cell in a separate diagram because, unlike the components of the timer in a washing machine, the proteins making up the control system in the cell are not actually located together in one place.

Research on the control of the cell cycle is one of the hottest areas in biology today. This research is leading to a better understanding of cancer, which we discuss next.

? At which of the three checkpoints described in this module do the chromosomes exist as duplicated sister chromatids?

■ G_2 and M

Figure 8.9A Mechanical model for the cell cycle control system

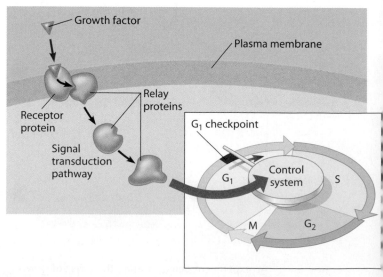

Figure 8.9B How a growth factor signals the cell cycle control system

8.10 Growing out of control, cancer cells produce malignant tumors

Cancer, which currently claims the lives of one out of every five people in the United States and other developed nations, is a disease of the cell cycle. Cancer cells do not respond normally to the cell cycle control system; they divide excessively and can invade other tissues of the body. If unchecked, cancer cells may continue to grow until they kill the organism.

The abnormal behavior of cancer cells begins when a single cell undergoes transformation, a process that converts a normal cell to a cancer cell. The body's immune system normally recognizes a transformed cell as abnormal and destroys it. However, if the cell evades destruction, it may proliferate to form a **tumor,** an abnormally growing mass of body cells. If the abnormal cells remain at the original site, the lump is called a **benign tumor.** Benign tumors can cause problems if they grow in and disrupt certain organs, such as the brain, but often they can be completely removed by surgery.

In contrast, a **malignant tumor** can spread into neighboring tissues and other parts of the body, displacing normal tissue and interrupting organ function as it goes (Figure 8.10). Cancer cells may separate from the original tumor or secrete signal molecules that cause blood vessels to grow toward the tumor. A few tumor cells may then enter the blood and lymph vessels of the circulatory system and move to other parts of the body, where they may proliferate and form new tumors. This spread of cancer cells via the circulatory system beyond their original site is called **metastasis.** An individual with a malignant tumor is said to have cancer.

Cancers are named according to the organ or tissue in which they originate. Liver cancer, for example, starts in liver tissue and may or may not spread from there. Based on their site of origin, cancers are grouped into four categories. **Carcinomas** are cancers that originate in the external or internal coverings of the body, such as the skin or the lining of the intestine. **Sarcomas** arise in tissues that support the body, such as bone and muscle. Cancers of blood-forming tissues, such as bone marrow, spleen, and lymph nodes, are called **leukemias** and **lymphomas.**

From studying cancer cells in culture, researchers have learned that these cells do not heed the normal signals that regulate the cell cycle. For example, cancer cells do not exhibit density-dependent inhibition; they continue to divide even at high densities, piling up on one another. Many cancer cells have defective cell cycle control systems that proceed past checkpoints even in the absence of growth factors. Other cancer cells themselves synthesize growth factors that make them divide continuously. If cancer cells do stop dividing, they seem to do so at random points in the cell cycle, rather than at the normal cell cycle checkpoints. Moreover, in culture, cancer

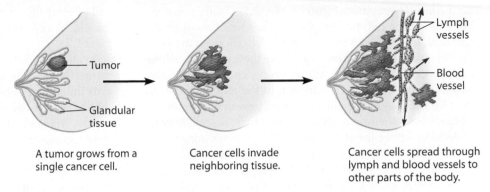

A tumor grows from a single cancer cell.

Cancer cells invade neighboring tissue.

Cancer cells spread through lymph and blood vessels to other parts of the body.

Figure 8.10   Growth and metastasis of a malignant (cancerous) tumor of the breast

cells are "immortal"; they can go on dividing indefinitely, as long as they have a supply of nutrients (whereas normal mammalian cells divide only about 20 to 50 times before they stop).

Luckily, many tumors can be successfully treated. A tumor that appears to be localized may be removed surgically. Alternatively, it can be treated with high-energy radiation, which damages DNA in cancer cells much more than it does in normal cells, apparently because cancer cells have lost the ability to repair such damage. However, there is sometimes enough damage to normal body cells to produce bad side effects. For example, radiation damage to cells of the ovaries or testes can lead to sterility.

To treat widespread or metastatic tumors, chemotherapy is used. During periodic chemotherapy treatments, drugs are administered that disrupt specific steps in the cell cycle. For example, the drug paclitaxel (trade name Taxol) "freezes" the mitotic spindle, which stops actively dividing cells from proceeding past metaphase. (Interestingly, Taxol was originally discovered in the bark of the Pacific yew tree, found mainly in the northwestern United States.) Vinblastin, a chemotherapeutic drug first obtained from the periwinkle plant (found in the rain forests of Madagascar), prevents the spindle from forming in the first place.

The side effects of chemotherapy are due to the drugs' effects on normal cells that rapidly divide. For example, nausea results from chemotherapy's effects on intestinal cells, hair loss from effects on hair follicle cells, and susceptibility to infection from effects on immune cell production.

We will return to the topic of cancer in Chapter 11, after studying the structure and function of genes. We will see that cancer results from changes in genes for proteins that control cell division.

?   What is metastasis?

■ Metastasis is the spread of cancer cells via the circulatory system from their original site of formation to sites in the body.

8.11 Review: Mitosis provides for growth, cell replacement, and asexual reproduction

The three micrographs in Figures 8.11A–8.11C summarize the roles that mitotic cell division plays in the lives of multicellular organisms. Figure 8.11A shows some of the cells from the tip of a rapidly growing onion plant root. Notice the several cells whose nuclei are in various stages of mitosis (as evidenced by the visibly compact chromosomes). Cell division in the root tip produces new cells, which elongate and bring about growth of the root.

Figure 8.11B shows a dividing bone marrow cell. Mitotic cell division within the red marrow of your body's bones (particularly within your ribs, vertebrae, breastbone, and pelvis) continuously creates new blood cells that replace older ones. Similar processes replace cells throughout your body. For example, dividing cells within your epidermis continuously replace dead cells that slough off the surface of your skin.

Figure 8.11C is a micrograph of a hydra, a common inhabitant of freshwater lakes. A hydra is a tiny multicellular animal that reproduces by either sexual or asexual means. This individual is reproducing asexually by budding. A bud starts out as a mass of mitotically dividing cells growing on the side of the parent. The bud develops into a small hydra like the one in the photo here. Eventually, the offspring detaches from the parent

and takes up life on its own. The offspring is literally a "chip off the old block," being genetically identical to (a clone of) its parent.

In all three of these cases—the growing onion root, replacement of blood cells, and budding hydra—the new cells have exactly the same number and types of chromosomes as the parent cells because of the way duplicated chromosomes divide during mitosis. Mitosis makes it possible for organisms to grow, regenerate and repair tissues, and reproduce asexually by producing cells that carry the same genes as the parent cells.

If we examine the cells of any individual organism, we see that almost all of them contain the same number and types of chromosomes. Likewise, if we examine cells from different individuals of any one species, we see that they have the same number and types of chromosomes. In the next module, we take a closer look at how chromosomes are organized in cells.

> **?** If a human skin cell with 46 chromosomes divides by mitosis, each daughter cell will have ___ chromosomes.
>
> 46 ■

Figure 8.11A   Growth (in an onion root)

LM 500×

Figure 8.11B   Cell replacement (in bone marrow)

LM 700×

Figure 8.11C   Asexual reproduction (of a hydra)

LM 20×

Meiosis and Crossing Over

8.12 Chromosomes are matched in homologous pairs

In humans, a typical body cell, called a **somatic cell,** has 46 chromosomes. If we use a microscope to examine human chromosomes in metaphase of mitosis, we see that each chromosome (consisting of two sister chromatids) has a twin chromosome that is identical in length and centromere position. Figure 8.12 (at the top of the next page) illustrates one pair of metaphase chromosomes. Altogether, the cell contains 23 such matched pairs of duplicated chromosomes. Other species have

different numbers of chromosomes, but these too usually occur in matched pairs. Moreover, when treated with special dyes, the chromosomes of a pair display matching staining patterns (represented by colored stripes in Figure 8.12). Notice that each chromosome consists of two sister chromatids joined at the centromere. The two chromosomes composing a pair are called **homologous chromosomes** (or homologs) because they both carry genes controlling the same inherited characteristics. For

Homologous pair of chromosomes

Centromere

Sister chromatids

One duplicated chromosome

Figure 8.12
A homologous pair of chromosomes

example, if a gene that determines whether a person has freckles is located at a particular place, or **locus** (plural, *loci*), on one chromosome—within the narrow orange band in our drawing, for instance—then the other chromosome of the homologous pair also has a gene for freckles at that locus. (However, the two homologs may have different versions of the freckles gene, perhaps one that promotes freckles and one that does not.)

The two distinct chromosomes called X and Y are an important exception to the general pattern of homologous chromosomes. Human females have a homologous pair of X chromosomes (XX), but males have one X and one Y chromosome (XY). Only small parts of the X and Y are homologous; most of the genes carried on the X chromosome do not have counterparts on the tiny Y, and the Y chromosome has genes lacking on the X. Because they determine an individual's sex, the X and Y chromosomes are called **sex chromosomes** (although they carry genes that perform other functions as well). The other 22 pairs of chromosomes are called **autosomes.**

For both autosomes and sex chromosomes, we inherit one chromosome of each pair from our mother and the other from our father, as discussed in the next module.

? What is the explanation for our having two of each type of chromosome?

■ We inherit one of each kind from each parent.

8.13 Gametes have a single set of chromosomes

Having two sets of chromosomes, one inherited from each parent, is a key factor in the human life cycle (outlined in Figure 8.13) and in the life cycles of all other species that reproduce sexually. (We examine other life cycles in Unit IV.)

Any cell with two homologous sets of chromosomes is called a **diploid cell,** and the total number of chromosomes is called the diploid number (abbreviated $2n$). For humans, the diploid number is 46; that is, $2n = 46$. Humans are said to be diploid

organisms because almost all our cells are diploid. The exceptions are the egg and sperm cells, collectively known as **gametes.** Each gamete has a single set of chromosomes: 22 autosomes plus a single sex chromosome, either X or Y. A cell with a single chromosome set is called a **haploid cell.** For humans, the haploid number (abbreviated n) is 23; that is, $n = 23$.

In humans, sexual intercourse allows a haploid sperm cell from the father to reach and fuse with a haploid egg cell of the mother in the process of **fertilization.** The resulting fertilized egg, called a **zygote,** is diploid. It has two haploid sets of chromosomes: one set from the mother and a homologous set from the father. The life cycle is completed as a sexually mature adult develops from the zygote. Mitotic cell division ensures that all somatic cells of the human body receive copies of all of the zygote's 46 chromosomes.

All sexual life cycles, including our own, involve an alternation of diploid and haploid stages. Having haploid gametes keeps the chromosome number from doubling in each generation. Gametes are made by a special sort of cell division called meiosis, which occurs only in reproductive organs (ovaries and testes in animals). Whereas mitosis produces daughter cells with the same numbers of chromosomes as the parent cell, meiosis reduces the chromosome number by half. We turn to meiosis next.

Web Activity *Asexual and Sexual Life Cycles*

? Imagine you stain a human cell and view it under a microscope. You observe 23 chromosomes, including a Y chromosome. You could conclude that this must be a _____ cell taken from the organ called the _____.

■ sperm . . . testes

Haploid gametes ($n = 23$)

Egg cell

Sperm cell

Meiosis

Fertilization

Diploid zygote ($2n = 46$)

Multicellular diploid adults ($2n = 46$)

Mitosis and development

Figure 8.13 The human life cycle

8.14 Meiosis reduces the chromosome number from diploid to haploid

Meiosis is a type of cell division that produces haploid gametes in diploid organisms. Many of the stages of meiosis closely resemble corresponding stages in mitosis. Meiosis, like mitosis, is preceded by the duplication of chromosomes. However, this single duplication is followed by two consecutive cell divisions, called meiosis I and meiosis II. These

Figure 8.14 The stages of meiosis

MEIOSIS I: Homologous chromosomes separate

INTERPHASE | PROPHASE I | METAPHASE I | ANAPHASE I

Centrosomes (with centriole pairs)
Sites of crossing over
Spindle
Microtubules attached to kinetochore
Metaphase plate
Sister chromatids remain attached

Nuclear envelope
Chromatin
Sister chromatids
Tetrad
Centromere (with kinetochore)
Homologous chromosomes separate

Interphase
Like mitosis, meiosis is preceded by an interphase, during which the chromosomes duplicate. At the end of this interphase, each chromosome consists of two genetically identical sister chromatids attached together. But at this stage the chromosomes are not yet visible under the microscope except as a mass of chromatin. The cell's centrosome has also duplicated by the end of this interphase.

Prophase I
Prophase I is the most complex phase of meiosis and typically occupies over 90% of the time required for meiotic cell division. Early in this phase, the chromatin coils up, so that individual chromosomes become visible with the microscope. In a process called **synapsis**, homologous chromosomes, each composed of two sister chromatids, come together as pairs. The resulting structure, consisting of four chromatids, is called a tetrad. During synapsis, chromatids of homologous chromosomes exchange segments in a process called crossing over. Because the

versions of the genes on a chromosome (or one of its chromatids) may be different from those on its homologue, crossing over rearranges genetic information. As we will discuss in Module 8.18, the genetic shuffling produced by crossing over can make an important contribution to the genetic variability resulting from sexual reproduction.

As prophase I continues, the chromosomes condense further as the nucleoli disappear. Now the centrosomes move away from each other, and a spindle starts to form between them. The nuclear envelope breaks into fragments, and the chromosome tetrads, captured by spindle microtubules, are moved toward the center of the cell.

Metaphase I
At metaphase I, the chromosome tetrads are aligned on the metaphase plate, midway between the two poles of the spindle. Each chromosome is condensed and thick, with its sister chromatids still attached at their centromeres. Spindle microtubules are attached to kinetochores at the centromeres. In each tetrad, the homologous chromosomes are

held together at sites of crossing over. Notice that, for each tetrad, the spindle microtubules attached to one of the homologous chromosomes come from one pole of the cell, and the microtubules attached to the other homologous chromosome come from the opposite pole. With this arrangement, the homologous chromosomes of each tetrad are poised to move toward opposite poles of the cell.

Anaphase I
Like anaphase of mitosis, anaphase I of meiosis is marked by the migration of chromosomes toward the two poles of the cell. In contrast to mitosis, however, the sister chromatids making up each doubled chromosome remain attached at their centromeres. Only the tetrads (pairs of homologous chromosomes) split up. Thus, in the drawing you see three still-doubled chromosomes (the haploid number) moving toward each spindle pole. If this were anaphase of mitosis, you would see six daughter chromosomes moving toward each pole.

divisions result in four daughter cells (rather than the two daughter cells of mitosis), each with a single haploid set of chromosomes. Thus, meiosis produces daughter cells with only half as many chromosomes as the parent cell. The drawings in **Figure 8.14** show the two meiotic divisions for an animal cell with a diploid number of 6.

🅱️ BioFlix *Meiosis*

🎧 MP3 Tutor *Meiosis*

❓ A cell has the haploid number of chromosomes, but each chromosome has two chromatids. The chromosomes are arranged at the center of the spindle. What is the meiotic stage?

■ Metaphase II

| TELOPHASE I AND CYTOKINESIS | PROPHASE II | METAPHASE II | ANAPHASE II | TELOPHASE II AND CYTOKINESIS |

MEIOSIS II: Sister chromatids separate

Cleavage furrow

Sister chromatids separate

Haploid daughter cells forming

Telophase I and Cytokinesis

In telophase I, the chromosomes arrive at the poles of the cell. When the chromosomes finish their journey, each pole of the cell has a haploid chromosome set, although each chromosome is still in duplicate form at this point. In other words, each chromosome still consists of two sister chromatids. Usually, cytokinesis occurs along with telophase I, and two haploid daughter cells are formed.

Following telophase I in some organisms, the chromosomes uncoil and the nuclear envelope re-forms, and there is an interphase before meiosis II begins. In other species, daughter cells produced in the first meiotic division immediately begin preparation for the second meiotic division. In either case, no chromosome duplication occurs between telophase I and the onset of meiosis II.

Meiosis II

In organisms having an interphase after meiosis I, the chromosomes condense again and the nuclear envelope breaks down during prophase II. In any case, meiosis II is essentially the same as mitosis. The important difference is that meiosis II starts with a haploid cell.

During prophase II, a spindle forms and moves the chromosomes toward the middle of the cell. During metaphase II, the chromosomes are aligned on the metaphase plate as they are in mitosis, with the kinetochores of the sister chromatids of each chromosome pointing toward opposite poles. In anaphase II, the centromeres of sister chromatids finally separate, and the sister chromatids of each pair, now individual daughter chromosomes, move toward opposite poles of the cell. In telophase II, nuclei form at the cell poles, and cytokinesis occurs at the same time. There are now four daughter cells, each with the haploid number of (single) chromosomes.

8.15 Mitosis and meiosis have important similarities and differences

We have now described the two ways that cells of eukaryotic organisms divide. Mitosis, which provides for growth, tissue repair, and asexual reproduction, produces daughter cells genetically identical to the parent cell. Meiosis, needed for sexual reproduction, yields haploid daughter cells—cells with one member of each homologous chromosome pair.

For both mitosis and meiosis, the chromosomes duplicate only once, in the preceding interphase. Mitosis involves one division of the nucleus, and it is usually accompanied by cytokinesis, producing two identical cells. Meiosis entails two nuclear and cytoplasmic divisions, yielding four haploid cells.

Figure 8.15 compares mitosis and meiosis, tracing these two processes for a diploid parent cell with four chromosomes. Homologous chromosomes are those matching in size.

All the events unique to meiosis occur during meiosis I. In prophase I, duplicated homologous chromosomes pair to form **tetrads,** four chromatids, with each pair of sister chromatids joined at their centromeres. Crossing over occurs between homologous (nonsister) chromatids. In metaphase I, tetrads (not individual chromosomes) are aligned at the metaphase plate. During anaphase I, homologous pairs of chromosomes separate, but the sister chromatids of each chromosome stay together. At the end of meiosis I, there are two haploid cells, but each chromosome still has two sister chromatids.

Meiosis II is virtually identical to mitosis and separates sister chromatids. But unlike mitosis, each daughter cell produced by meiosis II has only a *haploid* set of chromosomes.

🎧 **MP3 Tutor** *Mitosis–Meiosis Comparison*

❓ Explain how mitosis conserves chromosome number while meiosis reduces the number from diploid to haploid.

■ In mitosis, the duplication of chromosomes is followed by one division of the cell. In meiosis, homologous chromosomes separate in the first of two cell divisions; after the second division, each new cell ends up with just a single haploid set.

Figure 8.15 Comparison of mitosis and meiosis

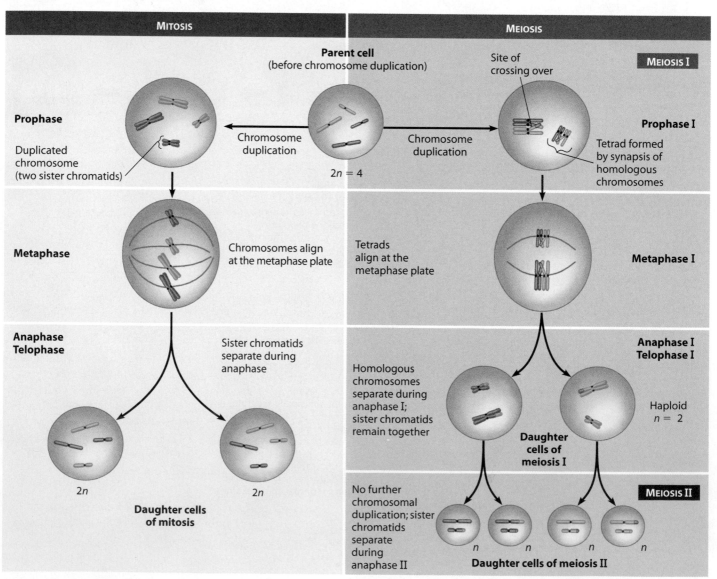

Independent orientation of chromosomes in meiosis and random fertilization lead to varied offspring

As we discussed in Module 8.1, offspring that result from sexual reproduction are highly varied; they are genetically different from their parents and from one another. How do we account for this genetic variation? As you will learn in later chapters, mutations are the original source of genetic diversity: Changes in an organism's DNA create different versions of genes. Once these differences arise, reshuffling of the different versions during sexual reproduction produces genetic variation. When we discuss natural selection and evolution in Unit III, we will see that this genetic variety in offspring is the raw material for natural selection.

Figure 8.16 illustrates one way in which the process of meiosis contributes to genetic differences in gametes. The

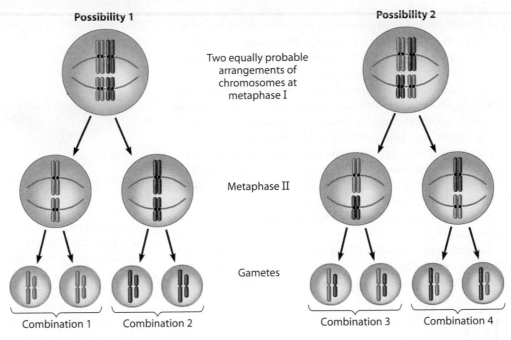

Figure 8.16 Results of the independent orientation of chromosomes at metaphase I

figure shows how the arrangement of homologous chromosome pairs at metaphase of meiosis I affects the resulting gametes. Here we use color to distinguish chromosomes that originated from the organism's two parents (red for maternal and blue for paternal). The colors highlight the important fact that each maternal chromosome differs genetically from its paternal homolog. In fact, each chromosome you received from your mother carries many genes that are different versions from those on the homologous chromosome you received from your father.

The orientation of the homologous pairs of chromosomes (tetrads) at metaphase I—whether the maternal or paternal chromosome is closer to a given pole—is as random as the flip of a coin. Thus, there is a 50% chance that a particular daughter cell will get the maternal (red) chromosome of a certain homologous pair and a 50% chance that it will receive the paternal (blue) chromosome. In this example, there are two possible ways that the two tetrads can align during metaphase I. In possibility 1, the tetrads are oriented with both red chromosomes on the same side of the metaphase plate. Therefore, the gametes produced in possibility 1 can each have only red *or* blue chromosomes (bottom row, combinations 1 and 2).

In possibility 2, the tetrads are oriented differently, with one red and one blue chromosome on each side of the metaphase I plate. This arrangement produces gametes that each have one red and one blue chromosome. Furthermore, half the gametes have a big blue chromosome and a small red one (combination 3), and half have a big red one and a small blue one (combination 4).

So we see that for this example, a total of four chromosome combinations is possible in the gametes, and in fact the organism will produce gametes of all four types in roughly equal quantities. For a species with more than two pairs of chromosomes, such as the human, *all* the chromosome pairs orient independently at metaphase I. (Chromosomes X and Y behave as a homologous pair in meiosis.)

For any species, the total number of combinations of chromosomes that meiosis can package into gametes is 2^n, where n is the haploid number. For the organism in this figure, $n = 2$, so the number of chromosome combinations is 2^2, or 4. For a human ($n = 23$), there are 2^{23}, or about 8 million possible chromosome combinations! This means that each gamete you produce contains one of roughly 8 million possible combinations of chromosomes inherited from your mother and father.

How many possibilities are there when a gamete from one individual unites with a gamete from another individual in fertilization? In humans, the random fusion of a single sperm with a single ovum during fertilization will produce a zygote with any of about 64 trillion (8 million × 8 million) combinations of chromosomes! While the random nature of fertilization adds a huge amount of potential variability to the offspring of sexual reproduction, there is in fact even more variety created during meiosis, as we see in the next two modules.

? A particular species of worm has a diploid number of 10. How many chromosomal combinations are possible for gametes formed by meiosis?

■ 32; 2n = 10, so n = 5 and 2^n = 32

8.17 Homologous chromosomes can carry different versions of genes

So far, we have focused on genetic variability in gametes and zygotes at the whole-chromosome level. We have yet to discuss the actual genetic information—the genes—contained in the chromosomes of gametes and zygotes. The question we need to answer now is this: What is the significance of the independent orientation of metaphase chromosomes at the level of genes?

Let's take a simple example, the single tetrad in Figure 8.17A. The letters on the homologous chromosomes represent genes. Recall that homologous chromosomes have genes for the same characteristic at corresponding loci. Our example involves hypothetical genes controlling the appearance of mice. *C* and *c* are different versions of a gene for one characteristic, coat color; *E* and *e* are different versions of a gene for another characteristic, eye color. (As you'll learn in later chapters, different versions of a gene contain slightly different nucleotide sequences in the chromosomal DNA.)

Let's say that *C* represents the gene for the brownish color of the mouse on the left in Figure 8.17B and that *c* represents the gene for white coat color (mouse on right). In the chromosome

Brown coat (*C*); black eyes (*E*)

White coat (*c*); pink eyes (*e*)

Figure 8.17B   Coat-color and eye-color traits in mice

diagram, notice that *C* is at the same locus on the red homolog as *c* is on the blue one. Likewise, gene *E* (for black eyes) is at the same locus as *e* (pink eyes).

The fact that homologous chromosomes can bear two different kinds of genetic information for the same characteristic (for instance, coat color) is what really makes gametes—and therefore offspring—different from one another. In our example, a gamete carrying a red chromosome would have genes specifying brownish coat color and black eye color, while a gamete with the homologous blue chromosome would have genes for white coat and pink eyes. Thus, we see how a tetrad with genes shown for only two characteristics can yield two genetically different kinds of gametes. In the next module, we go a step further and see how this same tetrad can actually yield *four* different kinds of gametes.

Figure 8.17A   Differing genetic information on homologous chromosomes

Coat-color genes → Brown / *C* ... White / *c*

Eye-color genes → Black / *E* ... Pink / *e*

Tetrad in parent cell (homologous pair of duplicated chromosomes)

→ Meiosis →

Chromosomes of the four gametes

?   In the tetrad of Figure 8.17A, use labels to distinguish the homologous pair of chromosomes from sister chromatids.

Homologous pair of chromosomes { Sister chromatids / Sister chromatids

Sister chromatids / Sister chromatids

8.18 Crossing over further increases genetic variability

Crossing over is an exchange of corresponding segments between two homologous chromosomes. The micrograph and drawing in Figure 8.18A show the results of crossing over between two homologous chromosomes during prophase I of meiosis. The chromosomes are a tetrad—four chromatids, with each pair of sister chromatids joined at their centromeres. The sites of crossing over appear as X-shaped regions; each is called a **chiasma** (Greek for "cross"). A chiasma (plural, *chiasmata*) is a place where two homologous (nonsister) chromatids are attached to each other. Figure 8.18B (on the facing page) illustrates how crossing over can produce new combinations of genes, using as examples the hypothetical mouse genes mentioned in the previous module.

TEM 2,200×

Tetrad

Chiasma

Centromere

Figure 8.18A
Chiasmata

Crossing over begins very early in prophase I of meiosis. At that time, homologous chromosomes are paired along their lengths. Each gene on one homolog is aligned precisely with the corresponding gene on the other homolog.

At the top of the figure is a tetrad with coat-color (*C, c*) and eye-color (*E, e*) genes labeled. ❶ The DNA molecules of two nonsister chromatids—one maternal (red) and one paternal (blue)—break at the same place. ❷ Immediately, the two broken chromatids join together in a new way (red to blue and blue to red). In effect, the two homologous segments trade places, or cross over, producing hybrid (red/blue and blue/red) chromosomes with new combinations of maternal and paternal genes. ❸ When the homologous chromosomes separate in anaphase I, each contains a new segment originating from its homolog. ❹ Finally, in meiosis II, the sister chromatids separate, each going to a different gamete.

In this example, if there were no crossing over, meiosis could produce only two genetic types of gametes. These would be the ones ending up with the "parental" types of chromosomes, carrying either genes *C* and *E* or genes *c* and *e*. These are the same two kinds of gametes we saw in Figure 8.17A. With crossing over, two other types of gametes can result. One of these carries genes *C* and *e,* and the other carries genes *c* and *E.* Chromosomes with these combinations of genes would not exist if not for crossing over; thus, they are called "recombinant" because they result from **genetic recombination,** the production of gene combinations different from those carried by the original chromosomes.

In meiosis in humans, an average of one to three crossover events occur per chromosome pair. Thus, if you were to examine a chromosome from one of your gametes, you would most likely find that it is not exactly like any one of your own chromosomes. Rather, it is probably a patchwork of segments derived from a pair of homologous chromosomes, cut and pasted together to form a chromosome with a unique combination of genes.

We have now examined three sources of genetic variability in sexually reproducing organisms: independent orientation of chromosomes at metaphase I, random fertilization, and crossing over during prophase I of meiosis. When we take up molecular genetics in Chapter 10, we will see yet another source of variability—mutations, or rare changes in the DNA of genes. The different versions of genes that homologous chromosomes may have at each locus originally arise from mutations, so mutations are ultimately responsible for genetic diversity in living organisms.

Our discussion of meiosis to this point has focused on the process as it normally and "correctly" occurs. In the next, and last, major section of the chapter, we consider some of the consequences of errors in the process.

Web Activity *Origins of Genetic Variation*

Web Process of Science *How Is Crossing Over Measured in the Fungus* Sordaria?

Figure 8.18B How crossing over leads to genetic recombination

? Describe how crossing over and the random alignment of homologous chromosomes account for the genetic variation among gametes formed by meiosis.

■ (1) Crossing over creates recombinant chromosomes having a combination of genes that were originally on different, though homologous, chromosomes. (2) Homologous chromosome pairs are oriented randomly at metaphase of meiosis I (see Figure 8.16).

8.19 A karyotype is a photographic inventory of an individual's chromosomes

Errors in meiosis can lead to gametes containing chromosomes in abnormal numbers or with major alterations in their structures. Fertilization of these abnormal gametes results in offspring with chromosomal abnormalities. Such conditions can be readily detected in a **karyotype,** an ordered display of magnified images of an individual's chromosomes arranged in pairs, starting with the longest. A karyotype shows the chromosomes condensed and doubled, as they appear in metaphase of mitosis.

To prepare a karyotype, medical scientists often use lymphocytes, a type of white blood cell. A blood sample is treated with a chemical that stimulates mitosis. After growing in culture for several days, the cells are treated with another chemical to arrest mitosis at metaphase, when the chromosomes, each consisting of two joined sister chromatids, are most highly condensed. Figure 8.19 outlines the steps in one method for the preparation of a karyotype from a blood sample.

The photograph in step 5 shows the karyotype of a normal human male. The 46 chromosomes of a single diploid cell are arranged in 23 homologous pairs: autosomes numbered from 1 to 22 and one pair of sex chromosomes (X and Y in this case). The chromosomes have been stained to reveal band patterns, which are helpful in differentiating the chromosomes and in detecting structural abnormalities. Among the alterations detected by karyotyping is trisomy 21, the basis of Down syndrome, which we discuss next.

? How would the karyotype of a human female differ from the male karyotype in Figure 8.19?

■ Instead of an XY combination for the sex chromosomes, there would be a homologous pair of X chromosomes (XX).

Figure 8.19 Preparation of a karyotype from a blood sample

Packed red and white blood cells

Hypotonic solution

Fixative

Stain

Blood culture

Centrifuge

Fluid

White blood cells

1 A blood culture is centrifuged to separate the blood cells from the culture fluid.

2 The fluid is discarded, and a hypotonic solution is mixed with the cells. This makes the red blood cells burst. The white blood cells swell but do not burst, and their chromosomes spread out.

3 Another centrifugation step separates the swollen white blood cells. The fluid containing the remnants of the red blood cells is poured off. A fixative (preservative) is mixed with the white blood cells. A drop of the cell suspension is spread on a microscope slide, dried, and stained.

Centromere

Sister chromatids

Pair of homologous chromosomes

2,600×

4 The slide is viewed with a microscope equipped with a digital camera. A photograph of the chromosomes is entered into a computer, which electronically arranges them by size and shape.

5 The resulting display is the karyotype. The 46 chromosomes here include 22 pairs of autosomes and 2 sex chromosomes, X and Y. Although difficult to discern in the karyotype, each of the chromosomes consists of two sister chromatids lying very close together (see diagram).

An extra copy of chromosome 21 causes Down syndrome

The karyotype in Figure 8.19 shows the normal human complement of 23 pairs of chromosomes. However, the karyotype in Figure 8.20A is different; notice that there are three number 21 chromosomes, making 47 chromosomes in total. This condition is called **trisomy 21.**

In most cases, a human embryo with an abnormal number of chromosomes is spontaneously aborted (miscarried) long before birth. But some aberrations in chromosome number, including trisomy 21, appear to upset the genetic balance less drastically, and individuals carrying them can survive. These individuals have a characteristic set of symptoms, called a syndrome. A person with an extra copy of chromosome 21, for instance, has a condition called **Down syndrome** (named after John Langdon Down, who characterized the syndrome in 1866).

Trisomy 21 is the most common chromosome number abnormality. Affecting about one out of every 700 children born, it is also the most common serious birth defect in the United States. Chromosome 21 is one of our smallest chromosomes, but an extra copy produces a number of effects. Down syndrome (Figure 8.20B) includes characteristic facial features, notably a round face, a skin fold at the inner corner of the eye, a flattened nose bridge, and small, irregular teeth, as well as short stature, heart defects, and susceptibility to respiratory infections, leukemia, and Alzheimer's disease.

People with Down syndrome usually have a life span shorter than normal. They also exhibit varying degrees of mental retardation. However, some individuals with the syndrome live to middle age or beyond, and many are socially adept and able to hold jobs. A few women with Down syndrome have had children, though most people with the syndrome are sexually underdeveloped and sterile. Half the eggs produced by a woman with Down syndrome will have the extra chromosome 21, so there is a 50% chance that she will transmit the syndrome to her child.

Figure 8.20B   A child with Down syndrome

As indicated in Figure 8.20C, the incidence of Down syndrome in the offspring of normal parents increases markedly with the age of the mother. Down syndrome strikes less than 0.05% of children (fewer than one in 2,000) born to women under age 30. The risk climbs to just under 1% (ten in 1,000) for mothers at age 40 and is even higher for older mothers. Because of this relatively high risk, pregnant women over 35 are candidates for fetal testing for trisomy 21 and other chromosomal abnormalities (see Module 9.10).

What causes trisomy 21? We address that question in the next module.

Figure 8.20A   A karyotype for trisomy 21 (Down syndrome)

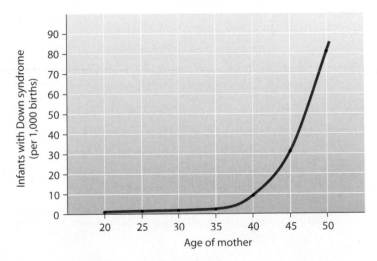

Figure 8.20C   Maternal age and incidence of Down syndrome

? For mothers of age 47, the risk of having a baby with Down syndrome is about _____ per thousand births, or _____%.

■ 40 . . . 4

8.21 Accidents during meiosis can alter chromosome number

Meiosis occurs repeatedly in a human lifetime as the testes or ovaries produce gametes. Almost always, the meiotic spindle distributes chromosomes to daughter cells without error. But there is an occasional mishap, called a **nondisjunction,** in which the members of a chromosome pair fail to separate. Figures 8.21A and 8.21B illustrate two ways that nondisjunction can occur. For simplicity, we use a hypothetical organism whose diploid chromosome number is 4. In both figures, the cell at the top is diploid ($2n = 4$), with two pairs of homologous chromosomes undergoing anaphase of meiosis I.

Sometimes, as in Figure 8.21A, a pair of homologous chromosomes does not separate during meiosis I. In this case, even though the rest of meiosis occurs normally, all the resulting gametes end up with abnormal numbers of chromosomes. Two of the gametes have three chromosomes; the other two gametes have only one chromosome each. In Figure 8.21B, meiosis I is normal, but one pair of sister chromatids fails to move apart during meiosis II. In this case, two of the resulting gametes are abnormal; the other two gametes are normal.

If an abnormal gamete produced by nondisjunction unites with a normal gamete in fertilization, the result is a zygote with an abnormal number of chromosomes. Mitosis will then transmit the anomaly to all embryonic cells. If this were a real organism and it survived, it would have an abnormal karyotype and probably a syndrome of disorders caused by the abnormal number of genes. For example, if there is nondisjunction affecting human chromosome 21, some resulting gametes will carry an extra chromosome 21. If one of these gametes unites with a normal gamete, trisomy 21 (Down syndrome) will result.

Nondisjunction explains how abnormal chromosome numbers come about, but what causes nondisjunction in the first place? We do not yet know the answer. We do know, however, that meiosis begins in a woman's ovaries before she is born but is not completed until years later, at the time of an ovulation (see Module 27.5). Because only one egg cell usually matures each month, a cell might remain arrested in the mid-meiosis state for decades. Some research points to an age-dependent error in one of the checkpoints that coordinates the process of meiosis. Nondisjunction can also affect chromosomes other than 21, as we see next.

? Explain how nondisjunction could result in a diploid gamete.

■ A diploid gamete would result if the nondisjunction affected all the chromosomes during one of the meiotic divisions.

Figure 8.21A Nondisjunction in meiosis I

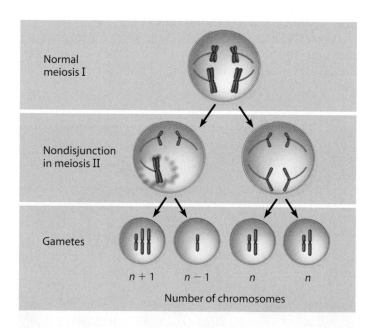

Figure 8.21B Nondisjunction in meiosis II

8.22 Abnormal numbers of sex chromosomes do not usually affect survival

Nondisjunction in meiosis does not affect just autosomes, such as chromosome 21. It can also lead to abnormal numbers of sex chromosomes, X and Y. Unusual numbers of sex chromosomes seem to upset the genetic balance less than unusual numbers of autosomes. This may be because the Y chromosome is very small and carries relatively few genes. Furthermore, mammalian cells usually operate with only one functioning X chromosome because other copies of the chromosome become inactivated in each cell (see Module 11.4).

Table 8.22 lists the most common human sex chromosome abnormalities. An extra X chromosome in a male, making him XXY, occurs approximately once in every 2,000 live births (once in every 1,000 male births). Men with this disorder, called *Klinefelter syndrome*, have male sex organs, but the testes are abnormally small and the individual is sterile. The syndrome often includes breast enlargement and other female body characteristics. The person is usually of normal intelligence. Klinefelter syndrome is also found in individuals with more than three sex chromosomes, such as XXYY, XXXY, or XXXXY. These abnormal numbers of sex chromosomes probably result from multiple nondisjunctions; such men are more likely to have developmental disabilities than XY or XXY individuals.

Human males with an extra Y chromosome (XYY) do not have any well-defined syndrome, although they tend to be taller than average. Females with an extra X chromosome (XXX) cannot be distinguished from XX females except by karyotype.

Females who are lacking an X chromosome are designated XO; the O indicates the absence of a second sex chromosome. These women have *Turner syndrome*. They have a characteristic appearance, including short stature and often a web of skin extending between the neck and the shoulders. Women with Turner syndrome are sterile because their sex organs do not

TABLE 8.22	ABNORMALITIES OF SEX CHROMOSOME NUMBER IN HUMANS		
Sex Chromosomes	Syndrome	Origin of Nondisjunction	Frequency in Population
XXY	Klinefelter syndrome (male)	Meiosis in egg or sperm formation	$\frac{1}{2,000}$
XYY	None (normal male)	Meiosis in sperm formation	$\frac{1}{2,000}$
XXX	None (normal female)	Meiosis in egg or sperm formation	$\frac{1}{1,000}$
XO	Turner syndrome (female)	Meiosis in egg or sperm formation	$\frac{1}{5,000}$

fully mature at adolescence. If left untreated, girls with Turner syndrome have poor development of breasts and other secondary sexual characteristics. Artificial administration of estrogen can alleviate these symptoms. Girls with Turner syndrome have normal intelligence. The XO condition is the sole known case where having only 45 chromosomes is not fatal in humans.

The sex chromosome abnormalities described here illustrate the crucial role of the Y chromosome in determining sex. In general, a single Y chromosome is enough to produce "maleness," even in combination with several X chromosomes. The absence of a Y chromosome yields "femaleness."

? What is the *total* number of chromosomes you would expect to find in the karyotype of a female with Turner syndrome?

■ 45

8.23 New species can arise from errors in cell division

Errors in meiosis or mitosis do not always lead to problems. In fact, biologists hypothesize that such errors have been instrumental in the evolution of many species. Numerous plant species, in particular, seem to have originated from accidents during cell division that resulted in extra sets of chromosomes. The new species is polyploid, meaning that it has more than two sets of homologous chromosomes in each somatic cell. At least half of all species of flowering plants are polyploid, including such useful ones as wheat, potatoes, apples, and cotton.

Let's consider one scenario by which a diploid (2*n*) plant species might generate a tetraploid (4*n*) plant. Imagine that, like many plants, our diploid plant produces both sperm and egg cells and can self-fertilize. If meiosis fails to occur in the plant's reproductive organs and gametes are instead produced by mitosis, the gametes will be diploid. The union of a diploid (2*n*) sperm with a diploid (2*n*) egg during self-fertilization will

produce a tetraploid (4*n*) zygote, which may develop into a mature tetraploid plant that can itself reproduce by self-fertilization. The tetraploid plants will constitute a new species, one that has evolved in just one generation.

Although polyploid animal species are less common than polyploid plants, they are known to occur among the fishes and amphibians. Moreover, researchers in Chile have identified the first candidate for polyploidy among the mammals, a rat whose cells seem to be tetraploid. Tetraploid organisms are sometimes strikingly different from their recent diploid ancestors—larger, for example. Scientists don't yet understand exactly how polyploidy brings about such differences.

? What is a polyploid organism?

■ One with more than two sets of homologous chromosomes in its genome

Chapter 8 *The Cellular Basis of Reproduction and Inheritance* **147**

8.24 Alterations of chromosome structure can cause birth defects and cancer

Even if all chromosomes are present in normal numbers, abnormalities in chromosome structure may cause disorders. Breakage of a chromosome can lead to a variety of rearrangements affecting the genes of that chromosome. Figure 8.24A shows three types of rearrangement. (The pink arrows indicate chromosome breaks.) If a fragment of a chromosome is lost, the remaining chromosome will then have a **deletion.** If a fragment from one chromosome joins to a sister chromatid or homologous chromosome, it will produce a **duplication.** If a fragment reattaches to the original chromosome but in the reverse direction, an **inversion** results.

Inversions are less likely than deletions or duplications to produce harmful effects, because in inversions all genes are still present in their normal number. Many deletions in human chromosomes, however, cause serious physical and mental problems. One example is a specific deletion in chromosome 5 that causes *cri du chat* ("cry of the cat") syndrome. A child born with this syndrome is mentally retarded, has a small head with unusual facial features, and has a cry that sounds like the mewing of a distressed cat. Such individuals usually die in infancy or early childhood.

Another type of chromosomal change is chromosomal **translocation,** the attachment of a chromosomal fragment to a nonhomologous chromosome. Figure 8.24B shows a translocation that is reciprocal; that is, two nonhomologous chromosomes exchange segments. Like inversions, translocations may or may not be harmful. Some people with Down syndrome have only part of a third chromosome 21; as the result of a translocation, this partial chromosome is attached to another (nonhomologous) chromosome.

Whereas chromosomal changes present in sperm or egg can cause congenital disorders, such changes in a somatic cell may contribute to the development of cancer. For example, a chromosomal translocation in somatic cells in the bone marrow is associated with *chronic myelogenous leukemia (CML).* CML is one of the most common of the leukemias, the cancers affecting cells that give rise to white blood cells (leukocytes). In the cancerous cells of most CML patients, a part of chromosome 22 has switched places with a small fragment from a tip of chromosome 9 (Figure 8.24C). This reciprocal translocation activates a gene that leads to leukemia. The chromosome ending up with the activated cancer-causing gene is called the "Philadelphia chromosome," after the city where it was discovered.

Because the chromosomal changes in cancer are usually confined to somatic cells, cancer is not usually inherited. We'll return to cancer in Chapter 11. In Chapter 9, we continue our study of genetic principles, looking first at the historical development of the science of genetics and then at the rules governing the way traits are passed from parents to offspring.

Figure 8.24A Alterations of chromosome structure involving one chromosome or a homologous pair

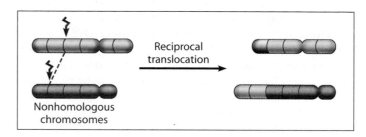

Figure 8.24B Chromosomal translocation between nonhomologous chromosomes

Figure 8.24C The translocation associated with chronic myelogenous leukemia

? How is reciprocal translocation different from normal crossing over?

■ Reciprocal translocation swaps chromosome segments between nonhomologous chromosomes. Crossing over normally exchanges corresponding segments between homologous chromosomes.

Chapter Review

Reviewing the Concepts

Connections Between Cell Division and Reproduction (Introduction–8.3)

Cell division is at the heart of the reproduction of cells and organisms, because cells come only from preexisting cells. Some organisms reproduce asexually, and their offspring are all genetic copies of the parent and of each other. Others reproduce sexually, creating a variety of offspring, each with a unique combination of traits (**Introduction–8.2**). Prokaryotic cells reproduce asexually by cell division. As the cell replicates its single chromosome, the copies move apart; the growing membrane then divides the cell (**8.3**).

The Eukaryotic Cell Cycle and Mitosis (8.4–8.11)

Chromosomes.   A eukaryotic cell has many more genes than a prokaryotic cell, and they are grouped into multiple chromosomes in the nucleus. Each chromosome contains a very long DNA molecule associated with proteins. Individual chromosomes are visible only when the cell is in the process of dividing; otherwise, they are in the form of thin, loosely packed chromatin fibers. Before a cell starts dividing, the chromosomes duplicate, producing sister chromatids (containing identical DNA) joined together at the centromere. Cell division involves the separation of sister chromatids and results in two daughter cells, each containing a complete and identical set of chromosomes (**8.4**).

The eukaryotic cell cycle (8.5):

Mitosis distributes duplicated chromosomes into two daughter nuclei. After the chromosomes coil up, a mitotic spindle made of microtubules moves them to the middle of the cell. The sister chromatids then separate and move to opposite poles of the cell, where two new nuclei form. Cytokinesis, in which the cell divides in two, overlaps the end of mitosis (**8.6**). In animals, cytokinesis occurs by a constriction of the cell (cleavage). In plants, a membranous cell plate splits the cell in two (**8.7**).

Cell cycle control.   Most animal cells divide only when stimulated, and some not at all. In laboratory cultures, most normal cells divide only when attached to a surface. They continue dividing until they touch one another. Growth factors are proteins secreted by cells that stimulate other cells to divide (**8.8**).

A set of proteins within the cell controls the cell cycle. Signals affecting critical checkpoints in the cell cycle determine whether a cell will go through the complete cycle and divide. The binding of growth factors to specific receptors on the plasma membrane is usually necessary for cell division (**8.9**).

Cancer cells divide excessively to form masses called tumors. Malignant tumors can invade other tissues. Radiation and chemotherapy are effective as cancer treatments because they interfere with cell division (**8.10**). When the cell cycle operates normally, mitotic cell division functions in growth, replacement of damaged and lost cells, and asexual reproduction (**8.11**).

Meiosis and Crossing Over (8.12–8.18)

Homologous chromosomes.   The somatic (body) cells of each species contain a specific number of chromosomes; for example, human cells have 46, making up 23 pairs (two sets) of homologous chromosomes. The chromosomes of a homologous pair carry genes for the same characteristics at the same place, or locus (**8.12**). Cells with two sets of homologous chromosomes are said to be diploid. Gametes—eggs and sperm—are haploid cells with a single set of chromosomes. Sexual life cycles involve the alternation of haploid and diploid stages (**8.13**):

Meiosis, like mitosis, is preceded by chromosome duplication, but in meiosis the cell divides twice to form four daughter cells. The first division, meiosis I, starts with synapsis, the pairing of homologous chromosomes. In crossing over, homologous chromosomes exchange corresponding segments. Meiosis I separates each homologous pair and produces two daughter cells, each with one set of chromosomes. Meiosis II is essentially the same as mitosis: In each of the cells, the sister chromatids of each chromosome separate; the result is a total of four haploid cells (**8.14**). Figure 8.15 reviews and compares mitosis and meiosis (**8.15**).

Genetic variation.   Each chromosome of a homologous pair differs at many points from the other member of the pair. Random arrangements of chromosome pairs at metaphase I of meiosis leads to many different combinations of chromosomes in eggs and sperm. Random fertilization of eggs by sperm greatly increases this variation (**8.16**). The differences between homologous chromosomes are based on the fact that they can bear different versions of a gene at corresponding loci (**8.17**). Genetic recombination, which results from crossing over during prophase I of meiosis, increases variation still further (**8.18**).

Alterations of Chromosome Number and Structure (8.19–8.24)

Chromosome number. A karyotype is an ordered arrangement of images of a cell's chromosomes (**8.19**). A person may have an abnormal number of chromosomes, which causes problems. Down syndrome is caused by trisomy 21, an extra copy of chromosome 21 (**8.20**). An abnormal chromosome count is the result of nondisjunction, the failure of a homologous pair of chromosomes to separate during meiosis I or of sister chromatids to separate during meiosis II (**8.21**). Nondisjunction can also produce gametes with extra or missing sex chromosomes, leading to varying degrees of malfunction in humans but not usually affecting survival (**8.22**). Nondisjunction can produce polyploid organisms, ones with extra sets of chromosomes. Such errors in mitosis are important in the evolution of new species (**8.23**). Chromosome breakage can lead to rearrangements—deletions, duplications, inversions, and translocations—that can produce genetic disorders or, if the changes occur in somatic cells, cancer (**8.24**).

Connecting the Concepts

1. Complete the following table to compare mitosis and meiosis.

	Mitosis	Meiosis
Number of chromosomal duplications		
Number of cell divisions		
Number of daughter cells produced		
Number of chromosomes in daughter cells		
How chromosomes line up during metaphase		
Genetic relationship of daughter cells to parent cell		
Functions performed in the human body		

Testing Your Knowledge

Multiple Choice

2. If an intestinal cell in a grasshopper contains 24 chromosomes, a grasshopper sperm cell contains _____ chromosomes.
   a. 3
   b. 6
   c. 12
   d. 24
   e. 48

3. Which of the following phases of mitosis is essentially the opposite of prophase in terms of nuclear changes?
   a. telophase
   b. metaphase
   c. S phase
   d. interphase
   e. anaphase

4. A biochemist measured the amount of DNA in cells growing in the laboratory and found that the quantity of DNA in a cell doubled
   a. between prophase and anaphase of mitosis.
   b. between the G_1 and G_2 phases of the cell cycle.
   c. during the M phase of the cell cycle.
   d. between prophase I and prophase II of meiosis.
   e. between anaphase and telophase of mitosis.

5. Which of the following is *not* a function of mitosis in humans?
   a. repair of wounds
   b. growth
   c. production of gametes from diploid cells
   d. replacement of lost or damaged cells
   e. multiplication of somatic cells

6. A micrograph of a dividing cell from a mouse showed 19 chromosomes, each consisting of two sister chromatids. During which of the following stages of cell division could this picture have been taken? (*Explain your answer.*)
   a. prophase of mitosis
   b. telophase II of meiosis
   c. prophase I of meiosis
   d. anaphase of mitosis
   e. prophase II of meiosis

7. Cytochalasin B is a chemical that disrupts microfilament formation. This chemical would interfere with
   a. DNA replication.
   b. formation of the mitotic spindle.
   c. cleavage.
   d. formation of the cell plate.
   e. crossing over.

8. It is difficult to observe individual chromosomes during interphase because
   a. the DNA has not been replicated yet.
   b. they are in the form of long, thin strands.
   c. they leave the nucleus and are dispersed to other parts of the cell.
   d. homologous chromosomes do not pair up until division starts.
   e. the spindle must move them to the metaphase plate before they become visible.

9. A fruit fly somatic cell contains 8 chromosomes. This means that _____ different combinations of chromosomes are possible in its gametes.
   a. 4
   b. 8
   c. 16
   d. 32
   e. 64

10. If a fragment of a chromosome breaks off and then re-attaches to the original chromosome but in the reverse direction, the resulting chromosomal abnormality is called
    a. a deletion.
    b. an inversion.
    c. a translocation.
    d. a nondisjunction.
    e. a reciprocal translocation.

11. Why are individuals with an extra chromosome 21, which causes Down syndrome, more numerous than individuals with an extra chromosome 3 or chromosome 16?
    a. There are probably more genes on chromosome 21 than on the others.
    b. Chromosome 21 is a sex chromosome and chromosomes 3 and 16 are not.
    c. Down syndrome is not more common, just more serious.
    d. Extra copies of the other chromosomes are probably fatal.
    e. Chromosome 21 is more likely to produce a nondisjunction error than other chromosomes.

Describing, Comparing, and Explaining

12. Briefly describe how three different processes that occur during a sexual life cycle increase the genetic diversity of offspring.

13. In the light micrograph below of dividing cells near the tip of an onion root, identify a cell in interphase, prophase, metaphase, anaphase, and telophase. Describe the major events occurring at each stage.

LM 500×

14. Discuss the factors that control the division of eukaryotic cells grown in the laboratory. Cancer cells are easier to grow in the lab than other cells. Why do you suppose this is the case?

15. Compare cytokinesis in plant and animal cells.

16. Sketch a cell with three pairs of chromosomes undergoing meiosis, and show how nondisjunction can result in the production of gametes with extra or missing chromosomes.

Applying the Concepts

17. Suppose you read in the newspaper that a genetic engineering laboratory has developed a procedure for fusing two gametes from the same person (two eggs or two sperm) to form a zygote. The article mentions that an early step in the procedure prevents crossing over from occurring during the formation of the gametes in the donor's body. The researchers are in the process of determining the genetic makeup of one of their new zygotes. Which of the following predictions do you think they would make? Justify your choice, and explain why you rejected each of the other choices.
    a. The zygote would have 46 chromosomes, all of which came from the gamete donor (its one parent), so the zygote would be genetically identical to the gamete donor.
    b. The zygote *could* be genetically identical to the gamete donor, but it is much more likely that it would have an unpredictable mixture of chromosomes from the gamete donor's parents.
    c. The zygote would not be genetically identical to the gamete donor, but it would be genetically identical to one of the donor's parents.
    d. The zygote would not be genetically identical to the gamete donor, but it would be genetically identical to one of the donor's grandparents.

18. Bacteria are able to divide on a much faster schedule than eukaryotic cells. Some bacteria can divide every 20 minutes, while the minimum time required by eukaryotic cells in a rapidly developing embryo is about once per hour, and most cells divide much less often than that. State several testable hypotheses explaining why bacteria can divide at a faster rate than eukaryotic cells.

19. Red blood cells, which carry oxygen to body tissues, live for only about 120 days. Replacement cells are produced by cell division in bone marrow. How many cell divisions must occur each second in your bone marrow just to replace red blood cells? Here is some information to use in calculating your answer: There are about 5 million red blood cells per cubic millimeter (mm^3) of blood. An average adult has about 5 L (5,000 cm^3) of blood. (*Hint:* What is the total number of red blood cells in the body? What fraction of them must be replaced each day if all are replaced in 120 days?)

20. A mule is the offspring of a horse and a donkey. A donkey sperm contains 31 chromosomes and a horse egg cell 32 chromosomes, so the zygote contains a total of 63 chromosomes. The zygote develops normally. The combined set of chromosomes is not a problem in mitosis, and the mule combines some of the best characteristics of horses and donkeys. However, a mule is sterile; meiosis cannot occur normally in its testes (or ovaries). Explain why mitosis is normal in cells containing both horse and donkey chromosomes but the mixed set of chromosomes interferes with meiosis.

21. Every year about a million Americans are diagnosed as having cancer. This means that about 75 million Americans now living will eventually have cancer, and one in five will die of the disease. There are many kinds of cancers and many causes of the disease. For example, smoking causes most lung cancers. Overexposure to ultraviolet rays in sunlight causes most skin cancers. There is evidence that a high-fat, low-fiber diet is a factor in breast, colon, and prostate cancers. And agents in the workplace such as asbestos and vinyl chloride are also implicated as causes of cancer. Hundreds of millions of dollars are spent each year in the search for effective treatments for cancer; far less money is spent preventing cancer. Why might this be the case? What kinds of lifestyle changes could we make to help prevent cancer? What kinds of prevention programs could be initiated or strengthened to encourage these changes? What factors might impede such changes and programs? Should we devote more of our resources to treating cancer or preventing it? Why?

Answers to all questions can be found in Appendix 4.

For Practice Quizzes, BioFlix, MP3 Tutors, and Activities, go to www.mybiology.com.

chapter 9

Patterns of Inheritance

Mendel's Laws

9.1 The science of genetics has ancient roots

9.2 Experimental genetics began in an abbey garden

9.3 Mendel's law of segregation describes the inheritance of a single character

9.4 Homologous chromosomes bear the alleles for each character

9.5 The law of independent assortment is revealed by tracking two characters at once

9.6 Geneticists use the testcross to determine unknown genotypes

9.7 Mendel's laws reflect the rules of probability

9.8 Genetic traits in humans can be tracked through family pedigrees

9.9 Many inherited disorders in humans are controlled by a single gene

9.10 New technologies can provide insight into one's genetic legacy

Variations on Mendel's Laws

9.11 Incomplete dominance results in intermediate phenotypes

9.12 Many genes have more than two alleles in the population

9.13 A single gene may affect many phenotypic characters

9.14 A single character may be influenced by many genes

9.15 The environment affects many characters

The Chromosomal Basis of Inheritance

 9.16 Chromosome behavior accounts for Mendel's laws

9.17 Genes on the same chromosome tend to be inherited together

9.18 Crossing over produces new combinations of alleles

9.19 Geneticists use crossover data to map genes

Sex Chromosomes and Sex-Linked Genes

9.20 Chromosomes determine sex in many species

9.21 Sex-linked genes exhibit a unique pattern of inheritance

9.22 Sex-linked disorders affect mostly males

9.23 The Y chromosome provides clues about human male evolution

Wolf

Ancestral canine

Chinese Shar-Pei

Akita

Siberian Husky

Basenji

Alaskan Malamute

Afghan hound

Saluki

Rottweiler

Sheepdog

Retriever

Barking Up the Genetic Tree

The proud pooch shown on the facing page is Kirby, winner of the Best in Show Trophy at the 123rd Westminster Kennel Club Dog Show. Formally known as Champion Loteki Supernatural Being, Kirby is considered one of the finest examples of his breed: the papillon. Kirby's championship rank also makes him highly sought after as a stud. Papillon breeders expect his offspring to inherit many of his desirable traits, such as the large butterfly-like ears that distinguish the breed. This is a reasonable expectation because Kirby's well-documented pedigree includes award-winning parents, grandparents, and great grandparents with very similar genetic makeup and appearance.

Kirby is living proof that dogs are more than man's best friend—they are also one of our longest-running genetic experiments. About 15,000 years ago, in East Asia, humans began to cohabit with ancestral canines that were predecessors of both modern wolves and dogs. As people settled into permanent, geographically isolated settlements, different populations of canines were separated from one another and eventually became inbred. At the same time, different groups of people chose dogs with different traits, depending on their needs. Herders selected dogs that were good at controlling flocks of animals. Hunters chose dogs that were good at retrieving wounded prey. Continued over millennia, the result of such genetic tinkering is an incredibly diverse array of dog body types and behaviors, from tiny, feisty Chihuahuas to huge, docile St. Bernards. But no matter what appearance a dog sports, we can ultimately explain their inborn traits through **genetics,** the science of heredity. In each breed, a distinct genetic makeup results in a distinct set of physical and behavioral characteristics.

Our understanding of canine genetics took a big leap forward in 2003 when researchers sequenced the complete genome of a dog. Using the genome sequence and a wealth of other data, canine geneticists produced the family tree of dog breeds shown above. Published in 2006, the tree is based on genetic analysis of 414 dogs from 85 recognized breeds. The analysis shows that the canine family tree includes a series of well-defined branch points. Each

fork represents purposeful artificial selection that produced a genetically distinct sub-population with specific desired traits. The genetic tree shows that the most ancient breeds, those with genetic makeups most closely resembling the wolf, are Asian species such as the shar-pei and Akita. Subsequent genetic splits created distinct breeds in Africa (basenji), the Arctic (Alaskan malamute and Siberian husky), and the Middle East (Afghan hound and saluki). The remaining breeds, primarily of European ancestry, can be grouped by genetic makeup into those bred for guarding (for example, the rottweiler), herding (such as various sheepdogs), and hunting (including the golden retriever and beagle).

Although humans have been applying genetics for thousands of years—by breeding food crops as well as domesticated animals—the biological basis of selective breeding has only recently been understood. In this chapter, we examine the rules that govern how inherited traits are passed from parents to offspring. We look at several kinds of inheritance patterns and how they allow us to predict the ratios of offspring with particular traits. Most importantly, we uncover a basic biological concept: how the behavior of chromosomes during gamete formation and fertilization (discussed in Chapter 8) accounts for the patterns of inheritance we observe. ■ ■ ■

9.1 The science of genetics has ancient roots

Attempts to explain inheritance date back at least to ancient Greece. The physician Hippocrates (approximately 460–370 B.C.) suggested an explanation called pangenesis. According to this idea, particles called pangenes travel from each part of an organism's body to the eggs or sperm and are then passed to the next generation; moreover, changes that occur in the body during an organism's life are passed on in this way. The Greek philosopher Aristotle (384–322 B.C.) rejected this idea as simplistic, saying that what is inherited is the potential to produce body features rather than particles of the features themselves.

Actually, pangenesis proves incorrect on several counts. The reproductive cells are not composed of particles from somatic (body) cells, and changes in somatic cells do not influence eggs and sperm. For instance, no matter how much you enlarge your biceps by lifting weights, muscle cells in your arms do not transmit genetic information to your gametes, and your offspring will not be changed by your weight-lifting efforts. This may seem like common sense today, but the pangenesis hypothesis and the idea that traits acquired during an individual's lifetime are passed on to offspring prevailed well into the 19th century.

By observing inheritance patterns in ornamental plants, biologists of the early 19th century established that offspring inherit traits from both parents. The favored explanation of inheritance then became the "blending" hypothesis, the idea that the hereditary materials contributed by the male and female parents mix in forming the offspring in the way that blue and yellow paints blend to make green. For example, according to this hypothesis, after the genetic information for the colors of black and chocolate brown Labrador retrievers is blended, the colors should be as inseparable as paint pigments. But this is not what happens: Instead, the offspring of a purebred black Lab and a purebred brown one will all be black, but some of the dogs in the next generation will be brown. The blending hypothesis was finally rejected because it does not explain how traits that disappear in one generation can reappear in later ones.

? Horse breeders sometimes speak of "mixing the bloodlines" of two pedigrees. How does this language relate back to the "blending" model of inheritance?

■ It implies that offspring are a blend of two parents, as in a liquid mixture.

9.2 Experimental genetics began in an abbey garden

The modern science of genetics began in the 1860s, when an Augustinian monk named Gregor Mendel deduced the fundamental principles of genetics by breeding garden peas (Figure 9.2A). Mendel lived and worked in an abbey in Brunn, Austria (now Brno, in the Czech Republic). Strongly influenced by his study of physics, mathematics, and chemistry at the University of Vienna, his research was both experimentally and mathematically rigorous, and these qualities were largely responsible for his success.

In a paper published in 1866, Mendel correctly argued that parents pass on to their offspring discrete heritable factors. (It is interesting to note that Mendel's publication came just seven years after Darwin's 1859 publication of *The Origin of Species,* making the 1860s a banner decade in the development of modern biology.) In his paper, Mendel stressed that the heritable factors (today called genes) retain their individuality generation after generation; that is, genes are like marbles of different colors. Just as marbles retain their colors permanently and do not blend, no matter how they are mixed, genes permanently retain their identities.

Mendel probably chose to study garden peas because they had short generation times, they produced large numbers of offspring from each mating, and they came in many readily distinguishable varieties. For example, one variety has purple flowers, and another variety has white flowers. A heritable feature that varies among individuals, such as flower color, is called a **character.** Each variant for a character, such as purple or white flowers, is called a **trait.**

Perhaps the most important advantage of pea plants as an experimental model was that Mendel could strictly control matings. As Figure 9.2B shows, the petals of the pea flower almost completely enclose the reproductive organs: the stamens and carpel. Consequently, pea plants usually **self-fertilize** in nature. That is, sperm-carrying pollen grains released from the stamens land on the egg-containing carpel of the same flower. Mendel could ensure self-fertilization by covering a flower with a small bag so that no pollen from another plant could reach the carpel. When he wanted **cross-fertilization** (fertilization of one

Figure 9.2A Gregor Mendel

Figure 9.2B Anatomy of a garden pea flower (with one petal removed to improve visibility)

Petal

Stamen

Carpel

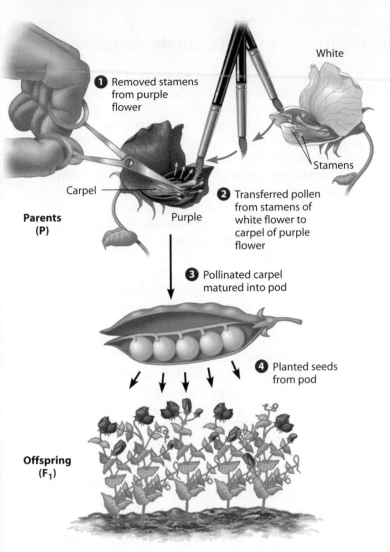

Figure 9.2C Mendel's technique for cross-fertilization of pea plants

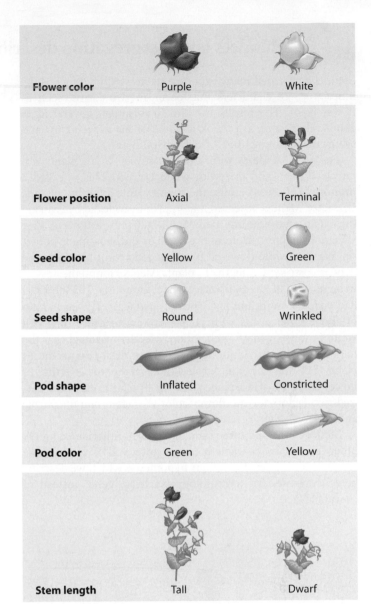

Figure 9.2D The seven pea characters studied by Mendel

plant by pollen from a different plant), he used the method shown in **Figure 9.2C**. ❶ He prevented self-fertilization by cutting off the immature stamens of a plant before they produced pollen. ❷ To cross-fertilize the stameless flower, he dusted its carpel with pollen from another plant. After pollination, ❸ the carpel developed into a pod, containing seeds (peas) that ❹ he planted. The seeds grew into offspring plants. Through these methods, Mendel could always be sure of the parentage of new plants.

Mendel's success was due not only to his experimental approach and choice of organism but also to his selection of characteristics to study. He chose to observe seven characters, each of which occurred in two distinct forms **(Figure 9.2D)**. Mendel worked with his plants until he was sure he had **true-breeding** varieties—that is, varieties for which self-fertilization produced offspring all identical to the parent. For instance, he identified a purple-flowered variety that, when self-fertilized, produced offspring plants that all had purple flowers.

Now Mendel was ready to ask what would happen when he crossed his different true-breeding varieties with each other.

For example, what offspring would result if plants with purple flowers and plants with white flowers were cross-fertilized? In the language of plant and animal breeders and geneticists, the offspring of two different varieties are called **hybrids,** and the cross-fertilization itself is referred to as a hybridization, or simply a **cross.** The true-breeding parental plants are called the **P generation** (P for parental), and their hybrid offspring are the **F₁ generation** (F for filial, from the Latin word for "son"). When F₁ plants self-fertilize or fertilize each other, their offspring are the **F₂ generation.** We turn to Mendel's results next.

? Why was the development of true-breeding varieties critical to the success of Mendel's experiments?

■ True-breeding varieties allowed Mendel to predict the outcome of specific crosses and therefore run controlled experiments.

Mendel's law of segregation describes the inheritance of a single character

Mendel performed many experiments in which he tracked the inheritance of characters that occur in two forms, such as flower color. The results led him to formulate several ideas about inheritance. Let's look at some of his experiments and follow the reasoning that led to his hypotheses.

Figure 9.3A starts with a cross between a pea plant with purple flowers and one with white flowers. This is called a **monohybrid cross** because the parent plants differ in only one character. Mendel observed that F_1 plants produced by crossing these two true-breeding parents all had purple flowers; they were not a lighter purple, as predicted by the blending hypothesis. Was the white-flowered plant's genetic contribution to the hybrids lost? By mating the F_1 plants, Mendel found the answer to be no. Out of 929 F_2 plants, Mendel found that 705 (about $\frac{3}{4}$) had purple flowers and 224 (about $\frac{1}{4}$) had white flowers, a ratio of about three plants with purple flowers to every one with white flowers in the F_2 generation. Mendel reasoned that the heritable factor for white flowers did not disappear in the F_1 plants, but that only the purple-flower factor was affecting F_1 flower color. He also deduced that the F_1 plants must have carried two factors for the flower-color character, one for purple and one for white.

Mendel observed these same patterns of inheritance for six other pea plant characters (see Figure 9.2D). From these results, Mendel developed four hypotheses, which we describe here using modern terminology (such as "gene" instead of "heritable factor"):

1. *There are alternative versions of genes that account for variations in inherited characters.* For example, the gene for flower color in pea plants exists in two versions, one for purple and the other for white. The alternative versions of a gene are now called **alleles.**

2. *For each character, an organism inherits two alleles, one from each parent.* These alleles may be the same or different. An organism that has two identical alleles for a gene is said to be **homozygous** for that gene (and is called a homozygote). An organism that has two different alleles for a gene is said to be **heterozygous** for that gene (and is called a heterozygote).

3. *If the two alleles of an inherited pair differ, then one determines the organism's appearance and is called the **dominant allele;** the other has no noticeable effect on the organism's appearance and is called the **recessive allele.*** We use uppercase letters to represent dominant alleles and lowercase letters to represent recessive alleles.

4. *A sperm or egg carries only one allele for each inherited character because allele pairs separate (segregate) from each other during the production of gametes.* This statement is now known as the **law of segregation.** When sperm and egg unite at fertilization, each contributes its allele, restoring the paired condition in the offspring.

Figure 9.3B shows how Mendel explained the results given in Figure 9.3A. In this example, the italic letter P represents the

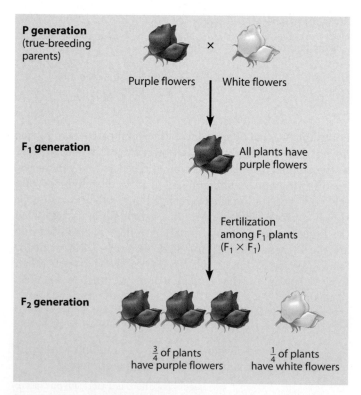

Figure 9.3A   Crosses tracking one character (flower color)

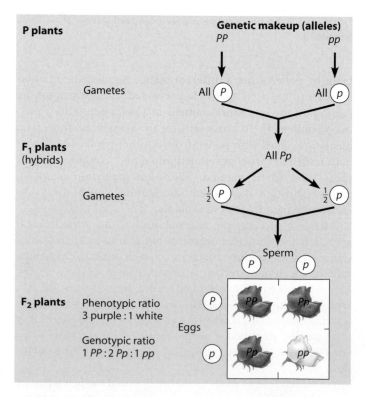

Figure 9.3B   Explanation of the crosses in Figure 9.3A

dominant allele (for purple flowers) and *p* stands for the recessive allele (for white flowers). At the top in Figure 9.3B, you see the alleles carried by the parental plants. Both plants were true-breeding, and Mendel's first two hypotheses propose that one parental variety had two alleles for purple flowers (*PP*) and the other had two alleles for white flowers (*pp*).

Consistent with hypothesis 4, the gametes of Mendel's parental plants each carried one allele; thus, the parental gametes in Figure 9.3B are either *P* or *p*. As a result of fertilization, the F₁ hybrids each inherited one allele for purple flowers and one for white. Hypothesis 3 explains why all of the F₁ hybrids (*Pp*) had purple flowers: The dominant *P* allele has its full effect in the heterozygote, while the recessive *p* allele has no effect on flower color.

Mendel's hypotheses also explain the 3 : 1 ratio ($\frac{3}{4}$ purple flowers to $\frac{1}{4}$ white flowers) in the F₂ generation. Because the F₁ hybrids are *Pp*, they make gametes *P* and *p* in equal numbers. The bottom diagram in Figure 9.3B, called a **Punnett square,** shows the four possible combinations of gametes.

The Punnett square shows the proportions of F₂ plants predicted by Mendel's hypotheses. If a sperm carrying allele *P* fertilizes an egg carrying allele *P*, the offspring (*PP*) will produce purple flowers. Mendel's hypotheses predict that this combination will occur in $\frac{1}{4}$ of the offspring. As shown in the Punnett square, the hypotheses also predict that $\frac{2}{4}$ of the offspring will inherit one *P* allele and one *p* allele. These offspring (*Pp*) will all have purple flowers because *P* is dominant. The remaining $\frac{1}{4}$ of the F₂ plants will inherit two *p* alleles and will have white flowers.

Because an organism's appearance does not always reveal its genetic composition, geneticists distinguish between an organism's expressed, or physical, traits, called its **phenotype** (such as purple or white flowers), and its genetic makeup, its **genotype** (in this example, *PP*, *Pp*, or *pp*). So now we see that Figure 9.3A shows the phenotypes and Figure 9.3B the genotypes in our sample crosses. For the F₂ plants, the ratio of plants with purple flowers to those with white flowers (3 : 1) is called the phenotypic ratio. The genotypic ratio, as shown by the Punnett square, is 1 *PP* : 2 *Pp* : 1 *pp*.

Mendel found that each of the seven characteristics he studied exhibited the same inheritance pattern: One parental trait disappeared in the F₁ generation, only to reappear in one-fourth of the F₂ offspring. The mechanism underlying this inheritance pattern is stated by Mendel's law of segregation: *Pairs of alleles segregate (separate) during gamete formation.* The fusion of gametes at fertilization creates allele pairs once again. Research since Mendel's time has established that the law of segregation applies to all sexually reproducing organisms, including humans. We'll return to Mendel and his experiments with pea plants in Module 9.5. But first let's see how some of the concepts we discussed in Chapter 8 fit with what we have said about genetics so far.

Web Activity *Monohybrid Cross*

? How can two plants with different genotypes for a particular inherited character be identical in phenotype?

■ One could be homozygous for the dominant allele, whereas the other is heterozygous.

9.4 Homologous chromosomes bear the alleles for each character

Figure 9.4 shows three gene loci on a pair of homologous chromosomes (homologues)—chromosomes that carry genes controlling the same inherited characteristics. Recall from Module 8.12 that every diploid cell, whether from pea plant or human, has two sets of homologous chromosomes. One set comes from the organism's female parent, the other from the male parent.

The labeled bands on the chromosomes in the figure represent three gene loci, specific locations of genes along the chromosome. The matching colors of corresponding loci on the two homologues highlight the fact that homologous chromosomes have genes for the same characters located at the same positions along their lengths. However, as the uppercase and lowercase letters next to the loci indicate, two homologous chromosomes may bear either the same alleles or different ones. Thus, we see the connection between Mendel's laws and homologous chromosomes: *Alleles (alternative versions) of a gene reside at the same locus on homologous chromosomes.*

The diagram here also serves as a review of some of the genetic terms we have encountered to this point. We will return to the chromosomal basis of inheritance in more detail beginning with Module 9.16.

Figure 9.4 Matching gene loci on homologous chromosomes

? An individual is heterozygous, *Gg*, for a gene. According to the law of segregation, each gamete formed by this individual will have *either* the *G* allele *or* the *g* allele. Recalling what you learned about meiosis in Chapter 8, explain the physical basis for this segregation of alleles.

■ The *G* and *g* alleles are located at the same gene locus on homologous chromosomes, which separate during meiosis and are packaged in separate gametes.

9.5 The law of independent assortment is revealed by tracking two characters at once

Two of the seven characters Mendel studied were seed shape and seed color. Mendel's seeds were either round or wrinkled in shape, and they were either yellow or green in color. From monohybrid crosses, Mendel knew that the allele for round shape (designated R) was dominant to the allele for wrinkled shape (r) and that the allele for yellow seed color (Y) was dominant to the allele for green seed color (y). What would result from a mating of parental varieties differing in two characters—a **dihybrid cross?** Mendel crossed homozygous plants having round yellow seeds (genotype $RRYY$) with plants having wrinkled green seeds ($rryy$). As shown in Figure 9.5A, the union of RY and ry gametes yielded hybrids heterozygous for both characteristics ($RrYy$)—that is, *dihybrids*. As we would expect, all of these offspring, the F_1 generation, had round yellow seeds. But were the two characters transmitted from parents to offspring as a package, or was each character inherited independently of the other?

The question was answered when Mendel allowed fertilization to occur among the F_1 plants. If the genes for the two characters were inherited together, as shown on the left in the figure, then the F_1 hybrids would produce only the same two kinds (genotypes) of gametes—RY and ry—that they received from their parents. This hypothesis predicts that the phenotypic ratio of the F_2 generation will be 3 : 1 (three plants with round yellow seeds for every one with wrinkled green seeds),

as in the left Punnett square. If, however, the two seed characters segregated independently, then the F_1 generation would produce four gamete genotypes—RY, rY, Ry, and ry—in equal quantities. The Punnett square on the right shows all possible combinations of alleles that can result in the F_2 generation from the union of four kinds of sperm with four kinds of eggs. This Punnett square shows that there are nine different genotypes in the F_2. However, there are only four phenotypes, with a ratio of 9 : 3 : 3 : 1.

The Punnett square on the right also reveals that a dihybrid cross is equivalent to two monohybrid crosses occurring simultaneously. From the 9 : 3 : 3 : 1 ratio, we can see that there are 12 plants with round seeds to 4 with wrinkled seeds and 12 yellow-seeded plants to 4 green-seeded ones. These 12 : 4 ratios each reduce to 3 : 1, which is the F_2 ratio for a monohybrid cross. Mendel tried his seven pea characters in various dihybrid combinations and always obtained data close to the predicted 9 : 3 : 3 : 1 ratio. These results supported the hypothesis that *each pair of alleles segregates independently of other pairs of alleles during gamete formation.* This is called Mendel's **law of independent assortment.**

Figure 9.5B shows how this law applies to the inheritance of two characters in Labrador retrievers: black versus chocolate coat color and normal vision versus the eye disorder called progressive retinal atrophy (PRA). As you would

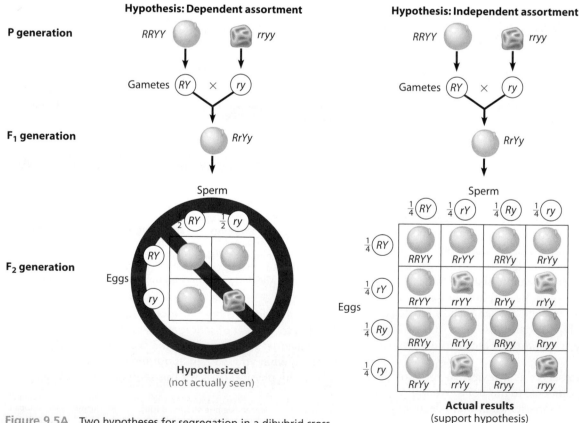

Figure 9.5A Two hypotheses for segregation in a dihybrid cross

| Phenotypes Genotypes | Black coat, normal vision B_N_ | Black coat, blind (PRA) B_nn | Chocolate coat, normal vision bbN_ | Chocolate coat, blind (PRA) bbnn |

Mating of heterozygotes (black, normal vision)

$BbNn \times BbNn$

Phenotypic ratio of offspring

| 9 black coat, normal vision | 3 black coat, blind (PRA) | 3 chocolate coat, normal vision | 1 chocolate coat, blind (PRA) |

Figure 9.5B Independent assortment of two genes in the Labrador retriever

expect, these characters are controlled by separate genes. Black Labs have at least one copy of an allele called *B*, which gives their hairs densely packed granules of a dark pigment. The *B* allele is dominant to *b*, which leads to a less tightly packed distribution of pigment granules. As a result, the coats of dogs with genotype *bb* are chocolate in color. The allele that causes PRA, called *n*, is recessive to allele *N*, which is necessary for normal vision. Thus, only dogs of genotype *nn* become blind from PRA. (In the figure, blanks in the genotypes indicate a second allele of either sort. And if you're wondering about yellow Labs, their color is controlled by a different gene altogether.)

The lower part of Figure 9.5B shows what happens when we mate two heterozygous Labs, both of genotype *BbNn*. The F$_2$ phenotypic ratio will be nine black dogs with normal eyes to three black with PRA to three chocolate with normal eyes to one chocolate with PRA. These results are analogous to the results in Figure 9.5A and demonstrate that the *B* and *N* genes are inherited independently.

? Predict the phenotypes of offspring obtained by mating a black Lab homozygous for both coat color and normal eyes with a chocolate Lab that is blind from PRA.

■ All offspring would be black with normal eyes ($BBNN \times bbnn \rightarrow BbNn$).

9.6 Geneticists use the testcross to determine unknown genotypes

Suppose you have a Labrador retriever with a chocolate coat. Referring to Figure 9.5B, you can tell that its genotype must be *bb*, the only combination of alleles that produces the chocolate-coat phenotype. But what if you had a black Lab? It could have one of two possible genotypes—*BB* or *Bb*—and there is no way

to tell which is correct simply by looking at the dog. To determine your dog's genotype, you need to perform a **testcross,** a mating between an individual of unknown genotype (your dog) and a homozygous recessive (*bb*) individual– in this case, a chocolate Lab.

Figure 9.6 shows the offspring that could result from such a mating. If, as shown on the left, the black parent's genotype is *BB*, we would expect all the offspring to be black because a cross between genotypes *BB* and *bb* can produce only *Bb* offspring. On the other hand, if the black parent is *Bb*, we would expect both black (*Bb*) and chocolate (*bb*) offspring. Thus, the appearance of the offspring reveals the original black dog's genotype.

Mendel used testcrosses to verify that he had true-breeding varieties of plants. The testcross continues to be an important tool of geneticists for determining genotypes.

Web Activity *Dihybrid Cross*

? You use a testcross to determine the genotype of a Lab with normal eyes. Half of the offspring of the testcross are normal and half develop PRA. What is the genotype of the normal parent?

Testcross:

Genotypes: B_ × bb

Two possibilities for the black dog:

BB or Bb

Gametes: B | B b

Offspring:

| | Bb |
| b | Bb |

All black

| | Bb | bb |
| b | Bb | bb |

1 black : 1 chocolate

Figure 9.6 Using a testcross to determine genotype

UN ■

9.7 Mendel's laws reflect the rules of probability

Mendel's strong background in mathematics served him well in his studies of inheritance. He understood, for instance, that the segregation of allele pairs during gamete formation and the re-forming of pairs at fertilization obey the rules of probability—the same rules that apply to the tossing of coins, the rolling of dice, and the drawing of cards. Mendel also appreciated the statistical nature of inheritance. He knew that he needed to obtain large samples—count many offspring from his crosses—before he could begin to interpret inheritance patterns.

Let's see how the rules of probability apply to inheritance. The probability scale ranges from 0 to 1. An event that is certain to occur has a probability of 1, whereas an event that is certain not to occur has a probability of 0. The probabilities of all possible outcomes for an event must add up to 1. With a coin, the chance of tossing heads is $\frac{1}{2}$, and the chance of tossing tails is $\frac{1}{2}$. In a standard deck of 52 playing cards, the chance of drawing a jack of diamonds is $\frac{1}{52}$, and the chance of drawing any card other than the jack of diamonds is $\frac{51}{52}$.

An important lesson we can learn from coin tossing is that for each and every toss of the coin, the probability of heads is $\frac{1}{2}$. In other words, the outcome of any particular toss is unaffected by what has happened on previous attempts. Each toss is an *independent event*.

If two coins are tossed simultaneously, the outcome for each coin is an independent event, unaffected by the other coin. What is the chance that both coins will land heads up? The probability of such a *compound event* is the product of the probabilities of each independent event—for the coins, $\frac{1}{2} \times \frac{1}{2} = \frac{1}{4}$. This is called the **rule of multiplication,** and it holds true for genetics as well as coin tosses. Figure 9.7 represents a cross between F_1 Labrador retrievers that have the *Bb* genotype for coat color. The genetic cross is represented by the tossing of two coins that represent the two gametes (a dime for the egg and a penny for the sperm); the heads side of each coin stands for the dominant *B* allele and the tails side of each coin the recessive *b* allele. What is the probability that a particular F_2 dog will have the *bb* genotype? To produce a *bb* offspring, both egg and sperm must carry the *b* allele. The probability that an egg will have the *b* allele is $\frac{1}{2}$, and the probability that a sperm will have the *b* allele is also $\frac{1}{2}$. By the rule of multiplication, the probability that two *b* alleles will come together at fertilization is $\frac{1}{2} \times \frac{1}{2} = \frac{1}{4}$. This is exactly the answer given by the Punnett square in Figure 9.7. If we know the genotypes of the parents, we can predict the probability for any genotype among the offspring.

Now consider the probability that an F_2 Lab will be heterozygous for the coat-color gene. As Figure 9.7 shows, there are two ways in which F_1 gametes can combine to produce a heterozygous offspring. The dominant (*B*) allele can come from the egg and the recessive (*b*) allele from the sperm, or vice versa. The probability that an event can occur in two or more alternative ways is the *sum* of the separate probabilities of the different ways; this is known as the **rule of addition.** Using this rule, we can calculate the probability of an F_2 heterozygote as $\frac{1}{4} + \frac{1}{4} = \frac{1}{2}$.

By applying the rules of probability to segregation and independent assortment, we can solve some rather complex genetics problems. For instance, we can predict the results of trihybrid crosses, in which three different characters are involved. Consider a cross between two organisms that both have the genotype *AaBbCc*. What is the probability that an offspring from this cross will be a recessive homozygote for all three genes (*aabbcc*)? Since each allele pair assorts independently, we can treat this trihybrid cross as three separate monohybrid crosses:

$Aa \times Aa$: Probability of *aa* offspring $= \frac{1}{4}$

$Bb \times Bb$: Probability of *bb* offspring $= \frac{1}{4}$

$Cc \times Cc$: Probability of *cc* offspring $= \frac{1}{4}$

Because the segregation of each allele pair is an independent event, we use the rule of multiplication to calculate the probability that the offspring will be *aabbcc*:

$$\tfrac{1}{4} aa \times \tfrac{1}{4} bb \times \tfrac{1}{4} cc = \tfrac{1}{64}$$

We could reach the same conclusion by constructing a 64-section Punnett square, but that would take a lot of space!

Web Activity *Gregor's Garden*

? A plant of genotype *AABbCC* is crossed with an *AaBbCc* plant. What is the probability of an offspring having the genotype *AABBCC*?

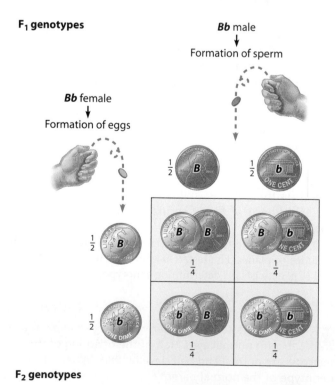

F₁ genotypes

Bb female
↓
Formation of eggs

Bb male
↓
Formation of sperm

$\frac{1}{2}$ **B** $\frac{1}{2}$ **b**

$\frac{1}{2}$ **B**   **BB** $\frac{1}{4}$ **Bb** $\frac{1}{4}$

$\frac{1}{2}$ **b**   **bB** $\frac{1}{4}$ **bb** $\frac{1}{4}$

F₂ genotypes

Figure 9.7 Segregation and fertilization as chance events

■ $\frac{1}{16}$ (that is, $\frac{1}{2} \times \frac{1}{4} \times \frac{1}{2}$)

Genetic traits in humans can be tracked through family pedigrees

Mendel's laws apply to the inheritance of many human traits. **Figure 9.8A** illustrates alternative forms of three human characters that are each thought to be determined by simple dominant-recessive inheritance at one gene locus. (The genetic basis of many other human characters—such as eye and hair color—involves several genes and is not well understood.) If we call the dominant allele of any such gene *A,* the dominant phenotype results from either the homozygous genotype *AA* or the heterozygous genotype *Aa.* Recessive phenotypes always result from the homozygous genotype *aa.* In genetics, the word *dominant* does not imply that a phenotype is either normal or more common than a recessive phenotype; wild-type traits (those prevailing in nature) are not necessarily specified by dominant alleles. In genetics, dominance means that a heterozygote (*Aa*), carrying only a single copy of a dominant allele, displays the dominant phenotype. By contrast, the phenotype of the corresponding recessive allele is seen only in a homozygote (*aa*). Recessive traits are often more common in the population than dominant ones. For example, the absence of freckles is more common than their presence.

How can we determine the inheritance pattern of a particular human trait? Since we obviously cannot control human matings, geneticists must analyze the results of matings that have already occurred. First, the geneticist collects as much information as possible about a family's history for the trait of interest. The next step is to assemble this information into a family tree—the family **pedigree.** (You may associate pedigrees with purebred animals—such as racehorses or championship dogs—but they can represent human matings just as well.) To analyze the pedigree, the geneticist applies logic and the Mendelian laws you have learned.

Let's apply this approach to the example in **Figure 9.8B,** which shows a pedigree that traces the incidence of free versus attached earlobes. The letter *F* stands for the dominant allele for free earlobes, and *f* symbolizes the recessive allele for attached earlobes. In the pedigree, squares represent males, circles represent females, and colored symbols indicate that the person is affected by the trait under investigation (in this case, attached earlobes). The earliest generation studied is at the top of the pedigree.

By applying Mendel's laws, we can deduce that the attached allele is recessive because that is the only way that

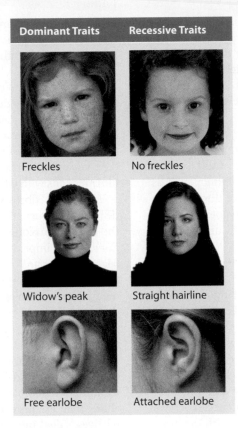

Figure 9.8A Examples of single-gene inherited traits in humans

one of the third-generation sisters (at the bottom of the pedigree) could have attached earlobes when both her parents did not. We can therefore label all the individuals with attached earlobes in the pedigree (that is, all those with colored circles or squares) as homozygous recessive (*ff*). Mendel's laws also enable us to deduce the genotypes for most of the people in the pedigree. For example, both of the second generation parents must have carried the *f* allele (which they passed on to the affected daughter) along with the *F* allele that gave them free earlobes. The same must be true of the first set of grandparents because they both had free earlobes but their two sons had attached earlobes.

Notice that we cannot deduce the genotype of every member of the pedigree. For example, the sister with the free earlobe must have at least one *F* allele, but it is possible that she could be *FF* or *Ff.* We cannot distinguish between these two possibilities using the available data.

Figure 9.8B Pedigree showing inheritance of attached versus free earlobe in a hypothetical family

? Imagine the second sister (who has attached earlobes) married a man with free earlobes and they had a daughter. What phenotype of this daughter would allow us to deduce all three genotypes in that family?

■ If the daughter had free earlobes, then she and her father must be *ff* and her mother must be *Ff.*

Many inherited disorders in humans are controlled by a single gene

The genetic disorders listed in Table 9.9 at the bottom of the next page are known to be inherited as dominant or recessive traits controlled by a single gene locus. These disorders show simple inheritance patterns like the traits Mendel studied in pea plants. The genes discussed in this module are all located on autosomes (chromosomes other than the sex chromosomes X and Y; see Module 8.12).

Recessive Disorders   Most human genetic disorders are recessive. They range in severity from relatively mild, such as albinism (lack of pigmentation), to life-threatening, such as cystic fibrosis. Most people who have recessive disorders are born to normal parents who are both heterozygotes—that is, who are **carriers** of the recessive allele for the disorder but are phenotypically normal.

Using Mendel's laws, we can predict the fract ion of affected offspring likely to result from a mating between two carriers. Consider a form of inherited deafness caused by a recessive allele (Figure 9.9A). Suppose two heterozygous carriers (*Dd*) had a child. What is the probability that this child would be deaf? As the Punnett square in Figure 9.9A shows, each child of two carriers has a $\frac{1}{4}$ chance of inheriting two recessive alleles. Thus, we can say that about one-fourth of the children of this marriage are likely to be deaf. We can also say that a hearing ("normal") child from such a marriage has a $\frac{2}{3}$ chance of being a carrier (that is, two out of three of the offspring with the hearing phenotype are likely to be carriers). We can apply this same method of pedigree analysis and prediction to any genetic trait controlled by a single gene locus.

The most common fatal genetic disease in the United States is **cystic fibrosis (CF).** Affecting about 30,000 children and adults in the United States and 70,000 worldwide, the CF allele is carried by about one in 25 people of European ancestry. A person with two copies of this allele has cystic fibrosis, which is characterized by an excessive secretion of very thick mucus from the lungs, pancreas, and other organs. This mucus can interfere with breathing, digestion, and liver function and makes the person vulnerable to recurrent bacterial infections. Although there is no cure for this fatal disease, strict adherence to a daily health regimen—including gentle pounding on the chest and back to clear the airway, inhaled antibiotics, and a high-calorie diet—can have a profound impact on the health of the affected person. Once invariably fatal in childhood, tremendous advances in treatment have raised the median survival age of Americans with CF to 37.

Like cystic fibrosis, most genetic disorders are not evenly distributed across all ethnic groups. Such uneven distribution is the result of prolonged geographic isolation of certain populations. For example, the isolated lives of the early inhabitants of Martha's Vineyard (an island off the coast of Massachusetts) led to frequent marriages between close relatives. Consequently, the frequency of an allele that causes deafness was high, and the deafness allele was rarely transmitted to outsiders.

With the increased mobility in most societies today, it is relatively unlikely that two carriers of a rare, harmful allele will meet and mate. However, the probability increases greatly if close relatives marry and have children. People with recent common ancestors are more likely to carry the same recessive alleles than are unrelated people. Therefore, a mating of close relatives, called **inbreeding,** is more likely to produce offspring homozygous for recessive traits. Such effects can be observed in many types of inbred animals. For example, dogs that have been inbred for appearance may have serious genetic disorders, such as weak hip joints, eye problems, or undesirable behaviors. The detrimental effects of inbreeding are also seen in some endangered species, such as cheetahs.

Geneticists debate the extent to which human inbreeding increases the risk of inherited diseases. Many harmful mutations have such severe effects that a homozygous embryo spontaneously aborts long before birth. Still, most societies have taboos and laws forbidding marriages between close relatives. These rules may have arisen out of the observation that stillbirths and birth defects are more common when parents are closely related.

Dominant Disorders   Although many harmful alleles are recessive, a number of human disorders are caused by dominant alleles. Some are nonlethal conditions, such as extra fingers and toes (called polydactyly) or webbed fingers and toes.

One serious dominant disorder is **achondroplasia,** a form of dwarfism. In people with this disorder, the head and torso of the body develop normally, but the arms and legs are short (Figure 9.9B, top of next page). About one out of every 25,000 people has achondroplasia. The homozygous dominant genotype causes death of the embryo, and therefore only heterozygotes, individuals with a single copy of the defective allele, have this disorder. (This also means that a person with achondroplasia

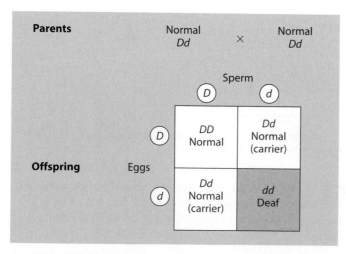

Parents	Normal *Dd*	×	Normal *Dd*

		Sperm	
		D	d
Offspring	Eggs		
	D	DD Normal	Dd Normal (carrier)
	d	Dd Normal (carrier)	dd Deaf

Figure 9.9A   Offspring produced by parents who are both carriers for a recessive disorder

has a 50% chance of passing the condition on to any children.) Therefore, all those who do not have achondroplasia, more than 99.99% of the population, are homozygous for the recessive allele. This example makes it clear that a dominant allele is not necessarily more common in a population than the corresponding recessive allele.

Dominant alleles that cause lethal diseases are, in fact, much less common than lethal recessives. One reason for this difference is that the dominant lethal allele cannot be carried by heterozygotes without affecting them. Many lethal dominant alleles result from mutations in a sperm or egg that subsequently kill the embryo. And if the afflicted individual is born but does not survive long enough to reproduce, he or she will not pass on the lethal allele to future generations. This is in contrast to lethal recessive mutations, which are perpetuated from generation to generation by healthy (unaffected) heterozygous carriers.

A lethal dominant allele can escape elimination, however, if it does not cause death until a relatively advanced age. One such example is the allele that causes **Huntington's disease,** a degenerative disorder of the nervous system that usually does not appear until 35 to 45 years of age. Once the deterioration of the nervous system begins, it is irreversible and inevitably

Figure 9.9B Dr. Michael C. Ain, a specialist in the repair of bone defects caused by achondroplasia and related disorders

fatal. Because the allele for Huntington's disease is dominant, any child born to a parent with the allele has a 50% chance of inheriting the allele and the disorder. This example makes it clear that the dominant allele is not necessarily "better" than the corresponding recessive allele.

Until relatively recently, the onset of symptoms was the only way to know if a person had inherited the Huntington's allele. This is no longer the case. By analyzing DNA samples from a large family with a high incidence of the disorder, geneticists tracked the Huntington's allele to a locus near the tip of chromosome 4, and the gene has now been sequenced. This information led to development of a test that can detect the presence of the Huntington's allele in an individual's genome. This is one of several genetic tests currently available. We'll discuss this topic in greater depth in the next module.

> **?** Peter is a 30-year-old man whose father died of Huntington's disease. Neither Peter's mother nor a much older sister show any signs of Huntington's. What is the probability that Peter has inherited Huntington's disease?

$\frac{1}{2}$ ■

TABLE 9.9	SOME AUTOSOMAL DISORDERS IN HUMANS			
Disorder	**Major Symptoms**		**Incidence**	**Comments**
Recessive disorders				
Albinism	Lack of pigment in skin, hair, and eyes		$\frac{1}{22,000}$	Prone to skin cancer
Cystic fibrosis	Excess mucus in lungs, digestive tract, liver; increased susceptibility to infections; death in early childhood unless treated		$\frac{1}{2,500}$ Caucasians	See Module 9.9
Galactosemia	Accumulation of galactose in tissues; mental retardation; eye and liver damage		$\frac{1}{100,000}$	Treated by eliminating galactose from diet
Phenylketonuria (PKU)	Accumulation of phenylalanine in blood; lack of normal skin pigment; mental retardation		$\frac{1}{10,000}$ in U.S. and Europe	See Module 9.10
Sickle-cell disease	Sickled red blood cells; damage to many tissues		$\frac{1}{400}$ African-Americans	See Module 9.13
Tay-Sachs disease	Lipid accumulation in brain cells; mental deficiency; blindness; death in childhood		$\frac{1}{3,500}$ Jews from central Europe	See Module 4.11
Dominant disorders				
Achondroplasia	Dwarfism		$\frac{1}{25,000}$	See Module 9.9
Alzheimer's disease (one type)	Mental deterioration; usually strikes late in life		Not known	
Huntington's disease	Mental deterioration and uncontrollable movements; strikes in middle age		$\frac{1}{25,000}$	See Module 9.9
Hypercholesterolemia	Excess cholesterol in blood; heart disease		$\frac{1}{500}$ are heterozygous	See Module 9.11

9.10 New technologies can provide insight into one's genetic legacy

Some prospective parents are aware that they have an increased risk of having a baby with a genetic disease. For example, many pregnant women over age 35 know that they have a heightened risk of bearing children with Down syndrome (see Module 8.20), and some couples are aware that a certain genetic disease runs in their families. These potential parents may want to learn more about their own and their baby's genetic makeup. Modern technologies offer ways to obtain such information before conception, during pregnancy, and after birth.

Genetic Testing Because most children with recessive disorders are born to healthy parents, the genetic risk for many diseases is determined by whether the prospective parents are carriers of the recessive allele. For an increasing number of genetic disorders, including Tay-Sachs disease, sickle-cell disease, and one form of cystic fibrosis (see Table 9.9), tests are available that can distinguish between individuals who have no disease-causing alleles and those who are heterozygous carriers. Other parents may know that a dominant but late-appearing disease, such as Huntington's disease, runs in their family. Such

people may benefit from genetic tests for dominant alleles. Information from genetic testing (also called genetic screening) can inform decisions about whether to have a child.

Fetal Testing Several technologies are available for detecting harmful genetic conditions in a fetus. Genetic testing before birth requires the collection of fetal cells. In a procedure called **amniocentesis,** performed between weeks 14 and 20 of pregnancy, a physician carefully inserts a needle into the mother's uterus, avoiding the fetus (Figure 9.10A, left). The physician extracts about 10 milliliters (2 teaspoonsful) of the amniotic fluid that bathes the developing fetus. Tests for genetic disorders can be performed on fetal cells (mostly shed skin) present in the fluid. Before testing, these cells are usually cultured in the laboratory for several weeks. By then, enough dividing cells can be harvested to allow karyotyping and the detection of chromosomal abnormalities such as Down syndrome. Biochemical tests can also be performed on the cultured cells, revealing conditions such as Tay-Sachs disease.

Figure 9.10A Testing a fetus for genetic disorders

In another procedure, **chorionic villus sampling (CVS),** a physician extracts a tiny sample of chorionic villus tissue from the placenta, the organ that carries nourishment and wastes between the fetus and the mother. The tissue can be obtained using a narrow, flexible tube inserted through the mother's vagina and cervix into the uterus (see Figure 9.10A, right). Results of karyotyping and some biochemical tests can be available within 24 hours. The speed of CVS is an advantage over amniocentesis. Another advantage is that CVS can be performed as early as the 8th to 10th week of pregnancy.

Unfortunately, both amniocentesis and CVS pose some risk of complications, such as maternal bleeding, miscarriage, or premature birth. Complication rates for amniocentesis and CVS are about 1% and 2%, respectively. Because of the risks, these procedures are usually reserved for situations in which the chance of a genetic disorder is reasonably high. Recently, medical scientists have developed methods for isolating fetal cells from the mother's blood or cervical mucus. Although very few in number, these cells can be cultured and tested with little risk to the mother or child.

Blood tests on the mother at 15 to 20 weeks of pregnancy can help identify fetuses at risk for certain birth defects—and thus candidates for further testing that may require more invasive procedures (such as amniocentesis). The most widely used blood test measures the mother's blood level of alpha-fetoprotein (AFP), a protein produced by the fetus. High levels of AFP may indicate a neural tube defect in the fetus. (The neural tube is an embryonic structure that develops into the brain and spinal cord.) Low levels of AFP may indicate Down syndrome. For a more complete risk profile, a woman's doctor may order a "triple screen test," which measures AFP as well as two other hormones produced by the placenta. Abnormal levels of these substances in the maternal blood may also point to a risk of Down syndrome.

Fetal Imaging Other techniques enable a physician to examine a fetus directly for anatomical deformities. The most widely used procedure is **ultrasound imaging,** which uses sound waves to produce a picture of the fetus. Figure 9.10B shows an ultrasound scanner, which emits high-frequency sounds, beyond the range of hearing. When the sound waves bounce off the fetus, the echoes produce an image on the monitor. The inset image in Figure 9.10B shows a fetus at about 18 weeks. Ultrasound imaging is noninvasive (no foreign objects are inserted into the mother's body) and has no known risk. In another imaging method, fetoscopy, a needle-thin tube containing a fiber optic viewing scope is inserted into the uterus. Fetoscopy can provide highly detailed images of the fetus but, unlike ultrasound, carries risk of complications.

Newborn Screening Some genetic disorders can be detected at birth by simple tests that are now routinely performed in most hospitals in the United States. One common screening program is for phenylketonuria (PKU), a recessively inherited disorder that occurs in about one out of every 10,000 births in the United States. Children with this disease cannot properly break down the naturally occurring amino acid phenylalanine; an accumulation of phenylalanine may lead to mental retardation. However, if the deficiency is

Figure 9.10B Ultrasound scanning of a fetus

detected in the newborn, a special diet low in phenylalanine can usually prevent retardation. Unfortunately, few other genetic disorders are currently treatable.

Ethical Considerations As new technologies such as fetal imaging and testing become more widespread, geneticists are working to make sure that they do not cause more problems than they solve. Consider the tests for identifying carriers of recessive diseases. Such information may enable people with family histories of genetic disorders to make informed decisions about having children. But these new methods for genetic screening pose problems, too. If confidentiality is breached, will carriers be stigmatized? For example, will they be denied health or life insurance, even though they themselves are healthy? Will misinformed employers equate "carrier" with disease? Geneticists stress that patients seeking genetic testing should receive counseling both before and after to clarify their family history, to explain the test, and to help them cope with the results. But will sufficient numbers of genetic counselors be available to help individuals understand their test results?

Couples at risk for conceiving children with genetic disorders may now learn a great deal about their unborn children. In particular, CVS gives parents a chance to become informed very early in pregnancy. What is to be done with such information? If fetal tests reveal a serious disorder, the parents must choose between terminating the pregnancy and preparing themselves for a baby with severe problems. Identifying a genetic disease early can give families time to prepare—emotionally, medically, and financially.

Advances in biotechnology offer possibilities for reducing human suffering, but not before key ethical issues are resolved. The dilemmas posed by human genetics reinforce one of this book's themes: the immense social implications of biology.

? What is the primary benefit of genetic screening by CVS? What is the primary risk?

■ CVS allows genetic screening to be performed very early in pregnancy, but it carries a risk of miscarriage.

9.11 Incomplete dominance results in intermediate phenotypes

Mendel's laws explain inheritance in terms of discrete factors—genes—that are passed along from generation to generation according to simple rules of probability. Mendel's laws are valid for all sexually reproducing organisms, including garden peas, show dogs, and human beings. But just as the basic rules of musical harmony cannot account for all the rich sounds of a symphony, Mendel's laws stop short of explaining some patterns of genetic inheritance. In fact, for most sexually reproducing organisms, cases where Mendel's laws can strictly account for the patterns of inheritance are relatively rare. More often, the inheritance patterns are more complex, as we will see in this and the next four modules.

The F_1 offspring of Mendel's pea crosses always looked like one of the two parental varieties. This situation is called **complete dominance;** the dominant allele had the same phenotypic effect whether present in one or two copies. But for some characters, the appearance of F_1 hybrids falls *between* the phenotypes of the two parental varieties, an effect called **incomplete dominance.** For instance, as **Figure 9.11A** illustrates, when red snapdragons are crossed with white snapdragons, all the F_1 hybrids have pink flowers. This third phenotype results from flowers of the heterozygote having less red pigment than the red homozygotes.

Incomplete dominance does *not* support the blending hypothesis, which would predict that the red and white traits could never be retrieved from the pink hybrids. As the Punnett square at the bottom of Figure 9.11A shows, the F_2 offspring appear in a phenotypic ratio of one red to two pink to one white, because the red and white alleles segregate during gamete formation in the pink F_1 hybrids. In incomplete dominance, the phenotypes of heterozygotes differ from the two homozygous varieties, and the genotypic ratio and the phenotypic ratio are both 1 : 2 : 1 in the F_2 generation.

We also see examples of incomplete dominance in humans. One case involves a recessive allele (h) that can cause *hypercholesterolemia,* dangerously high levels of cholesterol in the blood. Normal individuals are HH. Heterozygotes ($Hh;$ about one in 500 people) have blood cholesterol levels about twice normal. They are unusually prone to atherosclerosis, the blockage of arteries by cholesterol buildup in artery walls, and they may have heart attacks from blocked heart arteries by their mid-30s. Hypercholesterolemia is even more serious in homozygous individuals ($hh;$ about one in a million people). Homozygotes have about five times the normal amount of blood cholesterol and may have heart attacks as early as age 2.

Figure 9.11B illustrates the molecular basis for hypercholesterolemia. The dominant allele, which normal individuals carry in duplicate (HH), specifies a cell-surface protein called an LDL receptor. LDLs, or low-density lipoproteins, are cholesterol-containing particles in the blood. The LDL

P generation

Red
RR × White
rr

Gametes (R) (r)

F₁ generation

Pink
Rr

Gametes ½(R) ½(r)

Sperm
½(R) ½(r)

F₂ generation

Eggs ½(R) | RR | rR |
½(r) | Rr | rr |

Figure 9.11A Incomplete dominance in snapdragon color

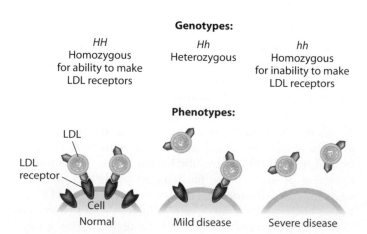

Genotypes:

HH
Homozygous
for ability to make
LDL receptors

Hh
Heterozygous

hh
Homozygous
for inability to make
LDL receptors

Phenotypes:

LDL

LDL
receptor

Cell

Normal   Mild disease   Severe disease

Figure 9.11B Incomplete dominance in human hypercholesterolemia receptors pick up LDL particles from the blood and promote their uptake by cells that break down the cholesterol. This process helps prevent the accumulation of cholesterol in arteries. Without the receptors, lethal levels of LDL build up in the blood. Heterozygotes (*Hh*) have only half the normal number of LDL receptors, and homozygous recessives (*hh*) have none.

? Why is a testcross unnecessary to determine whether a snapdragon with red flowers is homozygous or heterozygous?

■ Because the homozygotes and heterozygotes differ in phenotype: red flowers for the dominant homozygote and pink flowers for the heterozygote.

9.12 Many genes have more than two alleles in the population

So far, we have discussed inheritance patterns involving only two alleles per gene. But most genes can be found in populations in more than two versions, known as multiple alleles. Although any particular individual carries, at most, two different alleles for a particular gene, in cases of multiple alleles, more than two possible alleles exist in the wider population.

For instance, the **ABO blood group** phenotype in humans involves three alleles of a single gene. These three alleles, in various combinations, produce four phenotypes: A person's blood group may be either O, A, B, or AB. These letters refer to two carbohydrates, designated A and B, that may be found on the surface of red blood cells. A person's red blood cells may have carbohydrate A (type A blood), carbohydrate B (type B), both (type AB), or neither (type O). Matching compatible blood groups is critical for safe blood transfusions. If a donor's blood cells have a carbohydrate (A or B) that is foreign to the recipient, then the recipient's immune system produces blood proteins called antibodies (see Module 24.8) that bind specifically to the foreign carbohydrates and cause the donor blood cells to clump together, potentially killing the recipient. The clumping reaction is also the basis of a blood-typing test performed in the laboratory. Figure 9.12 shows which combinations of blood groups result in clumping.

The four blood groups result from various combinations of the three different alleles, symbolized as I^A (for the enzyme that adds carbohydrate A to red blood cells), I^B (for B), and i (for neither A nor B). Each person inherits one of these alleles from each parent. Because there are three alleles, there are six possible genotypes, as listed in the figure. Both the I^A and I^B alleles are dominant to the i allele. Thus, I^AI^A and I^Ai people have type A blood, and I^BI^B and I^Bi people have type B. Recessive homozygotes, ii, have type O blood because their blood cells have neither the A nor the B carbohydrate. The I^A and I^B alleles are **codominant;** both alleles are expressed in heterozygous individuals (I^AI^B), who have type AB blood. Note that codominance (the expression of both alleles) is different from incomplete dominance (the expression of one intermediate trait).

? Maria has type O blood and her sister has type AB blood. The girls know that both of their maternal grandparents are type A. What are the genotypes of the girls' parents?

■ Their mother is I^Ai; their father is I^Bi.

Blood Group (Phenotype)	Genotypes	Red Blood Cells	Antibodies Present in Blood	Reaction When Blood from Groups Below Is Mixed with Antibodies from Groups at Left			
				O	A	B	AB
O	*ii*		Anti-A Anti-B				
A	I^AI^A or I^Ai	Carbohydrate A	Anti-B				
B	I^BI^B or I^Bi	Carbohydrate B	Anti-A				
AB	I^AI^B		—				

Figure 9.12 Multiple alleles for the ABO blood groups

A single gene may affect many phenotypic characters

All of our genetic examples to this point have been cases in which each gene specifies only one hereditary character. Most genes, however, influence multiple characters, a property called **pleiotropy** (from the Greek *pleion*, more).

An example of pleiotropy in humans is sickle-cell disease, a disorder characterized by the diverse symptoms shown in **Figure 9.13**. The direct effect of the sickle-cell allele is to make red blood cells produce abnormal hemoglobin molecules. These molecules tend to link together and crystallize, especially when the oxygen content of the blood is lower than usual because of high altitude, overexertion, or respiratory ailments. As the hemoglobin crystallizes, the normally disk-shaped red blood cells deform to a sickle shape with jagged edges, as shown in the micrograph. Sickled cells are destroyed rapidly by the body, and the destruction of these cells may seriously lower the individual's red cell count, causing anemia and general weakening of the body. Also, because of their angular shape, sickled cells do not flow smoothly in the blood and tend to accumulate and clog tiny blood vessels.

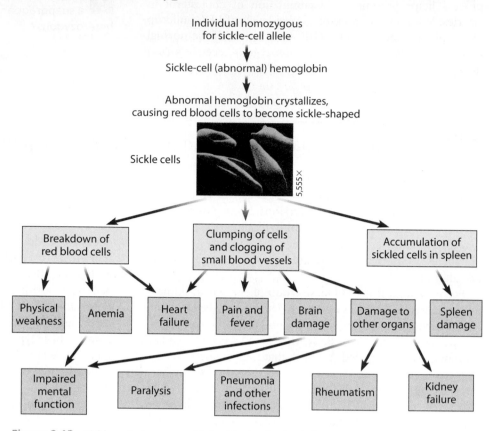

Figure 9.13 Sickle-cell disease, multiple effects of a single human gene

Blood flow to body parts is reduced, resulting in periodic fever, severe pain, and damage to various organs, including the heart, brain, and kidneys. Sickled cells also accumulate in the spleen, damaging it. Blood transfusions and certain drugs may relieve some of the symptoms, but there is no cure, and sickle-cell disease kills about 100,000 people in the world annually.

In most cases, only people who are homozygous for the sickle-cell allele suffer from the disease. Heterozygotes, who have one sickle-cell allele and one nonsickle allele, are usually healthy, although in rare cases they may experience some pleiotropic effects when oxygen in the blood is severely reduced, such as at very high altitudes. These effects may occur because the nonsickle and sickle-cell alleles are codominant: Both alleles are expressed in heterozygous individuals, and their red blood cells contain both normal and abnormal hemoglobin. Heterozygotes are said to have "sickle-cell trait."

Sickle-cell disease is the most common inherited disorder among people of African descent, striking one in 400 African-Americans. About one in ten African-Americans is a carrier—a heterozygote. Among Americans of other ancestry, the sickle-cell allele is extremely rare.

One in ten is an unusually high frequency of carriers for an allele with such harmful effects in homozygotes. We might expect that the frequency of the sickle-cell allele in the population would be much lower because many homozygotes die before passing their genes to the next generation. The high frequency appears to be a vestige of the roots of African-Americans. Sickle-cell disease is most common in tropical Africa, where the deadly disease malaria is also prevalent. The protistan parasite that causes malaria spends part of its life cycle inside red blood cells. When it enters those of a person with the sickle-cell allele, it triggers sickling. The body destroys most of the sickled cells, and the parasite does not grow well in those that remain. Consequently, sickle-cell carriers are resistant to malaria, and in many parts of Africa, they live longer and have more offspring than noncarriers who are exposed to malaria. In this way, malaria has kept the frequency of the sickle-cell allele relatively high in much of the African continent. To put it in evolutionary terms, as long as malaria is a danger, individuals with the sickle-cell allele have a selective advantage.

? How does sickle-cell disease exemplify the concept of pleiotropy?

Homozygosity for the sickle-cell allele causes abnormal hemoglobin, and the impact of the abnormal hemoglobin on the shape of red blood cells leads to a cascade of symptoms in multiple organs of the body.

A single character may be influenced by many genes

Mendel studied genetic characters that could be classified on an either-or basis, such as purple or white flower color. However, many characteristics, such as human skin color and height, vary in a population along a continuum. Many such features result from **polygenic inheritance,** the additive effects of two or more genes on a single phenotypic character. (This is the converse of pleiotropy, in which a single gene affects several characters.)

Let's consider a hypothetical example. Assume that the continuous variation in human skin color is controlled by three genes that are inherited separately, like Mendel's pea genes. (Actually, genetic evidence indicates that *at least* three genes control this character.) The "dark-skin" allele for each gene (*A*, *B*, or *C*) contributes one "unit" of darkness to the phenotype and is incompletely dominant to the other allele (*a*, *b*, or *c*). A person who is *AABBCC* would be very dark, whereas an *aabbcc* individual would be very light. An *AaBbCc* person (resulting, for example, from a mating between an *AABBCC* person and an *aabbcc* person) would have skin of an intermediate shade. Because the alleles have an additive effect, the genotype *AaBbCc* would produce the same skin color as any other genotype with just three dark-skin alleles, such as *AABbcc*.

The Punnett square in **Figure 9.14** shows all possible genotypes of offspring from a mating of two triple heterozygotes (the F₁ generation here). The row of squares below the Punnett square shows the seven skin-color phenotypes that would theoretically result from this mating. The seven bars in the graph at the bottom of the figure depict the relative numbers of each of the phenotypes in the F₂ generation. In real human populations, skin color has even more variations than shown in the figure, in part for reasons we discuss in the next module.

Up to this point in the chapter, we have presented four types of inheritance patterns that are extensions of Mendel's laws of inheritance: incomplete dominance, codominance, pleiotropy, and polygenic inheritance. It is important to realize that these patterns are extensions of Mendel's model, rather than exceptions to it. From Mendel's garden pea experiments came data supporting a particulate theory of inheritance, with the particles (genes) being transmitted according to the same rules of chance that govern the tossing of coins. The particulate theory holds true for all inheritance patterns. In the next module, we consider another important source of deviation from Mendel's standard model: the effect of the environment.

> **?** Based on the skin-color model in Figure 9.14, an *AaBbcc* individual would be indistinguishable in phenotype from which of the following individuals: *AAbbcc, aaBBcc, AabbCc, Aabbcc,* or *aaBbCc*?
>
> ■ *All except AabbCc*

Figure 9.14 A model for polygenic inheritance of skin color

9.15 The environment affects many characters

In the previous module, we saw how a set of three hypothetical human skin-color genes could produce seven different skin-color phenotypes. If we examine a real human population for the skin-color phenotype, we would see more shades than just seven. The true range might be similar to the entire spectrum of color under the bell-shaped curve in Figure 9.14. In fact, no matter how carefully we characterize the genes for skin color, a purely genetic description will always be incomplete. This is because some intermediate shades of skin color result from the effects of environmental factors, such as exposure to the sun.

Many characters result from a combination of heredity and environment. For example, although a single tree is locked into its inherited genotype, its leaves vary in size, shape, and color, depending on exposure to wind and sun and the tree's nutritional state. For humans, nutrition influences height; exercise alters build; sun-tanning darkens the skin; and experience improves performance on intelligence tests. As geneticists learn more and more about our genes, it is becoming clear that many human phenotypes—such as risk of heart disease and cancer and susceptibility to alcoholism and schizophrenia—are influenced by both genes and environment.

Whether human characters are more influenced by genes or by the environment—nature or nurture—is a very old and hotly contested debate. For some characters, such as the ABO blood group, a given genotype mandates a very specific phenotype. In contrast, a person's blood count of red and white cells varies quite a bit, depending on such factors as the altitude, the customary level of physical activity, and the presence of infectious agents.

It is important to realize that the individual features of any organism arise from a combination of genetic and environmental factors. Simply spending time with identical twins will convince anyone that environment, and not just genes, affects a

Figure 9.15 Varying phenotypes due to environmental factors in genetically identical twins

person's traits (**Figure 9.15**). However, there is an important difference between these two sources of variation: Only genetic influences are inherited. Any effects of the environment are not passed on to the next generation.

? Why was Mendel able to ignore environmental influences on his pea plants?

■ The characters he chose for study were all entirely genetically determined.

The Chromosomal Basis of Inheritance

9.16 Chromosome behavior accounts for Mendel's laws

Mendel published his results in 1866, but not until long after he died did biologists understand the significance of his work. Cell biologists worked out the processes of mitosis and meiosis in the late 1800s (see Chapter 8 to review these processes). Then, around 1900, researchers began to notice parallels between the behavior of chromosomes and the behavior of Mendel's heritable factors. One of biology's most important concepts—the **chromosome theory of inheritance**—was emerging. The chromosome theory states that genes occupy specific loci (positions) on chromosomes and it is the chromosomes that undergo segregation and independent assortment during

meiosis. Thus, it is the behavior of chromosomes during meiosis and fertilization that accounts for inheritance patterns.

We can see the chromosomal basis of Mendel's laws by following the fates of two genes during meiosis and fertilization in pea plants. In **Figure 9.16**, we picture the genes for seed shape (alleles R and r) and seed color (Y and y) as black bars on different chromosomes. We start with the F_1 generation, in which all plants have the $RrYy$ genotype. To simplify the diagram, we show only two of the seven pairs of pea chromosomes and three of the stages of meiosis: metaphase I, anaphase I, and metaphase II.

To see the chromosomal basis of the law of segregation, let's follow just the homologous pair of long chromosomes, the ones carrying R and r, taking either the left or the right branch from the F_1 cell. Whichever arrangement the chromosomes assume at metaphase I, the two alleles *segregate* as the homologous chromosomes separate in anaphase I. And at the end of meiosis II, a single long chromosome ends up in each of the gametes. Fertilization then recombines the two alleles at random, resulting in F_2 offspring that are $\frac{1}{4}$ *RR*, $\frac{1}{2}$ *Rr*, and $\frac{1}{4}$ *rr*. The ratio of round to wrinkled phenotypes is thus $3:1$ (12 round to 4 wrinkled), the ratio Mendel observed (see Figure 9.3A).

To see the chromosomal basis of the law of independent assortment, follow both the long and short (nonhomologous) chromosomes through the figure below. Two alternative, equally likely arrangements of tetrads can occur at metaphase I. The nonhomologous chromosomes (and their genes) assort independently, leading to four gamete genotypes. Random fertilization leads to the $9:3:3:1$ phenotypic ratio in the F_2 generation, as you saw in Figure 9.5A.

🎧 **MP3 Tutor** *Chromosomal Basis of Inheritance*

? Which of Mendel's laws have their physical basis in the following phases of meiosis: (a) the orientation of homologous chromosome pairs in metaphase I; (b) the separation of homologues in anaphase I?

■ (a) the law of independent assortment; (b) the law of segregation

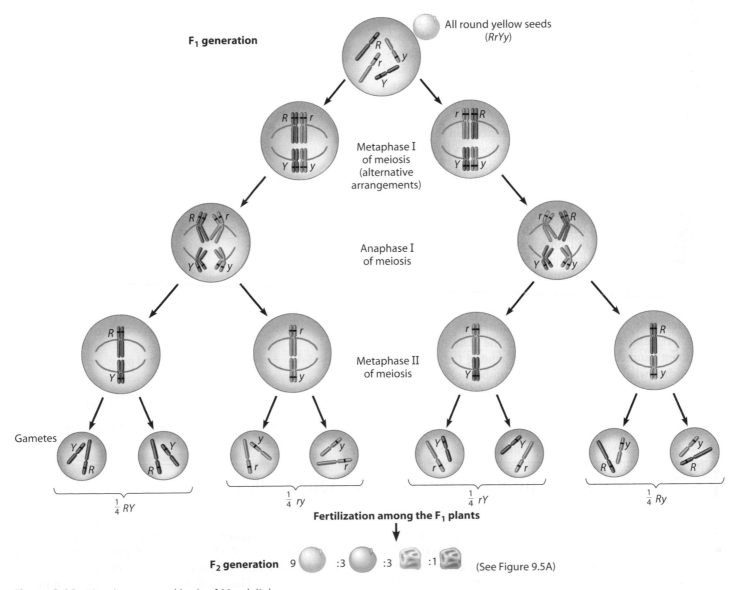

Figure 9.16 The chromosomal basis of Mendel's laws

10.2 DNA and RNA are polymers of nucleotides

By the time Hershey and Chase performed their experiments, much was already known about DNA. Scientists had identified all its atoms and knew how they were covalently bonded to one another. What was not understood was the specific arrangement of atoms that gave DNA its unique properties—the capacity to store genetic information, copy it, and pass it from generation to generation. However, only one year after Hershey and Chase published their results, scientists figured out the three-dimensional structure of DNA and the basic strategy of how it works. We will examine that momentous discovery in Module 10.3. First, let's look at the underlying chemical structure of DNA and its chemical cousin RNA.

Recall from Module 3.16 that DNA and RNA are nucleic acids consisting of long chains (polymers) of chemical units (monomers) called **nucleotides.** A very simple diagram of such a polymer, or **polynucleotide,** is shown on the far left in **Figure 10.2A**. This chain shows one arrangement of the four types of nucleotides that make up DNA. Each type of DNA nucleotide has a different nitrogenous base: adenine (A), cytosine (C), thymine (T), or guanine (G). Because nucleotides can occur in a polynucleotide in any sequence and polynucleotides

vary in length from long to very long, the number of possible polynucleotides is enormous.

Looking more closely at our polynucleotide, we see in the center of Figure 10.2A that each nucleotide consists of three components: a nitrogenous base (in DNA, A, C, T, or G), a sugar (blue), and a phosphate group (yellow). The nucleotides are joined to one another by covalent bonds between the sugar of one nucleotide and the phosphate of the next. This results in a **sugar-phosphate backbone,** a repeating pattern of sugar-phosphate-sugar-phosphate. The nitrogenous bases are arranged as appendages all along this backbone.

Examining a single nucleotide in even more detail (on the right in Figure 10.2A), we note the chemical structure of its three components. The phosphate group has a phosphorus atom (P) at its center and is the source of the *acid* in nucleic acid. The sugar has five carbon atoms (shown in red here for emphasis)—four in its ring and one extending above the ring. The ring also includes an oxygen atom. The sugar is called deoxyribose because, compared with the sugar ribose, it is missing an oxygen atom. (Notice that the C atom in the lower right corner of the ring is bonded to an H atom instead of to an

Figure 10.2A The structure of a DNA polynucleotide

Figure 10.2B   Nitrogenous bases of DNA

Figure 10.2C   An RNA nucleotide

Figure 10.2D   Part of an RNA polynucleotide

—OH group, as it is in ribose; see Figure 10.2C.) The full name for DNA is deoxyribonucleic acid, with the "nucleic" portion of the word coming from DNA's location in the nuclei of eukaryotic cells. The nitrogenous base (thymine, in our example) has a ring consisting of nitrogen and carbon atoms with various functional groups attached. In contrast to the acidic phosphate group, nitrogenous bases are basic (hence their name).

The four nucleotides found in DNA differ only in their nitrogenous bases. **Figure 10.2B** shows the structures of the four nitrogenous bases in DNA. At this point, the structural details are not as important as the fact that the bases are of two types. **Thymine (T)** and **cytosine (C)** are single-ring structures called *pyrimidines*. **Adenine (A)** and **guanine (G)** are larger, double-ring structures called *purines*. The one-letter abbreviations can be used for either the bases alone or for the nucleotides containing them.

What about RNA? As its name—ribonucleic acid—implies, its sugar is ribose rather than deoxyribose. Notice the ribose in the RNA nucleotide in **Figure 10.2C**; unlike deoxyribose, the sugar ring has an —OH group attached to the C atom at its lower-right corner. Another difference between RNA and DNA is that instead of thymine, RNA has a nitrogenous base called **uracil (U)**. (You can see the structure of uracil in Figure 10.2C; it is very similar to thymine.) Except for the presence of ribose and

uracil, an RNA polynucleotide chain is identical to a DNA polynucleotide chain. **Figure 10.2D** is a computer graphic of a piece of RNA polynucleotide about 20 nucleotides long. The yellow phosphorus atoms at the center of the phosphate groups makes it easy to spot the sugar-phosphate backbone.

In this module, we reviewed the structure of a polynucleotide. In the next module, we'll see how two polynucleotides join together in a molecule of DNA.

? Compare and contrast DNA and RNA polynucleotides.

■ Both are polymers of nucleotides consisting of a sugar + a nitrogenous base + a phosphate. In RNA, the sugar is ribose; in DNA, it is deoxyribose. Both RNA and DNA have the bases A, G, and C, but DNA has a T and RNA has a U.

10.3 DNA is a double-stranded helix

After the 1952 Hershey-Chase experiment convinced most biologists that DNA was the material that stored genetic information, a race was on to determine how the structure of this molecule could account for its role in heredity. By that time, the arrangement of covalent bonds in a nucleic acid polymer was well established, and researchers focused on discovering the three-dimensional structure of DNA. First to the finish line were two scientists who were relatively unknown at the time—American James D. Watson and Englishman Francis Crick.

The brief but celebrated partnership that solved the puzzle of DNA structure began soon after the 23-year-old Watson journeyed to Cambridge University, where Crick was studying protein structure with a technique called X-ray crystallography. While visiting the laboratory of Maurice Wilkins at King's College in London, Watson saw an X-ray crystallographic image of DNA produced by Wilkins's colleague Rosalind Franklin (Figure 10.3A). A careful study of the image enabled Watson to deduce the basic shape of DNA to be a helix with a uniform diameter of 2 nanometers (nm), with

Figure 10.3A Rosalind Franklin and her X-ray image

its nitrogenous bases stacked about one-third of a nanometer apart. (For comparison, the plasma membrane of a cell is about 8 nm thick.) The diameter of the helix suggested that it was made up of two polynucleotide strands. The presence of two strands accounts for the now-familiar term **double helix.**

Watson and Crick began trying to construct a double helix that would conform both to Franklin's data and to what was then known about the chemistry of DNA (Figure 10.3B). Franklin had concluded that the sugar-phosphate backbones must be on the outside of the double helix, forcing the nitrogenous bases to swivel to the interior of the molecule. But how were the bases arranged in the interior of the double helix?

At first, Watson and Crick imagined that the bases paired like with like—for example, A with A and C with C. But that kind of pairing did not fit the X-ray data, which suggested that the DNA molecule has a *uniform* diameter. An AA pair would be almost twice as wide as a CC pair, causing bulges in the molecule. It soon became apparent that a double-ringed base (purine) must always be paired with a single-ringed base (pyrimidine) on the opposite strand. Moreover, Watson and Crick realized that the individual structures of the bases dictated the pairings even more specifically. Each base has chemical side groups that can best form hydrogen bonds with one

appropriate partner (to review the hydrogen bond, see Module 2.10). Adenine can best form hydrogen bonds with thymine, and guanine with cytosine. In the biologist's shorthand, A pairs with T, and G pairs with C. A is also said to be "complementary" to T, and G to C.

Watson and Crick's pairing scheme not only fit what was known about the physical attributes and chemical bonding of DNA, but also explained some data obtained several years earlier by American biochemist Erwin Chargaff. Chargaff had discovered that the amount of adenine in the DNA of any one species was equal to the amount of thymine and that the amount of guanine was equal to that of cytosine. Chargaff's rules, as they are called, are explained by the fact that A on one of DNA's polynucleotide chains always pairs with T on the other polynucleotide chain, and G on one chain pairs only with C on the other chain.

You can picture the model of the DNA double helix proposed by Watson and Crick as a twisted rope ladder with wooden rungs (Figure 10.3C). The side ropes are the equivalent of the sugar-phosphate backbones, and the rungs represent pairs of nitrogenous bases joined by hydrogen bonds.

Figure 10.3D shows three representations of the double helix. The shapes of the base symbols in the ribbonlike diagram on the left indicate the bases' complementarity. In the center is an atomic-level version showing four base pairs, with the helix untwisted and the hydrogen bonds specified by dotted lines. You can see that the two sugar-phosphate backbones of the double helix are oriented in opposite directions. (Notice that the sugars on the two strands are upside down

Figure 10.3B Watson and Crick in 1953 with their model of the DNA double helix

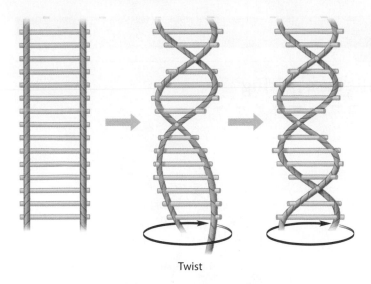

Twist

Figure 10.3C A rope-ladder model for the double helix

with respect to each other.) On the right is a computer graphic showing every atom of part of a double helix. The atoms that compose the deoxyribose sugars are shown as blue, phosphate groups as yellow, and nitrogenous bases as shades of green and orange.

Although the Watson-Crick base-pairing rules dictate the side-by-side combinations of nitrogenous bases that form the rungs of the double helix, they place no restrictions on the *sequence* of nucleotides along the length of a DNA strand. In fact, the sequence of bases can vary in countless ways, and each gene has a unique order of nucleotides, or base sequence.

In April 1953, Watson and Crick shook the scientific world with a succinct paper explaining their molecular model for DNA in the journal *Nature*. In 1962, Watson, Crick, and Wilkins received the Nobel Prize for their work. (Rosalind Franklin probably would have received the prize as well but for her death from cancer in 1958; Nobel Prizes are never awarded posthumously.) Few milestones in the history of biology have had as broad an impact as the discovery of the double helix, with its AT and CG base pairing.

The Watson-Crick model gave new meaning to the words *genes* and *chromosomes*—and to the chromosome theory of inheritance (see Module 9.16). With a complete picture of DNA, we can see that the genetic information in a chromosome must be encoded in the nucleotide sequence of the molecule. One powerful aspect of the Watson-Crick model is that the structure of DNA suggests a molecular explanation for genetic inheritance, as we see in the next module.

Web Activity *DNA and RNA Structure*

Web Activity *DNA Double Helix*

? Along one strand of a double helix is the nucleotide sequence GGCATAGGT. What is the complementary sequence for the other DNA strand?

■ CCGTATCCA

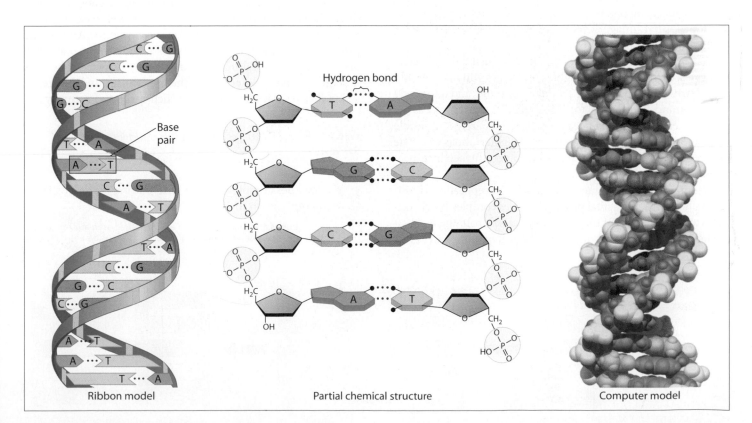

Ribbon model   Partial chemical structure   Computer model

Figure 10.3D Three representations of DNA

10.4 DNA replication depends on specific base pairing

One of biology's overarching themes—the relationship between structure and function—is evident in the double helix. The idea that there is specific pairing of bases in DNA was the flash of inspiration that led Watson and Crick to the correct structure of the double helix. At the same time, they saw the functional significance of the base-pairing rules. They ended their classic 1953 paper with this statement: "It has not escaped our notice that the specific pairing we have postulated immediately suggests a possible copying mechanism for the genetic material."

The logic behind the Watson-Crick proposal for how DNA is copied—by specific pairing of complementary bases—is quite simple. You can see this by covering one of the strands in the parental DNA molecule in Figure 10.4A. You can determine the sequence of bases in the covered strand by applying the base-pairing rules to the unmasked strand: A pairs with T, G with C.

Watson and Crick predicted that a cell applies the same rules when copying its genes. As shown in Figure 10.4A, the two strands of parental DNA (blue) separate. Each then becomes a template for the assembly of a complementary strand from a supply of free nucleotides (gray). The nucleotides line up one at a time along the template strand in accordance with the base-pairing rules. Enzymes link the nucleotides to form the new DNA strands. The completed new molecules, identical to the parental molecule, are known as daughter DNA. The copying mechanism is analogous to using a photographic negative to make a positive image, which can in turn be used to make another negative, and so on.

Watson and Crick's model predicts that when a double helix replicates, each of the two daughter molecules will have one old strand, which was part of the parental molecule, and one newly created strand. This model for DNA replication is known as the **semiconservative model** because half of the parental molecule is maintained (conserved) in each daughter molecule. The semiconservative model of replication was confirmed by experiments performed in the 1950s.

Although the general mechanism of DNA replication is conceptually simple, the actual process involves complex biochemical gymnastics. Some of the complexity arises from the fact that the helical DNA molecule must untwist as it replicates and must

Figure 10.4B Untwisting and replication of DNA

copy its two strands roughly simultaneously (Figure 10.4B). Another challenge is the speed of the process. *E.coli,* with about 4.6 million DNA base pairs, can copy its entire genome in less than an hour. Humans, with over 6 billion base pairs in 46 diploid chromosomes, require only a few hours. And yet the process is amazingly accurate; typically, only about one DNA nucleotide per several billion is incorrectly paired. In the next module, we take a closer look at the mechanisms of DNA replication that allow it to proceed with such speed and accuracy.

Web Process of Science *What Is the Correct Model for DNA Replication?*

? How does complementary base pairing make possible the replication of DNA?

■ When the two strands of the double helix separate, each serves as a "mold" for the base-pairing of the new complementary strands.

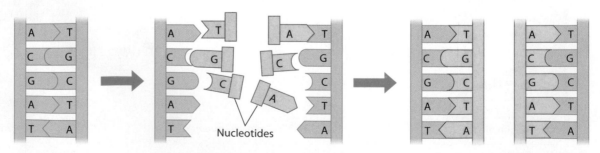

Figure 10.4A
A template model for DNA replication

Parental molecule of DNA

Both parental strands serve as templates

Two identical daughter molecules of DNA

DNA replication proceeds in two directions at many sites simultaneously

Altogether, DNA replication requires the cooperation of more than a dozen enzymes and other proteins. Replication of a DNA molecule begins at special sites called *origins of replication,* stretches of DNA having a specific sequence of nucleotides where proteins attach to the DNA and separate the strands. As shown in **Figure 10.5A**, replication then proceeds in both directions, creating what are called replication "bubbles." The parental DNA strands (blue) open up as daughter strands (gray) elongate on both sides of each bubble. The DNA molecule of a eukaryotic chromosome has many origins where replication can start simultaneously, shortening the total time needed for the process. Thus, thousands of bubbles can be present at once. Eventually, all the bubbles merge, yielding two completed daughter DNA molecules.

Figure 10.5B shows the molecular building blocks of a tiny segment of DNA, reminding us that the DNA's sugar-phosphate backbones run in opposite directions. Notice that each strand has a 3′ ("three-prime") end and a 5′ end. The primed numbers refer to the carbon atoms of the nucleotide sugars. At one end of each DNA strand, the sugar's 3′ carbon atom is attached to an —OH group; at the other end, the sugar's 5′ carbon has a phosphate group.

The opposite orientation of the strands is important in DNA replication. The enzymes that link DNA nucleotides to a growing daughter strand, called **DNA polymerases,** add nucleotides only to the 3′ end of the strand, never to the 5′ end. Thus, a daughter DNA strand can only grow in the 5′ → 3′ direction. You see the consequences of this enzyme specificity in **Figure 10.5C**. The forked structure represents one side of a replication bubble. One of the daughter strands (shown in gray) can be synthesized in one continuous piece by a DNA polymerase working toward the forking point of the parental DNA. However, to make the other daughter strand, polymerase molecules must work outward from the forking point. This new strand is synthesized in short pieces as the fork opens up. Another enzyme, called **DNA ligase,** then links (ligates) the pieces together into a single DNA strand.

In addition to their roles in linking nucleotides together, DNA polymerases carry out a proofreading step that quickly removes nucleotides that have base-paired incorrectly during replication. DNA polymerases and DNA ligase are also involved in repairing DNA damaged by harmful radiation (such as ultraviolet light and X-rays) or toxic chemicals in the environment, such as those found in tobacco smoke.

DNA replication ensures that all the somatic cells in a multicellular organism carry the same genetic information. It is also the means by which genetic instructions are copied for the next generation of the organism. In the next module, we begin to pursue the connection between DNA instructions and an organism's phenotypic traits.

Figure 10.5B The opposite orientations of DNA strands

Figure 10.5C How daughter DNA strands are synthesized

Web Activity *DNA Replication*

? **What is the function of DNA polymerase in DNA replication?**

Figure 10.5A Multiple "bubbles" in replicating DNA

■ This enzyme lines up new nucleotides along an existing strand according to the base-pairing rules and then covalently connects the nucleotides into the new strand.

10.6 The DNA genotype is expressed as proteins, which provide the molecular basis for phenotypic traits

With our knowledge of DNA, we can now define genotype and phenotype more precisely than we did in Chapter 9. An organism's genotype, its genetic makeup, is the heritable information contained in its DNA. The phenotype is the organism's specific traits. So what is the molecular connection between genotype and phenotype?

The answer is that the DNA inherited by an organism specifies traits by dictating the synthesis of proteins. In other words, proteins are the links between genotype and phenotype. However, a gene does not build a protein directly. Rather, a gene dispatches instructions in the form of RNA, which in turn programs protein synthesis. This central concept in biology (termed the "central dogma" by Francis Crick in 1956) is summarized in **Figure 10.6A**. The chain of command is from DNA in the nucleus of the cell (purple area) to RNA to protein synthesis in the cytoplasm (tan area). The two main stages are **transcription,** the transfer of genetic information from DNA into an RNA molecule, and **translation,** the transfer of the information in the RNA into a protein. In the next nine modules, we will explore the steps in this flow of molecular information from gene to protein.

The relationship between genes and proteins was first proposed in 1909, when English physician Archibald Garrod suggested that genes dictate phenotypes through enzymes, the proteins that catalyze chemical processes in the cell. Garrod's idea came from his observations of inherited diseases. He hypothesized that an inherited disease reflects a person's inability to make a particular enzyme, and he referred to such diseases as "inborn errors of metabolism." He gave as one example the hereditary condition called alkaptonuria, in which the urine appears black because it contains a chemical called alkapton. Garrod reasoned that normal individuals have an enzyme that breaks down alkapton, whereas alkaptonuric

individuals cannot make the enzyme. Garrod's hypothesis was ahead of its time, but research conducted decades later proved him right. In the intervening years, biochemists accumulated evidence that cells make and break down biologically important molecules via metabolic pathways, as in the synthesis of an amino acid or the breakdown of a sugar. As we described in Unit I, each step in a metabolic pathway is catalyzed by a specific enzyme. Therefore, individuals lacking one of the enzymes for a pathway are unable to complete it.

The major breakthrough in demonstrating the relationship between genes and enzymes came in the 1940s from the work of American geneticists George Beadle and Edward Tatum with the bread mold *Neurospora crassa* **(Figure 10.6B).** Beadle and Tatum studied strains of the mold that were unable to grow on a simple growth medium. Each of these so-called nutritional mutants turned out to lack an enzyme in a metabolic pathway that produced some molecule the mold needed, such as an amino acid. Beadle and Tatum also showed that each mutant was defective in a single gene. This result suggested the one gene–one enzyme hypothesis: the function of a gene is to dictate the production of a specific enzyme.

Figure 10.6B *Neurospora crassa* growing in a culture dish

The one gene–one enzyme hypothesis has been amply confirmed, but with some important modifications. First it was extended beyond enzymes to include *all* types of proteins. For example, keratin—the structural protein of hair—and the hormone insulin are two examples of proteins that are not enzymes. So biologists began to think in terms of one gene–one *protein.* However, many proteins are made from two or more polypeptide chains (see Module 3.14), with each polypeptide specified by its own gene. For example, hemoglobin, the oxygen-transporting protein in your blood, is built from two kinds of polypeptides, encoded by two different genes. Thus, Beadle and Tatum's hypothesis has come to be restated as the one gene–one *polypeptide* hypothesis.

(Bio Flix) **Bioflix** *Protein Synthesis*

(headphones) **MP3 Tutor** *DNA to RNA to Protein*

Web Process of Science *How Are Nutritional Mutations Identified?*

? What are the functions of transcription and translation?

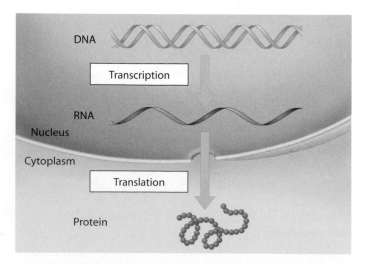

Figure 10.6A Flow of genetic information in a eukaryotic cell

■ Transcription is the transfer of information from DNA to RNA. Translation is the use of the RNA as information for making a protein.

10.7 Genetic information written in codons is translated into amino acid sequences

Genes provide the instructions for making specific proteins. But a gene does not build a protein directly. The bridge between DNA and protein synthesis is the nucleic acid RNA: DNA is transcribed into RNA, which is then translated into protein. Put another way, cells are governed by a molecular chain of command: DNA → RNA → protein.

Transcription and translation are linguistic terms, and it is useful to think of nucleic acids and proteins as having languages. To understand how genetic information passes from genotype to phenotype, we need to see how the chemical language of DNA is translated into the different chemical language of proteins.

What, exactly, is the language of nucleic acids? Both DNA and RNA are polymers made of nucleotide monomers. In DNA, there are four types of nucleotides, which differ in their nitrogenous bases (A, T, C, and G). The same is true for RNA, although it has the base U instead of T.

Figure 10.7 focuses on a small region of one of the genes (gene 3, shown in light blue) carried by a DNA molecule. DNA's language is written as a linear sequence of nucleotide bases on a polynucleotide, a sequence such as the one you see on the enlarged DNA strand in the figure. Specific sequences of bases, each with a beginning and an end, make up the genes on a DNA strand. A typical gene consists of hundreds or thousands of nucleotides in a specific sequence.

The pink strand underneath the enlarged DNA region represents the results of transcription: an RNA molecule. The process is called transcription because the nucleic acid language of DNA has been rewritten (transcribed) as a sequence of bases on RNA; the language is still that of nucleic acids.

DNA molecule —

Gene 1

Gene 2

Gene 3

Notice that the nucleotide bases on the RNA molecule are complementary to those on the DNA strand. As we will see in Module 10.9, this is because the RNA was synthesized using the DNA as a template.

The purple chain represents the results of translation, the conversion of the nucleic acid language into the polypeptide language (recall that proteins consist of one or more polypeptides). Like nucleic acids, polypeptides are polymers, but the monomers that compose them are the 20 amino acids common to all organisms. Again, the language is written in a linear sequence, and the sequence of nucleotides of the RNA molecule dictates the sequence of amino acids of the polypeptide. The RNA acts as a messenger carrying genetic information from DNA.

During translation, there is a change in language from the nucleotide sequence of the RNA into the amino acid sequence of the polypeptide. The brackets below the RNA indicate how genetic information is coded in nucleic acids. Notice that each bracket encloses *three* nucleotides on RNA. Recall that there are only four different kinds of nucleotides in DNA (A, G, C, T) and RNA (A, G, C, U). In translation, these four must somehow specify 20 amino acids. If each nucleotide base specified one amino acid, only 4 of the 20 amino acids could be accounted for. What if the language consisted of two-letter code words? If we read the bases of a gene two at a time, AG, for example, could specify one amino acid, whereas AT could designate a different amino acid. However, when the 4 bases are taken in doublets, there are only 16 (that is, 4^2) possible arrangements—still not enough to specify all 20 amino acids.

Triplets of bases are the smallest "words" of uniform length that can specify all the amino acids. Suppose each code word in DNA consists of a triplet, with each arrangement of three consecutive bases specifying an amino acid. Then there can be 64 (that is, 4^3) possible code words—more than enough to specify the 20 amino acids. Indeed, there are enough triplets to allow more than one coding for each amino acid. For example, the base triplets AAT and AAC both code for the same amino acid (leucine).

Experiments have verified that the flow of information from gene to protein is based on a **triplet code**: The genetic instructions for the amino acid sequence of a polypeptide chain are written in DNA and RNA as a series of three-base words, called **codons**. Notice in the figure that three-base codons in the DNA are transcribed into complementary three-base codons in the RNA, and then the RNA codons are translated into amino acids that form a polypeptide. We turn to the codons themselves in the next module.

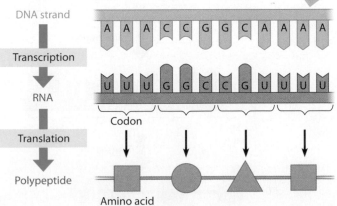

DNA strand

Transcription

RNA

Translation

Polypeptide

A A A C C G G C A A A A

U U U G G C C G U U U U

Codon

Amino acid

? A particular protein is 100 amino acids long. How many nucleotides are necessary to code for this protein?

Figure 10.7   Transcription and translation of codons

The genetic code is the Rosetta stone of life

In 1799, a large stone tablet was found in Rosetta, Egypt, carrying the same lengthy inscription in three ancient languages: Egyptian hieroglyphics, Egyptian script, and Greek. This stone provided the key that enabled scholars to crack the previously indecipherable hieroglyphic code.

To crack the genetic code, scientists wrote their own Rosetta stone. It was based on information gathered from a series of elegant experiments that disclosed the amino acid translations of each of the nucleotide-triplet code words. The first codon was deciphered in 1961 by American biochemist Marshall Nirenberg. He synthesized an artificial RNA molecule by linking together identical RNA nucleotides having uracil as their base. No matter where this message started or stopped, it could contain only one type of triplet codon: UUU. Nirenberg added this "poly U" to a test-tube mixture containing ribosomes and the other ingredients required for polypeptide synthesis. This mixture translated the poly U into a polypeptide containing a single kind of amino acid, phenylalanine. Thus, Nirenberg learned that the RNA codon UUU specifies the amino acid phenylalanine (Phe). By variations on this method, the amino acids specified by all the codons were soon determined.

The **genetic code** is the set of rules giving the correspondence between codons in RNA and amino acids in proteins. As Figure 10.8A shows, 61 of the 64 codons code for amino acids. The triplet AUG has a dual function: It codes for the amino acid methionine (Met) and also can provide a signal for the start of a polypeptide chain. Three of the other codons (in red

boxes in the figure) do not designate amino acids. They are the stop codons that mark the end of translation.

Notice in Figure 10.8A that there is redundancy in the code but no ambiguity. For example, although codons UUU and UUC both specify phenylalanine (redundancy), neither of them ever represents any other amino acid (no ambiguity). The codons in the figure are the triplets found in RNA. They have a straightforward, complementary relationship to the codons in DNA. The nucleotides making up the codons occur in a linear order along the DNA and RNA, with no gaps or "punctuation" separating the codons.

As an exercise in translating the genetic code, consider the 12-nucleotide segment of DNA in Figure 10.8B. Let's read this as a series of triplets. Using the base-pairing rules (with U in RNA instead of T), we see that the RNA codon corresponding to the first transcribed DNA triplet, TAC, is AUG. As you can see in Figure 10.8A, AUG indicates, "place Met as the first amino acid in the polypeptide." The second DNA triplet, TTC, dictates RNA codon AAG, which designates lysine (Lys) as the second amino acid. We continue until we reach a stop codon.

The genetic code is nearly universal, shared by organisms from the simplest bacteria to the most complex plants and animals. In experiments, bacteria can translate human genetic messages, and human cells can translate bacterial RNA. A language shared by all living things must have evolved early enough in the history of life to be present in the common ancestors of all modern organisms. A shared genetic vocabulary is a reminder of the kinship that connects all life on Earth.

		Second base			
First base	**U**	**C**	**A**	**G**	Third base
U	UUU UUC Phe / UUA UUG Leu	UCU UCC UCA UCG Ser	UAU UAC Tyr / UAA Stop / UAG Stop	UGU UGC Cys / UGA Stop / UGG Trp	U C A G
C	CUU CUC CUA CUG Leu	CCU CCC CCA CCG Pro	CAU CAC His / CAA CAG Gln	CGU CGC CGA CGG Arg	U C A G
A	AUU AUC AUA Ile / AUG Met or start	ACU ACC ACA ACG Thr	AAU AAC Asn / AAA AAG Lys	AGU AGC Ser / AGA AGG Arg	U C A G
G	GUU GUC GUA GUG Val	GCU GCC GCA GCG Ala	GAU GAC Asp / GAA GAG Glu	GGU GGC GGA GGG Gly	U C A G

Figure 10.8A Dictionary of the genetic code (RNA codons)

? Translate the RNA sequence CCAUUUACG into the corresponding amino acid sequence.

Pro-Phe-Thr

Figure 10.8B Deciphering the genetic information in DNA

10.9 Transcription produces genetic messages in the form of RNA

In eukaryotic cells, transcription, the transfer of genetic information from DNA to RNA, occurs in the nucleus. (The nucleus, after all, contains the DNA; see Figure 10.6A for a review.) An RNA molecule is transcribed from a DNA template by a process that resembles the synthesis of a DNA strand during DNA replication. Figure 10.9A is a close-up view of this process. As with replication, the two DNA strands must first separate at the place where the process will start. In transcription, however, only one of the DNA strands serves as a template for the newly forming molecule. The nucleotides that make up the new RNA molecule take their places one at a time along the DNA template strand by forming hydrogen bonds with the nucleotide bases there. Notice that the RNA nucleotides follow the same base-pairing rules that govern DNA replication, except that U, rather than T, pairs with A. The RNA nucleotides are linked by the transcription enzyme **RNA polymerase,** symbolized in the figure by the large gray shape in the background.

Figure 10.9B is an overview of the transcription of an entire prokaryotic gene. (We focus on prokaryotes here; eukaryotic transcription is a similar process but more complex.) Specific sequences of nucleotides along the DNA mark where transcription of a gene begins and ends. The "start transcribing" signal is a nucleotide sequence called a **promoter.** A promoter is a specific binding site for RNA polymerase and determines which of the two strands of the DNA double helix is used as the template in transcription.

❶ The first phase of transcription, called initiation, is the attachment of RNA polymerase to the promoter and the start of RNA synthesis. ❷ During a second phase of transcription, the RNA elongates. As RNA synthesis continues, the RNA strand peels away from its DNA template, allowing the two separated DNA strands to come back together in the region already transcribed. ❸ Finally, in the third phase, termination, the RNA polymerase reaches a sequence of bases in the DNA template

called a **terminator.** This sequence signals the end of the gene; at that point, the polymerase molecule detaches from the RNA molecule and the gene.

In addition to producing RNA that encodes amino acid sequences, transcription makes two other kinds of RNA that are involved in building polypeptides. We discuss these three kinds of RNA in the next three modules.

🎧 **MP3 Tutor** *DNA Transcription*

Web Activity *Transcription*

? What is a promoter? What molecule binds to it?

■ A promoter is a specific nucleotide sequence at the start of a gene where RNA polymerase attaches and begins transcription.

Figure 10.9B Transcription of a gene

Figure 10.9A A close-up view of transcription

10.10 Eukaryotic RNA is processed before leaving the nucleus

The kind of RNA that encodes amino acid sequences is called **messenger RNA (mRNA)** because it conveys genetic information from DNA to the translation machinery of the cell. Messenger RNA is transcribed from DNA, and the message in the mRNA is then translated into polypeptides. In prokaryotic cells, which lack a nucleus, transcription and translation occur in the same place (the cytoplasm). In eukaryotic cells, however, mRNA molecules and other RNA molecules required for translation must exit the nucleus via the nuclear pores and enter the cytoplasm, where the machinery for polypeptide synthesis is located.

Before leaving the nucleus as mRNA, eukaryotic transcripts are modified, or processed, in several ways. One kind of RNA processing is the addition of extra nucleotides to the ends of the RNA transcript (Figure 10.10). These additions include a small cap (a single G nucleotide) at one end and a long tail (a chain of 50 to 250 adenine nucleotides) at the other end. The cap and tail facilitate the export of the mRNA from the nucleus, protect

the mRNA from attack by cellular enzymes, and help ribosomes bind to the mRNA. The cap and tail themselves are not translated into protein.

Eukaryotes require an additional type of RNA processing because, in most protein-coding genes, the DNA sequence that codes for the polypeptides is not continuous. Most genes of plants and animals include internal noncoding regions called **introns** (for "intervening sequences"). The coding regions—the parts of a gene that are expressed as amino acids—are called **exons.** As Figure 10.10 shows, both exons (darker color) and introns (lighter color) are transcribed from DNA into RNA. However, before the RNA leaves the nucleus, the introns are removed, and the exons are joined to produce an mRNA molecule with a continuous coding sequence. (The short noncoding regions just inside the cap and tail are considered parts of the first and last exons.) This cutting-and-pasting process is called **RNA splicing.** In most cases, RNA splicing is catalyzed by a complex of proteins and small RNA molecules, but sometimes the RNA transcript itself catalyzes the process. In other words, RNA can sometimes act as an enzyme that removes its own introns! As we will see in the next chapter (Module 11.6), RNA splicing also provides a means to produce multiple polypeptides from a single gene.

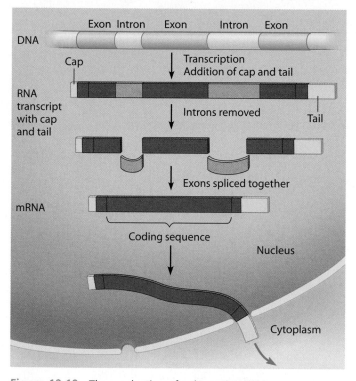

Figure 10.10 The production of eukaryotic mRNA

? Explain why many eukaryotic genes are longer than the mRNA that leaves the nucleus.

These genes have introns, noncoding sequences of nucleotides that are spliced out of the final RNA transcripts.

We are now ready to see how the translation process works. Translation of mRNA into protein involves more complicated machinery than transcription, including:

- Transfer RNA, another kind of RNA molecule
- Ribosomes, the organelles where translation occurs
- Enzymes and a number of protein "factors"
- Sources of chemical energy, such as adenosine triphosphate (ATP)

In the next two modules, we take a closer look at transfer RNA and ribosomes.

10.11 Transfer RNA molecules serve as interpreters during translation

Translation of any language requires an interpreter, someone who can recognize the words of one language and convert them to another. Translation of a message carried in mRNA into the amino acid language of proteins also requires an interpreter. To convert the three-letter words (codons) of nucleic

acids to the one-letter, amino acid words of proteins, a cell employs a molecular interpreter, a special type of RNA called **transfer RNA (tRNA).**

A cell that is ready to carry out translation has in its cytoplasm a supply of amino acids, either obtained from food or made from other chemicals. The amino acids themselves cannot recognize the codons in the mRNA. The amino acid tryptophan, for example, is no more attracted by codons for tryptophan than by any other codons. It is up to the cell's molecular interpreters, tRNA molecules, to match amino acids to the appropriate codons to form the new polypeptide. To perform this task, tRNA molecules must carry out two functions: (1) picking up the appropriate amino acids and (2) recognizing the appropriate codons in the mRNA. The unique structure of tRNA molecules enables them to perform both tasks.

As shown in **Figure 10.11A**, a tRNA molecule is made of a single strand of RNA—one polynucleotide chain—consisting of about 80 nucleotides. By twisting and folding upon itself, tRNA forms several double-stranded regions in which short stretches of RNA base-pair with other stretches. A single-stranded loop at one end of the folded molecule contains a special triplet of bases called an **anticodon.** The anticodon triplet is complementary to a codon triplet on mRNA. During translation, the anticodon on tRNA recognizes a particular codon on mRNA by using base-pairing rules. At the other end of the tRNA molecule is a site where an amino acid can attach.

In the modules that follow, in which we trace the process of translation, we represent tRNA with the simplified shape that is shown on the right in Figure 10.11A. This symbol emphasizes two parts of the molecule—the anticodon and the amino acid attachment site—that give tRNA its ability to match a particular nucleic acid word (codon) with its corresponding protein word (amino acid). Although all tRNA molecules are similar, there is a slightly different variety of tRNA for each amino acid.

Each amino acid is joined to the correct tRNA by a specific enzyme. There is a family of 20 versions of these enzymes, one enzyme for each amino acid. Each enzyme specifically binds one type of amino acid to all tRNA molecules that code for that amino acid, using a molecule of ATP as energy to drive the reaction. The resulting amino acid–tRNA complex can then furnish its amino acid to a growing polypeptide chain, a process that we describe in Module 10.12.

The computer graphic in **Figure 10.11B** shows a tRNA molecule (red and yellow) and an ATP molecule (purple) bound to the enzyme molecule (blue). In this picture, you can see the proportional sizes of these three molecules. The amino acid that would attach to the tRNA is not shown; it would be less than half the size of the ATP.

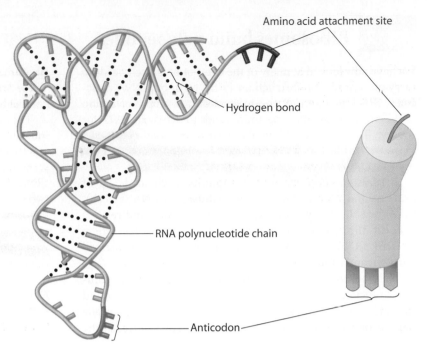

Figure 10.11A   The structure of tRNA

Figure 10.11B   A molecule of tRNA binding to an enzyme molecule (blue)

? What is an anticodon, and what is its function?

■ It is the base triplet of a tRNA molecule that couples the tRNA to a complementary codon in the mRNA. This is a key step in translating mRNA to polypeptide.

10.12 Ribosomes build polypeptides

We have now looked at many of the components a cell needs to carry out translation: instructions in the form of mRNA molecules, tRNA to interpret the instructions, a supply of amino acids, enzymes for attaching amino acids to tRNA, and ATP for energy. The final components needed are the ribosomes, organelles in the cytoplasm that coordinate the functioning of the mRNA and tRNA and actually make polypeptides.

A ribosome consists of two subunits, each made up of proteins and a kind of RNA called **ribosomal RNA (rRNA).** In Figure 10.12A, you can see the actual shapes and relative sizes of the ribosomal subunits. You can also see where mRNA, tRNA, and the growing polypeptide are located during translation.

The ribosomes of prokaryotes and eukaryotes are very similar in function, but those of eukaryotes are slightly larger and are different in composition. The differences are medically significant. Certain antibiotic drugs can inactivate prokaryotic ribosomes while leaving eukaryotic ribosomes unaffected. These drugs, such as tetracycline and streptomycin, are used to combat bacterial infections.

The simplified drawings in Figures 10.12B and 10.12C indicate how tRNA anticodons and mRNA codons fit together on ribosomes. As Figure 10.12B shows, each ribosome has a binding site for mRNA and two binding sites for tRNA. Figure 10.12C shows tRNA molecules occupying these two sites. The subunits of the ribosome act like a vise, holding the tRNA and mRNA molecules close together, allowing the amino acids carried by the tRNA molecules to be connected into a polypeptide chain. In the next two modules, we examine the steps of translation in detail.

? How does a ribosome function in protein synthesis?

■ A ribosome holds mRNA and tRNAs together and connects amino acids from the tRNAs to the growing polypeptide chain.

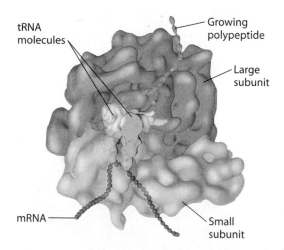

Figure 10.12A The true shape of a functioning ribosome

tRNA molecules
Growing polypeptide
Large subunit
mRNA
Small subunit

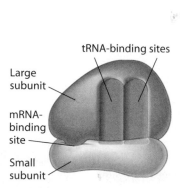

Figure 10.12B Binding sites of a ribosome

tRNA-binding sites
Large subunit
mRNA-binding site
Small subunit

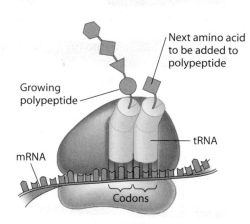

Figure 10.12C A ribosome with occupied binding sites

Next amino acid to be added to polypeptide
Growing polypeptide
tRNA
mRNA
Codons

10.13 An initiation codon marks the start of an mRNA message

Translation can be divided into the same three phases as transcription: initiation, elongation, and termination. The process of polypeptide initiation brings together the mRNA, a tRNA bearing the first amino acid, and the two subunits of a ribosome.

As indicated in Figure 10.13A, an mRNA molecule transcribed from DNA is longer than the genetic message it carries. A sequence of nucleotides (light pink) at either end of the molecule is not part of the message but helps the mRNA bind to the ribosome. The role of the initiation process is to establish exactly where translation will begin, ensuring that the mRNA codons are translated into the correct sequence of amino acids.

Initiation occurs in two steps (Figure 10.13B, top of next page). ❶ An mRNA molecule binds to a small ribosomal subunit. A special initiator tRNA binds to the specific codon, called the **start codon,** where translation is to begin on the mRNA

Start of genetic message

End

Figure 10.13A
A molecule of mRNA

Figure 10.13B
The initiation of translation

molecule. The initiator tRNA carries the amino acid methionine (Met); its anticodon, UAC, binds to the start codon, AUG. ❷ Next, a large ribosomal subunit binds to the small one, creating a functional ribosome. The initiator tRNA fits into one of the two tRNA-binding sites on the ribosome. This site, called the **P site,** will hold the growing polypeptide. The other tRNA-binding site, called the **A site,** is vacant and ready for the next amino-acid-bearing tRNA.

? What would happen if a genetic mutation changed a start codon to some other codon?

■ Any messenger RNA transcribed from the mutated gene would be nonfunctional because ribosomes could not initiate translation correctly.

10.14 **Elongation adds amino acids to the polypeptide chain until a stop codon terminates translation**

Once initiation is complete, amino acids are added one by one to the first amino acid. Each addition occurs in a three-step elongation process (Figure 10.14; the small green arrows indicate movement):

❶ **Codon recognition.** The anticodon of an incoming tRNA molecule, carrying its amino acid, pairs with the mRNA codon in the A site of the ribosome.

❷ **Peptide bond formation.** The polypeptide separates from the tRNA to which it was bound (the one in the P site) and attaches by a peptide bond to the amino acid carried by the tRNA in the A site. The ribosome catalyzes formation of the bond. Thus, one more amino acid is added to the chain.

❸ **Translocation.** The P site tRNA now leaves the ribosome, and the ribosome translocates (moves) the tRNA in the A site, with its attached polypeptide, to the P site. The codon and anticodon remain bonded, and the mRNA and tRNA move as a unit. This movement brings into the A site the next mRNA codon to be translated, and the process can start again with step 1.

Elongation continues until a **stop codon** reaches the ribosome's A site. Stop codons—UAA, UAG, and UGA—do not code for amino acids but instead act as signals to stop translation. This is the termination stage of translation. The completed polypeptide is released from the last tRNA and exits the ribosome, which then splits into its separate subunits.

Web Activity *Translation*

? What happens as a tRNA passes through the A and P binding sites on the ribosome?

■ In the A site, its amino acid receives the growing polypeptide from the tRNA that precedes it. In the P site, it gives up the polypeptide to the tRNA that follows it.

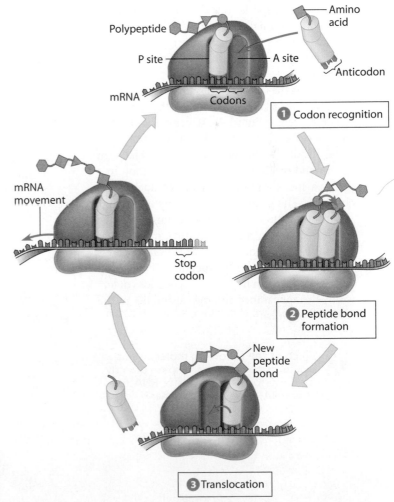

Figure 10.14 Polypeptide elongation

10.15 Review: The flow of genetic information in the cell is DNA → RNA → protein

Figure 10.15 summarizes the main stages in the flow of genetic information from DNA to RNA to protein. ❶ In transcription (DNA → RNA), the RNA is synthesized on a DNA template. In eukaryotic cells, transcription occurs in the nucleus, and the messenger RNA must travel from the nucleus to the cytoplasm.

❷–❺ Translation (RNA → protein) can be divided into four steps, all of which occur in the cytoplasm. When the polypeptide is complete at the end of step 5, the two ribosomal subunits come apart, and the tRNA and mRNA are released (not shown in this figure). Translation is rapid; a single ribosome can make an average-sized polypeptide in less than a minute. Typically, an mRNA molecule is translated simultaneously by a number of ribosomes. Once the start codon emerges from the first ribosome, a second ribosome can attach to it; thus, several ribosomes may trail along on the same mRNA molecule.

Each polypeptide coils and folds, assuming a three-dimensional shape, its tertiary structure. Several polypeptides may come together, forming a protein with quaternary structure (see Module 3.14).

What is the overall significance of transcription and translation? These are the processes whereby genes control the structures and activities of cells, or, more broadly, the way the genotype produces the phenotype. The chain of command originates with the information in a gene, a specific linear sequence of nucleotides in DNA. The gene serves as a template, dictating transcription of a complementary sequence of nucleotides in mRNA. In turn, mRNA dictates the linear sequence in which amino acids appear in a specific polypeptide. Finally, the proteins that form from the polypeptides determine the appearance and the capabilities of the cell and organism.

? Which of the following molecules or structures does not participate directly in translation: ribosomes, transfer RNA, messenger RNA, DNA, ATP, enzymes?

■ DNA

Figure 10.15 Summary of transcription and translation

❶ mRNA is transcribed from a DNA template.

❷ Each amino acid attaches to its proper tRNA with the help of a specific enzyme and ATP.

❸ **Initiation of polypeptide synthesis**
The mRNA, the first tRNA, and the ribosomal sub-units come together.

❹ **Elongation**
A succession of tRNAs add their amino acids to the polypeptide chain as the mRNA is moved through the ribosome, one codon at a time.

❺ **Termination**
The ribosome recognizes a stop codon. The polypeptide is terminated and released.

Mutations can change the meaning of genes

Since discovering how genes are translated into proteins, scientists have been able to describe many inherited traits in molecular terms. For instance, when a child is born with sickle-cell disease (see Module 9.9), the condition can be traced back through a difference in a protein to one tiny change in a gene. In one of the two kinds of polypeptides in the hemoglobin protein, the sickle-cell child has a single different amino acid. This difference is caused by the change of a single nucleotide in the coding strand of DNA (Figure 10.16A). In the double helix, one base *pair* is changed.

We now know that the alternative alleles of many genes result from changes in single base pairs in DNA. Any change in the nucleotide sequence of DNA is called a **mutation.** Mutations can involve large regions of a chromosome or just a single nucleotide pair, as in sickle-cell disease. Here we consider how mutations involving only one or a few nucleotide pairs can affect gene translation.

Mutations within a gene can be divided into two general categories: base substitutions and base insertions or deletions (Figure 10.16B). A base substitution is the replacement of one nucleotide with another. For example, in the second row in Figure 10.16B, A replaces G in the fourth codon of the mRNA. What effect does a base substitution have? Because the genetic code is redundant, some substitution mutations have no effect at all. If a mutation causes an mRNA codon to change from GAA to GAG, for instance, no change in the protein product would result because GAA and GAG both code for the same amino acid (Glu). Other base substitutions may alter an amino acid but have little effect (perhaps because that amino acid is uninvolved in the protein's function). But as in the example in Figure 10.16A, base substitutions may cause changes in a protein that prevent it from functioning normally. Occasionally, a base substitution leads to an improved protein that enhances the success of the mutant organism and its descendants. Much more often, though, mutations are harmful. And if a base substitution changes an amino-acid codon to a stop codon, a shortened, probably nonfunctional, polypeptide will result.

Mutations involving the insertion or deletion of one or more nucleotides in a gene often have disastrous effects. Because mRNA is read as a series of nucleotide triplets (codons) during translation, adding or subtracting nucleotides may alter the **reading frame** (triplet grouping) of the message. All the nucleotides that are "downstream" of the insertion or deletion will be regrouped into different codons (Figure 10.16B, bottom). The result will most likely be a nonfunctional polypeptide.

The production of mutations, called **mutagenesis,** can occur in a number of ways. Errors that occur during DNA replication or recombination are called spontaneous mutations. Another source of mutation is a physical or chemical agent, called a **mutagen.** The most common physical mutagen in nature is high-energy radiation, such as X-rays and ultraviolet light. Chemical mutagens fall into several categories. One type, for example, consists of chemicals that are similar to normal DNA bases but that pair incorrectly.

Although mutations are often harmful, they are also extremely useful, both in nature and in the laboratory. It is because of mutations that there is such a rich diversity of genes in the living world, a diversity that makes evolution by natural selection possible. Mutations are also essential tools for geneticists. Whether naturally occurring (as in Mendel's peas) or created in the laboratory (Morgan used X-rays to make most of his fruit fly mutants), mutations create the different alleles needed for genetic research.

Figure 10.16A The molecular basis of sickle-cell disease

Figure 10.16B Types of mutations and their effects

Web Process of Science *Connection: How Do You Diagnose a Genetic Disorder?*

? How could a single base substitution result in a shortened protein product?

■ A substitution that changed an amino acid codon into a stop codon would produce a prematurely terminated polypeptide.

10.17 Viral DNA may become part of the host chromosome

As we discussed in Module 10.1, bacteria and viruses served as models in experiments that uncovered the molecular details of heredity. Now let's take a closer look at viruses, focusing on the relationship between viral structure and the processes of nucleic acid replication, transcription, and translation. (Viruses, though not considered alive, are often grouped with microscopic organisms under the general term "microbes"; hence, this section is called "microbial genetics.")

In a sense, viruses are nothing more than "genes in a box": infectious particles consisting of nucleic acid enclosed in a protein coat called a **capsid** and, in some cases, a membrane envelope. Viruses are parasites that can reproduce only inside cells. In fact, the host cell provides most of the components necessary for replicating, transcribing, and translating the viral nucleic acid.

In Figure 10.1C, we described the reproductive cycle of phage T2. This sort of cycle is called a **lytic cycle** because it results in the lysis (breaking open) of the host cell and the release of the viruses that were produced within the cell. Some phages can also reproduce by an alternative route called the lysogenic cycle. During a **lysogenic cycle,** viral DNA replication occurs without destroying the host cell.

In Figure 10.17, you see the two kinds of cycles for a phage called lambda that infects E. coli. Both cycles begin when the phage DNA ❶ enters the bacterium and ❷ forms a circle. The DNA then embarks on one of the two pathways. In the lytic cycle (left), ❸ lambda's DNA immediately turns the cell into a virus-producing factory, and ❹ the cell soon lyses and releases its viral products. In the lysogenic cycle, however, ❺ the DNA is inserted by genetic recombination into the bacterial chromosome. Once inserted, the phage DNA is referred to as a **prophage,** and most of its genes are inactive. ❻ Every time the E. coli cell prepares to divide, it replicates the phage DNA along with its own and passes the copies on to daughter cells. A single infected cell can quickly give rise to a large population of bacteria carrying the virus in prophage form. The lysogenic cycle enables viruses to propagate without killing the host cells on which they depend. The prophages may remain in the bacterial cells indefinitely. ❼ Occasionally, however, an environmental signal such as radiation or a certain chemical triggers a switchover from the lysogenic cycle to the lytic cycle.

Sometimes the few prophage genes active in a lysogenic bacterium can cause medical problems. For example, the bacteria that cause diphtheria, botulism, and scarlet fever would be harmless to humans if it were not for the prophage genes they carry. Certain of these genes direct the bacteria to produce the toxins responsible for making people ill. In the next module, we will explore animal viruses.

Web Activity *Phage Lysogenic and Lytic Cycles*

? Describe one way a virus can perpetuate its genes without destroying its host cell. What is this type of reproductive cycle called?

■ Some viruses can insert their DNA into a chromosome of the host cell, which replicates the viral genes when it replicates its own DNA prior to cell division. This is called the lysogenic cycle.

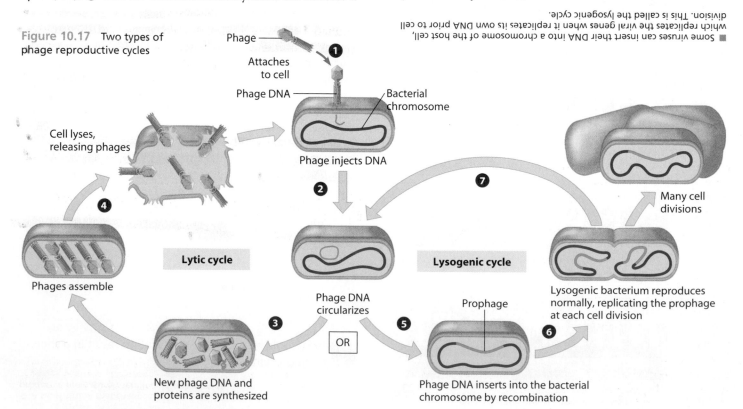

Figure 10.17 Two types of phage reproductive cycles

Phage

Attaches to cell

Phage DNA

Bacterial chromosome

Phage injects DNA

❶

❷

Cell lyses, releasing phages

❹

Phages assemble

Lytic cycle

Phage DNA circularizes

❸

OR

New phage DNA and proteins are synthesized

❺

Prophage

Phage DNA inserts into the bacterial chromosome by recombination

❻

❼

Many cell divisions

Lysogenic cycle

Lysogenic bacterium reproduces normally, replicating the prophage at each cell division

10.18 Many viruses cause disease in animals and plants

Viruses can cause disease in both animals and plants. A typical animal virus has a membranous outer envelope and projecting spikes of glycoprotein (protein with attached sugars). The envelope helps the virus enter and leave the host cell. Many animal viruses have RNA rather than DNA as their genetic material. Examples of RNA viruses include those that cause the common cold, measles, and mumps, as well as ones that cause more serious human diseases, such as AIDS and polio. Examples of diseases caused by DNA viruses are hepatitis, chicken pox, and herpes infections.

Figure 10.18 shows the reproductive cycle of a typical enveloped RNA virus (the mumps virus). When the virus contacts a host cell, the glycoprotein spikes attach to receptor proteins on the cell's plasma membrane. The envelope fuses with the cell's membrane, allowing the protein-coated RNA to ❶ enter the cytoplasm. ❷ Enzymes then remove the protein coat. ❸ An enzyme that entered the cell as part of the virus uses the virus's RNA genome as a template for making complementary strands of RNA (pink strand). The new strands have two functions: ❹ They serve as mRNA for the synthesis of new viral proteins, and ❺ they serve as templates for synthesizing new viral genome RNA. ❻ The new coat proteins assemble around the new viral RNA. ❼ Finally, the viruses leave the cell by cloaking themselves in plasma membrane. Thus, the virus obtains its envelope from the host cell, leaving the cell without necessarily lysing it.

Not all animal viruses reproduce in the cytoplasm. For example, herpesviruses, which you read about in the chapter introduction, are enveloped DNA viruses that reproduce in the host cell's nucleus; they acquire their envelopes from the cell's nuclear membranes. While inside the nuclei of certain nerve cells, herpesvirus DNA may remain latent, without destroying these cells. From time to time, physical stress, such as a cold or sunburn, or emotional stress may stimulate the herpesvirus DNA to begin production of the virus, which then infects cells at the body's surface and brings about cold sores or genital sores.

The amount of damage a virus causes our body depends partly on how quickly our immune system responds to fight the infection and partly on the ability of the infected tissue to repair itself. We usually recover completely from colds because our respiratory tract tissue can efficiently replace damaged cells by mitosis. In contrast, the poliovirus attacks nerve cells, which do not divide. The damage to such cells, unfortunately, is permanent. In such cases, we try to prevent the disease with vaccines (see Module 24.4).

Viruses that infect plants can stunt plant growth and diminish crop yields. Most plant viruses discovered to date are RNA viruses. To infect a plant, a virus must first get past the plant's outer protective layer of cells. Once a virus enters a plant cell and begins reproducing, it can spread throughout the entire plant through plasmodesmata, the cytoplasmic connections that penetrate the walls between adjacent plant cells (see Figure 4.22).

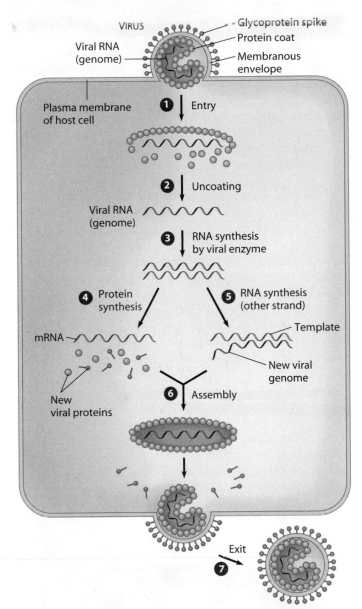

Figure 10.18   The reproductive cycle of an enveloped virus

Plant viruses may spread to other plants by insects, herbivores, humans, or farming tools. As with animal viruses, there are no cures for most viral diseases of plants. Agricultural scientists focus instead on preventing infections and on breeding resistant varieties of crop plants.

Web Activity *Simplified Reproductive Cycle of a DNA Virus*

❓ Explain how some viruses replicate without having DNA.

■ The genetic material of these viruses is RNA, which is replicated inside the host cell by special enzymes encoded by the virus. The viral genome (or its complement) serves as mRNA for the synthesis of viral proteins.

10.19 Emerging viruses threaten human health

Viruses that appear suddenly or are new to medical scientists are called **emerging viruses.** HIV, the AIDS virus, is a classic example: This virus appeared in San Francisco, Los Angeles, and New York in the early 1980s, seemingly out of nowhere. The deadly Ebola virus, recognized initially in 1976 in central Africa, is one of several emerging viruses that cause hemorrhagic fever, an often fatal syndrome characterized by fever, vomiting, massive bleeding, and circulatory system collapse. A number of other dangerous new viruses cause encephalitis, inflammation of the brain. One example is the West Nile virus, which appeared for the first time in North America in 1999 and has since spread to all 48 contiguous U.S. states. Severe acute respiratory syndrome (SARS) first appeared in China in 2002. Within eight months, about 8,000 people were infected, of whom some 10% died. Researchers quickly identified the infectious agent as a previously unknown, single-stranded RNA coronavirus, so named for its halo-like "corona" of spikes.

From where and how do such viruses burst on the human scene, giving rise to rare or previously unknown diseases? Three processes contribute to the emergence of viral diseases: mutations, contact between species, and spread from isolated populations.

The mutation of existing viruses is a major source of new viral diseases. RNA viruses tend to have unusually high rates of mutation because errors in replicating their RNA genomes are not subject to the kind of proofreading mechanisms that help reduce errors in DNA replication (see Module 10.5). Some mutations enable existing viruses to evolve into new strains (genetic varieties) that can cause disease in individuals who have developed immunity to the ancestral virus. Flu epidemics, for instance, are caused by new influenza virus strains that are genetically different enough from earlier strains that people have little immunity to them.

New viral diseases often arise from the spread of existing viruses from one host species to another. Scientists estimate that about three-quarters of new human diseases have originated in other animals. For example, bats have been identified as the likely natural reservoir of the SARS virus: Large numbers of bats carry the virus and are able to transmit it to humans or to other animals that can infect humans.

In 1997, at least 18 people in Hong Kong were infected with a strain of flu virus previously seen only in birds. A mass culling of all of Hong Kong's 1.5 million domestic birds appeared to stop that outbreak. Beginning in 2002, however, new cases of human infection by this bird strain began to crop up around southeast Asia. As of 2007, the disease caused by this virus, now called "avian flu," has killed more than 180 people, and more than 100 million birds have either died from the disease or been killed to prevent the spread of infection (Figure 10.19). If this virus evolves so that it can spread easily from person to person, the potential for a major human outbreak is significant. Indeed, evidence is strong that the flu pandemic of 1918–1919, which killed about 40 million people, originated in birds.

The spread of a viral disease from a small, isolated population can lead to widespread epidemics. For instance, AIDS went unnamed and virtually unnoticed for decades before it began to spread around the world. In this case, technological and social factors, including affordable international travel, blood transfusions, sexual promiscuity, and the abuse of intravenous drugs, allowed a previously rare human disease to become a global scourge. It is likely that when we do find the means to control HIV and other emerging viruses, molecular biologists will be responsible for the discovery.

Colorized TEM 160,000×

Web Process of Science Connection: Why Do AIDS Rates Differ Across the United States?

? Why doesn't a bout of flu give us immunity to flu in subsequent years?

Figure 10.19 Ducks in Vietnam being checked for infection by the Avian flu virus (inset)

■ Influenza viruses evolve rapidly by frequent mutation; thus, the strains that infect us later will most likely be different from the ones to which we've developed immunity.

10.20 The AIDS virus makes DNA on an RNA template

The devastating disease AIDS is caused by a type of RNA virus with some special twists. In outward appearance, the AIDS virus (HIV) resembles the flu or mumps virus. As illustrated in Figure 10.20A, HIV has a membranous envelope and glycoprotein spikes. These components enable HIV to enter and leave a host cell much the way the mumps virus does (see Figure 10.18B). Notice, however, that HIV contains two identical copies of its RNA instead of one. HIV also has a different mode of reproduction. HIV carries molecules of an enzyme called **reverse transcriptase**, which catalyzes reverse transcription, the synthesis of DNA on an RNA template. This unusual phenomenon, which is opposite the usual DNA → RNA flow of genetic information, characterizes **retroviruses** ("retro" means "backward").

Figure 10.20B illustrates what happens after HIV RNA is uncoated in the cytoplasm of a host cell. ❶ The reverse transcriptase (○) uses the RNA as a template to make a DNA strand and then ❷ adds a second, complementary DNA strand. ❸ The resulting double-stranded DNA then enters the cell's nucleus and inserts itself into the chromosomal DNA, becoming a *provirus* (analogous to a prophage). Occasionally, the

Figure 10.20B   The behavior of HIV nucleic acid in a host cell

provirus is ❹ transcribed into RNA and ❺ translated into viral proteins. ❻ New viruses assembled from these components leave the cell and can then infect other cells. This is the standard reproductive cycle for retroviruses.

AIDS stands for acquired immunodeficiency syndrome and **HIV** for human immunodeficiency virus; these terms describe the main effect of the virus on the body. HIV infects and eventually kills white blood cells that are important in immunity. We discuss AIDS in more detail when we take up the immune system in Chapter 24.

Web Activity *Retrovirus (HIV) Reproductive Cycle*

Web Process of Science *Connection: What Causes Infections in AIDS Patients?*

❓ Why is HIV classified as a retrovirus?

■ Because it synthesizes DNA from its RNA genome. This is the reverse ("retro") of the usual DNA → RNA information flow.

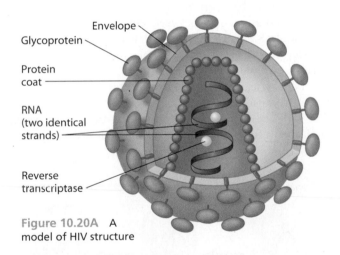

Envelope
Glycoprotein
Protein coat
RNA (two identical strands)
Reverse transcriptase

Figure 10.20A   A model of HIV structure

10.21 Viroids and prions are formidable pathogens in plants and animals

Viruses may be small and simple, but they dwarf another class of pathogens: viroids. **Viroids** are small circular RNA molecules that infect plants. Viroids do not encode proteins but can replicate in host plant cells, apparently using cellular enzymes. These small RNA molecules seem to cause errors in the regulatory systems that control plant growth. The typical signs of viroid diseases are abnormal development and stunted growth.

An important lesson to learn from viroids is that a single molecule can be an infectious agent. Viroids are nucleic acid, whose ability to be replicated is well known. Even more surprising is the evidence for infectious proteins, called **prions**, which appear to cause a number of degenerative brain diseases in various animal species, including scrapie in sheep, mad cow

disease, and Creutzfeldt-Jakob disease in humans. Although much remains to be learned, a prion is thought to be a misfolded form of a protein normally present in brain cells. When the prion enters a cell containing the normal form of protein, the prion somehow converts the normal protein molecules to the misfolded prion versions. To date, there is no known cure for prion diseases, and the only hope for developing effective treatments lies in understanding and preventing the process of infection.

❓ What makes prions different from all other known infectious agents?

■ Prions are proteins and have no nucleic acid.

10.22 Bacteria can transfer DNA in three ways

By studying viral reproduction, researchers also learn about the mechanisms that regulate DNA replication and gene expression in cells. Bacteria are equally valuable as microbial models in genetics research, but for different reasons. As prokaryotic cells, bacteria allow researchers to investigate molecular genetics in the simplest living organisms.

Most of a bacterium's DNA is found in a single chromosome, a closed loop of DNA with associated proteins. In the diagrams here, we show the chromosome much smaller than it actually is relative to the cell. A bacterial chromosome is hundreds of times longer than its cell; it fits inside the cell because it is tightly folded.

Bacterial cells divide by replication of the bacterial chromosome and then by binary fission (see Module 8.3). Because binary fission is an asexual process involving only a single parent, the bacteria in a colony are genetically identical to the parental cell. But this does not mean that bacteria lack ways to produce new combinations of genes. In fact, in the bacterial world, there are three mechanisms by which genes can move from one cell to another: transformation, transduction, and conjugation.

Figure 10.22A
Transformation

Figure 10.22A illustrates **transformation**, the uptake of foreign DNA from the surrounding environment. In Frederick Griffith's "transforming factor" experiment (see Module 10.1), a harmless strain of bacteria took up pieces of DNA left from the dead cells of a disease-causing strain. The DNA from the pathogenic bacteria carried a gene that made the cells resistant to an animal's defenses, and when the previously harmless bacteria acquired this gene, it could cause pneumonia in infected animals.

Bacteriophages provide the second means of bringing together genes of different bacteria. The transfer of bacterial genes by a phage is called **transduction.** In this process, a fragment of DNA belonging to a phage's previous host cell is packaged within the phage's coat instead of the phage's DNA. When the phage infects a new bacterial cell, the DNA stowaway from the former host cell is injected into the new host (Figure 10.22B).

Figure 10.22C is an illustration of what happens at the DNA level when two bacterial cells mate. This physical union

Figure 10.22B Transduction

of cells and the DNA transfer between them is called **conjugation** (from the Latin *conjugatus,* united). Notice that the "male" donor cell has hollow appendages called sex pili, one of which is attached to the "female" recipient cell. The outside layers of the cells have fused, and a cytoplasmic bridge has formed between them. Through this mating bridge, donor cell DNA (bright blue in the figure) passes to the recipient cell. The donor cell replicates its DNA as it transfers it, so the cell doesn't end up lacking any genes. The DNA replication is a special type that allows one copy to peel off and transfer into the recipient cell.

Figure 10.22C Conjugation

Once new DNA gets into a bacterial cell, by whatever mechanism, part of it may then integrate into the recipient's chromosome. As Figure 10.22D indicates, integration occurs by crossing over between the two DNA molecules, a process similar to crossing over between eukaryotic chromosomes (see Module 8.18). Here we see that two crossovers result in a piece of the donated DNA replacing part of the recipient cell's original DNA. The leftover pieces of DNA are broken down, leaving the recipient bacterium with a recombinant chromosome.

As we'll see in the next module, the transfer of genetic material between bacteria has important medical consequences.

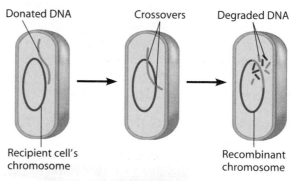

Figure 10.22D Integration of donated DNA into the recipient cell's chromosome

? The three modes of gene transfer between bacteria are _____, which is transfer via a virus; _____, which is the uptake of DNA from the surrounding environment; and _____, which is bacterial "sex."

■ transduction . . . transformation . . . conjugation

10.23 Bacterial plasmids can serve as carriers for gene transfer

The ability of a donor *E. coli* cell to carry out conjugation is usually due to a specific piece of DNA called the **F factor** (F for fertility). The F factor carries genes for making sex pili and other requirements for conjugation; it also contains an origin of replication, where DNA replication can start.

Let's see how the F factor behaves during conjugation. In Figure 10.23A, the F factor (light blue) is integrated into the male bacterium's chromosome. When this cell conjugates with a recipient cell, the male chromosome starts replicating at the F factor's origin of replication, indicated by the blue dot on the DNA. The growing copy of the DNA peels off the chromosome and heads into the recipient cell. Thus, part of the F factor serves as the leading end of the transferred DNA, but right behind it are genes from the donor's original chromosome. The rest of the F factor stays in the donor cell. Once inside the recipient cell, the transferred donor genes can recombine with the corresponding part of the recipient chromosome by crossing over. If crossing over occurs, the recipient cell may be genetically changed, but it usually remains female because the two cells break apart before the rest of the F factor transfers.

Alternatively, as Figure 10.23B shows, an F factor can exist as a **plasmid,** a small, circular DNA molecule separate from the bacterial chromosome. Every plasmid has an origin of replication, required for its replication within the cell. Some plasmids, including the F-factor plasmid, can bring about conjugation and move to another cell. When the male cell in Figure 10.23B mates with a recipient cell, the F factor replicates and at the same time transfers one whole copy of itself, in linear rather than circular form, to the recipient cell. The transferred plasmid re-forms a circle in the recipient cell, and the cell becomes male.

E. coli and other bacteria have many different kinds of plasmids. You can see several from one cell in Figure 10.23C, along with part of the bacterial chromosome, which extends in loops from the ruptured cell. Some plasmids carry genes that can affect the survival of the cell. Plasmids of one class, called **R plasmids,** pose serious problems for human medicine. Transferable R plasmids carry genes for enzymes that destroy antibiotics such as penicillin and tetracycline. Bacteria containing R plasmids are resistant (hence the designation R) to antibiotics that would otherwise kill them. The widespread use of antibiotics in medicine and agriculture has tended to kill off bacteria that lack R plasmids, whereas those with R plasmids have multiplied. As a result, an increasing number of bacteria that cause human diseases, such as food poisoning and gonorrhea, are becoming resistant to antibiotics (see Module 13.15).

We will return to the topic of plasmids in Chapter 12. But first, we continue our study of molecular genetics in Chapter 11, where we explore what is known about how genes themselves are controlled.

Figure 10.23A Transfer of chromosomal DNA by an integrated F factor

Figure 10.23B Transfer of an F-factor plasmid

Figure 10.23C Plasmids and part of a bacterial chromosome released from a ruptured *E. coli* cell

? In Chapter 12, you will learn that plasmids are useful tools for genetic engineering. Can you guess why?

■ Because plasmids can carry foreign genes and are duplicated and passed along by bacterial cells

Chapter Review

Reviewing the Concepts

The Structure of the Genetic Material (Introduction–10.3)

DNA as the genetic material. Viruses provided some of the earliest evidence that genes are made of DNA. One key experiment showed that certain bacterial viruses (phages) reprogram host cells to produce more phages by injecting their DNA (**Introduction–10.1**).

DNA is a nucleic acid, made of long chains of nucleotide monomers (**10.2**):

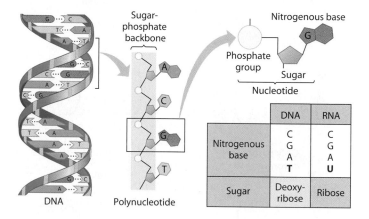

	DNA	RNA
Nitrogenous base	C G A **T**	C G A **U**
Sugar	Deoxy-ribose	Ribose

Watson and Crick worked out the three-dimensional structure of DNA: two polynucleotide strands wrapped around each other in a double helix. Hydrogen bonds between bases hold the strands together. Each base pairs with a complementary partner: A with T and G with C (**10.3**).

DNA Replication (10.4–10.5)

DNA replication starts with the separation of DNA strands. Enzymes then use each strand as a template to assemble new nucleotides into a complementary strand. Using the enzyme DNA polymerase, the cell synthesizes one daughter strand as a continuous piece, the other as a series of short pieces, which are then connected by the enzyme DNA ligase (**10.4–10.5**).

The Flow of Genetic Information from DNA to RNA to Protein (10.6–10.16)

From genotype to phenotype. The information constituting an organism's genotype is carried in the sequence of its DNA bases. A particular gene—a linear sequence of many nucleotides—specifies a polypeptide. The DNA of the gene is transcribed into RNA, which is translated into the polypeptide (**10.6**). The "words" of the DNA "language" are triplets of bases called codons. The codons in a gene specify the amino acid sequence of a polypeptide. Nearly all organisms use exactly the same genetic code (**10.7–10.8**).

Transcription. In the nucleus, the DNA helix unzips, and RNA nucleotides line up and hydrogen-bond along one strand of the DNA, following the base-pairing rules. As the single-stranded messenger RNA (mRNA) peels away from the gene, the DNA strands rejoin (**10.9**). Eukaryotic RNA is processed before leaving the nucleus as mRNA. Noncoding segments called introns are spliced out, and a cap and tail are added to the ends (**10.10**).

Translation takes place in the cytoplasm. A ribosome attaches to the mRNA and translates its message into a specific polypeptide, aided by transfer RNAs (tRNAs) that act as interpreters. Each tRNA is a folded molecule bearing a base triplet called an anticodon on one end; a specific amino acid is added to the other end (**10.11**). The mRNA moves a codon at a time relative to the ribosome, and a tRNA with a complementary anticodon pairs with each codon, adding its amino acid to the peptide chain (**10.12–10.14**):

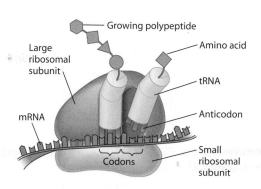

The sequence of codons in DNA, via the sequence of codons in mRNA, spells out the primary structure of a polypeptide (**10.15**).

Mutations are changes in the DNA base sequence, caused by errors in DNA replication or recombination, or by mutagens. Substituting, inserting, or deleting nucleotides alters a gene, with varying effects on the organism (**10.16**).

Microbial Genetics (10.17–10.23)

Viruses can be regarded as genes packaged in protein. When phage DNA enters a lytic cycle inside a bacterium, it is replicated, transcribed, and translated; the new viral DNA and protein molecules then assemble into new phages, which burst from the host cell. In the lysogenic cycle, phage DNA inserts into the host chromosome and is passed on to generations of daughter cells. Much later, it may initiate phage production (**10.17**). Many viruses cause disease when they invade animal or plant cells. Many, such as flu viruses and most plant viruses, have RNA, rather than DNA, as their genetic material. Some animal viruses steal a bit of host cell membrane as a protective envelope. Some viruses can remain latent in the host's body for long periods (**10.18**). Emerging viral diseases pose a threat to human health (**10.19**). HIV, the AIDS virus, is a retrovirus. Inside a cell it uses its RNA as a template for making DNA, which then inserts into a host chromosome (**10.20**). Viroids are RNA molecules that can infect plants. Prions are infectious proteins that can cause brain diseases in animals (**10.21**).

Bacteria can transfer genes from cell to cell by one of three processes: transformation, transduction, or conjugation (**10.22**). Plasmids, small circular DNA molecules separate from the bacterial chromosome, can serve as carriers for the transfer of genes (**10.23**).

Connecting the Concepts

1. Check your understanding of the flow of genetic information through a cell by filling in the blanks.

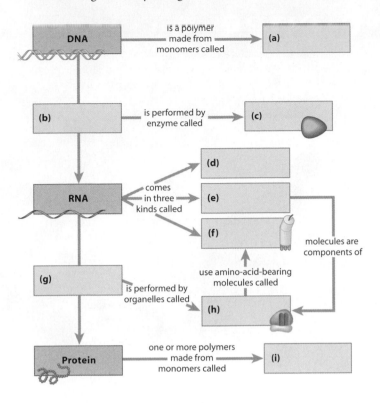

Testing Your Knowledge

Multiple Choice

2. Scientists have discovered how to put together a bacteriophage with the protein coat of phage T2 and the DNA of phage lambda. If this composite phage were allowed to infect a bacterium, the phages produced in the host cell would have _____. (*Explain your answer.*)
   a. the protein of T2 and the DNA of lambda
   b. the protein of lambda and the DNA of T2
   c. a mixture of the DNA and proteins of both phages
   d. the protein and DNA of T2
   e. the protein and DNA of lambda

3. A geneticist found that a particular mutation had no effect on the polypeptide coded by a gene. This mutation probably involved
   a. deletion of one nucleotide.
   b. alteration of the start codon.
   c. insertion of one nucleotide.
   d. deletion of the entire gene.
   e. substitution of one nucleotide.

4. Which of the following correctly ranks the structures in order of size, from largest to smallest?
   a. gene-chromosome-nucleotide-codon
   b. chromosome-gene-codon-nucleotide
   c. nucleotide-chromosome-gene-codon
   d. chromosome-nucleotide-gene-codon
   e. gene-chromosome-codon-nucleotide

5. The nucleotide sequence of a DNA codon is GTA. A messenger RNA molecule with a complementary codon is transcribed from the DNA. In the process of protein synthesis, a transfer RNA pairs with the mRNA codon. What is the nucleotide sequence of the tRNA anticodon?
   a. CAT   d. CAU
   b. CUT   e. GT
   c. GUA

Describing, Comparing, and Explaining

6. Describe the process of DNA replication: the ingredients needed, the steps in the process, and the final product.

7. Describe the process by which the information in a gene is transcribed and translated into a protein. Correctly use these words in your description: tRNA, amino acid, start codon, transcription, RNA splicing, exons, introns, mRNA, gene, codon, RNA polymerase, ribosome, translation, anticodon, peptide bond, stop codon.

Applying the Concepts

8. A cell containing a single chromosome is placed in a medium containing radioactive phosphate so that any new DNA strands formed by DNA replication will be radioactive. The cell replicates its DNA and divides. Then the daughter cells (still in the radioactive medium) replicate their DNA and divide, and a total of four cells are present. Sketch the DNA molecules in all four cells, showing a normal (nonradioactive) DNA strand as a solid line and a radioactive DNA strand as a dashed line.

9. The base sequence of the gene coding for a short polypeptide is CTACGCTAGGCGATTGACT. What would be the base sequence of the mRNA transcribed from this gene? Using the genetic code in Figure 10.8A, give the amino acid sequence of the polypeptide translated from this mRNA. (*Hint:* What is the start codon?)

10. Researchers on the Human Genome Project have determined the nucleotide sequences of human genes and in many cases identified the proteins encoded by the genes. Knowledge of the nucleotide sequences of genes might be used to develop lifesaving medicines or treatments for genetic defects. In the United States, both government agencies and biotechnology companies have applied for patents on their discoveries of genes. In Britain, the courts have ruled that a naturally occurring gene cannot be patented. Do you think individuals and companies should be able to patent genes and gene products? Before answering, consider the following: What are the purposes of a patent? How might the discoverer of a gene benefit from a patent? How might the public benefit? What might be some positive and negative results of patenting genes?

Answers to all questions can be found in Appendix 4.

For Practice Quizzes, BioFlix, MP3 Tutors, and Activities, go to www.mybiology.com.

Control of Gene Expression

🎧 **11.1** Proteins interacting with DNA turn prokaryotic genes on or off in response to environmental changes

11.2 Differentiation results from the expression of different combination of genes

11.3 DNA packing in eukaryotic chromosomes helps regulate gene expression

11.4 In female mammals, one X chromosome is inactive in each somatic cell

11.5 Complex assemblies of proteins control eukaryotic transcription

11.6 Eukaryotic RNA may be spliced in more than one way

11.7 Small RNAs play multiple roles in controlling gene expression

11.8 Translation and later stages of gene expression are also subject to regulation

11.9 Review: Multiple mechanisms regulate gene expression in eukaryotes

11.10 Cascades of gene expression direct the development of an animal

11.11 DNA microarrays test for the transcription of many genes at once

11.12 Signal transduction pathways convert messages received at the cell surface to responses within the cell

11.13 Cell-signaling systems appeared early in the evolution of life

Cloning of Plants and Animals

11.14 Plant cloning shows that differentiated cells may retain all of their genetic potential

11.15 Nuclear transplantation can be used to clone animals

11.16 Reproductive cloning has valuable applications, but human reproductive cloning raises ethical issues

11.17 Therapeutic cloning can produce stem cells with great medical potential

The Genetic Basis of Cancer

11.18 Cancer results from mutations in genes that control cell division

11.19 Multiple genetic changes underlie the development of cancer

11.20 Faulty proteins can interfere with normal signal transduction pathways

11.21 Lifestyle choices can reduce the risk of cancer

Cloning to the Rescue?

All the animals shown on these pages share two unusual features. First, they are all members of endangered species. Second, they are all clones. In this usage, a **clone** is an individual created by asexual reproduction (that is, reproduction that does not involve fusion of sperm and egg) and thus genetically identical to a single parent. First demonstrated in the 1950s with frogs, animal cloning became much more commonplace after 1997, when Scottish researchers announced the first successful cloning of a mammal: the celebrated Dolly the sheep, cloned using a mammary cell from an adult ewe. In the years since Dolly's landmark birth, researchers have cloned a variety of other mammals, including mules, horses, cats, cows, goats, pigs, monkeys, mice, and, most recently, dogs.

Some researchers have concentrated their efforts on cloning members of endangered species. Among the rare animals that have been cloned are a gaur (an Asian ox) and a mouflon (a small European sheep). At the Audubon Center for Research of Endangered Species in New Orleans, cloners have focused their efforts on endangered felines, such as the African wildcat (*Felis silvestris*) shown at right. And in 2006, South Korean researchers announced the successful cloning of two gray wolves, a species that nearly became extinct in the United States in the early 20th century. One of these wolves is shown at left.

One remarkable case was the 2003 cloning of a banteng (a Javanese bovine whose numbers have dwindled to just a few in the wild) using frozen skin cells from a zoo-raised banteng that had died 23 years previously. Nuclei from the donor were inserted into denucleated eggs from ordinary cows. The resulting embryos were implanted into surrogate Angus cows, leading to the birth of a healthy baby banteng (above). This case proves the possibility of producing new animals even when a female of the donor species is unavailable. Scientists may someday be able to use similar cross-species methods to clone an animal from a recently extinct species.

The use of cloning to slow or reverse extinction and repopulate endangered species holds tremendous promise. However, conservationists object that cloning may trivialize the tragedy of extinction and detract from efforts to preserve natural habitats. They correctly point out that cloning, like other forms of asexual reproduction, does not increase genetic diversity and is therefore not as beneficial to endangered species as natural reproduction.

Researchers are also concerned that cloned animals are less healthy than those arising from a fertilized egg. In 2003, at age 6, Dolly was euthanized after suffering complications from a lung disease normally seen only in much older sheep. Dolly's premature death, as well as her arthritic condition, led to speculation that her cells were somehow "older" than those of normal sheep. Many other cloned animals exhibit defects. Cloned mice, for instance, are prone to obesity, pneumonia, liver failure, and premature death. Scientists believe that even cloned animals that appear normal are likely to have subtle defects. Recent work traces these problems to physical changes within the chromosomes of the cloned organism that derail the normal regulation of genes.

The ability to clone an animal using a transplanted nucleus demonstrates an important point: The nuclei of adult body cells contain a complete genome capable of directing the production of all the cell types in an organism. The development of a multicellular organism, with many different kinds of cells, thus depends on the turning on and off of genes—the control of gene expression. The health problems associated with cloned animals underscore the fact that proper gene regulation is important to the well-being of all organisms.

This chapter focuses first on how genes are controlled, beginning with simple prokaryotic systems and then describing gene regulation in eukaryotes. Next we look at the methods and applications of animal cloning. Finally, we discuss cancer, a disease that results from defects in the regulation of cell division. ■ ■ ■

209

11.1 Proteins interacting with DNA turn prokaryotic genes on or off in response to environmental changes

Gene regulation—the turning on and off of genes—can help organisms respond to environmental changes. But what do we actually mean when we say that genes are turned on or off? As we discussed in Chapter 10, genes determine the nucleotide sequences of specific RNA molecules; if this RNA is mRNA, it in turn determines the sequences of amino acids in protein molecules. Thus, a gene that is turned on is being transcribed into RNA, and that message is being translated into specific protein molecules. The overall process by which genetic information flows from genes to proteins—that is, from genotype to phenotype—is called **gene expression**. The control of gene expression makes it possible for cells to produce specific kinds of proteins when and where they are needed. The turning on and off of transcription is the main way that gene expression is regulated in all organisms.

Our earliest understanding of gene control came from studies of the bacterium *Escherichia coli* (Figure 11.1A). *E. coli* can change its metabolic activities in response to changes in its environment. For example, when a certain nutrient is plentiful, *E. coli* does not squander valuable resources to make it from scratch. Bacterial cells that can conserve resources and energy have an advantage over cells that are unable to do so. Thus, natural selection has favored bacteria that express only the genes whose products are needed by the cell. Let's look at how the regulation of gene transcription helps *E. coli* accomplish such control.

The* lac *Operon Picture an *E. coli* cell living in your intestine. It is dependent on your dietary whims for its nutrients. If

Figure 11.1A Cells of *E. coli* bacteria

Colorized SEM 7,000×

you eat a sweet roll for breakfast, the bacterium will soon be bathed in sugars and broken-down fats. Later on, if you have a glass of fat-free milk and a salad for lunch, *E. coli*'s environment will change drastically.

Let's focus on your glass of milk for a moment. One of the main nutrients in milk is the disaccharide sugar lactose (see Module 3.5). When lactose is plentiful in the intestine, *E. coli* makes the enzymes necessary to absorb the sugar and use it as an energy source. Conversely, when lactose is not plentiful, *E. coli* does not waste its energy producing these enzymes.

Remember that enzymes are proteins; their production is an outcome of gene expression. *E. coli* can make lactose-utilization enzymes because it has genes that code for these enzymes. Figure 11.1B (on the facing page) presents a model (first proposed in 1961 by French biologists François Jacob and Jacques Monod) to explain how an *E. coli* cell can turn genes coding for lactose-utilization enzymes off or on, depending on whether lactose is available.

E. coli uses three enzymes to take up and start metabolizing lactose, and the genes coding for these three enzymes are regulated as a single unit. The DNA at the top of Figure 11.1B represents a small segment of the bacterium's chromosome. Notice that the three genes that code for the lactose-utilization enzymes (light blue) are next to each other in the DNA.

Adjacent to the group of lactose enzyme genes are two *control sequences*, short sections of DNA that help control the enzyme genes. One stretch of nucleotides is a **promoter** (green), a site where the transcription enzyme, RNA polymerase, attaches and initiates transcription—in this case, transcription of all three lactose enzyme genes (as depicted in the bottom panel of Figure 11.1B). Between the promoter and the enzyme genes, a DNA segment called an **operator** (yellow) acts as a switch. The operator determines whether RNA polymerase can attach to the promoter and start transcribing the genes.

Such a cluster of genes with related functions, along with a promoter and an operator, is called an **operon**; with rare exceptions, operons exist only in prokaryotes. The key advantage to the grouping of related genes into operons is that a single "on-off switch" can control the whole cluster. The operon discussed here is called the *lac* operon, short for lactose operon. When an *E. coli* encounters lactose, all the enzymes needed for its use are made at once because the operon's genes are all controlled by a single switch, the operator. But what determines whether the operator switch is on or off?

The top panel of Figure 11.1B shows the *lac* operon in "off" mode, its status when there is no lactose in the cell's environment. Transcription is turned off by a molecule called a **repressor** ( ), a protein that functions by binding to the operator and physically blocking the attachment of RNA polymerase ( ) to the promoter. On the left side of the figure, you can see where the repressor comes from. A gene called a

regulatory gene (dark blue), located outside the operon, codes for the repressor. The regulatory gene is expressed continually, so the cell always has a small supply of repressor molecules.

How can an operon be turned on if its repressor is always present? As the bottom panel of Figure 11.1B indicates, lactose (○) interferes with the attachment of the *lac* repressor to the operator by binding to the repressor and changing its shape. With its new shape (●), the repressor cannot bind to the operator, and the operator switch remains on. RNA polymerase can now bind to the promoter (since it is no longer being blocked) and from there transcribe the genes of the operon. The resulting mRNA carries coding sequences for all three enzymes (purple) needed for lactose use. The cell can translate the message in this single mRNA into three separate polypeptides because the mRNA has multiple codons signaling the start and stop of translation.

The newly produced mRNA and protein molecules will remain intact for only a short time before cellular enzymes break them down. When the synthesis of mRNA and protein stops because lactose is no longer present, the molecules quickly disappear.

Figure 11.1B   The *lac* operon

Other Kinds of Operons   The *lac* operon is only one type of operon in bacteria. Other types also have a promoter, an operator, and several adjacent genes, but they differ in the way the operator switch is controlled. **Figure 11.1C** shows two types of repressor-controlled operons. The *lac* operon's repressor is active when alone and inactive when bound to lactose. A second type of operon, represented here by the *trp* operon, is controlled by a repressor that is *inactive* alone. To be active, this type of repressor must combine with a specific small molecule. In our example, the small molecule is tryptophan, an amino acid essential for protein synthesis. *E. coli* can make tryptophan from scratch, using enzymes encoded in the *trp* operon. But it will stop making tryptophan and simply absorb it in prefabricated form from the surroundings whenever possible. When *E. coli* is swimming in tryptophan, which occurs in large amounts in such foods as milk and poultry, tryptophan binds to the repressor of the *trp* operon. This activates the *trp* repressor, enabling it to switch off the operon. Thus, this type of operon allows bacteria to stop making certain essential molecules when the molecules are already present in the environment, saving materials and energy for the cells.

Another type of operon control involves **activators,** proteins that turn operons *on* by binding to DNA. These proteins act by making it easier for RNA polymerase to bind to the promoter, rather than by blocking RNA polymerase, as repressors do. Activators help control a wide variety of operons.

Figure 11.1C   Two types of repressor-controlled operons

Armed with a variety of operons and regulated by repressors and activators, *E. coli* and other prokaryotes can thrive in frequently changing environments. Next we'll examine how more complex eukaryotes achieve gene regulation.

🎧 MP3 Tutor *Control of Gene Expression*

Web Activity *The* lac *operon in* E. coli

? A certain mutation in *E. coli* impairs the ability of the *lac* repressor to bind to the *lac* operator. How would this affect the cell?

■ The cell would wastefully produce the enzymes for lactose metabolism continuously, even when lactose is not present.

11.2 Differentiation results from the expression of different combinations of genes

Compared with bacteria, eukaryotic organisms, especially multicellular ones, face elaborate gene regulation challenges. During the repeated cell divisions that lead from a zygote to a multicellular adult, individual cells must undergo **differentiation**—that is, become specialized in structure and function. Differentiation results from selective gene expression, the turning on and off of specific genes.

The light micrographs in **Figure 11.2** show several types of human cells. Each sample was stained with dyes to bring out important cellular details, and all three micrographs are printed at about the same magnification (900×). The micrograph on the left shows a short segment of a muscle cell, which is a long fiber with multiple nuclei (dark horizontal rods). The vertical stripes result from the arrangement of the proteins that bring about muscle contraction. As you'd expect, the genes encoding these proteins are active in muscle cells.

The center micrograph shows cells from the pancreas, the organ that produces the hormones glucagon and insulin, which regulate blood sugar. The gene for glucagon is turned on only in the alpha cells (pink) and the gene for insulin only in the beta cells (light purple). The dark blue spots are cell nuclei.

In the micrograph on the right, we see a single white blood cell (purple with a dark, two-part nucleus) surrounded by red blood cells (pink). In immature red blood cells, the genes for the oxygen-carrying protein hemoglobin are turned on full blast. Later in differentiation, mammalian red blood cells lose their nuclei and other organelles. Mature red blood cells (shown in the micrograph) are packed full with hemoglobin.

| Muscle cell | Pancreas cells | Blood cells |

Figure 11.2 Some types of human cells (all shown at 900×)

The genes for "housekeeping" enzymes, such as those involved in glycolysis, are active in all metabolizing cells. In contrast, the genes for specialized proteins are turned on only in particular types of cells.

In summary, the particular genes that are active in each type of differentiated cell are the source of its particular function and structure. As you'll see later, such differentiated cells still retain their full genetic potential. But first, let's examine how genes are regulated in eukaryotes.

? If a nerve cell and a skin cell in your body have the same genes, how can the cells be so different?

■ Each cell type must be expressing certain genes that are present in, but not expressed in, the other cell types.

11.3 DNA packing in eukaryotic chromosomes helps regulate gene expression

Let's begin our exploration of gene regulation in eukaryotes by looking at the chromosomes, where almost all of the cell's genes are located. The DNA in just a single human chromosome averages 4 cm in length, thousands of times more than the diameter of the nucleus. All this DNA can fit within the nucleus because of an elaborate, multilevel system of coiling and folding, or *packing*, of the DNA in each chromosome. A crucial aspect of DNA packing is the association of the DNA with small proteins called **histones**. In fact, histone proteins account for about half the mass of eukaryotic chromosomes. (Prokaryotes have analogous proteins, but lack the degree of DNA packing in eukaryotes.)

Figure 11.3 (top of next page) shows a model for the main levels of DNA packing. At the left, notice that the double-helical molecule of DNA has a diameter of 2 nm, which is not altered by packing. At the first level of packing, histones attach to the DNA. In electron micrographs, the DNA-histone complex has the appearance of beads on a string. Each "bead," called a **nucleosome**, consists of DNA wound around a protein core of eight histone molecules. Short stretches of DNA, called linkers, join consecutive nucleosomes (the "string" between the "beads").

At the next level of packing, the beaded string is wrapped into a tight helical fiber. Then this fiber coils further into a thick supercoil with a diameter of about 300 nm. Looping and folding can further compact the DNA, as you can see in the metaphase chromosome at the right of the figure. Viewed as a whole, Figure 11.3 gives a sense of how successive levels of coiling and folding enable a huge amount of DNA to fit into a cell nucleus.

DNA packing tends to prevent gene expression by preventing transcription proteins from contacting the DNA. Cells seem to use higher levels of packing for long-term inactivation of genes. Highly compacted chromatin, which is found not only in metaphase chromosomes but also in varying regions of interphase chromosomes, is generally not expressed at all. One intriguing instance of this phenomenon is described in the next module.

? How does dense packing of DNA in chromosomes prevent gene expression?

■ RNA polymerase and other proteins required for transcription do not have access to the DNA in tightly packed regions of a chromosome.

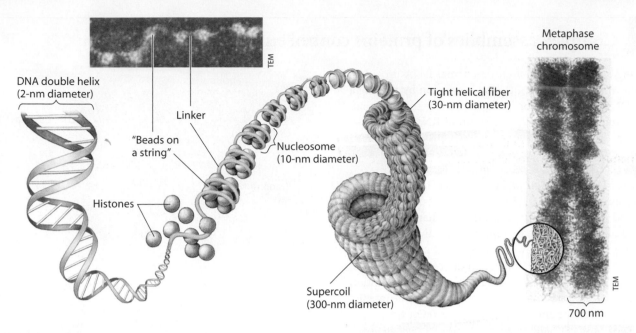

Figure 11.3   DNA packing in a eukaryotic chromosome

11.4   In female mammals, one X chromosome is inactive in each somatic cell

Female mammals, including humans, inherit two X chromosomes. So why don't females make twice as much of the proteins encoded by genes on the X chromosome compared to the amount in males? It turns out that in female mammals, one X chromosome in each somatic cell exists in a highly compacted and almost entirely inactive form. This **X chromosome inactivation** is initiated early in embryonic development, when one of the two X chromosomes in each cell is inactivated at random. As a result, the cells of females and males have the same effective dose (one copy) of these genes. The inactive X in each cell of a female condenses into a compact object called a **Barr body.**

Which X chromosome is inactivated is a matter of chance in each embryonic cell, but once an X chromosome is inactivated, all descendant cells have the same copy turned off. Consequently, females consist of a mosaic of two types of cells: those with the active X derived from the father and those with the active X derived from the mother. Thus, if a female is heterozygous for a gene on the X chromosome (a sex-linked gene; see Module 9.21), about half her cells will express one allele, while the others will express the alternate allele.

A striking example of this phenomenon is the tortoiseshell cat, which has orange and black patches of fur (Figure 11.4). The relevant fur-color gene is on the X chromosome, and the

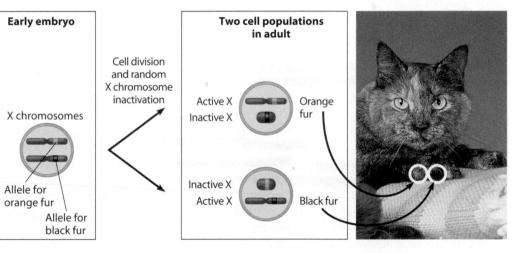

Figure 11.4   Tortoiseshell pattern on a cat, a result of X chromosome inactivation

tortoiseshell phenotype requires the presence of two different alleles, one for orange fur and one for black fur. Normally, only females can have both alleles because only they have two X chromosomes. If a female is heterozygous for the tortoiseshell gene, she will have the tortoiseshell phenotype. Orange patches are formed by populations of cells in which the X chromosome with the orange allele is active; black patches have cells in which the X chromosome with the nonorange allele is active.

? Why are tortoiseshell cats usually female?

In general, only females have two X chromosomes (but see Module 8.22).

11.5 Complex assemblies of proteins control eukaryotic transcription

The packing and unpacking of chromosomal DNA provide a coarse adjustment for eukaryotic gene expression by making a region of DNA either more or less available for transcription. The fine-tuning begins with the initiation of RNA synthesis—transcription. In both prokaryotes and eukaryotes, the initiation of transcription (whether transcription starts or not) is the most important stage for regulating gene expression.

Like prokaryotes (see Module 11.1), eukaryotes employ regulatory proteins that bind to DNA and turn the transcription of genes on and off. The eukaryotic control mechanisms involve proteins that, like prokaryotic repressors and activators, bind to specific segments of DNA. However, eukaryotic cells have more regulatory proteins and more control sequences in their DNA. The current model for the initiation of eukaryotic transcription features an intricate array of regulatory proteins that interact with DNA and with one another to turn genes on or off.

In contrast to the clustered genes of bacterial operons, each eukaryotic gene usually has its own promoter and other control sequences. Moreover, activator proteins seem to be more important in eukaryotes than repressors. In multicellular eukaryotes, the "default" state for most genes seems to be "off." A typical animal or plant cell needs to turn on (transcribe) only a small percentage of its genes, those required for the cell's specialized structure and function. Housekeeping genes, those continually active in virtually all cells for routine activities such as glycolysis, may be in an "on" state by default.

In order to function, eukaryotic RNA polymerase requires the assistance of proteins called **transcription factors.** In the model depicted in **Figure 11.5**, the first step in initiating gene transcription is the binding of activator proteins (green) to DNA sequences called **enhancers** (yellow). In contrast to the operators of prokaryotic operons, enhancers are usually far away from the gene they help regulate. The binding of activators to enhancers leads to bending of the DNA. Once the DNA is bent, the bound activators interact with other transcription factor proteins (purple), which then bind as a complex at the gene's promoter. This large assembly of proteins facilitates the correct attachment of RNA polymerase to the promoter and the initiation of transcription. As shown in the figure, several enhancers and activators may be involved. Not shown are *repressor* proteins called **silencers** that may bind to DNA sequences and *inhibit* the start of transcription.

If eukaryotic genomes only rarely have operons, how does the eukaryotic cell deal with genes of related function that

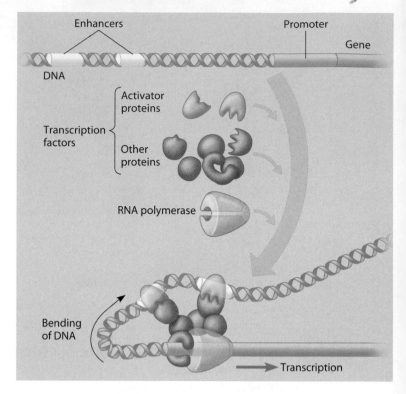

Figure 11.5 A model for the turning on of a eukaryotic gene

need to be turned on or off at the same time? Genes coding for the enzymes of a metabolic pathway, for example, are often scattered over different chromosomes. Coordinated gene expression in eukaryotes seems to depend on the association of a specific enhancer (or collection of enhancers) with every gene of a particular metabolic pathway. Copies of the transcription factors that recognize these DNA sequences bind to them all at once, promoting simultaneous transcription of the genes, no matter where they are in the genome.

Web Process of Science *How Do You Design a Gene Expression System?*

? What must occur before RNA polymerase can bind to a promoter and transcribe a specific eukaryotic gene?

■ Enhancers must bind to transcription factors to facilitate the attachment of RNA polymerase to the promoter.

11.6 Eukaryotic RNA may be spliced in more than one way

Once transcription of a eukaryotic RNA molecule is completed, the noncoding segments called introns are removed by splicing (see Module 10.10). RNA splicing provides several possible ways for regulating gene expression. Some scientists think that the splicing process itself may help control the flow of mRNA from nucleus to cytoplasm because until splicing is completed, the RNA is attached to the molecules of the splicing machinery and cannot pass through the nuclear pores. Moreover, in some cases, the cell can carry out splicing in more than one way, generating different mRNA molecules from the same RNA transcript. Notice in **Figure 11.6**, for example, that one mRNA molecule ends up with the green exon and the other with the brown exon.

(The light blue and pink segments are the introns.) With this sort of **alternative RNA splicing,** an organism can get more than one type of polypeptide from a single gene.

One interesting example of two-way splicing is found in the fruit fly. In this animal, the differences between males and females are largely due to different patterns of RNA splicing. And as you will learn in Chapter 12, recent results from the Human Genome Project suggest that alternative splicing is very common in humans. Included among the many instances already known is one gene whose transcript can be spliced to encode *seven* alternative versions of a certain protein involved in cellular contraction. Each of the seven is made in a different type of cell.

? How does alternative RNA splicing enable a single gene to encode more than one kind of polypeptide?

■ Each kind of polypeptide is encoded by an mRNA molecule containing a different combination of exons.

Figure 11.6 Production of two different mRNAs from the same gene

---

11.7 Small RNAs play multiple roles in controlling gene expression

Recall that only 1.5% of the human genome—and a similarly small percentage of the genomes of many other multicellular eukaryotes—codes for proteins. Another very small fraction of DNA consists of genes for ribosomal RNA and transfer RNA. Until recently, most of the remaining DNA was considered to be "noncoding," meaning that it neither coded for proteins nor was transcribed into functional RNA of the few known types. In other words, it was thought not to contain meaningful genetic information. However, a flood of recent data has contradicted this view. Biologists currently think that a significant amount of the genome may be transcribed into non-protein-coding RNAs, including a variety of small RNAs. While many questions about the functions of these RNAs remain unanswered, researchers are uncovering more evidence of their biological roles every day.

In 1993, researchers discovered small single-stranded RNA molecules, called microRNAs (miRNAs), that can bind to complementary sequences on mRNA molecules (Figure 11.7). Each miRNA, typically about 20 nucleotides long, ❶ associates with a large protein complex. The complex can ❷ bind to any mRNA molecule with the complementary sequence. Then the miRNA-protein complex either ❸ degrades the target mRNA or ❹ blocks its translation. It has been estimated that miRNAs may regulate the expression of up to one-third of all human genes, a striking figure given that miRNAs were unknown a mere 20 years ago.

Researchers can take advantage of the miRNA mechanism to artificially control gene expression. For example, injecting miRNAs into a cell can turn off expression of a gene with a sequence that matches the miRNA. This procedure is called **RNA interference (RNAi).** As you learned in Chapter 10, some viruses that infect cells have double-stranded RNA genomes. The RNAi pathway may have evolved as a natural defense against infection by such viruses.

Biologists are excited about these recent discoveries, which hint at a large, diverse population of RNA molecules in the cell that play crucial roles in regulating gene expression—and have gone largely unnoticed until now. Clearly, we must revise the long-standing view that because they code for proteins, mRNAs are the most important RNAs in terms of cellular function.

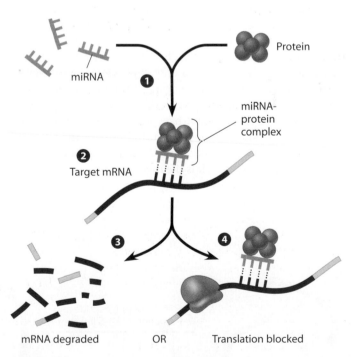

Figure 11.7 The mechanism of RNA interference

? If a gene has the sequence AATTCGCG, what would be the sequence of an miRNA that turns off the gene?

■ The gene will be transcribed as the mRNA sequence UUAAGCG; an miRNA of sequence AAUUCGCG would bind to and disable this mRNA.

Translation and later stages of gene expression are also subject to regulation

After a eukaryotic mRNA is fully processed and transported to the cytoplasm, there are additional opportunities for regulation. These include mRNA breakdown, initiation of translation, protein activation, and protein breakdown.

Breakdown of mRNA Molecules of mRNA do not remain intact forever. Enzymes in the cytoplasm eventually break them down, and the timing of this event is an important factor regulating the amounts of various proteins that are produced in the cell. Long-lived mRNAs can be translated into many more protein molecules than short-lived ones. Prokaryotic mRNAs have very short lifetimes; they are degraded by enzymes within a few minutes after their synthesis. This is one reason bacteria can change their proteins relatively quickly in response to environmental changes. In contrast, the mRNA of eukaryotes can have lifetimes of hours or even weeks.

A striking example of long-lived mRNA is found in vertebrate red blood cells, which manufacture large quantities of the protein hemoglobin. In most species of vertebrates, the mRNAs for hemoglobin are unusually stable. They probably last as long as the red blood cells that contain them—about a month or a bit longer in reptiles, amphibians, and fishes—and are translated again and again. Mammals are an exception, as you learned in Module 11.2. When their red blood cells mature, they lose their ribosomes (along with their other organelles) and thus cease to make new hemoglobin. However, mammalian hemoglobin itself lasts about as long as the red blood cells last, around four months.

Initiation of Translation The process of translating an mRNA into a polypeptide also offers opportunities for regulation. Among the molecules involved in translation are a great many proteins that control the start of polypeptide synthesis. Red blood cells, for instance, have an inhibitory protein that prevents translation of hemoglobin mRNA unless the cell has a supply of heme, the iron-containing chemical group essential for hemoglobin function. (It is the iron atom of the heme group to which oxygen molecules actually attach.)

Protein Activation After translation is complete, polypeptides may require alteration to become functional. Post-translational control mechanisms in eukaryotes often involve the cleavage (cutting) of a polypeptide to yield a smaller final product that is the active protein, able to carry out a specific function in the organism. In Figure 11.8 we see the example of the hormone insulin, which is a protein. Insulin is synthesized in the cells of the pancreas as one long polypeptide that has no hormonal activity. After translation is completed, the polypeptide folds up, and covalent bonds form between the sulfur (S) atoms of sulfur-containing amino acids (see Figure 3.12C). (Two H atoms are lost as each S—S bond forms.) The result is that parts of the polypeptide are linked together in a specific way. Finally, a large center portion is cut away, leaving two shorter chains held together by the sulfur linkages. This combination of two shorter polypeptides is the form of insulin that functions as a hormone.

Protein Breakdown The final control mechanism operating after translation is the selective breakdown of proteins. Though mammalian hemoglobin may last as long as the red blood cell housing it, the lifetimes of many other proteins are closely regulated. Some of the proteins that trigger metabolic changes in cells are broken down within a few minutes or hours. This regulation allows a cell to adjust the kinds and amounts of its proteins in response to changes in its environment. It also enables the cell to maintain its proteins in prime working order. Indeed, when proteins are damaged, they are usually broken down right away and replaced by new ones that function properly.

Web Activity *Gene Regulation in Eukaryotes*

? Review Figure 11.8. If the enzyme responsible for cleaving inactive insulin is deactivated, what effect will this have on the form and function of insulin?

■ The final molecule will have a different shape and therefore not be able to perform the proper function of insulin.

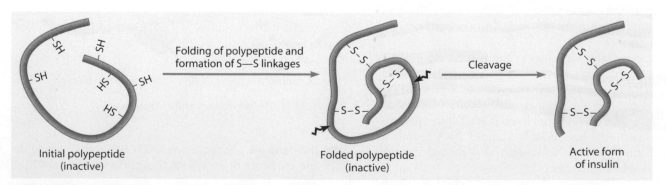

Figure 11.8 Protein activation: The role of polypeptide cleavage in producing the active insulin protein

Initial polypeptide (inactive)

Folding of polypeptide and formation of S—S linkages

Folded polypeptide (inactive)

Cleavage

Active form of insulin

Figure 11.9 provides a review of eukaryotic gene expression and highlights the multiple control points where the process can be turned on or off, speeded up, or slowed down. Picture the series of pipes that carry water from your local water supply, perhaps a reservoir, to a faucet in your home. At various points, valves control the flow of water. We use this model in the figure to illustrate the flow of genetic information from a chromosome—a reservoir of genetic information—to an active protein that has been synthesized in the cell's cytoplasm. The multiple mechanisms that control gene expression are analogous to the control valves in water pipes. In the figure, each gene expression "valve" is indicated by a control knob. Note that these knobs represent *possible* control points; for most proteins, only a few control points are probably important. As we have seen, the most important control point, in both eukaryotes and prokaryotes, is usually the start of transcription. In the diagram, the large yellow knob represents the mechanisms that regulate the start of transcription.

After transcription, RNA processing in the nucleus adds nucleotides to the ends of the RNA (cap and tail) and splices out introns. As we discussed in Module 11.7, a growing body of evidence suggests the importance of control at this stage. Once mRNA reaches the cytoplasm, additional stages subject to regulation include mRNA translation and eventual breakdown, possible alteration of the polypeptide to give the active protein, and the eventual breakdown of the protein.

Despite its numerous steps, Figure 11.9 oversimplifies the control of gene expression. What it does not show is the web of control that connects different genes, often through their products. We have seen examples in both prokaryotes and eukaryotes of the actions of gene products (usually proteins) on other genes or on other gene products within the same cell. The genes of operons in *E. coli*, for instance, are controlled by repressor or activator proteins encoded by regulatory genes on the same DNA molecule. In eukaryotes, many genes are controlled by proteins encoded by regulatory genes on different chromosomes.

In eukaryotes, cellular differentiation results from the selective turning on and off of genes. In the next module, we will examine the stage in the life cycle of a multicellular eukaryote when cellular differentiation by selective gene expression is most vital: the development of a multicellular embryo from a unicellular zygote.

Web Activity *Review: Gene Regulation in Eukaryotes*

? Of the nine regulatory "valves" in Figure 11.9, which five can also operate in a prokaryotic cell?

■ (1) Control of transcription; (2) control of mRNA breakdown; (3) control of translation; (4) control of protein activation; and (5) control of protein breakdown

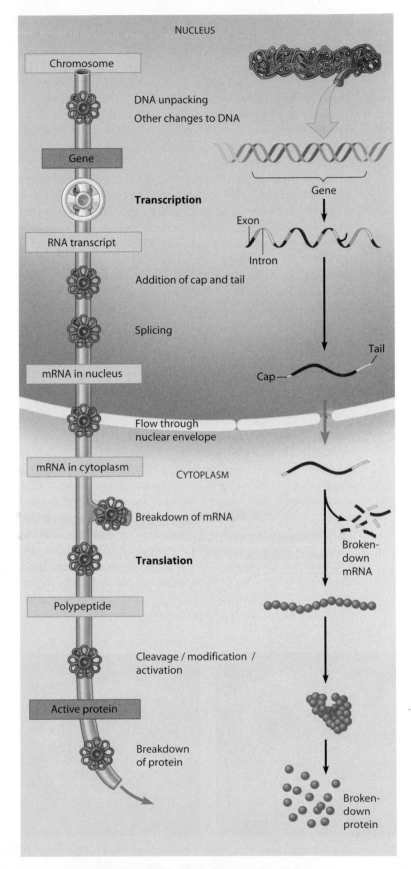

Figure 11.9 The gene expression "pipeline" in a eukaryotic cell

Some of the first glimpses into the relationship between gene expression and embryonic development came from studies of mutants of the fruit fly *Drosophila melanogaster* (see Module 9.18). Figure 11.10A, showing front views of the heads of two fruit flies, includes a mutant that developed in a strikingly abnormal way: It has two legs where its antennae should be! Research on this and other developmental mutants has led to the identification of many of the genes that program development in the normal fly. This genetic approach has revolutionized developmental biology.

Among the earliest events in fruit fly development are ones that determine which end of the egg cell will become the head and which end will become the tail. These events occur in the ovaries of the mother fly and involve communication between an unfertilized egg cell and cells adjacent to it in its follicle (egg chamber). As Figure 11.10B indicates, ❶ early genes in the egg produce proteins and mRNAs that establish which end of the embryo will become the head and which the tail. In a similar way, other egg cell genes direct the positioning of the top-to-bottom and side-to-side axes.

After the egg is fertilized and laid, repeated mitoses transform the zygote into an embryo. ❷ Translation within the early embryo produces further cascades of proteins that diffuse through the cell layers. Cell signaling—now among the cells of the embryo—helps drive the process. ❸ The result is the subdivision of the embryo's body into segments.

Now finer details of the fly can take shape. Protein products of some of the axis-specifying genes and segment-forming genes activate yet another set of genes. These genes, called homeotic genes, determine what body parts will develop from each segment. A **homeotic gene** is a master control gene that regulates batteries of other genes that actually determine the anatomy of parts of the body. For example, one set of homeotic genes in fruit flies instructs cells in the segments of the head and thorax (midbody) to form antennae and legs, respectively. Elsewhere, these homeotic genes remain turned off, while others are turned on. (To learn more about the evolutionary significance of homeotic genes, see Module 27.14) ❹ The eventual outcome is an adult fly. Notice that the adult's body segments correspond to those of the embryo in step 3. It was mutation of a homeotic gene that was responsible for the abnormal fly in Figure 11.9A.

Cascades of gene expression, with the protein products of one set of genes activating another set of genes, and so on, are a common theme in development. Next, we'll look at how new DNA technologies can help elucidate gene expression in any type of cell.

Web Activity *Development of Head-Tail Polarity*

Web Process of Science *How Can the "Head" Gene Be Regulated to Alter Development?*

? What determines which end of a developing fruit fly will become the head?

■ A specific kind of mRNA localizes at the end of the unfertilized egg that will become the head.

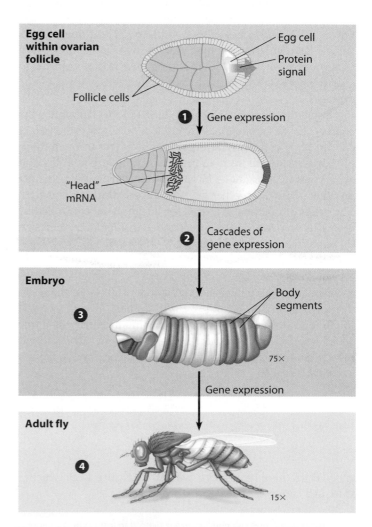

Figure 11.10B Key steps in the early development of head-tail polarity in a fruit fly

Head of a normal fruit fly   Head of a developmental mutant

Figure 11.10A A mutant fruit fly with legs coming out of its head, compared with a normal fruit fly

11.11 DNA microarrays test for the transcription of many genes at once

A major goal of biologists is to learn how genes act together within a functioning organism. Now that a number of whole genomes have been sequenced, it is possible to study the expression of large groups of genes. Researchers can use gene sequences as probes to investigate which genes are transcribed in different situations, such as in different tissues or at different stages of development. They also look for groups of genes that are expressed in a coordinated manner, with the aim of identifying networks of gene expression across an entire genome.

Genome-wide expression studies are made possible by the use of DNA microarrays. A **DNA microarray** is a glass slide with thousands of different kinds of single-stranded DNA fragments fixed to it in a tightly spaced array, or grid. (A DNA microarray is also called a *DNA chip* or *gene chip* by analogy to a computer chip.) Each fixed DNA fragment is obtained from a particular gene; a single microarray thus carries DNA from thousands of genes, perhaps even all the genes of an organism.

Figure 11.11 outlines how microarrays are used. ❶ A researcher isolates all of the mRNA transcribed from genes in a particular type of cell. ❷ This collection of mRNAs is mixed with reverse transcriptase (see Module 10.20) to produce a mixture of DNA fragments. These fragments are called cDNAs (complementary DNAs) because each one is complementary to one of the mRNAs. The cDNAs are produced in the presence of nucleotides that have been modified to fluoresce (glow). The fluorescent cDNA collection thus represents all of the genes being transcribed in the cell under investigation. ❸ A small amount of the fluorescently labeled cDNA mixture is added to each of the fixed DNA fragments in the microarray. If a molecule in the cDNA mixture is complementary to a DNA fragment

at a particular location on the grid, the cDNA molecule binds to it, becoming fixed there. ❹ After nonbinding cDNA is rinsed away, the remaining cDNA produces a detectable glow in the microarray. The pattern of glowing spots enables the researcher to determine which genes are being transcribed in the starting cells.

DNA microarrays are a potential boon to medical research. For example, a 2002 study showed that DNA microarray data can classify different types of leukemia into specific subtypes based on the activity of 17 genes. This information can be used to predict which of several available regimens of chemotherapy is likely to be most effective. Further research suggests that many cancers have a variety of subtypes with different gene expressions that can be identified with DNA microarrays. Indeed, some oncologists predict that DNA microarrays will usher in a new era where medical treatment is customized to each patient.

DNA microarrays can also reveal general profiles of gene expression over the lifetime of an organism. In one example of a global expression study using this technique, researchers performed DNA microarray experiments on more than 90% of the genes of the nematode *C. elegans* during every stage of its life cycle. The results showed that expression of nearly 60% of the genes changed dramatically during development. This study supported the model held by most developmental biologists that embryonic development involves a complex and elaborate program of gene expression, rather than simple expression of a small number of important genes.

? What is learned from a DNA microarray?

■ What genes are active (transcribed) in a particular sample of cells

Figure 11.11   DNA microarray

11.12 Signal transduction pathways convert messages received at the cell surface to responses within the cell

Cell-to-cell signaling, with proteins or other kinds of molecules carrying messages from signaling cells to receiving (target) cells, is a key mechanism in the coordination of cellular activities. In most cases, a signal molecule acts by binding to a receptor protein in the plasma membrane of the target cell and initiating a **signal transduction pathway** in the cell. A signal transduction pathway is a series of molecular changes that converts a signal on a target cell's surface to a specific response inside the cell.

Figure 11.12 shows the main elements of a signal transduction pathway in which the target cell's response is the transcription of a gene. ❶ The signaling cell secretes a signal molecule. ❷ This molecule binds to a receptor protein embedded in the target cell's plasma membrane. ❸ The binding activates the first in a series of relay proteins within the target cell. Each relay molecule activates another. ❹ The last relay molecule in the series activates a transcription factor that ❺ triggers transcription of a specific gene. ❻ Translation of the mRNA produces a protein.

Signal transduction pathways are crucial to many cellular functions. Throughout your study of biology, you'll see their importance again and again. We encountered them when we studied the cell cycle control system in Module 8.9; we'll revisit them when we discuss cancer later in this chapter; and we'll see how they are used to control hormone function in Chapters 26 and 33.

Web Activity *Signal Transduction Pathway*

? How can a signal molecule from one cell alter gene expression in a target cell without even entering the target cell?

■ By binding to a receptor protein in the membrane of the target cell and triggering a signal transduction pathway that activates transcription factors

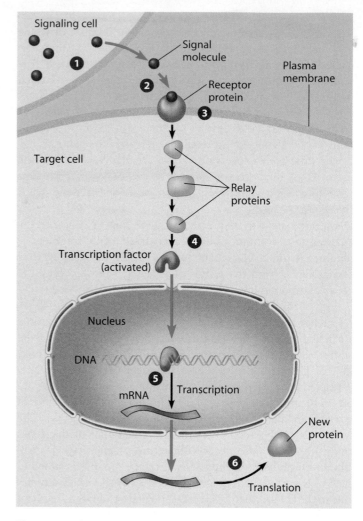

Figure 11.12 A signal transduction pathway that turns on a gene

11.13 Cell-signaling systems appeared early in the evolution of life

As explained in Module 11.12, one cell can communicate with another by secreting molecules that bind to surface proteins on a target cell. How ancient and widespread are such signaling systems among Earth's organisms? To answer these questions we can look at communication among microorganisms, for modern microbes are a window on the role of cell signaling in the evolution of life on Earth.

One topic of cell "conversation" is sex—at least for the yeast *Saccharomyces cerevisiae,* which people have used for millenia to make bread, wine, and beer. Researchers have learned that cells of this yeast identify their mates by chemical signaling. There are two sexes, or mating types, called **a** and **α** (Figure 11.13, top of facing page). Cells of mating type **a** secrete a chemical signal called **a** factor, which can bind to

specific receptor proteins on nearby **α** cells. At the same time, **α** cells secrete **α** factor, which binds to receptors on **a** cells. Without actually entering the target cells, the two mating factors cause the cells to grow toward each other and bring about other cellular changes. The result is the fusion, or mating, of two cells of opposite type. The new **a/α** cell contains all the genes of both original cells, a combination of genetic resources that provides advantages to the cell's descendants, which arise by subsequent cell divisions.

The yeast mating pathway is just one of many signal transduction pathways that have been extensively studied in both yeast and animal cells. Amazingly, the molecular details of signal transduction in yeast and mammals are strikingly similar, even though the last common ancestor of

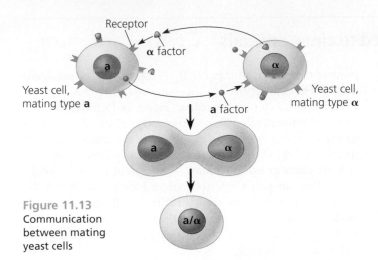

Figure 11.13 Communication between mating yeast cells

these two groups of organisms lived over a billion years ago. These similarities—and others more recently uncovered between signaling systems in bacteria and plants—suggest that early versions of the cell-signaling mechanisms used today evolved well before the first multicellular creatures appeared on Earth. Scientists think that signaling mechanisms evolved first in ancient prokaryotes and single-celled eukaryotes and then became adapted for new uses in their multicellular descendants.

? In what sense is the joining of yeast mating types "sex"?

■ The process results in the creation of a diploid cell that is a genetic blend of two parental haploid cells.

Cloning of Plants and Animals

11.14 Plant cloning shows that differentiated cells may retain all of their genetic potential

One of the most important "take home lessons" from this chapter is that differentiated cells express only a small percentage of their genes. So then how do we know that all the genes are still present? And if all the genes are still there, do differentiated cells retain the potential to express them?

One way to approach these questions is to see if a differentiated cell can generate a whole new organism. In plants, this ability is common, as was first demonstrated during the 1950s by F. C. Steward and his students at Cornell University. As shown in **Figure 11.14**, they found that when they transferred cells from a carrot to a culture medium, a single cell could begin dividing and eventually grow into an adult plant, a genetic replica of the parent plant. The fact that a mature plant cell can dedifferentiate (reverse its differentiation) and then give rise to all the different kinds of specialized cells of a new plant shows that differentiation does not necessarily involve irreversible changes in the plant's DNA.

Figure 11.14 Growth of a carrot plant from a differentiated root cell

Plant cloning is now used extensively in agriculture. For some plants, such as orchids, cloning is the only commercially practical means of reproducing plants. In other cases, cloning has been used to reproduce a plant with valuable characteristics, such as the ability to resist a plant pathogen. You yourself may be a plant cloner if you have ever grown a new plant from a cutting.

But is this sort of cloning possible in animals? An indication that differentiation need not impair an animal cell's genetic potential is the natural process of **regeneration,** the regrowth of lost body parts. When a salamander loses a leg, for example, certain cells in the leg stump dedifferentiate, divide, and then redifferentiate, giving rise to a new leg. Many animals can regenerate lost parts, especially among the invertebrates, and in a few relatively simple animals, isolated differentiated cells can dedifferentiate and then develop into an organism. Further evidence for the complete genetic potential of animal cells comes from cloning experiments, our next topic.

? How does the cloning of plants from differentiated cells support the view that differentiation is based on the control of gene expression rather than on irreversible changes in the genome?

■ Cloning shows that all the genes of a fully differentiated plant are still present, but some may be turned off.

11.15 Nuclear transplantation can be used to clone animals

Animal cloning, including the various cases described in the chapter introduction, is achieved through a procedure called **nuclear transplantation** (Figure 11.15). First performed in the 1950s using cells from frog embryos, nuclear transplantation involves replacing the nucleus of an egg cell or a zygote with the nucleus of an adult somatic cell. The recipient cell may then begin to divide. About 5 days later, repeated cell divisions form a blastocyst, a ball of cells. At this point, the blastocyst may be used for different purposes, as indicated by the branching in Figure 11.15.

If the animal to be cloned is a mammal, further development requires implanting the blastocyst into the uterus of a surrogate mother (Figure 11.15, upper branch). The resulting animal will be genetically identical to the donor of the nucleus—a "clone" of the donor. This type of cloning, which results in birth of a new individual, is called **reproductive cloning.** Scottish researcher Ian Wilmut and his colleagues used reproductive cloning to produce the celebrated sheep Dolly. A fully differentiated mammary cell of an adult ewe was the source of the nucleus.

In a different cloning procedure (Figure 11.15, lower branch), **embryonic stem (ES) cells** are harvested from the blastocyst. In nature, embryonic stem cells give rise to all the different kinds of specialized cells of the body. In the laboratory, embryonic stem cells are easily grown in culture, where, given the right conditions, they can perpetuate themselves indefinitely. When the major aim is to produce embryonic stem cells for therapeutic treatments, the process is called **therapeutic cloning.** In the next two modules, we will discuss applications of reproductive and therapeutic cloning.

? What are the intended products of reproductive cloning and therapeutic cloning?

■ Reproductive cloning is used to produce new individuals. Therapeutic cloning is used to harvest embryonic stem cells.

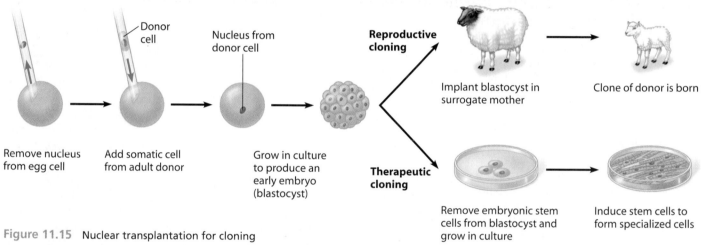

Figure 11.15 Nuclear transplantation for cloning

Remove nucleus from egg cell → Add somatic cell from adult donor → Grow in culture to produce an early embryo (blastocyst)

Reproductive cloning: Implant blastocyst in surrogate mother → Clone of donor is born

Therapeutic cloning: Remove embryonic stem cells from blastocyst and grow in culture → Induce stem cells to form specialized cells

Donor cell / Nucleus from donor cell

11.16 Reproductive cloning has valuable applications, but human reproductive cloning raises ethical issues

Since Dolly's birth in 1997, researchers have cloned many other mammals, including mice, cats, horses, cows, mules, pigs, and dogs. We have already learned much from such experiments. For example, cloned animals of the same species do not always look or behave identically. In a herd of cows cloned from the same line of cultured cells, certain cows are dominant and others are more submissive. Another example is the first cloned cat, named CC for Carbon Copy (Figure 11.16). She has a calico coat, like her single female parent, but the color and pattern are different due to random X chromosome inactivation (see Module 11.4). Besides appearance, CC and her lone parent behave differently; CC is playful while her mother is more reserved. You probably know that identical human twins, which are naturally occurring "clones," are always slightly different. Clearly, environmental influences and random phenomena can play a significant role during development.

Reproductive cloning has potential for many practical applications. On an experimental basis, agricultural scientists are cloning farm animals with specific sets of desirable traits in the hope of creating high-yielding, genetically identical herds. The pharmaceutical industry is experimentally cloning mammals for the production of potentially valuable drugs. Figure 12.6 shows cloned sheep that secrete a human blood protein into their milk, one that could prove useful in treating cystic fibrosis. Other researchers have produced piglet clones that lack one of two copies of a gene for a protein that can cause immune system rejection in humans. Such pigs may one day provide organs for transplant into humans. Some wildlife biologists hope that reproductive cloning can be used to restock the populations of endangered animals (although others caution against such an approach, as discussed in the chapter introduction).

The successful cloning of various mammals has heightened speculation that humans could be cloned. Critics point out that there are many obstacles—both practical and ethical—to human cloning. Practically, animal cloning is extremely difficult and inefficient. Only a small percentage of cloned embryos develop normally. Ethically, creating human embryos for such purposes raises many troubling questions. An ethical consensus on the status of the human blastocyst is unlikely any time soon. Meanwhile, the research and the debate continue.

? If you cloned your dog, would you expect the mother and baby to look and act just alike?

■ No. While cloning produces genetically identical dogs, appearance and behavior are affected by environment.

Figure 11.16　CC, the world's first cloned cat (right), and her lone parent (left)

11.17　Therapeutic cloning can produce stem cells with great medical potential

Therapeutic cloning produces embryonic stem cells, cells that in the early animal embryo differentiate to give rise to all the cell types in the body. When grown in laboratory culture, embryonic stem cells can divide indefinitely (like cancer cells; see Module 8.10). Furthermore, the right conditions can induce changes in gene expression that cause differentiation into a variety of cell types (Figure 11.17).

The adult body also has stem cells, which serve to replace nonreproducing specialized cells as needed. In contrast to embryonic stem cells, **adult stem cells** are able to give rise to many but not all cell types in the organism. For example, bone marrow contains several types of stem cells, including one that can generate all the different kinds of blood cells. Although adult animals have only tiny numbers of stem cells, scientists are learning to identify and isolate these cells from various tissues and, in some cases, to grow them in culture.

The ultimate aim of therapeutic cloning is to supply cells for the repair of damaged or diseased organs: for example, insulin-producing pancreatic cells for people with diabetes or certain kinds of brain cells for people with Parkinson's disease or Huntington's disease. Adult stem cells from donor bone marrow have long been used as a source of immune system cells in patients whose own immune systems are destroyed by genetic disorders or radiation treatments for cancer. More recently, clinical trials using bone marrow stem cells have shown slight success in promoting regeneration of heart tissue in patients whose hearts have been damaged by heart attacks.

The developmental potential of adult stem cells is limited to certain tissues, so embryonic stem cells are considered more promising than adult stem cells for medical applications, at least for now. However, the derivation of embryonic stem cells from donated human embryos raises ethical and political issues. In late 2007, two research groups discovered a procedure for using viruses to turn human skin cells into ES-like cells with the potential to develop into many kinds of body cells. The procedure does not involve the destruction of embryos. In the future, a donor nucleus from a patient with a particular disease could allow production of embryonic stem cells for treatment that match the patient and are thus not rejected by his or her immune system.

While many people believe that reproductive cloning of humans is unethical, opinions vary more widely about the morality of therapeutic cloning using embryonic stem cells. As with reproductive cloning, the research and the debate continue.

? In nature, how do embryonic stem cells differ from adult stem cells?

■ Embryonic cells give rise to all the different kinds of cells in the body. Adult stem cells generate only a few related types of cells.

Blood cells

Adult stem cells in bone marrow

Nerve cells

Cultured embryonic stem cells

Heart muscle cells

Different culture conditions

Different types of differentiated cells

Figure 11.17　Differentiation of stem cells in culture

11.18 Cancer results from mutations in genes that control cell division

In Chapter 8, you learned that cancerous cells have escaped from the control mechanisms that normally limit their growth. Scientists have learned that such escape is often due to changes in gene expression.

The abnormal behavior of cancer cells was observed years before anything was known about the cell cycle, its control, or the role genes play in making cells cancerous. One of the earliest clues to the cancer puzzle was the discovery, in 1911, of a virus that causes cancer in chickens. Recall that viruses are simply molecules of DNA or RNA coated with protein and in some cases a membranous envelope. Viruses that cause cancer can become permanent residents in host cells by inserting their nucleic acid into the DNA of host chromosomes. Researchers have identified several examples of viruses that harbor cancer-causing genes. When inserted into a host cell, these genes can make the cell cancerous. Such a gene, which can cause cancer when present in a single copy in the cell, is called an **oncogene** (from the Greek *onkos*, tumor).

Proto-Oncogenes In 1976, American molecular biologists J. Michael Bishop, Harold Varmus, and their colleagues made a startling discovery. They found that a virus that causes cancer in chickens contains an oncogene that is an altered version of a gene found in normal chicken cells. Subsequent research has shown that the chromosomes of many animals, including humans, contain genes that can be converted to oncogenes. A normal gene that has the potential to become an oncogene is called a **proto-oncogene.** Thus, a cell can acquire an oncogene either from a virus or from the mutation of one of its own genes.

The work by Bishop and Varmus focused cancer research on proto-oncogenes. Searching for the normal role of these genes, researchers found that many proto-oncogenes code for growth factors—proteins that stimulate cell division—or for other proteins that somehow affect growth factor function or some other aspect of the cell cycle. When all these proteins are functioning normally, in the right amounts at the right times, they help control cell division and cellular differentiation.

How might a proto-oncogene—a gene that has an essential function in normal cells—become an oncogene, a cancer-causing gene? In general, an oncogene arises from a genetic change that leads to an increase either in the amount of the proto-oncogene's protein product or in the rate of activity of each protein molecule. Figure 11.18A illustrates

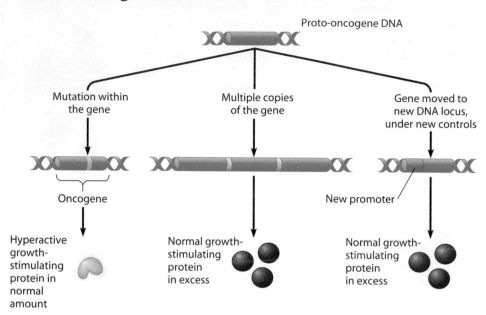

Figure 11.18A Alternative ways to make oncogenes from a proto-oncogene (all leading to excessive cell growth)

three kinds of changes in somatic (non-gamete-forming) cell DNA that can produce active oncogenes. Let's assume that the starting proto-oncogene codes for a protein that stimulates cell division. On the left in the figure, a mutation (green) in the proto-oncogene itself creates an oncogene that codes for a hyperactive protein, one whose stimulating effect is stronger than normal. In the center, an error in DNA replication or recombination generates multiple copies of the gene, which are all transcribed and translated; the result is an excess of the normal stimulatory protein. On the right, the proto-oncogene has been moved from its normal location in the cell's DNA to another location. At its new site, the gene is under the control of a different promoter, one that causes it to be transcribed more often than normal; and the normal protein is again made in excess. So in all three cases, normal gene expression is changed, and the cell is stimulated to divide excessively.

Tumor-Suppressor Genes In addition to genes whose products normally *promote* cell division, cells contain genes whose normal products *inhibit* cell division. Such genes are called **tumor-suppressor genes** because the proteins they encode help prevent uncontrolled cell growth. Any mutation that decreases the normal activity of a tumor-suppressor protein may contribute to the onset of cancer, in effect stimulating growth through the absence of suppression (Figure 11.18B, top of the facing page). Recently, scientists have discovered a new class of tumor-suppressor genes that function in the repair of damaged DNA. When these genes are mutated, other cancer-causing mutations are more likely to accumulate.

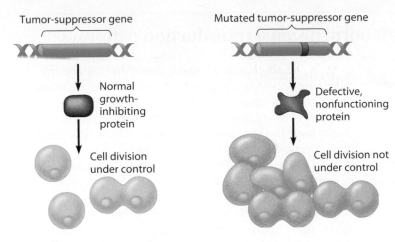

Figure 11.18B The effect of a mutation in a tumor-suppressor gene

? How do proto-oncogenes relate to oncogenes?

■ A proto-oncogene is a normal gene that, if mutated, can become a cancer-causing oncogene.

11.19 Multiple genetic changes underlie the development of cancer

Over 150,000 Americans will be stricken by cancer of the colon (large intestine) or rectum this year, perhaps including some of your own relatives or friends. One of the best-understood types of human cancer, colon cancer illustrates an important principle about how cancer develops: *More than one somatic mutation is needed to produce a full-fledged cancer cell.* As in many cancers, the development of malignant colon cancer is gradual. (See Module 8.10 to review cancer terms.)

The fact that more than one somatic mutation is generally needed to produce a full-fledged cancer cell may help explain why the incidence of cancer increases greatly with age. If cancer results from an accumulation of mutations and if mutations occur throughout life, then the longer we live, the more likely we are to develop cancer.

Figure 11.19A illustrates this idea using colorectal cancer as an example. ❶ Colorectal cancer begins when an oncogene is activated, causing unusually frequent division of apparently normal cells in the colon lining. ❷ Later, additional DNA mutations (such as the inactivation of a tumor-suppressor gene) causes the growth of a small benign tumor (polyp) in the colon wall. ❸ Still more mutations eventually lead to formation of a malignant tumor (a carcinoma). The requirement for several mutations—the actual number is usually four or more—explains why cancers can take a long time to develop.

The development of a malignant tumor is paralleled by a gradual accumulation of mutations that convert proto-oncogenes to oncogenes and knock out tumor-suppressor genes. Multiple changes must occur at the DNA level for a cell to become fully cancerous. Such changes usually include the appearance of at least one active oncogene and the mutation or loss of several tumor-suppressor genes. In Figure 11.19B, colors distinguish the normal cell (tan) from cells (red) with one or more mutations leading to increased cell division and cancer. Once a cancer-promoting mutation occurs (red band on chromosome), it is passed to all the descendants of the cell carrying it. Cancer researchers hope to learn about mutations that cause cancer through the Cancer Genome Project, a 10-year multi-million dollar effort to map all human cancer-causing genes.

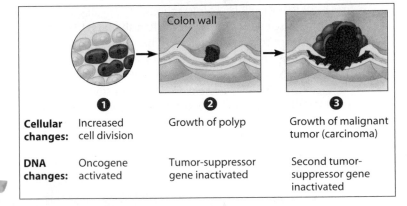

Figure 11.19A Stepwise development of a typical colon cancer

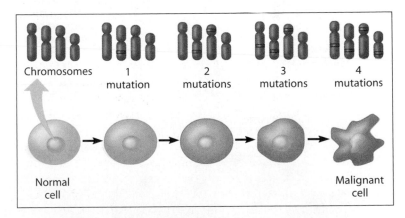

Figure 11.19B Accumulation of mutations in the development of a cancer cell

? Epithelial cells, those that line body cavities, are frequently replaced and so divide more often than most other types of body cells. Will epithelial cells become cancerous more or less frequently than other types of body cells?

■ More frequently. More frequent cell divisions will result in more frequent mutations and thus a greater chance of cancer.

Faulty proteins can interfere with normal signal transduction pathways

To understand how oncogenes and defective tumor-suppressor genes can contribute to uncontrolled cell growth, we need to look more closely at the normal functions of proto-oncogenes and tumor-suppressor genes. Genes in both categories often code for proteins involved in signal transduction pathways leading to gene expression (see Module 11.12).

The figures below (excluding, for the moment, the white boxes) illustrate two types of signal transduction pathways leading to the synthesis of proteins that influence the cell cycle. In Figure 11.20A, the pathway leads to the stimulation of cell division. The initial signal is a growth factor (●), and the target cell's ultimate response is the production of a protein that stimulates the cell to divide. By contrast, Figure 11.20B shows an inhibitory pathway, in which a growth-*inhibiting* factor (▽) causes the target cell to make a protein that inhibits cell division. In both cases, the newly made proteins function by interacting with components of the cell cycle control system (see Module 8.9). The figures here do not show these interactions.

Now let's see what can happen when the target cell undergoes a cancer-causing mutation. The white box in Figure 11.20A shows the protein product of an oncogene resulting from mutation of a proto-oncogene called *ras*. The normal product of *ras* is a relay protein. Ordinarily, a stimulatory pathway like this will not operate unless the growth factor is available. However, an oncogene protein that is a hyperactive version of a protein in the pathway may trigger the pathway even in the absence of a growth factor. In this example, the oncogene protein is a hyperactive version of the *ras* relay protein that issues signals on its own. In fact, abnormal versions or amounts of any of the pathway's components—from the growth factor itself to the transcription factor—could have the same final effect: overstimulation of cell division.

The white box in Figure 11.20B indicates how a mutant tumor-suppressor protein can affect cell division. In this case, the mutation affects a gene called *p53*, which codes for the transcription factor. This mutation leads to the production of a faulty transcription factor, one that the signal transduction pathway cannot activate. As a result, the gene for the inhibitory protein at the bottom of the figure remains turned off, and excessive cell division may occur.

Mutations of the *ras* and *p53* genes have been implicated in many kinds of cancer. In fact, mutations in *ras* occur in about 30% of human cancers, and mutations in *p53* occur in more than 50%. As we see next, carcinogens are responsible for causing many mutations that lead to cancer.

? Contrast the action of an oncogene with that of a cancer-causing mutation in a tumor-suppressor gene.

■ An oncogene produces an abnormal protein that stimulates cell division via a signal transduction pathway; a mutant tumor-suppressor gene produces a defective protein unable to function in a pathway that normally inhibits cell division.

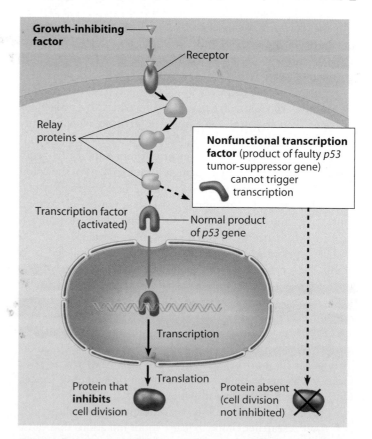

Figure 11.20A   A stimulatory signal transduction pathway and the effect of an oncogene protein

Figure 11.20B   An inhibitory signal transduction pathway and the effect of a faulty tumor-suppressor protein

11.21   Lifestyle choices can reduce the risk of cancer

Cancer is the second-leading cause of death in the United States, exceeded only by heart disease. Death rates due to certain forms of cancer (including stomach, cervical, and uterine cancers) have decreased in recent years, but the overall cancer death rate is still on the rise, currently increasing at about 1% per decade. Table 11.21 lists the most common cancers in the United States and associated risk factors for each.

The fact that multiple genetic changes are required to produce a cancer cell helps explain the observation that cancers can run in families. An individual inheriting an oncogene or a mutant allele of a tumor-suppressor gene is one step closer to accumulating the necessary mutations for cancer to develop than an individual without any such mutations.

But the majority of cancers cannot be associated with a mutation that is passed from parent to offspring; they arise from new mutations caused by environmental factors. Cancer-causing agents, factors that alter DNA and make cells cancerous, are called **carcinogens**. Most mutagens (substances that promote mutations) are carcinogens. Two of the most potent carcinogens (and mutagens) are X-rays and ultraviolet radiation in sunlight. X-rays are a significant cause of leukemia and brain cancer. Exposure to UV radiation from the sun is known to cause skin cancer, including a deadly type called melanoma.

The one substance known to cause more cases and types of cancer than any other single agent is tobacco. More people die of lung cancer (over 160,000 Americans in 2007) than any other form of cancer. Most tobacco-related cancers come from actually smoking, but the passive inhalation of secondhand smoke is also a risk. As Table 11.21 indicates, tobacco use, sometimes in combination with alcohol consumption, causes a number of other types of cancer in addition to lung cancer. In nearly all cases, cigarettes are the main culprit, but smokeless tobacco products (snuff and chewing tobacco) are linked to cancer of the mouth and throat.

How do carcinogens cause cancer? In many cases, the genetic changes that cause cancer result from decades of exposure to the mutagenic effects of carcinogens. Carcinogens can also produce their effect by promoting cell division. Generally, the higher the rate of cell division, the greater the chance for mutations resulting from errors in DNA replication or recombination. Some carcinogens seem to have both effects. For instance, the hormones that cause breast and uterine cancers promote cell division and may also cause genetic changes that lead to cancer. In other cases, several different agents, such as viruses and one or more carcinogens, may together produce cancer.

Avoiding carcinogens is not the whole story, for there is growing evidence that some food choices significantly reduce cancer risk. For instance, eating 20–30 grams (g) of plant fiber daily (about twice the amount the average American consumes) and at the same time reducing animal fat intake may help prevent colon cancer. There is also evidence that other substances in fruits and vegetables, including vitamins C and E and certain compounds related to vitamin A, may offer protection against a variety of cancers. Cabbage and its relatives, such as broccoli and

TABLE 11.21	CANCER IN THE UNITED STATES	
Cancer	Risk Factors	Estimated Number of Cases in 2007
Prostate	African heritage; possibly dietary fat	218,900
Lung	Tobacco smoke	213,400
Breast	Estrogen	180,500
Colon, rectum	High dietary fat; smoking; alcohol	153,800
Lymphomas	Viruses (for some types)	71,400
Urinary bladder	Cigarette smoke	67,200
Melanoma of skin	Ultraviolet light	59,900
Kidney	Cigarette smoke	51,200
Leukemias	X-rays; benzene; virus (for one type)	44,200
Uterus	Estrogen	39,000
Pancreas	Tobacco smoke; obesity	37,200
Mouth and throat	Tobacco in various forms; alcohol	34,400
Ovary	Obesity; many ovulation cycles	22,400
Stomach	Table salt; cigarette smoke	21,300
Liver	Alcohol; hepatitis viruses	19,200
Brain and nerve	Trauma; X-rays	20,500
Cervix	Sexually transmitted viruses; tobacco	11,200
All others		179,400

cauliflower (see Figure 13.2), are thought to be especially rich in substances that help prevent cancer, although the identities of these substances are not yet established. Determining how diet influences cancer has become a major research goal.

The battle against cancer is being waged on many fronts, and there is reason for optimism in the progress being made. It is especially encouraging that we can help reduce our risk of acquiring and increase our chance of surviving some of the most common forms of cancer by the choices we make in our daily life. Not smoking, exercising adequately, avoiding overexposure to the sun, and eating a high-fiber, low-fat diet can all help prevent cancer. Furthermore, seven types of cancer can be easily detected: skin and oral (via physical exam), breast (via self-exams and mammograms for higher-risk women), prostate (via rectal exam), cervical (via Pap smear), testicular (via self-exam), and colon (via colonoscopy) cancers. Regular visits to the doctor can help identify tumors early, thereby significantly increasing the possibility of successful treatment.

Web Activity *Connection: Causes of Cancer*

? Which type of cancer is the most frequently diagnosed in the United States? Which causes the most deaths?

Prostate; lung

Reviewing the Concepts

A clone is an individual created by asexual reproduction and thus genetically identical to a single parent (**Introduction**).

Control of Gene Expression (11.1–11.13)

In prokaryotes, genes for related enzymes are often controlled together in units called operons. Regulatory proteins bind to control sequences in the DNA and turn operons on or off in response to environmental changes (**11.1**):

In multicellular eukaryotes, cells become specialized, or differentiated, as a zygote develops into a mature organism. Different types of cells make different proteins because different combinations of genes are active in each type (**11.2**). A chromosome contains DNA wound around clusters of histone proteins, forming a string of bead-like nucleosomes. This beaded fiber is further wound and folded. DNA packing tends to block gene expression, presumably by preventing access of transcription proteins to the DNA (**11.3**). An extreme example of DNA packing in interphase cells is X chromosome inactivation in the cells of female mammals (**11.4**). A variety of regulatory proteins interact with DNA and with each other to turn the transcription of eukaryotic genes on or off (**11.5**). After transcription, alternative RNA splicing may generate two or more types of mRNA from the same transcript (**11.6**). Small RNAs help regulate gene expression in a variety of ways (**11.7**). The lifetime of an mRNA molecule helps determine how much protein is made, as do protein factors involved in translation. A protein may need to be activated in some way, and eventually the cell will break it down (**11.8**). Figure 11.9 reviews the multiple stages of eukaryotic gene expression, each stage offering an opportunity for regulation (**11.9**).

Cascades of gene expression control the development of an animal from a fertilized egg (**11.10**). A DNA microarray can test for the transcription of many genes at once (**11.11**).

Signal transduction pathways convert molecular messages to cell responses (**11.12**). Similarities among organisms suggest that signal transduction pathways evolved early in the history of life (**11.13**).

Cloning of Plants and Animals (11.14–11.17)

Differentiated cells retain a complete set of genes (**11.14**).

Nuclear transplantation is used to clone animals (**11.15**):

Reproductive cloning of nonhuman mammals has practical applications (**11.16**). The goal of therapeutic cloning is to produce embryonic stem cells. Like embryonic stem cells, adult stem cells can both perpetuate themselves in culture and give rise to differentiated cells. Unlike embryonic stem cells, however, adult stem cells normally give rise to only a limited range of cell types (**11.17**):

The Genetic Basis of Cancer (11.18–11.21)

Cancer cells, which divide uncontrollably, result from mutations in genes whose protein products affect the cell cycle. A mutation can change a proto-oncogene (a normal gene that promotes cell division) into an oncogene, which causes cells to divide excessively. Mutations that inactivate tumor-suppressor genes have similar effects (**11.18**). Cancers result from a *series* of genetic changes in a cell lineage (**11.19**). Many proto-oncogenes and tumor-suppressor genes code for proteins active in signal transduction pathways regulating cell division (**11.20**). Reducing exposure to carcinogens (which induce cancer-causing mutations) and making other lifestyle choices can help reduce cancer risk (**11.21**).

Connecting the Concepts

1. Complete the following concept map to test your knowledge of gene regulation.

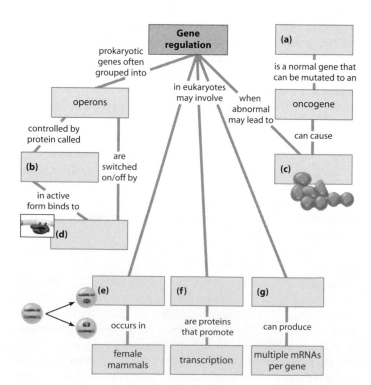

Testing Your Knowledge

Multiple Choice

2. The control of gene expression is more complex in multi-cellular eukaryotes than in prokaryotes because_____. (*Explain your answer.*)
   a. eukaryotic cells are much smaller
   b. in a multicellular eukaryote, different cells are specialized for different functions
   c. prokaryotes are restricted to stable environments
   d. eukaryotes have fewer genes, so each gene must do several jobs
   e. eukaryotic genes code for proteins

3. Your bone cells, muscle cells, and skin cells look different because
   a. each cell contains different kinds of genes.
   b. they are present in different organs.
   c. different genes are active in each kind of cell.
   d. they contain different numbers of genes.
   e. each cell has different mutations.

4. Which of the following methods of gene regulation do eukaryotes and prokaryotes have in common?
   a. elaborate packing of DNA in chromosomes
   b. activator and repressor proteins, which attach to DNA
   c. the addition of a cap and tail to mRNA after transcription
   d. *lac* and *trp* operons
   e. the removal of noncoding portions of RNA

5. A eukaryotic gene was inserted into the DNA of a bacterium. The bacterium then transcribed this gene into mRNA and translated the mRNA into protein. The protein produced was useless; it contained many more amino acids than the protein made by the eukaryotic cell. Why?
   a. The mRNA was not spliced, as it is in eukaryotes.
   b. Eukaryotes and prokaryotes use different genetic codes.
   c. Repressor proteins interfered with transcription and translation.
   d. The lifetime of the bacterial mRNA was too short.
   e. Ribosomes were not able to bind to the mRNA.

6. A homeotic gene does which of the following?
   a. It serves as the ultimate control for prokaryotic operons.
   b. It regulates the expression of groups of other genes during development.
   c. It represses the histone proteins that package eukaryotic DNA.
   d. It helps splice mRNA after transcription.
   e. It inactivates one of the X chromosomes in a female mammal.

7. All your cells contain proto-oncogenes, which can change into cancer-causing genes. Why do cells possess such potential time bombs?
   a. Viruses infect cells with proto-oncogenes.
   b. Proto-oncogenes are genetic "junk" with no known function.
   c. Proto-oncogenes are unavoidable environmental carcinogens.
   d. Cells produce proto-oncogenes as a by-product of mitosis.
   e. Proto-oncogenes normally control cell division.

8. Which of the following is a valid difference between embryonic stem cells and the stem cells found in adult tissues?
   a. In laboratory culture, only adult stem cells are immortal.
   b. In nature, only embryonic stem cells give rise to all the different types of cells in the organism.
   c. Only adult stem cells can differentiate in culture.
   d. Embryonic stem cells are generally more difficult to grow in culture than adult stem cells.
   e. Only embryonic stem cells are found in every tissue of the adult body.

Describing, Comparing, and Explaining

9. A mutation in a single gene may cause a major change in the body of a fruit fly, such as an extra pair of legs or wings. Yet it probably takes the combined action of hundreds or thousands of genes to produce a wing or leg. How can a change in just one gene cause such a big change in the body?

Applying the Concepts

10. Study the illustrations of the *lac* operon in Module 11.1. Normally, the genes are turned off when lactose is not present. Lactose activates the genes, which code for enzymes that enable the cell to use lactose. Mutations can alter the function of this operon; in fact, it was the effects of various mutations that enabled Jacob and Monod to figure out how the operon works. Predict how the following mutations would affect the function of the operon in the presence and absence of lactose:
    a. Mutation of regulatory gene; repressor will not bind to lactose.
    b. Mutation of operator; repressor will not bind to operator.
    c. Mutation of regulatory gene; repressor will not bind to operator.
    d. Mutation of promoter; RNA polymerase will not attach to promoter.

11. A chemical called dioxin is produced as a by-product of some chemical manufacturing processes. Trace amounts of this substance were present in Agent Orange, a defoliant sprayed on vegetation during the Vietnam War. There has been a continuing controversy over its effects on soldiers exposed to it during the war. Animal tests have suggested that dioxin can be lethal and can cause birth defects, cancer, liver and thymus damage, and immune system suppression. But its effects on humans are unclear, and even animal tests are inconclusive; a hamster is not affected by a dose that can kill a guinea pig. Researchers have discovered that dioxin enters a cell and binds to a protein that in turn attaches to the cell's DNA. How might this mechanism help explain the variety of dioxin's effects on different body systems and in different animals? How might you determine whether a particular individual became ill as a result of exposure to dioxin?

Answers to all questions can be found in Appendix 4.

For Practice Quizzes, BioFlix, MP3 Tutors, and Activities, go to www.mybiology.com.

12.1 Genes can be cloned in recombinant plasmids

Although it may seem like a modern field, **biotechnology,** the manipulation of organisms or their components to make useful products, actually dates back to the dawn of civilization. Consider such ancient practices as the use of microbes to make wine and cheese and the selective breeding of animals (livestock, dogs, and so forth). But when people use the term *biotechnology* today, they are usually referring to DNA technology, modern laboratory techniques that involve the manipulation of DNA. Using these techniques scientists can, for instance, modify specific genes and move them between organisms as different as bacteria, plants, and animals.

The field of DNA technology grew out of discoveries made about 60 years ago by American geneticists Joshua Lederberg and Edward Tatum. They performed a series of experiments with *E. coli* that demonstrated that two individual bacteria can combine genes—a phenomenon that was previously thought to be limited to sexually reproducing eukaryotic organisms. With this work, they pioneered bacterial genetics, a field that within 20 years made *E. coli* the most thoroughly studied and understood organism at the molecular level.

In the 1970s, the uses of biotechnology exploded with the invention of methods for making recombinant DNA in the laboratory. **Recombinant DNA** is formed when scientists combine nucleotide sequences (pieces of DNA) from two different sources—often different species—to form a single DNA molecule. Today, recombinant DNA technology is widely used to alter the genes of many types of cells for practical purposes. Scientists have genetically engineered bacteria to mass-produce a variety of useful chemicals, from cancer drugs to pesticides. Scientists have also transferred genes from bacteria into plants and from humans into farm animals (see Table 12.6).

To manipulate genes in the laboratory, biologists often use bacterial **plasmids,** which are small, circular DNA molecules that replicate separately from the much larger bacterial chromosome (see Module 10.23). Because plasmids can carry virtually any gene and are passed on from one generation of bacteria to the next, they are key tools for **gene cloning,** the production of multiple identical copies of a gene-carrying piece of DNA. Gene-cloning methods are central to **genetic engineering,** the branch of biotechnology that involves the direct manipulation of genes for practical purposes.

Consider a typical genetic engineering challenge: A molecular biologist at a pharmaceutical company has identified a gene that codes for a valuable product: a hypothetical substance called protein V. The biologist wants to manufacture large amounts of this protein. **Figure 12.1** (on the facing page) illustrates how the techniques of gene cloning are used to make many copies of the gene that codes for protein V.

To begin, the biologist isolates two kinds of DNA: ❶ a bacterial plasmid that will serve as the **vector** (gene carrier) and ❷ the DNA containing gene *V.* In this example, the plasmid comes from the bacterium *E. coli.* The DNA containing gene *V*

could come from a variety of sources such as a different bacterium, a plant, a nonhuman animal, or even human tissue cells growing in laboratory culture.

The researcher treats both the plasmid and the gene *V* source DNA with an enzyme that cuts each DNA. ❸ An enzyme is chosen that cleaves the plasmid in only one place. ❹ The other DNA, which is usually much longer in sequence, may be cut into many fragments, one of which carries gene *V.* The figure shows the processing of just one DNA fragment and one plasmid, but actually millions of plasmids and DNA fragments (most of which do *not* contain gene *V*) are treated simultaneously. The cuts leave single-stranded ends, as we'll explain in Module 12.2.

❺ The cut DNA from both sources (plasmid and target) are mixed. The single-stranded ends of the plasmid base-pair with the complementary ends of the target DNA fragment. ❻ The enzyme **DNA ligase** joins the two DNA molecules by covalent bonds. This enzyme, which the cell normally uses in DNA replication (see Module 10.5), is a "DNA pasting" enzyme that catalyzes the formation of covalent bonds between adjacent nucleotides, joining the strands. The result is a recombinant DNA plasmid containing gene *V* (as well as many other recombinant DNA plasmids carrying other genes not shown here).

❼ The recombinant plasmid containing the targeted gene is mixed with a culture of bacteria. Under the right conditions, a bacterium takes up the plasmid DNA by transformation (see Module 10.22). ❽ This recombinant bacterium then reproduces to form a **clone** of cells (a group of identical cells descended from a single ancestral cell), each carrying a copy of gene *V.* This step is the actual gene cloning. In our example, the biologist will eventually grow a cell clone large enough to produce protein V in marketable quantities.

As shown along the right side of the figure, gene cloning can be used to produce a variety of desirable products. In the examples in the upper box, copies of the gene itself are the immediate product, to be used in further genetic engineering projects. In the examples in the lower box, the protein product of the cloned gene is harvested and used.

In the next four modules, we will discuss the methods outlined in Figure 12.1. You may find it useful to turn back to this summary figure as each technique is discussed.

🎧 MP3 Tutor *DNA Technology*

Web Activity *Connection: Applications of DNA Technology*

Web Process of Science *How Can Antibiotic-Resistant Plasmids Transform* E. coli?

? Why does the rapid reproduction of bacteria make them a good choice for cloning a foreign gene?

■ A foreign gene located within plasmid DNA inside a bacterium is replicated each time the cell divides, resulting in rapid accumulation of many copies of the gene.

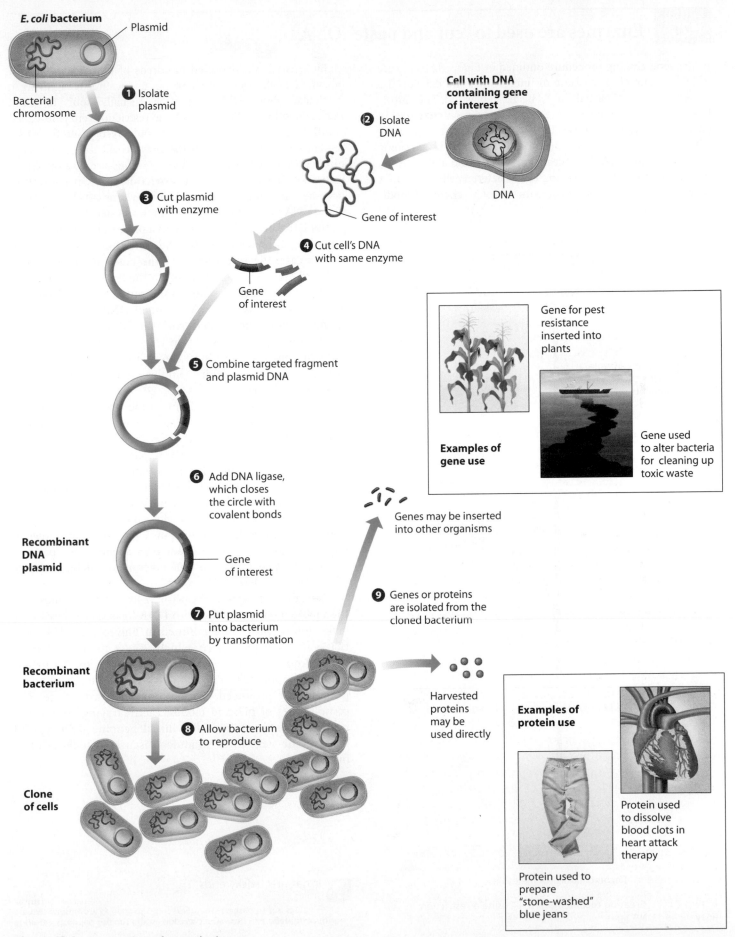

E. coli bacterium

Plasmid

Bacterial chromosome

1 Isolate plasmid

Cell with DNA containing gene of interest

2 Isolate DNA

DNA

Gene of interest

3 Cut plasmid with enzyme

4 Cut cell's DNA with same enzyme

Gene of interest

5 Combine targeted fragment and plasmid DNA

6 Add DNA ligase, which closes the circle with covalent bonds

Recombinant DNA plasmid

Gene of interest

7 Put plasmid into bacterium by transformation

Recombinant bacterium

8 Allow bacterium to reproduce

Clone of cells

Genes may be inserted into other organisms

9 Genes or proteins are isolated from the cloned bacterium

Harvested proteins may be used directly

Gene for pest resistance inserted into plants

Examples of gene use

Gene used to alter bacteria for cleaning up toxic waste

Examples of protein use

Protein used to dissolve blood clots in heart attack therapy

Protein used to prepare "stone-washed" blue jeans

Figure 12.1 An overview of gene cloning

12.2 Enzymes are used to "cut and paste" DNA

In the gene-cloning procedure outlined in Figure 12.1, a piece of DNA containing the gene of interest must be cut out of a chromosome and "pasted" into a bacterial plasmid. The cutting tools used are bacterial enzymes called **restriction enzymes.** In nature, these enzymes protect bacterial cells against intruding DNA from other organisms or viruses. They work by chopping up the foreign DNA, a process that *restricts* the ability of the invader to infect the bacterium. (The bacterial cell's own DNA is protected from restriction enzymes through chemical modification by other enzymes.)

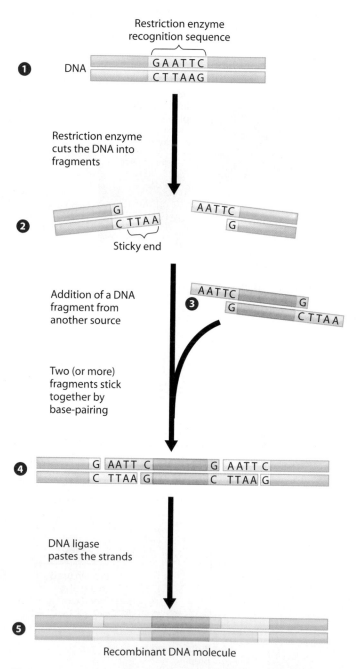

Figure 12.2 Creating recombinant DNA using a restriction enzyme and DNA ligase

Biologists have identified hundreds of different restriction enzymes. Each restriction enzyme is specific, recognizing a particular short DNA sequence (usually four to eight nucleotides long). For example, a restriction enzyme called *Eco*RI (found naturally in *E. coli*) only recognizes the DNA sequence GAATTC, whereas the enzyme called *Bam*HI recognizes GGATCC. The DNA sequence recognized by a particular restriction enzyme is called a **restriction site.** Once a restriction site is recognized, the restriction enzyme cuts both strands of the DNA at specific points within the sequence.

In **Figure 12.2,** ❶ we start with a piece of DNA containing one recognition sequence for the restriction enzyme *Eco*RI. In this case, the restriction enzyme cuts the DNA strands between the bases A and G within the sequence, producing pieces of DNA called **restriction fragments.** ❷ The staggered cuts yield two double-stranded DNA fragments with single-stranded ends, called "sticky ends." Sticky ends are the key to joining DNA restriction fragments originating from different sources. These short extensions can form hydrogen-bonded base pairs with complementary single-stranded stretches of DNA.

❸ A piece of DNA (gray) from another source is now added. Notice that the gray DNA has single-stranded ends identical in base sequence to the sticky ends on the blue DNA. The gray, "foreign" DNA has ends with this particular base sequence because it was cut from a larger molecule by the same restriction enzyme used to cut the blue DNA. ❹ The complementary ends on the blue and gray fragments allow them to stick together by base-pairing. (The hydrogen bonds are not shown.) The union between the blue and gray DNA fragments shown in step 4 of Figure 12.2 is then made permanent by the "pasting" enzyme DNA ligase. ❺ The final outcome is a stable molecule of recombinant DNA.

The ability to cut DNA with restriction enzymes and then paste it back together with DNA ligase is the key to the gene-cloning procedure outlined in Figure 12.1. This particular cloning procedure, which uses a mixture of fragments from the entire genome of an organism, is called a "shotgun" approach. Thousands of different recombinant plasmids are produced, and a clone of each is made. The complete set of plasmid clones, each carrying copies of a particular segment from the initial genome, is a type of library. The next three modules discuss such libraries in more detail.

Web Activity *Restriction Enzymes*

Web Activity *Cloning a Gene in Bacteria*

? What are "sticky ends"?

■ Single-stranded regions whose unpaired bases can hydrogen-bond to the complementary sticky ends of other fragments created by the same restriction enzyme

12.3 Cloned genes can be stored in genomic libraries

Each bacterial clone from the procedure in Figure 12.1 consists of identical cells with recombinant plasmids carrying one particular fragment of target DNA. The entire collection of all the cloned DNA fragments from a genome is called a **genomic library.** On the left side of Figure 12.3, the red, yellow, and green DNA segments represent three of the thousands of different library "books" that are "shelved" in plasmids inside bacterial cells. A typical cloned DNA fragment is big enough to carry one or a few genes, and together the fragments include the entire genome of the organism from which the DNA was derived.

In addition to bacterial plasmids, phages can also serve as vectors (DNA carriers) when cloning genes (Figure 12.3, right). When a phage is used, the DNA fragments are inserted into phage DNA molecules. The recombinant phage DNA can then be introduced into a bacterial cell through the normal infection process (see Figure 10.22B). Inside the cell, phage DNA is replicated, producing new phage particles, each carrying the foreign DNA. Another type of vector commonly used in library construction is a bacterial artificial chromosome (BAC). BACs are essentially large plasmids containing only the genes necessary to ensure replication. The primary advantage of BACs is that they can carry much larger pieces of foriegn DNA than plasmids or phages. In the next module, we look at another source of DNA for cloning: eukaryotic mRNA.

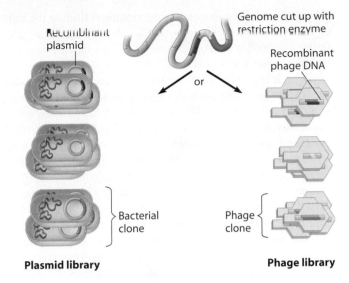

Figure 12.3   Genomic libraries

? In what sense does a genomic library have multiple copies of each "book"?

■ Each "book"—a piece of DNA from the genome that was the source of the library—is present in every recombinant bacterium or phage in a clone.

12.4 Reverse transcriptase can help make genes for cloning

Rather than starting with an entire eukaryotic genome, a researcher can focus on the genes *expressed* in a particular kind of cell by using its mRNA as the starting material for cloning. As shown in Figure 12.4, ❶ the chosen cells transcribe their genes and ❷ process the transcripts to produce mRNA. ❸ The researcher isolates the mRNA and makes single-stranded DNA transcripts from it using the enzyme **reverse transcriptase** (yellow in the figure), which is obtained from retroviruses (see Module 10.20). ❹ Another enzyme is added to break down the mRNA, and ❺ DNA polymerase is used to synthesize a second DNA strand.

The DNA that results from such a procedure, called **complementary DNA (cDNA),** represents only the subset of genes that had been transcribed into mRNA in the starting cells. Among other purposes, a cDNA library is useful for studying the genes responsible for the specialized functions of a particular cell type, such as brain or liver cells. And because cDNAs lack introns, they are shorter than the full versions of the genes, and therefore easier to work with.

In the next module, you will learn how to find one particular "book" (piece of DNA) from among the thousands that are stored in a genomic library.

? Why is a cDNA gene made using reverse transcriptase often shorter than the natural form of the gene?

■ Because cDNAs are made from spliced mRNAs, which lack introns

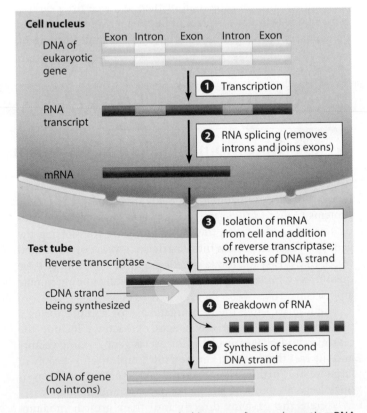

Figure 12.4   Making an intron-lacking gene from eukaryotic mRNA

12.5 Nucleic acid probes identify clones carrying specific genes

Often the most difficult task in gene cloning is finding the right "shelf" in a genomic library—that is, identifying clones containing a desired gene from among all those created (for example, pulling out just the bacteria from Figure 12.3 that have the red gene). If bacterial clones containing a specific gene actually translate the gene into protein, they can be identified by testing for the protein product. This is not always the case, however. Fortunately, researchers can also test directly for the gene itself.

Methods for detecting genes directly depend on base pairing between the gene and a complementary sequence on another nucleic acid molecule, either DNA or RNA. When at least part of the nucleotide sequence of a gene is already known or can be guessed, this information can be used to advantage. Taking a simplified example, if we know that a hypothetical gene contains the sequence TAGGCT, a biochemist can synthesize a short single strand of DNA with the complementary sequence (ATCCGA) and label it with a radioactive isotope or fluorescent tag. This labeled, complementary molecule is called a **nucleic acid probe** because it is used to find a specific gene or other nucleotide sequence within a mass of DNA. (In practice, probe molecules are usually considerably longer than six nucleotides.)

Figure 12.5 shows how a probe works. The DNA sample to be tested is treated with heat or alkali to separate the DNA strands. When the DNA probe is added to these strands, it tags the correct molecule—finds the correct shelf in the library—by hydrogen-bonding to the complementary sequence in the gene of interest. Such a probe can be simultaneously applied to many bacterial colonies to screen all of them at once for a desired gene. In one technique, a piece of filter paper is pressed against the colonies growing on a solid growth medium, picking up

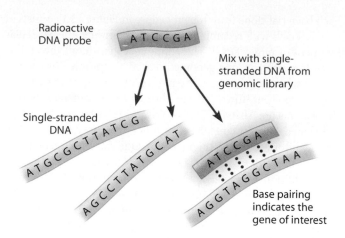

Figure 12.5   How a DNA probe tags a gene by base pairing

cells from each colony, treated to break the cells and separate the DNA strands, and then soaked in probe solution. Any bacterial colonies carrying the gene of interest will be tagged on the filter paper, marking them for easy identification. Once the researcher identifies a colony carrying the desired gene, the cells can be grown further and the gene of interest (and/or its protein product) isolated in large amounts.

? How does a probe consisting of radioactive DNA or RNA enable a researcher to find the bacterial clones carrying a particular gene?

■ The probe molecules bind to and label DNA only in the cells containing the gene of interest, which contains a complementary DNA sequence.

Genetically Modified Organisms

12.6 Recombinant cells and organisms can mass-produce gene products

Recombinant cells and organisms constructed by DNA technology are used to manufacture many useful products, chiefly proteins (Table 12.6, on the facing page). Most of these products are made by cells grown in culture. By transferring the gene for a desired protein into a bacterium, yeast, or other kind of cell that is easy to grow, a genetic engineer can produce large quantities of proteins that are present naturally in only minute amounts.

Bacteria are often the best organisms for manufacturing a protein product. Major advantages of bacteria include the plasmids and phages available for use as gene-cloning vectors and the fact that bacteria can be grown rapidly and cheaply in large tanks. Furthermore, bacteria can be engineered to produce large amounts of particular proteins and in some cases to secrete the proteins directly into their growth medium,

simplifying the task of collecting and purifying the products. As Table 12.6 shows, a number of proteins of importance in human medicine and agriculture are being produced in the bacterium *Escherichia coli*.

Despite the advantages of bacteria, it is sometimes desirable or necessary to use eukaryotic cells to produce a protein product. Often, the first-choice eukaryotic organism for protein production is the yeast used in making bread and beer, *Saccharomyces cerevisiae*. As bakers and brewers have recognized for centuries, yeast cells are easy to grow. And like *E. coli*, yeast cells can take up foreign DNA and integrate it into their genomes. Yeast cells also have plasmids that can be used as gene vectors, and yeast is often better than bacteria at synthesizing and secreting eukaryotic proteins. *S. cerevisiae* is currently used to produce a number of proteins. In certain cases, the same product (for example, interferons used in cancer research) can be made in either yeast or bacteria. In other cases, such as the hepatitis B vaccine, yeast alone is used.

The cells of choice for making some gene products come from mammals. For example, recombinant mammalian cells growing in laboratory cultures are currently used to produce human erythropoietin (EPO), a hormone that stimulates the production of red blood cells. EPO is used as a treatment for anemia; the drug is also abused by some athletes who seek the advantage of artificially high levels of oxygen-carrying red blood cells (called "blood doping").

Genes for products produced in mammalian cells are often cloned in bacteria as a preliminary step. For example, the gene for Factor VIII, a protein that affects blood clotting, is cloned in a bacterial plasmid before transfer to mammalian cells for large-scale production. Many proteins that mammalian cells normally secrete are glycoproteins, proteins with chains of sugars attached. Because only mammalian cells can attach the sugars correctly, mammalian cells must be used for making these products.

Recently, pharmaceutical researchers have been exploring the mass production of gene products by whole animals or plants rather than cultured cells. For example, using recombinant DNA technology, genetic engineers can add a gene for a desired human protein to the genome of a mammal in such a way that the gene's product is secreted in the animal's milk.

Figure 12.6 shows a herd of recombinant sheep that carry a gene for a human blood protein. The human protein can be harvested from the sheep's milk and is being tested as a treatment for cystic fibrosis. Because recombinant animals are difficult to produce, researchers may create a single one and then

Figure 12.6 "Pharm" animals that produce a human protein

clone it. The resulting herd of genetically identical recombinant animals, all carrying a recombinant human gene, could then serve as a grazing pharmaceutical factory—"pharm" animals. We continue an exploration of the medical applications of DNA technology in the next module.

? Why can't glycoproteins be mass-produced by engineered bacteria or yeast cells?

■ Because bacteria and yeast cells cannot correctly attach the sugar groups to the protein of glycoproteins

TABLE 12-6	SOME PROTEIN PRODUCTS OF RECOMBINANT DNA TECHNOLOGY	
Product	Made In	Use
Human insulin	E. coli	Treatment for diabetes
Human growth hormone (HGH)	E. coli	Treatment for growth defects
Epidermal growth factor (EGF)	E. coli	Treatment for burns, ulcers
Interleukin-2 (IL-2)	E. coli	Possible treatment for cancer
Bovine growth hormone (BGH)	E. coli	Improving weight gain in cattle
Cellulase	E. coli	Breaking down cellulose for animal feeds
Taxol	E. coli	Treatment for ovarian cancer
Interferons (alpha and gamma)	S. cerevisiae; E. coli	Possible treatment for cancer and viral infections
Hepatitis B vaccine	S. cerevisiae	Prevention of viral hepatitis
Erythropoietin (EPO)	Mammalian cells	Treatment for anemia
Factor VIII	Mammalian cells	Treatment for hemophilia
Tissue plasminogen activator (TPA)	Mammalian cells	Treatment for heart attacks and some strokes

12.11 The analysis of genetic markers can produce a DNA profile

As discussed in the chapter introduction, DNA technology has rapidly transformed the field of **forensics,** the scientific analysis of evidence for crime scene investigations and other legal proceedings. The most important application of biology to forensics is **DNA profiling,** the analysis of DNA fragments to determine whether they come from a particular individual. (The term "DNA profiling" is preferred over "DNA fingerprinting" by forensics scientists, who want to emphasize the genetic, inheritable basis for this procedure.)

How do you prove that two samples of DNA come from the same person? You could compare the entire genomes found in the two samples. But such an approach would be extremely impractical, requiring a lot of time and money. Instead, scientists compare genetic markers, sequences in the genome that vary from person to person. Like a gene (which is also a type of genetic marker), a noncoding genetic marker is more likely to be a match between relatives than between unrelated individuals.

Figure 12.11 summarizes the basic steps in creating a DNA profile. ❶ First, DNA samples are collected from the crime scene, suspects, victims, or stored evidence. ❷ Next, the selected markers from each DNA sample are amplified (copied many times), producing an adequate supply for testing. ❸ Finally, the amplified DNA markers are compared. In the next four modules, we'll explore the methods behind these steps.

Figure 12.11   An overview of DNA fingerprinting

❓ Why does DNA profiling rely on comparing specific genetic markers rather than the entire genome?

■ It would be too costly and time consuming to compare whole genomes.

12.12 The PCR method is used to amplify DNA sequences

Cloning DNA in host cells is often the best method for preparing large quantities of DNA from a particular gene (see Module 12.1). However, when the source of DNA is scanty or impure, the **polymerase chain reaction (PCR)** is a much better method. In this technique, a specific segment of a DNA molecule can be targeted and quickly amplified in a test tube. Starting with a single DNA segment, automated PCR can generate billions of copies in just a few hours.

In the PCR procedure (Figure 12.12), a three-step cycle brings about a chain reaction that doubles the population of identical DNA molecules each round. The key to amplifying one particular segment of DNA (and no others) are **primers,** short (usually 15–20 nucleotides long), chemically synthesized single-stranded DNA molecules with sequences that are complementary to sequences at each end of the target sequence. One primer is complimentary to one strand at one end of the target sequence; the second primer is complementary to the other strand at the other end of the sequence. The primers thus bind to sequences that flank the target sequence, marking the start and end points for the segment of DNA being amplified. ❶ In the first step of each PCR cycle, the reaction mixture is heated to separate the strands of the DNA double helices. ❷ Next, the strands are cooled. As they cool, primer molecules hydrogen-bond to their target sequences on the DNA. ❸ In the third step,

a heat-stable DNA polymerase builds new DNA strands by extending the primers in the $5' \rightarrow 3'$ direction. These three steps are repeated over and over, doubling the amount of DNA after each 3-step cycle. PCR became automated after the discovery of an unusual heat-stable DNA polymerase, first isolated from a bacterium living in hot springs, that could withstand the heat at the start of each cycle; standard DNA polymerases would denature (unfold) during the heating step of each cycle.

Just as impressive as the speed of PCR is its sensitivity. Only minute amounts of DNA need to be present in the starting material, and this DNA can even be in a partially degraded state. The key to the high sensitivity is the primers. Because DNA polymerase extends the primers, only the desired segments of DNA are duplicated. Other DNA will not be bound by primers and thus not copied by DNA polymerase.

Devised in 1985, PCR has had a major impact on biological research and biotechnology. PCR has been used to amplify DNA from a wide variety of sources: fragments of ancient DNA from a 40,000-year-old frozen woolly mammoth; DNA from fingerprints or from tiny amounts of blood, tissue, or semen found at crime scenes; DNA from single embryonic cells for rapid prenatal diagnosis of genetic disorders; and DNA of viral genes from cells infected with viruses that are difficult to detect, such as HIV.

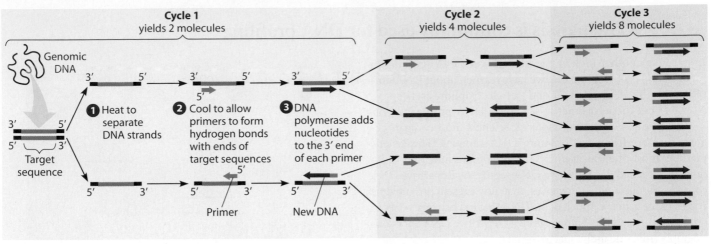

Cycle 1
yields 2 molecules

Cycle 2
yields 4 molecules

Cycle 3
yields 8 molecules

Genomic DNA

Target sequence

1 Heat to separate DNA strands

2 Cool to allow primers to form hydrogen bonds with ends of target sequences

3 DNA polymerase adds nucleotides to the 3′ end of each primer

Primer

New DNA

Figure 12.12   DNA amplification by PCR

? Why is amplification of DNA from a crime scene often necessary?

■ The DNA retrievable from a crime scene is often scanty and impure.

12.13   Gel electrophoresis sorts DNA molecules by size

Many approaches for studying DNA molecules make use of **gel electrophoresis.** This technique uses a gel (a thin slab of jellylike material) as a molecular sieve to separate macromolecules—usually proteins or nucleic acids—on the basis of size, electrical charge, or other physical properties.

Figure 12.13 outlines how gel electrophoresis can be used to separate mixtures of DNA fragments obtained from three different sources. A sample of each mixture is placed in a well (hole) at one end of a flat, rectangular gel. A negatively charged electrode from a power supply is attached near the end of the gel containing the DNA, and a positive electrode is attached near the other end. Because phosphate (PO_4^-) groups give DNA a negative charge (see Module 10.2), the DNA molecules all travel through the gel toward the positive pole. However, the longer DNA fragments are held back by a thicket of polymer fibers within the gel, so they move more slowly than the shorter fragments. Over time, shorter molecules move further through the gel than longer fragments. Gel electrophoresis thus separates DNA molecules by length, with shorter molecules migrating toward the bottom faster than longer molecules.

When the current is turned off, a series of bands is left in each "lane" of the gel. Each band is a collection of DNA molecules of the same length. The bands can be made visible by staining, by exposure onto photographic film (if the DNA is radioactively labeled), or by measuring fluorescence (if the DNA is labeled with a fluorescent dye).

Web Activity *Gel Electrophoresis of DNA*

Web Process of Science *How Can Gel Electrophoresis Be Used to Analyze DNA?*

? (a) What causes DNA molecules to move toward the positive pole during electrophoresis? (b) Why do large molecules move more slowly than smaller ones?

■ (a) The negatively charged phosphate groups of the DNA are attracted to the positive pole. (b) The gel restricts their movement more.

Mixture of DNA fragments of different sizes

Power source

Gel

Longer (slower) molecules

Shorter (faster) molecules

Completed gel

Figure 12.13   Gel electrophoresis of DNA

12.14 STR analysis is commonly used for DNA profiling

If you take another look at the overview of DNA profiling in Figure 12.11, you will see that we have learned about DNA amplification by PCR (step 2) and gel electrophoresis (step 3). Now let's put them together to see how a DNA profile is made.

To create a DNA profile, a forensic scientist must compare genetic markers from two or more DNA samples. The genetic markers most often used in DNA profiling are inherited variations in the lengths of repetitive DNA segments. **Repetitive DNA** consists of nucleotide sequences that are present in multiple copies in the genome; much of the DNA that lies between genes in humans is of this type. Some regions of repetitive DNA vary considerably from one individual to the next.

For DNA profiling, the relevant type of repetitive DNA consists of short sequences repeated many times in a row (tandemly); such sequences are called **short tandem repeats (STRs).** For example, one person might have the sequence AGAT repeated 12 times in a row at one place in the genome, the sequence GATA repeated 45 times in a row at a second place, and so on. Another person is likely to have the same sequences at the same places but with different numbers of repeats.

STR analysis is a method of DNA profiling that compares the lengths of STR sequences at specific sites in the genome. Most commonly, STR analysis compares the number of repeats of specific four-nucleotide DNA sequences at 13 sites scattered throughout the genome. Each of these repeat sites, which typically contain from 3 to 50 four-nucleotide repeats in a row, vary widely from person to person. In fact, some of the short tandem repeats used in the standard procedure can be found in up to 80 different variations in the human population.

Consider the two samples of DNA shown in Figure 12.14A. Imagine that the top DNA was obtained at a crime scene and the bottom DNA from a suspect's blood. The two segments have the same number of repeats at the first site: 7 repeats of the four-nucleotide DNA sequence AGAT (shown in orange). Notice, however, that they differ in the number of repeats at the second site: 8 repeats of GATA (shown in purple) in the crime scene DNA, compared to 13 repeats in the suspect's DNA. To create a DNA profile, a scientist uses PCR to specifically amplify the regions of DNA that include these STR sites. This can be done by using primers matching nucleotide sequences known to flank the STR sites. The resulting DNA molecules are then compared by gel electrophoresis.

Figure 12.14B DNA profiles generated from the STRs in Figure 12.14A

Figure 12.14B shows a gel that could have resulted from the STR fragments in Figure 12.14A. The differences in the locations of the bands reflect the different lengths of the DNA fragments. (A gel from an actual DNA profile would typically contain more than just two bands in each lane.) This gel would provide evidence that the crime scene DNA did not come from the suspect. Notice that electrophoresis allows us to see similarities as well as differences between mixtures of DNA molecules. Thus, data from DNA profiling can provide evidence of either innocence or guilt.

Although other methods have been used in the past, STR analysis of 13 predetermined STR sites is the current standard for DNA profiling in forensic and legal systems. Once determined, the number of repeats at each of these sites can be entered into the Combined DNA Index System (CODIS) database, administered by the Federal Bureau of Investigation. In the next module, we'll examine several real-world examples of how this technology has been used.

Web Activity *Analyzing DNA Fragments Using Gel Electrophoresis*

? (a) What are STRs? (b) What is STR analysis?

■ (a) Regions of the genome that contain varying numbers of in-a-row repeats of a short nucleotide sequence (b) A technique for determining whether two DNA samples have identical STRs

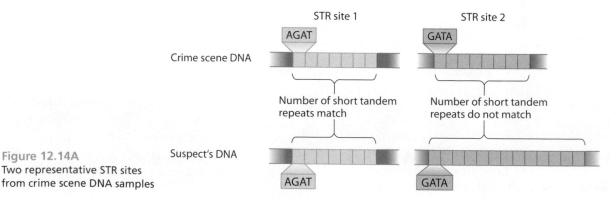

Figure 12.14A
Two representative STR sites from crime scene DNA samples

12.15 | DNA profiling has provided evidence in many forensic investigations

When a violent crime is committed, body fluids or small pieces of tissue may be left at the crime scene or on the clothes of the victim or assailant. If rape has occurred, semen may be recovered from the victim's body. DNA profiling can match such samples to the person they came from with a high degree of certainty because the DNA sequence of every person is unique (except for identical twins). And with PCR amplification of DNA, a tissue sample as small as 20 cells can be sufficient for testing.

Since its introduction in 1986, DNA profiling has become a standard tool of criminalistics and has provided crucial evidence in many famous cases. In the O. J. Simpson murder trial, DNA analysis proved that blood in Simpson's car belonged to the victims and that blood at the crime scene belonged to Simpson. (The jury in this case did not find the DNA evidence alone to be sufficient to convict the suspect, and Simpson was found not guilty.) During the investigation that led up to his impeachment, President Bill Clinton repeatedly denied that he had sexual relations with Monica Lewinsky—until DNA profiling proved that his semen was on her dress.

Figure 12.15A   STR analysis proved that convicted murderer Earl Washington was innocent, freeing him after 17 years in prison.

Of course, DNA evidence can prove innocence as well as guilt. The Innocence Project, associated with the Yeshiva University School of Law in New York City, has used DNA technology and legal work to exonerate over 200 convicted criminals since 1989, including 15 on death row (Figure 12.15A). In more than a third of these cases, DNA evidence pointed toward the true suspects. These facts have prompted several states to impose or consider moratoriums on the death penalty.

The use of DNA profiling extends beyond crimes. For instance, a comparison of the DNA of a child and the purported father can conclusively settle a question of paternity. Sometimes paternity is of historical interest: DNA profiling proved that Thomas Jefferson or one of his close male relatives fathered at least one child with his young slave, Sally Hemings. Going back much farther, one of the strangest cases of DNA profiling is that of Cheddar Man, a 9,000-year-old skeleton found in a cave near Cheddar, England (Figure 12.15B). DNA was extracted from his tooth and analyzed. The DNA profile showed that Cheddar Man was a direct ancestor (through approximately 300 generations) of a present-day schoolteacher who lived only a half mile from the cave!

DNA profiling can also identify victims of mass casualties. The largest such effort in history occurred after the World Trade Center attack on September 11, 2001. Forensic scientists under the coordination of the Office of the Chief Medical Examiner of New York City worked for years to identify over 20,000 samples of victims' remains. Tissue samples from the disaster site were matched to known DNA profiles (when available) or to DNA-carrying items provided by families, such as toothbrushes. When no sample of a victim's DNA was available, blood samples from close relatives were used to confirm identity through near matches. Over half of the identified victims at the World Trade Center site were identified solely by DNA evidence, providing closure to many grieving families.

Figure 12.15B   Cheddar Man and his modern-day descendant

Just how reliable is DNA profiling? When the standard CODIS set of 13 STR sites (see Module 12.14) is used, the probability of finding the same DNA profile in randomly selected, unrelated individuals is less than one in 10 billion. Put another way, a standard DNA profile can provide a statistical match of a particular DNA sample to just *one living human*. For this reason, DNA analyses are now accepted as compelling evidence by legal experts and scientists alike. In fact, DNA analysis on stored forensic samples has provided the evidence needed to solve many "cold cases" in recent years. DNA analysis has also been used to probe the origin of nonhuman materials. In 1998, the U.S. Fish and Wildlife Service began testing the DNA in caviar to determine if the fish eggs originated from the species claimed on the label. By conclusively proving the origin of contraband animal products, DNA profiling could help protect endangered species. In another example, a 2005 study determined that DNA extracted from a 27,000-year-old Siberian mammoth was 98.6% identical to DNA from modern African elephants.

Although DNA profiling has provided definitive evidence in many investigations, the method is far from foolproof. Problems can arise from insufficient data, human error, or flawed evidence. While the science behind DNA profiling is irrefutable, the human element remains a possible confounding factor.

Web Activity *Connection: DNA Fingerprinting*

?   In what way is DNA profiling valuable for determining innocence as well as guilt?

■ A DNA profile can prove with near certainty that a sample of DNA does or does not come from a particular individual. DNA profiling therefore can provide evidence in support of guilt or innocence.

12.16 RFLPs can be used to detect differences in DNA sequences

Recall that a genetic marker is a DNA sequence that varies in a population. Like different alleles of a gene, the DNA sequence at a specific place on a chromosome may exhibit small nucleotide differences, or polymorphisms (from the Greek for "many forms"). Geneticists have catalogued many single base-pair variations in the genome. Such a variation found in at least 1% of the population is called a **single nucleotide polymorphism** (**SNP,** pronounced "snip"). SNPs occur on average about once in 100 to 300 base pairs in the human genome in either the coding sequence of a gene or in a noncoding sequence. Methods have been developed that can detect a particular SNP.

SNPs may alter a restriction site (the sequence recognized by a restriction enzyme). Such alterations change the lengths of the restriction fragments formed by that enzyme when it cuts the DNA. This type of sequence change is called a **restriction fragment length polymorphism** (**RFLP,** pronounced "rif-lip"). Thus, RFLPs serve as genetic markers for particular loci in the genome. RFLPs have many uses. For example, disease-causing alleles can be diagnosed with reasonable accuracy if a closely linked SNP or RFLP marker has been found. Alleles for Huntington's disease and a number of other genetic diseases were first detected by means of RFLPs in this indirect way.

Restriction fragment analysis involves two of the methods you have learned about: DNA fragments produced by restriction enzymes (see Module 12.2) are sorted by gel electrophoresis (see Module 12.13). The number of restriction fragments and their sizes reflect the specific sequence of nucleotides in the starting DNA.

At the top of Figure 12.16, we see corresponding segments of DNA from two DNA samples prepared from human tissue. Notice that the DNA sequences differ by a single base pair (highlighted in gold). In this case, the restriction enzyme cuts the DNA between two cytosine (C) bases in the sequence CCGG and in its complement, GGCC. Because DNA from the first sample has two recognition sequences for the restriction enzyme, it is cleaved in two places, yielding three restriction fragments (labeled *w, x,* and *y*). DNA from the second sample, however, has only one recognition sequence and yields only two restriction fragments (*z* and *y*). Notice that the lengths of restriction fragments, as well as their numbers, differ depending on the exact sequence of bases in the DNA.

To detect the differences between the collections of restriction fragments, we need to separate the restriction fragments in the two mixtures and compare their lengths. This process, called RFLP analysis, is accomplished through gel electrophoresis. As shown in the bottom of the figure, the three kinds of restriction fragments from sample 1 separate into three bands in the gel, while those from sample 2 separate into only two bands. Notice that the shortest fragment from sample 1 (*y*) produces a band at the same location as the identical short fragment from the sample 2. So you can see that electrophoresis allows us to see similarities as well as differences between mixtures of restriction fragments—and

Figure 12.16   RFLP analysis

similarities as well as differences between the base sequences in DNA from two individuals. The restriction fragment analysis in Figure 12.16 clearly shows that the two DNA samples differ in sequence.

? **Explain the meaning of the statement "A population has restriction fragment length polymorphisms."**

■ There are differences (polymorphisms) in the lengths of restriction fragments produced when restriction enzymes cut comparable DNA samples from different individuals.

12.17 Genomics is the scientific study of whole genomes

By the 1980s, biologists were using RFLPs to help map important genes in humans and some other organisms. It didn't take long for biologists to think on a larger scale. In 1995, a team of scientists announced that they had determined the nucleotide sequence of the entire genome of *Haemophilus influenzae*, a bacterium that can cause several human diseases, including pneumonia and meningitis. **Genomics,** the science of studying a complete set of genes (a genome) and their interactions, was born.

Since 1995, researchers have used the tools and techniques of DNA technology to develop more and more detailed maps of the genomes of a number of species. The first targets of genomics research were bacteria, which have relatively little DNA. The genome of *H. influenzae,* for example, contains only 1.8 million nucleotides and 1,709 genes. But soon the attention of genomics researchers turned toward more complex organisms with much larger genomes. As of 2007, the genomes of over 600 species have been published, and over 1,000 more are in progress. Table 12.17 lists a few of the completed genomes. The vast majority of genomes under study are from prokaryotes, including *Escherichia coli* and a few hundred other bacteria (some of medical importance), and a few dozen archaea. There are 50 or so eukaryotic species that have been sequenced, including vertebrates, invertebrates, fungi, and plants.

Baker's yeast (*Saccharomyces cerevisiae*) was the first eukaryote to have its full sequence determined, and the roundworm *Caenorhabditis elegans* was the first multicellular organism. Other sequenced animals include the fruit fly (*Drosophila melanogaster*) and the lab mouse (*Mus musculus*), both model organisms for genetics. Plants, such as *Arabidopsis thaliana* (another important research organism) and rice (*Oryza sativa*, one of the world's most economically important crops), have also been completed. Other recently completed eukaryotic genomes include the honeybee, the dog, the chicken, and the sea urchin.

In 2005, researchers completed the genome sequence for our closest living relative on the evolutionary tree of life, the chimpanzee (*Pan troglodytes*). Comparisons with human DNA revealed that we share 96% of our genome with our closest animal relative. As you will see in Module 12.21, genomic scientists are currently finding and studying the important differences, shedding scientific light on the age-old question of what makes us human.

Why map so many genomes? Not only are all genomes of interest in their own right, but comparative analysis provides invaluable insights into the evolutionary relationships among organisms. Also, the maps of a variety of genomes help scientists interpret the human genome. For example, when scientists find a nucleotide sequence in the human genome similar to a yeast gene whose function is known, they have a valuable clue to the function of the human sequence. Indeed, several yeast protein-coding genes are so similar to certain human disease-causing genes that researchers have figured out the functions of the disease genes by studying their normal yeast counterparts. Many genes of disparate organisms are turning out to be astonishingly similar, to the point that one researcher has joked that he now views fruit flies as "little people with wings."

? Why is it useful to sequence nonhuman genomes?

■ Besides their value in understanding evolution, comparative analysis of nonhuman genes helps scientists interpret human data.

| | | TABLE 12.17 SOME IMPORTANT COMPLETED GENOMES |

Organism	Year Completed	Size of Genome (in Base Pairs)	Approximate Number of Genes
Haemophilus influenzae (bacterium)	1995	1.8 million	1,700
Saccharomyces cerevisiae (yeast)	1996	13 million	6,200
Escherichia coli (bacterium)	1997	4.6 million	4,400
Caenorhabditis elegans (nematode)	1998	97 million	19,000
Drosophila melanogaster (fruit fly)	2000	180 million	13,700
Arabidopsis thaliana (mustard plant)	2000	118 million	25,500
Mus musculus (mouse)	2001	2.6 billion	22,000
Oryza sativa (rice)	2002	430 million	60,000
Homo sapiens (humans)	2003	3.2 billion	21,000
Rattus norvegius (lab rat)	2004	2.8 billion	25,000
Pan troglodytes (chimpanzee)	2005	3.1 billion	22,000
Macaca mulatta (macaque)	2007	2.9 billion	22,000

12.18 The Human Genome Project revealed that most of the human genome does not consist of genes

The most ambitious genomics project to date has been the **Human Genome Project (HGP).** The goals of the HGP were to determine the nucleotide sequence of all DNA in the human genome and to identify the location and sequence of every gene. The HGP began in 1990 as an effort by a consortium of 20 government-funded research centers in six countries. Several years into the project, private companies, chiefly Celera Genomics in the United States, joined the effort. At the completion of the final draft of the sequence in 2004, over 99% of the genome had been determined to 99.999% accuracy. As of 2007, there remain a few hundred gaps of unknown sequences within the human genome that will require special methods to figure out. The DNA sequences determined by the HGP have been deposited in a database, called Genbank, that is publically available via the Internet.

The chromosomes in the human genome (22 autosomes plus the X and Y sex chromosomes) contain approximately 3.2 billion nucleotide pairs of DNA. To try to get a sense of this quantity of DNA, imagine that its nucleotide sequence is printed in letters (A, T, C, and G) like the letters in this book. At this size, the sequence would fill a stack of books 18 stories high! The biggest surprise from the HGP is the small number of human genes. The current estimate is about 21,000 genes—very close to the number found in the nematode worm. How, then, do we account for human complexity? Part of the answer may lie in alternative RNA splicing (see Module 11.6); scientists think that a typical human gene probably specifies several polypeptides.

In humans, like most complex eukaryotes, only a small amount of our total DNA (about 1.5%) is contained in genes that code for proteins, tRNAs, or rRNAs (Figure 12.18). Most multicellular eukaryotes have a huge amount of noncoding DNA—about 98.5% of human DNA is of this type. Some noncoding DNA is made up of gene control sequences such as promoters and enhancers (see Chapter 11). The remaining noncoding DNA has been dubbed "junk DNA," a tongue-in-cheek way of saying that scientists don't fully understand its functions.

Much of the DNA between genes consists of repetitive DNA, nucleotide sequences present in many copies in the genome. Some of this noncoding DNA is used to create DNA profiles by STR analysis, as discussed in Module 12.14. Stretches of DNA with thousands of such repetitions are also prominent at the centromeres and ends of chromosomes—called **telomeres**—suggesting that this DNA plays a role in chromosome structure.

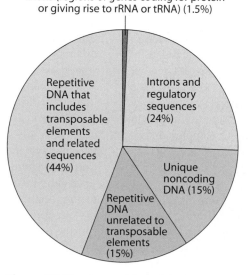

Exons (regions of genes coding for protein or giving rise to rRNA or tRNA) (1.5%)

Repetitive DNA that includes transposable elements and related sequences (44%)

Introns and regulatory sequences (24%)

Unique noncoding DNA (15%)

Repetitive DNA unrelated to transposable elements (15%)

Figure 12.18 Composition of the human genome

In the second main type of repetitive DNA, each repeated unit is hundreds of nucleotides long, and the copies are scattered around the genome. Most of these sequences seem to be associated with **transposable elements** ("jumping genes"), DNA segments that can move or be copied from one location to another in a chromosome and even between chromosomes. Researchers believe that transposable elements, through their copy-and-paste mechanism, are responsible for the proliferation of dispersed repetitive DNA in the human genome.

The potential benefits of having a complete map of the human genome are enormous. For instance, hundreds of disease-associated genes have already been identified. One example is the gene that is mutated in an inherited type of Parkinson's disease, a debilitating brain disorder that causes tremors of increasing severity. Until recently, Parkinson's disease was thought to have only an environmental basis; there was no evidence of a hereditary component. But data from the Human Genome Project mapped a very small number of cases of Parkinson's disease to a specific gene. Interestingly, an altered version of the protein encoded by this gene has also been tied to Alzheimer's disease, suggesting a link between these two brain disorders. Moreover, the same gene is also found in rats, where it plays a role in the sense of smell, and in zebra finches, where it is thought to be involved in song learning. Cross-species comparisons such as these may uncover clues about the role played by the normal version of the protein in the brain. And such knowledge could eventually lead to treatment for the half a million Americans with Parkinson's disease.

One interesting question about the Human Genome Project is: *Whose genome* was sequenced? The answer is no one's—or at least not any one person's. The human genome sequenced by the public consortium was actually a reference genome compiled from a group of individuals. The genome sequenced by Celera consisted primarily of DNA sampled from the company's president. These representative sequences will serve as standards so that comparisons of individual differences and similarities can be made. Eventually, as the amount of sequence data multiplies, the small differences that account for individual variation within our species will come to light.

? The human genome consists of about _____ nucleotides and _____ genes spread over _____ different chromosomes (provide three numbers).

■ 3.2 billion . . . 21,000 . . . 24 (22 autosomes plus two sex chromosomes)

12.19 The whole-genome shotgun method of sequencing a genome can provide a wealth of data quickly

Sequencing an entire genome is a complex task that requires careful work. The Human Genome Project proceeded through three stages that provided progressively more detailed views of the human genome. First, geneticists combined pedigree analyses of large families to map over 5,000 genetic markers (mostly RFLPs) spaced throughout all of the chromosomes. The resulting low-resolution *linkage map* provided a framework for mapping other markers and for arranging later, more detailed maps of particular regions. Next, researchers determined the number of base pairs between the markers in the linkage map. These data helped them construct a *physical map* of the human genome. Finally came the most arduous part of the project: determining the nucleotide sequences of the set of DNA fragments that had been mapped. Advances in automated DNA sequencing were crucial to this endeavor.

This three-stage approach is logical and thorough. However, in 1992, molecular biologist J. Craig Venter proposed an alternative strategy called the **whole-genome shotgun method** and set up the company Celera Genomics to implement it. His idea was essentially to skip the genetic and physical mapping stages and start directly with the sequencing step. In the whole genome shotgun method, an entire genome is chopped by restriction enzymes into fragments that are cloned and sequenced in just one stage (Figure 12.19). High-performance computers running specialized mapping software can assemble the millions of overlapping short sequences into a single continuous sequence.

Today, the whole-genome shotgun approach is the method of choice for genomic researchers because it is fast and relatively inexpensive. However, recent research has revealed some limitations of this method, suggesting that a hybrid approach that combines whole genome shotgunning with physical or genetic maps may prove to be the most useful method in the long run.

Figure 12.19   The whole-genome shotgun method

? What is the primary advantage of the whole-genome shotgun method?

■ It is faster and cheaper than the three-stage method of genome sequencing.

12.20 Proteomics is the scientific study of the full set of proteins encoded by a genome

The successes in the field of genomics have encouraged scientists to attempt similar systematic study of the full protein sets (proteomes) encoded by genomes, an approach called **proteomics.** The number of proteins in humans far exceeds the number of genes (about 100,000 proteins versus about 21,000 genes). And since proteins, not genes, actually carry out most of the activities of the cell, scientists must study when and where proteins are produced in an organism and how they interact in order to understand the functioning of cells and organisms. Assembling and analyzing proteomes pose many experimental challenges, but ongoing advances are providing the tools to meet those challenges.

Genomics and proteomics are enabling biologists to approach the study of life from an increasingly holistic perspective. Biologists are now in a position to compile catalogs of genes and proteins—that is, a listing of all the "parts" that contribute to the operation of cells, tissues, and organisms. With such catalogs in hand, researchers are shifting their attention from the individual parts to how they function together in biological systems.

? If every protein is encoded by a gene, how can humans have many more proteins than genes? *Hint:* See Module 11.6.

■ The mRNA from one gene may be spliced several different ways to produce several different proteins.

12.21 Genomes hold clues to the evolutionary divergence of humans and chimps

Comparisons of genome sequences from different species allow geneticists to evaluate the evolutionary relationships between those species. The more similar in sequence the same gene is in two species, the more closely related those species are in their evolutionary history. Comparing genes of closely related species sheds light on recent evolutionary events, whereas comparing those of distantly related species helps us understand more ancient evolutionary history. Indeed, comparisons of the completed genome sequences of bacteria, archaea, and eukarya strongly support the theory that these are the three fundamental domains of life.

The small number of gene differences between closely related species makes it easier to correlate phenotypic differences between the species with particular genetic differences. The completion of the chimpanzee genome in 2005 allows us to compare human, chimp, and other sequenced mammalian genomes, such as those of the mouse or rat. Identifying the genes shared by all of these species, but not by non-mammals, may give clues about what it takes to make a mammal, while the genes shared by chimps and humans, but absent from the rodents, may tell us something about primates (Figure 12.21).

An analysis of the overall composition of the human and chimp genomes reveals that they differ by 1.2% in single-base substitutions. Researchers were surprised when they found a further 2.7% difference due to insertions or deletions of larger regions in the genome of one or the other species, with many of the insertions being duplications or other repetitive DNA. In fact, a third of the human duplications are not present in the chimp genome, and some of these duplications contain regions associated with human diseases. All of these observations provide clues to the forces that might have swept the two genomes along different paths, but we don't have a complete picture yet.

What about specific genes and types of genes that differ between humans and chimps? Using evolutionary analyses, biologists have identified a number of genes that have evolved or are evolving faster in humans than in either mouse or chimp. Among them are genes involved in defense against malaria and tuberculosis and at least one gene regulating brain size.

One gene that shows evidence of rapid change in the human lineage is called *FOXP2*. Several lines of evidence suggest that *FOXP2* functions in speech and vocalization, characteristics that obviously distinguish the two species. For example, humans with mutations in this gene generally have severe speech and language impairment. Additionally, there is evidence that the *FOXP2* gene is expressed in the brains of zebra finches and canaries at the time when these songbirds are learning their songs, showing that the role of this gene in communication may be more widespread than in just mammals. These results support the idea that the differences between the *FOXP2* gene in humans and chimps may play a role in the ability of humans, but not chimps, to communicate by speech. The functional effect of the specific amino acid differences between the human and chimp FOXP2 proteins remains to be determined and is of great interest to scientists.

Figure 12.21 What genomic information makes us human or chimp?

Other research efforts are under way to extend genomic studies to many more microbial species, additional primates, and neglected species from diverse branches of the tree of life. These studies will advance our understanding of all aspects of biology, including health and ecology as well as evolution.

? How can cross-species comparisons of the nucleotide sequences of a gene provide insight into evolution?

■ Similarities in gene sequences correlate with evolutionary relatedness; greater genetic similarities reflect a more recent shared ancestry.

Chapter Review

Reviewing the Concepts

DNA technology, methods for studying and manipulating genetic material, has revolutionized the field of forensics (**Introduction**).

Gene Cloning (12.1–12.5)

Gene cloning is one application of biotechnology, the manipulation of organisms or their components to make useful products. Researchers can insert desired genes into plasmids, creating recombinant DNA, and insert those plasmids into bacteria. If the recombinant bacteria multiply into a clone,

the foreign genes are also copied and the desired product (more copies of the gene or its protein product) can be harvested (**12.1**). The tools used to make recombinant DNA include restriction enzymes, which cut DNA at specific sequences (called restriction sites) forming restriction fragments, and DNA ligase, which "pastes" DNA fragments together (**12.2**).

Genomic libraries, sets of DNA fragments containing all of an organism's genes, can be constructed and stored in cloned bacterial plasmids, phages, or bacterial artificial chromosomes (BACs) (**12.3**):

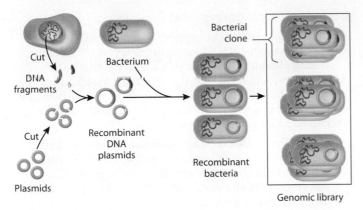

Reverse transcriptase can be used to make cDNA libraries containing only the genes that are transcribed by a particular type of cell (12.4). A nucleic acid probe, a short, single-stranded molecule of labeled DNA or RNA, can tag a desired gene in a library (12.5).

Genetically Modified Organisms (12.6–12.10)

Applications of gene cloning include the mass production of gene products for medical and other uses. Different organisms, including bacteria, yeast, and mammals, can be used for this purpose (12.6). Researchers use gene cloning to produce hormones, diagnose and treat diseases, and produce vaccines (12.7).

Recombinant DNA technology can be used to produce new genetic varieties of plants and animals; a number of important crop plants are genetically modified (12.8). Genetic engineering involves risks, such as ecological damage from GM crops (12.9). Gene therapy may one day be used to treat both genetic diseases and nongenetic disorders; progress is slow, however (12.10).

DNA Profiling (12.11–12.16)

DNA profiling, the analysis of DNA fragments, can conclusively determine whether two samples of DNA come from the same individual (12.11). The polymerase chain reaction (PCR) can be used to clone a small sample of DNA quickly, producing enough copies for analysis. The use of specific primers that flank the desired sequence ensures that only a particular subset of the DNA sample will be copied (12.12). Gel electrophoresis can sort DNA molecules by size (12.13):

Short tandem repeats (STRs) are stretches of DNA within the genome that contain short nucleotide sequences repeated many times in a row. DNA profiling by STR analysis involves amplifying a standard set of 13 STRs and visualizing them on a gel (12.14). DNA profiling has many practical applications, including helping to solve crimes, establishing paternity, and identifying crime victims (12.15). Restriction fragment length polymorphisms (RFLPs) reflect differences in the sequences of DNA samples. After being cut by restriction enzymes, the fragments are run through a gel (12.16).

Genomics (12.17–12.21)

Genomics, the study of whole genomes, has advanced rapidly in recent years with the sequencing of many prokaryotic and eukaryotic genomes. Besides being interesting themselves, nonhuman genomes can be compared with the human genome (12.17). Data from the Human Genome Project (HGP) revealed that the haploid human genome contains about 21,000 genes and a huge amount of noncoding DNA. Much of the noncoding DNA consists of repetitive nucleotide sequences and transposable elements that can move about within the genome (12.18). The HGP used genetic and physical mapping of chromosomes followed by DNA sequencing. Modern genomic analysis often uses the faster whole-genome shotgun method (12.19). Proteomics is the study of organisms' full sets of proteins (12.20). Genomic data provides insight into recent and ancient evolution (12.21).

Connecting the Concepts

1. Imagine you have found a small quantity of DNA. Fill in the following diagram, which outlines a series of DNA technology experiments you could perform to study this DNA.

Testing Your Knowledge

Multiple Choice

2. Which of the following would be considered a transgenic organism?
   a. a bacterium that has received genes via conjugation
   b. a human given a corrected human blood-clotting gene
   c. a fern grown in cell culture from a single fern root cell
   d. a rat with rabbit hemoglobin genes
   e. a human treated with insulin produced by bacteria

3. When a typical restriction enzyme cuts a DNA molecule, the cuts are uneven so that the DNA fragments have single-stranded ends. These ends are useful in recombinant DNA work because
   a. they enable a cell to recognize fragments produced by the enzyme.
   b. they serve as starting points for DNA replication.
   c. the fragments will bond to other fragments with complementary ends.
   d. they enable researchers to use the fragments as molecular probes.
   e. only single-stranded DNA segments can code for proteins.

4. The DNA profiles used as evidence in a murder trial look something like supermarket bar codes. The pattern of bars in a DNA profile shows
   a. the order of bases in a particular gene.
   b. the presence of various-sized fragments from chopped-up DNA.
   c. the presence of dominant or recessive alleles for particular traits.
   d. the order of genes along particular chromosomes.
   e. the exact location of a specific gene in a genomic library.

5. A biologist isolated a gene from a human cell, attached it to a plasmid, and inserted the plasmid into a bacterium. The bacterium made a new protein, but it was nothing like the protein normally produced in a human cell. Why? (*Explain your answer.*)
   a. The bacterium had undergone transformation.
   b. The gene did not have sticky ends.
   c. The gene contained introns.
   d. The gene did not come from a genomic library.
   e. The biologist should have cloned the gene first.

6. A paleontologist has recovered a tiny bit of organic material from the 400-year-old preserved skin of an extinct dodo. She would like to compare DNA from the sample with DNA from living birds. Which of the following would be most useful for increasing the amount of DNA available for testing?
   a. restriction fragment analysis
   b. polymerase chain reaction
   c. molecular probe analysis
   d. electrophoresis
   e. Ti plasmid technology

7. How many genes are there in a human sperm cell?
   a. 23
   b. 46
   c. 5,000–10,000
   d. about 25,000
   e. about 3 billion

Describing, Comparing, and Explaining

8. Explain how you might engineer *E. coli* to produce human growth hormone (HGH) using the following: *E. coli* containing plasmids, DNA carrying a gene for HGH, DNA ligase, a restriction enzyme, equipment for manipulating and growing bacteria, a method for extracting and purifying the hormone, an appropriate DNA probe. (Assume that the human HGH gene lacks introns.)

9. Recombinant DNA techniques are used to custom-build bacteria for two main purposes: to obtain multiple copies of certain genes and to obtain useful proteins produced by certain genes. Give an example of each of these applications in medicine and agriculture.

Applying the Concepts

10. A biochemist hopes to find a gene in human liver cells that codes for an important blood-clotting protein. She knows that the nucleotide sequence of a small part of the gene is CTGGACTGACA. Briefly explain how to obtain the desired gene.

11. What is left for genetic researchers to do now that the Human Genome Project has determined the complete nucleotide sequences of nearly all of the human chromosomes? Explain.

12. Today, it is fairly easy to make transgenic plants and animals. What are some important safety and ethical issues raised by this use of recombinant DNA technology? What are some of the possible dangers of introducing genetically engineered organisms into the environment? What are some reasons for and against leaving decisions in these areas to scientists? To business owners and executives? What are some reasons for and against more public involvement? How might these decisions affect you? How do you think these decisions should be made?

13. In the not-too-distant future, gene therapy may be an option for the treatment and cure of some inherited disorders. What do you think are the most serious ethical issues that must be dealt with before human gene therapy is used on a large scale? Why do you think these issues are important?

14. The possibility of extensive genetic testing raises questions about how personal genetic information should be used. For example, should employers or potential employers have access to such information? Why or why not? Should the information be available to insurance companies? Why or why not? Is there any reason for the government to keep genetic files? Is there any obligation to warn relatives who might share a defective gene? Might some people avoid being tested for fear of being labeled genetic outcasts? Or might they be compelled to be tested against their wishes? Can you think of other reasons to proceed with caution?

Answers to all questions can be found in Appendix 4.

For Practice Quizzes, BioFlix, MP3 Tutors, and Activities, go to www.mybiology.com.

Concepts of Evolution

UNITTHREE

13 How Populations Evolve

14 The Origin of Species

15 Tracing Evolutionary History

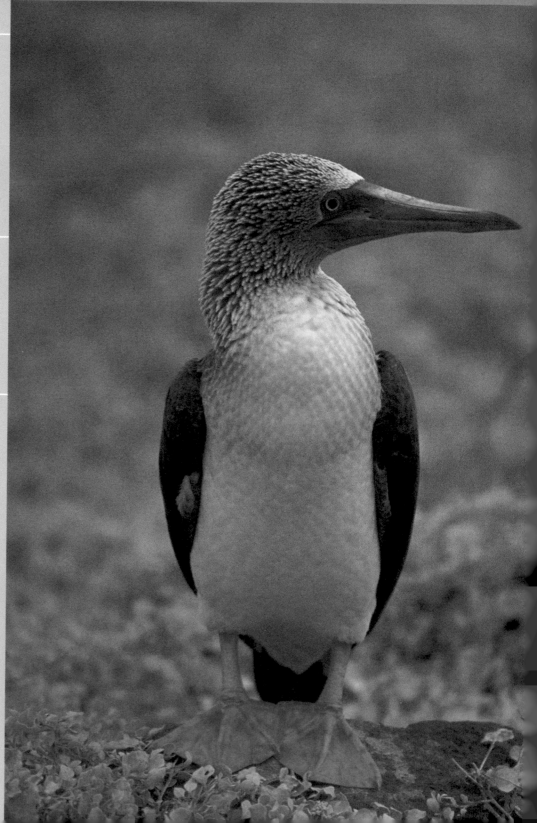

chapter

13

How Populations Evolve

Darwin's Theory of Evolution

13.1 A sea voyage helped Darwin frame his theory of evolution

13.2 Darwin proposed natural selection as the mechanism of evolution

13.3 Scientists can observe natural selection in action

13.4 The study of fossils provides strong evidence for evolution

13.5 A mass of other evidence reinforces the evolutionary view of life

13.6 Homologies indicate patterns of descent that can be shown on an evolutionary tree

The Evolution of Populations

13.7 Populations are the units of evolution

13.8 Mutation and sexual reproduction produce genetic variation, making evolution possible

13.9 The Hardy-Weinberg equation can be used to test whether a population is evolving

13.10 The Hardy-Weinberg equation is useful in public health science

Mechanisms of Microevolution

13.11 Natural selection, genetic drift, and gene flow can alter allele frequencies in a population

13.12 Natural selection is the only mechanism that consistently leads to adaptive evolution

13.13 Natural selection can alter variation in a population in three ways

13.14 Sexual selection may lead to phenotypic differences between males and females

13.15 The evolution of antibiotic resistance in bacteria is a serious public health concern

13.16 Diploidy and balancing selection preserve genetic variation

13.17 Natural selection cannot fashion perfect organisms

Clown, Fool, or Simply Well Adapted?

Is the blue-footed booby really as awkward or foolish as its name implies? With its bright blue feet and trusting demeanor, boobies were certainly noticed by early travelers to the Galápagos Islands, a chain of relatively young volcanic islands located about 900 km off the Pacific coast of South America. Spanish sailors may have called them "clown" (bobo in Spanish). British seamen may have called them "booby" (slang for "stupid"), as the birds were so approachable that they were easily killed. Either way, their comical feet are hard to miss.

Charles Darwin, whose observations in the Galápagos contributed greatly to his theory of evolution, no doubt encountered this friendly bird. And like the other species he observed, boobies have physical features that suit them to their environment. For example, their large, webbed feet make great flippers, propelling the birds through the water at high speeds. In the clear Galápagos waters, boobies gracefully "fly" beneath the surface. Their feet are thus a huge advantage when hunting fish. On land, however, those same feet are awkward, making for klutzy walking and for an even clumsier flight takeoff; their wings often touch the ground before they become airborne.

Boobies have other traits that serve them well in their seafaring life. The booby's body and bill are streamlined, like a torpedo, minimizing friction when it dives from heights of up to 24 meters into the shallow water below. To pull themselves out of this high-speed dive once they hit the water, boobies use their large tail. Specialized glands help boobies manage salt intake. A gland in the bird's eye socket accumulates excess salt from body fluids. This salty liquid then trickles into the nasal cavity. The bird expels this liquid by shaking its head from side to side, a characteristic clown-like movement.

The booby's big webbed feet, streamlined shape, large tail, and specialized salt-excreting glands are all good examples of evolutionary **adaptations,** inherited traits that enhance an organism's ability to survive and reproduce in a particular environment. As useful as adaptations may be, however, they often represent a trade-off between different needs. The booby's webbed feet are a case in point: extremely functional in water, but clumsy on dry land. But because boobies spend a great deal of time in the water, and especially because they find most of their food there, this adaptation represents a net advantage.

In this chapter, we examine how such adaptations evolve. We thus begin our study of **evolution,** the core theme of biology. We explore Darwin's theory of evolution—that Earth's many species are descendants of ancestral organisms that were different from those living today. In Chapter 14 we trace Darwin's ideas on the origin of new species. And in Chapter 15 we present the milestones in the long history of life on Earth and consider the mechanisms involved in such large evolutionary changes. It is these changes in species over time that have transformed life on Earth from its earliest forms to the vast diversity that we see today. Let's begin this grand journey with Darwin's sea voyage. ■ ■ ■

13.1 A sea voyage helped Darwin frame his theory of evolution

If you visit the Galápagos Islands today, you will see many of the same sights that fascinated Darwin over a century ago: blue-footed boobies waddling around; lumbering, long-necked giant tortoises (whose Spanish name is *galápagos*) (Figure 13.1A); and iguanas basking on dark lava rocks (Figure 13.1B). The marine iguanas feed on algae in the ocean. Their partially webbed feet and flattened tail suit their aquatic life. You might also observe some of the finches Darwin collected—closely related small birds that represent more than a dozen different species. (For now, we can define *species* as a group of organisms with similar anatomical features.) The most striking differences among these birds are the shapes of their beaks, which are adapted for crushing seeds, feeding on cactus flowers, or snagging insects. Some finches find their meals on tortoises, who raise themselves up on their legs and stretch out their necks to allow the birds to hop aboard and rid them of ticks and other parasites.

One of Darwin's lasting contributions is the scientific explanation for the striking ways in which organisms, such as these diverse inhabitants of the Galápagos Islands, are suited for life in their environment. Let's trace the path Darwin took to his theory of evolution.

Darwin's Cultural and Scientific Context Some early Greek philosophers suggested that life might change gradually over time. But the Greek philosopher Aristotle, whose views had an enormous impact on Western culture, generally viewed species as perfect and permanent. Judeo-Christian culture fortified this idea with a literal interpretation of the Book of Genesis, which holds that species were individually designed by a divine creator. The two ideas dominating the intellectual and cultural climate of the Western world for centuries were that Earth was only about 6,000 years old and that all living species were static in their form.

In the century prior to Darwin, only a few scientists questioned the belief that species are fixed, unchanging, and perfect.

In the mid-1700s, the study of **fossils** (the imprints or remains of organisms that lived in the past) revealed a succession of fossil forms in layers of sedimentary rock that differed from current life forms. In the early 1800s, French naturalist Jean Baptiste Lamarck suggested that the best explanation for the relationship of fossils to current organisms is that life evolves. Today, we remember Lamarck mainly for his erroneous view of *how* species evolve. He proposed that by using or not using its body parts, an individual may change its traits and then pass those changes on to its offspring. Lamarck's idea is known as the inheritance of acquired characteristics. He suggested, for instance, that the ancestors of the giraffe had lengthened their necks by stretching higher and higher into the trees to reach leaves. Our understanding of genetics refutes Lamarck's acquired characteristic mechanism. But the important fact remains that by strongly advocating evolution and by proposing that species evolve as a result of interactions with their environment, Lamarck helped set the stage for Darwin.

Darwin's Sea Voyage Charles Darwin was born in 1809. Even as a boy, Darwin had a consuming interest in nature. When not reading nature books, he was fishing, hunting, and collecting insects. His father, an eminent physician, could see no future for his son as a naturalist and sent him to medical school. But Darwin found medicine boring and surgery before the days of anesthesia horrifying. He enrolled at Cambridge University, intending to become a clergyman. At that time, many scholars of science belonged to the clergy.

Soon after graduation, Darwin's botany professor and mentor recommended him to the captain of the HMS *Beagle,* who was preparing a voyage to chart poorly known stretches of the South American coast. In December 1831, at the age of 22, Darwin began the round-the-world voyage (Figure 13.1C) that profoundly influenced his thinking and eventually the thinking of the world.

Figure 13.1A A giant tortoise, one of the unique inhabitants of the Galápagos Islands

Figure 13.1B A marine iguana basking on lava rocks

Figure 13.1C The voyage of the *Beagle* (1831–1836). The insets show a young Charles Darwin and his ship.

While the ship's crew surveyed the coast, Darwin spent most of his time onshore, collecting thousands of plants and animals, as well as fossils. He noted the unique adaptations of these organisms in places as different as the Brazilian jungle, the grasslands of Argentina, and the desolate and frigid lands at the southern tip of South America. Darwin asked himself why fossils found on the South American continent were more similar to present-day South American species than to fossils found on other continents. During his visit to the Galápagos Islands, Darwin observed that these islands had many unique organisms, most of which were similar to, but different from, the plants and animals of the nearest mainland. Even the individual islands had species different from those on other islands.

While on the voyage, Darwin was strongly influenced by Charles Lyell's newly published *Principles of Geology*. Having read Lyell's book and witnessed an earthquake that raised part of the coastline of Chile almost a meter, Darwin realized that natural forces gradually changed Earth's surface and that these forces are still operating in modern times. Thus, the growth of mountains as a result of earthquakes could account for the presence of the marine snail fossils that he had collected on mountaintops in the Andes.

By the time Darwin returned to Great Britain five years after the Beagle first set sail, his experiences and reading had led him to seriously doubt that Earth and all its living organisms had been specially created only a few thousand years earlier. Darwin had come to realize that Earth was very old and constantly changing. Once in Great Britain, Darwin began to analyze his collections and to discuss them with colleagues. He continued to read, correspond with other scientists, and to maintain extensive journals of his observations, studies, and thoughts.

Darwin's Writings By the early 1840s, Darwin had composed a long essay describing the major features of his theory of evolution. He realized that his ideas would cause a social furor, however, and he delayed publishing his essay. Even as he procrastinated, Darwin continued to compile evidence in support of his hypothesis. In the mid-1850s, Alfred Wallace, a British naturalist doing fieldwork in Indonesia, conceived a theory almost identical to Darwin's. Wallace asked Darwin to evaluate the manuscript he had written about his theory to see if it merited publication. In 1858, two of Darwin's colleagues presented Wallace's paper and excerpts of Darwin's earlier essay together to the scientific community. With the publication in 1859 of his book, *On the Origin of Species by Means of Natural Selection*, Darwin presented the world with a strong, logical explanation for evolution.

Darwin presented evidence that present-day species arose from a succession of ancestors. He called this evolutionary history of life "descent with modification." As the descendants of a remote ancestor spread into various habitats over millions and millions of years, they accumulated diverse modifications, or adaptations, that fit them to specific ways of life. Darwin's proposed mechanism for this descent with modification is natural selection, the topic of our next module.

Web Activity *Darwin and the Galápagos Islands*

Web Activity *The Voyage of the* **Beagle**: *Darwin's Trip Around the World*

? What was Darwin's phrase for evolution? What does it mean?

■ Descent with modification. An ancestral species could diversify into many descendant species by the accumulation of adaptations to various environments.

Darwin proposed natural selection as the mechanism of evolution

Darwin devoted much of *On the Origin of Species* to how organisms become adapted to their environment. First, he discussed familiar examples of domesticated plants and animals. Humans have modified other species by selecting and breeding individuals that possess desired traits—a process called **artificial selection.** We see evidence of artificial selection in the varied vegetables illustrated in Figure 13.2, all varieties of a single species of wild mustard. Crop plants and animals bred as livestock or pets often bear little resemblance to their wild ancestors.

Darwin then explained how a similar selection process could occur in nature, a process he called **natural selection.** He described two observations from which he drew two inferences:

OBSERVATION #1: Members of a population often vary in their traits, and most traits are inherited from parent to offspring.

OBSERVATION #2: All species are capable of producing more offspring than the environment can support.

INFERENCE #1: Individuals whose inherited traits give them a higher probability of surviving and reproducing in a given environment tend to leave more offspring than other individuals.

INFERENCE #2: This unequal production of offspring will cause favorable traits to accumulate in a population over generations.

Darwin recognized the connection between the capacity of organisms to produce excessive numbers of offspring and the process of natural selection. He had read an essay on human population written in 1798 by economist Thomas Malthus. Malthus contended that much of human suffering—disease, famine, and war—was the inescapable consequence of human populations increasing faster than food supplies and other resources. Darwin deduced that the production of more individuals than the limited resources can support leads to a struggle for existence, with only some offspring surviving in each generation. Of the many eggs laid, young born, and seeds spread, only a tiny fraction complete development and leave offspring. The rest are eaten, starved, diseased, unmated, or unable to reproduce for other reasons. The essence of natural selection is this unequal reproduction. Individuals whose traits enable them to better obtain food or escape predators or tolerate physical conditions will survive and reproduce more successfully than individuals without those traits.

Darwin reasoned that if artificial selection brings about so much change in a relatively short period of time, then natural selection could modify species considerably over hundreds or thousands of generations. Over vast spans of time, many traits that adapt a population to its environment will accumulate. If the environment changes, however, or if individuals move to a new environment, natural selection will select for adaptations to these new conditions. Major environmental changes, however, often lead to **extinction,** a frequent event in Earth's history resulting in the irrevocable loss of a species.

It is important to emphasize three key but subtle points about evolution by natural selection. The first point is that although natural selection occurs through interactions between individual organisms and their environment, individuals do not evolve. Evolution refers to generation-to-generation changes in populations.

A second key point is that natural selection can amplify or diminish only heritable traits. Certainly an organism may become modified through its own interactions with the environment during its lifetime, and those acquired characteristics may help the organism survive there. But unless coded for in the genes of an organism's gametes, such acquired characteristics cannot be passed on to offspring.

Third, evolution is not goal directed; it does not lead to perfectly adapted organisms. Natural selection is the result of environmental factors that vary from place to place and from time to time. A trait that is favorable in one situation may be useless—or even detrimental—in different circumstances. And adaptations are often compromises: A blue-footed booby's feet may be clumsy on land but efficient in water.

🎧 **MP3 Tutor** *Natural Selection*

Web Process of Science *How Do Environmental Changes Affect a Population?*

? Compare artificial selection and natural selection.

In artificial selection, humans choose the desirable traits and breed only organisms with those traits. In natural selection, the environment does the choosing; individuals with traits best suited to the environment survive and reproduce most successfully, passing those adaptive traits to offspring.

Cabbage — Terminal bud

Brussels sprouts — Lateral buds

Cauliflower — Flower clusters

Kale — Leaves

Broccoli — Flowers and stems

Kohlrabi — Stem

Wild mustard

Figure 13.2 Artificial selection: different vegetables produced by selecting variations in different parts of the plant

Scientists can observe natural selection in action

The blue-footed boobies described in the chapter introduction exhibit traits that are evolutionary adaptations to their ocean-based life. The exquisite camouflage adaptations shown in Figure 13.3A by insects that evolved in different environments are also examples of the results of natural selection. But do we have examples of natural selection in action?

Indeed, biologists have documented evolutionary change in thousands of scientific studies. A classic example involves Peter and Rosemary Grant's work with finches in the Galápagos Islands over a period of 20 years (see Module 14.9). As part of their research, they measured changes in beak size in a population of a ground finch species. These birds eat mostly small seeds. In dry years, when all seeds are in short supply, birds must eat more large seeds. Birds with larger, stronger beaks have a feeding advantage and greater reproductive success, and the average beak depth for the population increases. During wet years, smaller beaks are more efficient for eating the now abundant small seeds, and the average beak depth decreases.

An unsettling example of natural selection in action is the evolution of pesticide resistance in hundreds of insect species. Pesticides are poisons used to kill insect pests in farmlands, swamps, backyards, and homes. Whenever a new type of pesticide is used to control agricultural pests, the story is similar (Figure 13.3B): A relatively small amount of poison dusted onto a crop may kill 99% of the insects, but subsequent sprayings are less and less effective. The few survivors of the first

pesticide wave are insects that are genetically resistant, carrying an allele (alternative form of a gene, colored red in the figure) that somehow enables them to resist the chemical attack. So the poison kills most members of the population, leaving the resistant individuals to reproduce and pass the alleles for pesticide resistance to their offspring. The proportion of pesticide-resistant individuals increases in each generation. Like the finches, the insect population has adapted to environmental change through natural selection.

These two examples of evolutionary adaptation highlight three key points about natural selection. First, natural selection is more of an editing process than a creative mechanism. A pesticide does not create alleles that allow insects to resist it. Rather the presence of the pesticide leads to natural selection for insects already in the population who have those alleles. Second, natural selection is contingent on time and place: It favors those characteristics in a varying population that fit the current, local environment. For instance, mutations that endow houseflies with resistance to the pesticide DDT also reduce their growth rate. Before DDT was introduced, such mutations were a handicap to the flies that had them. But once DDT was part of the environment, the mutant alleles were advantageous, and natural selection increased their frequency in fly populations. Finally, these examples show that significant evolutionary change can occur in a short time.

> **?** In what sense is natural selection more of an editing process than a creative process?

■ Natural selection cannot create beneficial traits on demand, but "edits" variation in a population by selecting for those traits that work best in the current environment.

A flower mantid in Malaysia

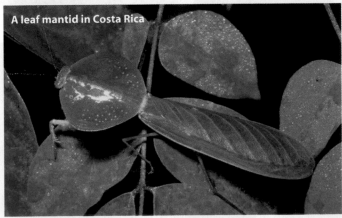

A leaf mantid in Costa Rica

Figure 13.3A Camouflage as an example of evolutionary adaptation. Look carefully for the mantids in these pictures.

Pesticide application

Chromosome with allele conferring resistance to pesticide

Survivors

Additional applications of the same pesticide will be less effective, and the frequency of resistant insects in the population will grow

Figure 13.3B Evolution of pesticide resistance in an insect population

13.5 A mass of other evidence reinforces the evolutionary view of life

Darwin's careful documentation convinced many of the scientists of his day that organisms do indeed evolve. Let's continue to explore Darwin's evidence as well as some new types of data that provide overwhelming support for evolution.

Biogeography It was the geographic distribution of species, known as **biogeography,** that first suggested to Darwin that organisms evolve from ancestral species. Darwin noted that Galápagos animals resembled species of the South American mainland more than they resembled animals on islands that were similar but much more distant. The logical explanation was that the Galápagos species evolved from animals that migrated from South America. These immigrants eventually gave rise to new species as they became adapted to their new environments. There are many other examples from biogeography that make sense only in the historical context of evolution. The unique collection of marsupials (pouched mammals) in Australia, such as kangaroos and koalas, evolved in isolation after geologic activities separated that island continent from the landmasses on which placental mammals diversified.

Comparative Anatomy Also providing support for evolution and cited extensively by Darwin is comparative anatomy. Anatomical similarities between many species give signs of common descent. Similarity in characteristics that results from common ancestry is known as **homology.** As Figure 13.5A shows, the same skeletal elements make up the forelimbs of humans, cats, whales, and bats. The functions of these forelimbs differ. A whale's flipper does not do the same job as a bat's wing, so if these structures had been uniquely engineered, we would expect that their basic designs would be very different. The logical explanation is, in fact, that the arms, forelegs, flippers, and wings of these different mammals are variations on the anatomical structures of an ancestral organism, structures that over millions of years have become adapted to different functions.

Biologists call such anatomical similarities in different organisms **homologous structures**—features that often have different functions but are structurally similar because of common ancestry.

Comparative anatomy illustrates that evolution is a remodeling process in which ancestral structures that originally functioned in one capacity become modified as they take on new functions—the kind of process that Darwin called descent with modification.

Comparing early stages of development in different animal species reveals additional homologies not visible in adult organisms. For example, at some point in their development, all vertebrate embryos have a tail posterior to the anus, as well as structures called pharyngeal (throat) pouches. These homologous pharyngeal pouches ultimately develop into structures with very different functions, such as gills in fishes and parts of the ears and throat in humans. Note the pharyngeal pouches and tails of the bird embryo (left) and the human embryo (right) in Figure 13.5B, on facing page.

Some of the most interesting homologous structures are **vestigial organs,** structures that are of marginal or perhaps no importance to the organism. Vestigial organs are remnants of structures that served important functions in the organism's ancestors. The small hind-leg and foot bones of modern whales discussed in Module 13.4 are examples of vestigial organs.

Molecular Biology Anatomical homology is not helpful in linking very distantly related organisms such as plants and animals and microorganisms. But in recent decades, advances in molecular biology have enabled biologists to read a molecular history of evolution in the DNA sequences of organisms. As we saw in Chapter 10, the hereditary background of an organism is documented in its DNA and in the proteins encoded there. Siblings have greater similarity in their DNA and proteins than do unrelated individuals of the same species. And if two species have homologous genes with sequences that match closely, biologists conclude that these sequences must have been inherited from a relatively recent common ancestor. In contrast, the greater the number of sequence differences between species, the more distant is their last common ancestor. Molecular comparisons between diverse organisms have allowed biologists to develop hypotheses about the evolutionary divergence of major branches on the tree of life.

Darwin's boldest hypothesis is that all life-forms are related. Molecular biology provides strong evidence for this claim: All forms of life use the same genetic language of DNA and

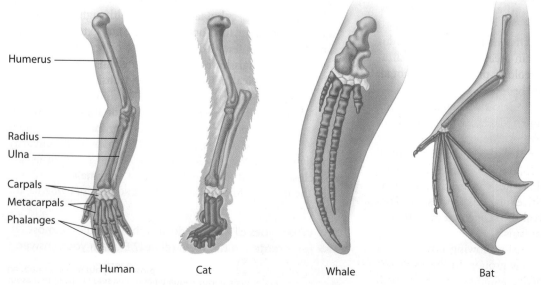

Humerus

Radius

Ulna

Carpals

Metacarpals

Phalanges

Human   Cat   Whale   Bat

Figure 13.5A   Homologous structures: vertebrate forelimbs

RNA, and the genetic code (how RNA triplets are translated into amino acids) is essentially universal. Thus it is likely that all species descended from one or a few common ancestors that used this code. But molecular homologies go beyond a shared code. For example, organisms as dissimilar as humans and bacteria share genes that have been inherited from a very distant common ancestor. Once again, homologies help identify common ancestry.

Web Activity *Reconstructing Forelimbs*

? What is homology? How does the concept of homology relate to molecular biology?

■ Homology is similarity in different species due to evolution from a common ancestor. Similarities in genes or other DNA sequences or proteins reflect the evolutionary relationship that is the basis of homology.

Chick embryo   Human embryo

Figure 13.5B Homologous structures in vertebrate embryos

13.6 Homologies indicate patterns of descent that can be shown on an evolutionary tree

Darwin was the first to view the history of life as a tree, with multiple branchings from a common ancestral trunk to the descendant species at the tips of the twigs. Biologists represent these patterns of descent with an **evolutionary tree**, although today they usually turn the trees sideways as in Figure 13.6.

Homologous structures, both anatomical and molecular, can be used to determine the branching sequence of such a tree. Some homologous characteristics, such as the genetic code, are shared by all species because they date to the deep ancestral past. In contrast, characteristics that evolved more recently are shared only within smaller groups of organisms. For example, all tetrapods (from the Greek *tetra,* four, and *pod,* foot) possess the same basic limb bone structure illustrated in Figure 13.5A, but their ancestors do not.

Figure 13.6 is an evolutionary tree of tetrapods (amphibians, mammals, and reptiles, including birds) and their closest living relatives, the lungfishes. In this diagram, each branch point represents the common ancestor of all species that descended from it. For example, lungfishes and all tetrapods descended from ancestor ❶. Three homologies are shown by the purple hatch marks on the tree—tetrapod limbs, the amnion (a protective embryonic membrane), and feathers. Tetrapod limbs were present in common ancestor ❷ and hence are found in all of its descendants (the tetrapods). The amnion was present only in ancestor ❸ and thus is shared only by mammals and reptiles. Feathers were present only in ancestor ❻, and hence are found only in birds.

Evolutionary trees are hypotheses reflecting our current understanding of patterns of evolutionary descent. Some trees are more speculative because less data may be available. Others, are based on strong combinations of fossil, anatomical, and DNA sequence data.

? Refer to the evolutionary tree in Figure 13.6. Are crocodiles more closely related to lizards or birds?

■ Look for the most recent common ancestor of these groups. Crocodiles are more closely related to birds because they share a more recent common ancestor with birds (ancestor ❺) than with lizards (ancestor ❹).

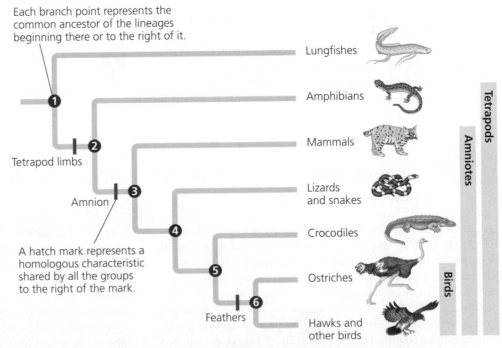

Each branch point represents the common ancestor of the lineages beginning there or to the right of it.

Tetrapod limbs

Amnion

A hatch mark represents a homologous characteristic shared by all the groups to the right of the mark.

Feathers

Lungfishes
Amphibians
Mammals
Lizards and snakes
Crocodiles
Ostriches
Hawks and other birds

Tetrapods
Amniotes
Birds

Figure 13.6 Evolutionary tree for tetrapods and their closest living relatives, the lungfishes. The purple hatch marks indicate the origin of three important homologies.

13.7 Populations are the units of evolution

One common misconception about evolution is that individual organisms evolve during their lifetimes. It is true that natural selection acts on individuals: Each organism's combination of traits affects its survival and reproductive success. But the evolutionary impact of natural selection is only apparent in the changes in a population of organisms over time.

A **population** is a group of individuals of the same species living in the same place at the same time. We can measure evolution as a change in the prevalence of certain heritable traits in a population over a span of generations. The increasing proportion of resistant insects in areas sprayed with pesticide is one example (see Module 13.3). Natural selection favored insects with alleles for pesticide resistance; these insects left more offspring, and the population changed, or evolved.

Let's examine some key features of populations. Different populations of the same species may be isolated from one another, with little interbreeding and thus little exchange of genes between them. Such isolation is common for populations confined to widely separated islands or in different lakes. However, populations are not usually so isolated, and they rarely have sharp boundaries. Figure 13.7 is a nighttime satellite photograph showing the lights of population centers in North America. We know that these populations are not really isolated; people move around, and there are suburban and rural communities between cities. Nevertheless, people are most likely to choose mates locally. As a result, for humans and other species, individuals in one population are generally more closely related to one another than to members of other populations.

In studying evolution at the population level, biologists focus on what is called the **gene pool,** the total collection of genes in a population at any one time. The gene pool consists of all alleles in all the individuals making up a population. For many genes, there are two or more alleles in the gene pool. For example, in an insect population, there may be two alleles relating to pesticide

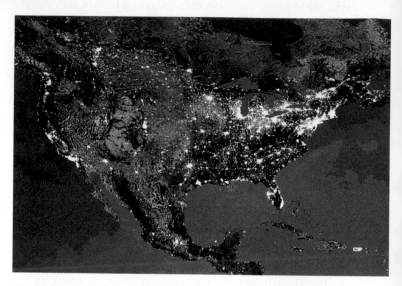

Figure 13.7 Human population centers in North America

breakdown, one that codes for an enzyme that breaks down a certain pesticide and one for a version of the enzyme that does not. In fields sprayed with pesticide, the allele for the enzyme conferring resistance will increase in frequency and the other allele will decrease in frequency. When the relative frequencies of alleles in a population change like this over a number of generations, evolution is occurring on its smallest scale. Such a change in a gene pool is often called **microevolution.**

Next let's look at the genetic variation that makes microevolution possible.

? Why can't an individual evolve?

■ Evolution is only apparent as the changes in the genetic makeup of a population over time. An individual's genes don't change during its lifetime.

13.8 Mutation and sexual reproduction produce genetic variation, making evolution possible

In *The Origin of Species,* Darwin provided evidence that life on Earth has evolved over time, and he proposed that natural selection, in favoring some heritable traits over others, was the primary mechanism for that change. But, he could not explain the cause of variation among the individuals making up a population, nor could he account for how those variations passed from parents to offspring. By breeding peas in his abbey garden, Mendel discovered the very hereditary processes required for natural selection (see Chapter 9). Although Darwin and Mendel were contemporaries, the significance of Mendel's work was not recognized during his or Darwin's lifetime.

Genetic Variation We have no trouble recognizing our friends in a crowd. Each person has a unique genome, reflected in individual variations in appearance and other traits. Indeed, individual variation occurs in all species. In addition to anatomical differences, most populations have a great deal of variation that can be observed at the molecular level.

Of course, not all variation in a population is heritable. The phenotype results from a combination of the genotype, which is inherited, and many environmental influences. For instance, a strength-training program can build up your muscle mass, though you would not pass this environmentally produced physique on to your offspring. Only the genetic component of variation is relevant to natural selection.

Many of the variable traits of the individuals in a population result from the combined effect of several genes. As we saw in Module 9.14, polygenic inheritance produces traits that vary more or less continuously—in human height, for instance, from very short individuals to very tall ones. By contrast, other features, such as human ABO blood groups (see Module 9.12), are determined by a single gene locus, with different alleles producing distinct phenotypes. But where do these alleles come from?

Mutation   New alleles originate by **mutation,** a change in the nucleotide sequence of DNA. Thus, mutation is the ultimate source of the genetic variation that serves as raw material for evolution. In multicellular organisms, however, most mutations occur in body cells and are lost when the individual dies. Only mutations in cells that produce gametes can be passed to offspring and affect a population's genetic variability.

A mutation that substitutes one nucleotide for another will be harmless if it does not affect the function of the protein the DNA encodes. However, if it does affect the protein's function, the mutation will probably be harmful. An organism is a refined product of thousands of generations of past selection, and a random change in its DNA is not likely to improve its genome any more than randomly changing some words on a page is likely to improve a story.

On rare occasions, however, a mutant allele may actually improve the adaptation of an individual to its environment and enhance its reproductive success. This kind of effect is more likely when the environment is changing in such a way that mutations that were once disadvantageous are favorable under the new conditions. The evolution of DDT-resistant houseflies (see Module 13.3) illustrates this point.

Chromosomal mutations that delete, disrupt, or rearrange many gene loci at once are almost certain to be harmful (see Figures 8.24A and 8.24B). But duplication of part of a chromosome is an important source of genetic variation. If a repeated segment of a chromosome can persist over the generations, it may provide a bigger genome with extra genes that may eventually take on new functions by further mutation. For example, the remote ancestors of mammals carried a single gene for an olfactory receptor, which is involved in detecting odors. This gene has been duplicated repeatedly. As a result, mice have about 1,300 different olfactory receptor genes, and humans have about 1,000. It is likely that such dramatic increases in the number of olfactory receptor genes helped early mammals by enabling them to distinguish among many different smells.

In prokaryotes, mutations can quickly generate genetic variation. Bacteria multiply so rapidly that a beneficial mutation can increase its frequency in descendant populations in a matter of hours or days. Because bacteria are haploid, with a single gene for each inherited character, a new allele can have an effect immediately.

Mutation rates in animals and plants average about one in every 100,000 genes per generation. For these organisms, low mutation rates, long time spans between generations, and diploid genomes prevent most mutations from significantly affecting genetic variation from one generation to the next.

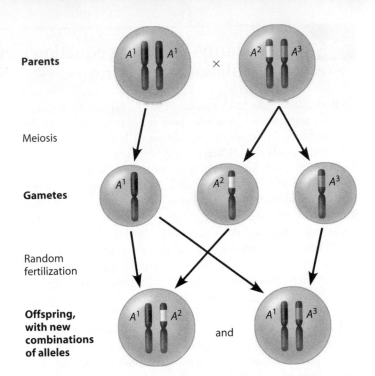

Figure 13.8   New allele combinations from sexual reproduction

Sexual Reproduction   In organisms that reproduce sexually, most of the genetic variation in a population results from the unique combination of alleles that each individual inherits. (Of course, the origin of that allele variation is past mutation.)

As we saw in Modules 8.16 and 8.18, fresh assortments of existing alleles arise every generation from three random components of sexual reproduction: independent orientation of homologous chromosomes at metaphase I of meiosis, random fertilization, and crossing over. During prophase I of meiosis, pairs of homologous chromosomes, one set inherited from each parent, trade some of their genes by crossing over, and then each pair separates into gametes independently of other chromosome pairs. Gametes from one individual vary extensively in their genetic makeup, and each zygote made by a mating pair has a unique assortment of alleles resulting from the random union of sperm and egg.

Figure 13.8 shows a simple example of the production of new allele combinations in sexual reproduction. We see the results of a mating of parents with the genotypes A^1A^1 and A^2A^3, where A^1, A^2, and A^3 are different alleles for a gene. Even without considering crossing over or the independent assortment of chromosomes, the offspring (A^1A^2 and A^1A^3) have different combinations of alleles than were present in their parents.

Genetic variation is necessary for a population to evolve, but variation alone does not guarantee that microevolution will occur. In the next module, we'll explore how to test whether evolution is occurring in a population.

Web Activity *Genetic Variation from Sexual Recombination*

? What is the ultimate source of genetic variation? What is the source of most genetic variation in a population that reproduces sexually?

■ Mutation. Unique combinations of alleles resulting from sexual reproduction

13.9 The Hardy-Weinberg equation can be used to test whether a population is evolving

To understand how microevolution works, let us first examine a simple population whose gene pool is not changing. Consider an imaginary, nonevolving population of blue-footed boobies with individuals that differ in foot webbing (Figure 13.9A). Let's assume that foot webbing is controlled by a single gene and that the allele for nonwebbed feet (*W*) is completely dominant to the allele for webbed feet (*w*). The term *dominant* (see Module 9.3) may seem to suggest that over many generations of sexual reproduction, the *W* allele will somehow come to "dominate," becoming more and more common at the expense of the recessive *w* allele. In fact, this is not what happens. The shuffling of alleles that accompanies sexual reproduction does not alter the genetic makeup of the population. In other words, sexual reproduction alone does not lead to evolution. No matter how many times alleles are segregated into different gametes by meiosis and united in different combinations by fertilization, the frequency of each allele in the gene pool will remain constant unless other factors are operating. This principle is known as **Hardy-Weinberg equilibrium,** named for the two scientists who derived it independently in 1908.

To test Hardy-Weinberg equilibrium, let's look at two generations of our booby population. Figure 13.9B shows the gene pool of the original population. We have a total of 500 boobies; of these, 320 birds have the genotype *WW* (nonwebbed feet), 160 have the heterozygous genotype, *Ww* (also nonwebbed feet, since *W* is dominant), and 20 have the genotype *ww* (webbed feet). The proportions of the three possible genotypes (the genotype frequencies) are shown in the middle of Figure 13.9B: 0.64 for *WW* $(\frac{320}{500})$, 0.32 for *Ww* $(\frac{160}{500})$, and 0.04 for *ww* $(\frac{20}{500})$.

From genotype frequencies, we can calculate the frequency of each allele in the population. Each booby carries two alleles for foot type, so this population of 500 has 1,000 alleles for foot type. To find the number of *W* alleles, we add the number carried by the *WW* boobies, $2 \times 320 = 640$, to the number carried by the *Ww* boobies, 160. The total number of *W* alleles is thus 800. The frequency of the *W* allele, which we will call *p*, is $\frac{800}{1,000}$, or 0.8. We can calculate the frequency of the *w* allele in a similar way; this frequency, called *q*, is 0.2. (The letters *p* and *q*

are often used to represent allele frequencies. Note that $p + q = 1$. The combined frequencies of all alleles must be 100% of the alleles for that gene in the population. If there are only two alleles and we know the frequency of one, we can calculate the frequency of the other.)

What happens when the boobies of this parent population form gametes? At the end of meiosis, each gamete has one allele for foot type, either *W* or *w*. The frequency of the two alleles in the gametes will be the same as it is in the gene pool of the parental population, 0.8 for *W* and 0.2 for *w*.

Figure 13.9C shows a Punnett square that uses these gamete allele frequencies and the rule of multiplication (see Module 9.7) to calculate the frequencies of the three possible genotypes in the next generation. The probability of producing a *WW* individual (by combining two *W* alleles from the pool of gametes) is $p \times p = p^2$, or $0.8 \times 0.8 = 0.64$. Thus, the frequency of *WW* boobies in the next generation would be 0.64. Likewise, the frequency of *ww* individuals would be $q^2 = 0.04$. For heterozygous individuals, *Ww*, the genotype can form in two ways, depending on whether the sperm or egg supplies the dominant allele. In other words, the frequency of *Ww* would be $2pq = 2 \times 0.8 \times 0.2 = 0.32$. Notice that the three possible genotypes have the same frequency in the next generation as they did in the parent generation.

Finally, what about the frequencies of the alleles in this next generation? Since the genotype frequencies are the same as in the parent population, the allele frequencies *p* and *q* are also the same. In fact, we could follow the frequencies through many generations, and the results would continue to be the same. Thus, the gene pool of this population is in a state of equilibrium—Hardy-Weinberg equilibrium.

Now let's write a general formula for calculating the frequencies of genotypes in a gene pool from the frequencies of alleles. In our imaginary blue-footed booby population, the frequency of the *W* allele (*p*) is 0.8, and the frequency of the *w* allele (*q*) is 0.2. (Again note that $p + q = 1$.)

Figure 13.9A
Imaginary blue-footed boobies, with and without foot webbing

Webbing   No webbing

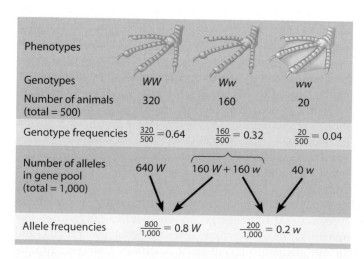

Phenotypes			
Genotypes	*WW*	*Ww*	*ww*
Number of animals (total = 500)	320	160	20
Genotype frequencies	$\frac{320}{500} = 0.64$	$\frac{160}{500} = 0.32$	$\frac{20}{500} = 0.04$
Number of alleles in gene pool (total = 1,000)	640 *W*	160 *W* + 160 *w*	40 *w*
Allele frequencies	$\frac{800}{1,000} = 0.8$ *W*		$\frac{200}{1,000} = 0.2$ *w*

Figure 13.9B Gene pool of original population of boobies

Gametes reflect allele frequencies of parental gene pool	Sperm	
	W sperm $p = 0.8$	w sperm $q = 0.2$
W egg $p = 0.8$	WW $p^2 = 0.64$	Ww $pq = 0.16$
w egg $q = 0.2$	wW $qp = 0.16$	ww $q^2 = 0.04$

Next generation:

Genotype frequencies	0.64 WW	0.32 Ww	0.04 ww
Allele frequencies		0.8 W	0.2 w

Figure 13.9C Gene pool of next generation of boobies

Notice in Figures 13.9B and 13.9C that the frequencies of all possible genotypes in the populations also add up to 1 (that is, 0.64 + 0.32 + 0.04 = 1). We can represent these relationships symbolically with the Hardy-Weinberg equation:

$$p^2 + 2pq + q^2 = 1$$

Frequency of homozygous dominants   Frequency of heterozygotes   Frequency of homozygous recessives

If a population is in Hardy-Weinberg equilibrium and its members continue to mate randomly, allele and genotype frequencies will remain constant generation after generation. Hardy-Weinberg equilibrium tells us that something other than the reshuffling processes of sexual reproduction is required to change allele frequencies in a population (result in microevolu-

tion). One way to find out what factors *can* change a gene pool is to identify the conditions that must be met if genetic equilibrium is to be maintained. For a population to be in Hardy-Weinberg equilibrium, it must satisfy five main conditions:

1. Very large population
2. No gene flow between populations
3. No mutations
4. Random mating
5. No natural selection

These five conditions are rarely met, and thus, we do not really expect a natural population to be in Hardy-Weinberg equilibrium. Let's expand on those conditions: (1) The smaller the population, the more likely it is that allele frequencies will fluctuate by chance from one generation to the next. (2) When individuals move into or out of populations, they add or remove alleles. Thus, gene flow can alter the gene pool. (3) By altering alleles or deleting or duplicating entire genes, mutations modify the gene pool. (4) If individuals mate preferentially, such as with close relatives (inbreeding), random mixing of gametes does not occur, and genotype frequencies change. Allele frequencies, however, usually stay the same. (5) The differential survival and reproductive success of individuals (natural selection) can alter allele frequencies.

The Hardy-Weinberg equation is often used to test whether evolution is occurring in a population. The equation also has many human medical applications, as we see next.

Web Process of Science How Can Frequency of Alleles Be Calculated?

? Which is least likely to alter allele and genotype frequencies in a few generations of a large, sexually reproducing population: gene flow, mutation, or natural selection?

■ Because mutations are rare, their effect on allele and genotype frequencies from one generation to the next is likely to be small.

Connection

13.10   The Hardy-Weinberg equation is useful in public health science

Public health scientists use the Hardy-Weinberg equation to estimate how many people carry alleles for certain inherited diseases. Consider the case of phenylketonuria (PKU), which is an inherited inability to break down the amino acid phenylalanine. PKU occurs in about one out of 10,000 babies born in the United States and, if untreated, results in severe mental retardation. Newborn babies are now routinely tested for PKU. For those who test positively for PKU, symptoms can be prevented or lessened if individuals follow a diet that strictly regulates the intake of phenylalanine. Packaged foods with ingredients such as aspartame, a common artificial sweetener that contains phenylalanine, must list warnings for people with PKU.

PKU is due to a recessive allele, so the frequency of individuals in the U.S. population born with PKU corresponds to the q^2 term in the Hardy-Weinberg equation. Given one PKU

occurrence per 10,000 births, $q^2 = 0.0001$. Therefore, the frequency of the recessive allele for PKU in the population, q, equals the square root of 0.0001, or 0.01. And the frequency of the dominant allele, p, equals $1 - q$, or 0.99. The frequency of carriers, heterozygous people who do not have PKU but may pass the PKU allele on to offspring, is $2pq$, which equals $2 \times 0.99 \times 0.01$, or 0.0198. Thus, the equation tells us that about 2% (actually 1.98%) of the U.S. population are carriers of the PKU allele. Estimating the frequency of a harmful allele is part of any public health program dealing with genetic diseases.

? Which term in the Hardy-Weinberg equation—p^2, $2pq$, or q^2—corresponds to the frequency of individuals who have no alleles for the disease PKU?

■ The frequency of individuals with no PKU alleles is p^2.

13.11 Natural selection, genetic drift, and gene flow can alter allele frequencies in a population

Deviations from the five conditions for Hardy-Weinberg equilibrium can cause changes in gene pools (microevolution). Although new genes and new alleles originate by mutation, these random and rare events probably change allele frequencies little from one generation of sexually reproducing organisms to the next. Nonrandom mating can affect the frequencies of homozygous and heterozygous genotypes but by itself usually does not affect allele frequencies. The three main causes of evolutionary change are natural selection, genetic drift, and gene flow.

Natural Selection   The condition for Hardy-Weinberg equilibrium that there be no natural selection—that all individuals in a population be equal in their ability to reproduce—is probably never met in nature. Populations consist of varied individuals, and some variants leave more offspring than others. In our imaginary blue-footed booby population, birds with webbed feet (genotype *ww*) might survive better and produce more offspring because they are more efficient at swimming and catching food than birds without webbed feet (genotype *Ww* or *WW*). Genetic equilibrium would be disturbed as the frequency of the *w* allele increased in the gene pool.

Genetic Drift   Flip a coin a thousand times, and a result of 700 heads and 300 tails would make you very suspicious about that coin. But flip a coin ten times, and an outcome of seven heads and three tails would seem within reason. The smaller the sample, the greater the chance of deviation from an idealized result—in the case of the flipped coin, an equal number of heads and tails. Let's apply that logic to a population's gene pool. The frequencies of alleles in a gene pool will be more stable from one generation to the next when a population is large. If a population of organisms is small, its allele frequencies may vary unpredictably from generation to generation.

Genetic drift is a change in the gene pool of a population due to chance. The smaller the population, the more impact genetic drift is likely to have. In many cases, an allele may be lost from a population by such chance fluctuations. Thus, genetic drift tends to reduce genetic variation through such losses. Two situations in which genetic drift can have a significant impact on a population are the bottleneck effect and the founder effect.

Earthquakes, floods, or fires may kill large numbers of individuals, leaving a small surviving population that is unlikely to have the same genetic makeup as the original population. Such a drastic reduction in population size and change in allele frequencies is called a **bottleneck effect,** analogous to shaking just a few marbles through a bottleneck. As illustrated in Figure 13.11A, certain alleles (purple marbles) may be present at higher frequency in the surviving population than in the original population, others (green marbles) may be present at lower frequency, and some (orange marbles) may not be present at all. After a bottleneck, genetic drift may continue for many generations until the population is again large enough for fluctuations due to chance to have less of an impact. Even if a population that has passed through a bottleneck ultimately recovers its size, it may have low levels of genetic variation—a legacy of the genetic drift that occurred when the population was small.

One reason it is important to understand the bottleneck effect is that human actions may create severe bottlenecks for other species, such as the endangered Florida panther and the African cheetah (see Figure 13.12). The greater prairie chicken (Figure 13.11B) is another example. Millions of these birds once lived on the prairies of Illinois. As these prairies were converted to farmland and other uses during the 19th and 20th centuries, the number of greater prairie chickens plummeted. By 1993, only two Illinois populations remained, with a total of fewer than 50 birds. Less than 50% of the eggs of these birds hatched. Researchers compared the DNA of the 1993 population with DNA extracted from museum specimens dating back to the 1930s. They surveyed six gene loci and found that the modern birds had lost 30% of the alleles that were present in the museum specimens. Thus, genetic drift as a result of the bottleneck reduced the genetic variation of the population and may have increased the frequency of harmful alleles, leading to the low egg-hatching rate.

Original population → Bottlenecking event → Surviving population

Figure 13.11A   The bottleneck effect

Figure 13.11B
Greater prairie chicken (*Tympanuchus cupido*). Illinois populations have reduced genetic variation as a result of a bottleneck.

Genetic drift is also likely when a few individuals colonize an isolated island or other new habitat. The smaller the group, the less likely the genetic makeup of the colonists will represent the gene pool of the larger population they left. Such differences in the gene pool of a small colony compared with the original population is called the **founder effect.**

The founder effect explains the relatively high frequency of certain inherited disorders among some human populations established by small numbers of colonists. In 1814, 15 people founded a British colony on Tristan da Cunha, a group of small islands in the middle of the Atlantic Ocean. Apparently, one of the colonists carried a recessive allele for retinitis pigmentosa, a progressive form of blindness. Of the 240 descendants who still lived on the islands in the 1960s, four had retinitis pigmentosa, and at least nine others were known to be heterozygous carriers of the allele. The frequency of this allele is ten times higher on Tristan da Cunha than in the population from which the founders came.

Gene Flow   Allele frequencies in a population can also change as a result of **gene flow,** where a population may gain or lose alleles when fertile individuals move into or out of a population or when gametes (such as plant pollen) are transferred between populations. Gene flow tends to reduce differences between populations. For example, humans today move more freely about the world than in the past, and gene flow has become an important agent of evolutionary change in previously isolated human populations.

Let's return to the Illinois greater prairie chickens and see how gene flow improved their fate. Between 1992 and 1996 researchers added a total of 271 birds from neighboring states to the Illinois populations. This strategy succeeded. New alleles entered the population, and the egg-hatching rate improved to over 90%.

Web Activity *Causes of Microevolution*

? How might gene flow between populations living in different habitats actually interfere with each population's adaptation to its local environment?

■ The introduction of alleles that may not be beneficial in a particular habitat prevents the population living there from becoming fully adapted to its local conditions.

13.12 Natural selection is the only mechanism that consistently leads to adaptive evolution

Genetic drift, gene flow, and even mutation can cause microevolution. But these are chance events, and only blind luck could result in their improving a population's fit to its environment. Evolution by natural selection, on the other hand, is a blend of chance and "sorting": chance in the random collection of genetic variation packaged in gametes and combined in offspring and sorting in that some alleles are favored over others. Because of this sorting effect, only natural selection consistently leads to adaptive evolution—evolution that results in a better fit between organisms and their environment.

The adaptations of organisms include many striking examples. Remember the adaptations of blue-footed boobies to their marine environment and the amazing camouflage of mantids shown in Figure 13.3A. Or consider the remarkable speed of the cheetah (**Figure 13.12**). The cheetah can accelerate from 0 to 40 mph in three strides and to full speed of 70 mph in seconds. Its entire body—skeleton, muscles, joints, heart, and lungs—is built for speed.

Such adaptations for speed are the result of natural selection. By consistently favoring some alleles over others, natural selection improves the match between organisms and their environment. However, an organism's environment may change over time. As a result, what constitutes a "good match" between an organism and its environment is a moving target, making adaptive evolution a continuous, dynamic process.

Let's take a closer look at natural selection. The commonly used phrases "struggle for existence" and "survival of the fittest" are misleading if we take them to mean direct competitive contests between individuals. There *are* animal species in which individuals lock horns or otherwise do combat to determine mating privilege. But reproductive success is generally more subtle and passive. In a varying population of moths, certain individuals may produce more offspring than others because their wing colors hide them from predators better. Plants in a wildflower population may differ in reproductive success because some attract more pollinators, owing to slight variations in flower color, shape, or fragrance. These examples point to a biological definition of **fitness:** the contribution an individual makes to the gene pool of the next generation relative to the contributions of other individuals. Thus, the fittest individuals in the context of evolution are those that produce the largest number of viable, fertile offspring and thus pass on the most genes to the next generation.

? Explain how the phrase "survival of the fittest" differs from the biological definition of fitness.

■ Survival alone does not guarantee reproductive success. An organism's fitness is determined by the number of fertile offspring it leaves and thus its contribution to the gene pool of the next generation.

Figure 13.12   The flexible spine of a cheetah stretches out in the middle of its 7 m (23 ft) stride.

Evolutionary fitness is related to genes, but it is an organism's phenotype—its physical traits, metabolism, and behavior—that is directly exposed to the environment. Let's see how natural selection can affect the distribution of phenotypes using an imaginary deer mouse population. The bell-shaped curve in the top graph of Figure 13.13 depicts the frequencies of individuals that could result from a polygenic inheritance pattern for variation in fur color. In this initial population, fur color varies along a continuum from very light (only a few individuals) through various intermediate shades (many individuals) to very dark (few individuals). The other graphs show three ways in which natural selection could alter the phenotypic variation in the deer mouse population. The blue downward arrows symbolize the pressure of natural selection working against certain phenotypes.

Stabilizing selection favors intermediate phenotypes. It typically occurs in relatively stable environments, where conditions tend to reduce phenotypic variation. In the mouse population depicted in the graph on the bottom left, stabilizing selection has eliminated the extremely light and dark individuals, and the population has a greater number of intermediate phenotypes, which may be best suited to a stable environment. Stabilizing selection probably prevails most of the time in most populations. For example, this type of selection keeps the majority of human birth weights in the range of 3–4 kg (6.5–9 pounds). For babies a lot smaller or larger than this size, infant mortality may be greater.

Directional selection shifts the overall makeup of the population by acting against individuals at *one* of the phenotypic extremes. For the mouse population in the bottom center graph, the trend is toward darker fur color, as might occur if the landscape consists of dark rocks, where darker fur would more readily camouflage the animal. Directional selection is most common during periods of environmental change or when members of a species migrate to some new habitat with different environmental conditions. The changes we described in populations of insects exposed to pesticides is an example of directional selection.

Disruptive selection typically occurs when environmental conditions are varied in a way that favors individuals at *both* extremes of a phenotypic range. For the mice in the graph on the bottom right, individuals with light and dark fur have increased numbers. Perhaps the mice colonized a patchy habitat where a background of light soil was studded with areas of dark rocks. Disruptive selection can lead to two or more contrasting phenotypes in a population. For example, in a population of African seedcracker finches, large-billed birds, who specialize in cracking hard seeds, and small-billed birds, who feed mainly on soft seeds, survive better than birds with intermediate-sized bills, who are fairly inefficient at cracking both types of seeds.

Next we consider a special case of selection, one that leads to phenotypic differences between males and females.

? Of the three modes of natural selection, which is most common?

■ Stabilizing selection

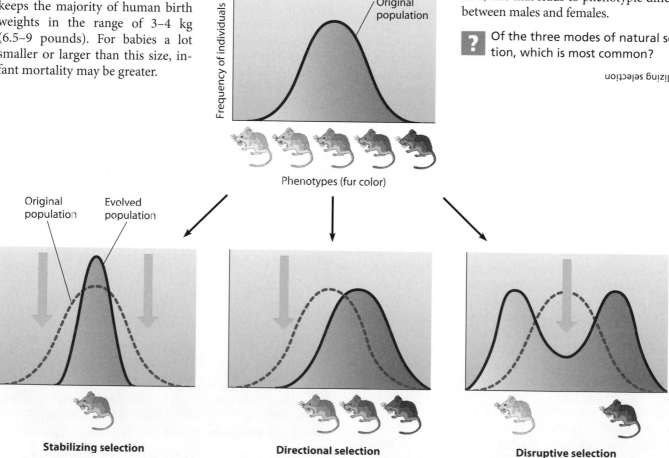

Figure 13.13 Three possible effects of natural selection on a phenotypic character

13.14 Sexual selection may lead to phenotypic differences between males and females

The males and females of an animal species obviously have different reproductive organs. But they may also have other noticeable differences, not directly associated with reproduction or survival, called secondary sexual characteristics. This distinction in appearance is called **sexual dimorphism.** It is often manifested in a size difference, but can also be evident in the form of male adornment, such as manes on lions, antlers on deer, or colorful plumage in birds (Figure 13.14A). Males are usually the showier sex, at least among vertebrates.

Darwin was the first to explore the implications of **sexual selection,** a form of natural selection in which individuals with certain characteristics are more likely than other individuals to obtain mates. Sexual selection can result in sexual dimorphism.

In some species, secondary sex structures may be used to compete with members of the same sex for mates (Figure 13.14B). This type of sexual selection is called intrasexual selection (within the same sex, most often the males). Contests may involve physical combat, but are more often ritualized displays (see Chapter 35). Intrasexual selection is common in species where the winning individual garners a harem of mates.

In a more common type of sexual selection, called intersexual selection (between sexes) or mate choice, individuals of one sex (usually females) are choosy in selecting their mates. Males with the largest or most colorful adornments are often the most attractive to females. The extraordinary feathers of a peacock's tail are an example of this sort of "choose me" statement (Figure 13.14A). What intrigued Darwin is that some of these mate-attracting features do not seem to be otherwise adaptive and may in fact pose some risks. For example, showy plumage may make male birds more visible to predators. But if such secondary sexual characteristics help a male gain a mate, then they will be reinforced over the generations for the most Darwinian of reasons—because they enhance reproductive success. Every time a female chooses a mate based on a certain appearance or behavior, she perpetuates the alleles that caused her to make that choice and allows a male with that particular phenotype to perpetuate his alleles.

What is the advantage to females of being choosy? One hypothesis is that females prefer male traits that are correlated with "good genes." In several bird species, research has shown that traits preferred by females, such as bright beaks or long tails, are related to overall male health. The "good genes" hypothesis was also tested in gray tree frogs. Female frogs prefer to mate with males that give long mating calls (Figure 13.14C). Researchers collected eggs from wild gray tree frogs. One half of each female's eggs was fertilized with sperm from long-calling males, the other with sperm from short-calling males. The offspring of long-calling male frogs grew bigger, faster, and survived better than their half-siblings fathered by short-calling males. The duration of a male's mating call was shown to be indicative of the male's overall genetic quality, supporting the hypothesis that female mate choice can be based on a trait that indicates whether the male has "good genes."

Figure 13.14A Extreme sexual dimorphism (peacock at right; peahen at left)

Figure 13.14B A contest for access to mates

Figure 13.14C A male gray tree frog calling for mates

Next, we return to the concept of directional selection with the evolution of antibiotic resistance in bacteria.

? Males with the most elaborate ornamentation may garner the most mates. How might choosing such a mate be advantageous to a female?

■ An elaborate display may signal good health and therefore good genes, which would be provided to the female's offspring.

13.15 The evolution of antibiotic resistance in bacteria is a serious public health concern

Antibiotics are drugs that kill infectious microorganisms. Many antibiotics are naturally occurring chemicals derived from soil-dwelling fungi or bacteria. For these microbes, antibiotic production is an adaptation that helps them destroy bacteria that compete with them for space and nutrients. Penicillin, originally isolated from a fungus, has been widely prescribed since the 1940s. A revolution in human health rapidly followed its introduction, rendering many previously fatal diseases easily curable (such as strep throat and surgical infections). During the 1950s, some doctors even predicted the end of human infectious disease.

Why hasn't that optimistic prediction come true? It did not take into account the force of evolution. In the same way that pesticides select for resistant insects (see Module 13.3), antibiotics select for resistant bacteria. Penicillin works by preventing the formation of bacterial cell walls. Resistant bacteria contain a gene that codes for a protein that breaks down penicillin. Many antibiotics bind to bacterial ribosomes and block protein synthesis. But existing or new mutations may alter the sites on the ribosomes where the antibiotic binds, making the bacterium and its offspring resistant to that antibiotic. Again we see the chance and sorting aspects of natural selection (see Module 13.12): the chance genetic variations in bacteria and the sorting effect of antibiotics as nonresistant bacteria are killed and resistant strains are left to flourish.

In what ways do we contribute to the problem of antibiotic resistance? Livestock producers add antibiotics to animal feed as a growth promoter and to prevent illness. These practices may select for bacteria that are resistant to standard antibiotics.

Doctors contribute to the problem by overprescribing antibiotics—for example, to patients with viral infections, which do not respond to antibiotic treatment. And patients misuse prescribed antibiotics, for example, by prematurely stopping the medication because they feel better. This allows mutant bacteria that may be killed more slowly by the drug to survive and multiply. Subsequent mutations in such bacteria may lead to full-blown antibiotic resistance.

Difficulty in treating common human infections is a serious public health concern. Penicillin, effective against many bacterial infections in the 1940s, is virtually useless today in its original form. New drugs have since been developed, but they continue to be rendered ineffective as resistant bacteria evolve. Natural selection for antibiotic resistance is particularly strong in hospitals, where antibiotic use is extensive. Nearly 100,000 people die each year in the United States from infections they contract in the hospital, often because the bacteria that cause hospital-acquired infections are resistant to antibiotics. The medical community and pharmaceutical companies are engaged in an ongoing race against the powerful force of bacterial evolution.

Web Process of Science *What Are the Patterns of Antibiotic Resistance?*

? Explain why the following statement is incorrect: "Antibiotics have created resistant bacteria."

■ The use of antibiotics has increased the frequency of alleles for resistance that were already naturally present in bacterial populations.

13.16 Diploidy and balancing selection preserve genetic variation

Natural selection acting on variations within a population adapts that population to its environment. But what prevents natural selection from eliminating the variation as it selects against unfavorable genotypes? Why aren't less adaptive alleles eliminated as the best alleles are passed to the next generation? The tendency for natural selection to reduce variation in a population is countered by mechanisms that maintain variation.

Most eukaryotes are diploid. Having two sets of chromosomes helps to prevent populations from becoming genetically uniform. The effects of recessive alleles are not often displayed in diploid organisms. A recessive allele is subject to natural selection only when it influences the phenotype, and that occurs only in individuals who are homozygous for that allele. In a heterozygote, a recessive allele is, in effect, hidden, or protected, from natural selection. The hiding of recessive alleles in the presence of dominant ones can allow a large number of recessive alleles to remain in a gene pool. Although these alleles may not be favored under present conditions, some could prove advantageous when the environment changes.

Genetic variability may also be preserved by natural selection, the very same force that generally reduces it. **Balancing selection** occurs when natural selection maintains stable frequencies of two or more phenotypic forms in a population.

In the type of balancing selection known as **heterozygote advantage,** heterozygous individuals have greater reproductive success than homozygotes, with the result that two or more alleles for a character are maintained in the population. An example of heterozygote advantage is the protection from malaria conferred by the sickle-cell allele (see Module 9.13). The frequency of the sickle-cell allele in Africa is generally highest in areas where malaria is a major cause of death. The environment in those areas favors heterozygotes, who are protected from the most severe effects of malaria. Less favored are individuals homozygous for the normal hemoglobin allele, who are susceptible to malaria, and individuals homozygous for the sickle-cell allele, who develop sickle-cell disease.

Frequency-dependent selection is a type of balancing selection that maintains two different phenotypic forms in a population. In this case, selection acts against either phenotypic form if it becomes too common in the population. An example of frequency-dependent selection is the scale-eating fish in Lake Tanganyika, Africa, which attack other fish from behind, darting in to remove a few scales from the side of its prey. As you can see in Figure 13.16, some of these fish are "left-mouthed" and others are "right-mouthed." Because their mouth twists to the left, left-mouthed fish always attack their prey's right side—to see why, twist your lower jaw and lips to the left and imagine which side of a fish you could take a bite from. Similarly, right-mouthed fish attack from the left. Prey fish guard more effectively against attack from whichever phenotype is most common in the lake. Thus, fish with the less common phenotype have a feeding advantage that enhances survival and reproductive success. As you can see on the graph, the frequency of left-mouthed fish oscillates over time, as frequency-dependent selection keeps each phenotype close to 50%.

Much of the DNA variation in populations probably has little or no impact on reproductive success. In humans, many of the nucleotide differences found in noncoding sequences of DNA (see Module 10.10) appear to confer no selective advantage or disadvantage. Such differences may be considered **neutral variation.** Even mutational changes that alter proteins can be neutral if they have little effect on protein function. Over time, the frequencies of alleles that are not affected by natural selection will vary by the chance effects of genetic drift. But even if only a fraction of the variation in a gene pool affects reproductive success, that is still an enormous resource of raw material for natural selection and the adaptive evolution it causes.

Figure 13.16 Frequency-dependent selection for left-mouthed and right-mouthed scale-eating fish

? Why would natural selection tend to reduce genetic variation more in populations of haploid organisms than in populations of diploid organisms?

■ All alleles in a haploid organism are phenotypically expressed and are hence screened by natural selection.

13.17 Natural selection cannot fashion perfect organisms

Though natural selection leads to adaptation, there are several reasons why nature abounds with organisms that seem to be less than ideally "engineered" for their lifestyles.

1. *Selection can act only on existing variations.* Natural selection favors only the fittest variations from the phenotypes that are available, which may not be the ideal traits. New, advantageous alleles do not arise on demand.

2. *Evolution is limited by historical constraints.* Each species has a legacy of descent with modification from a long line of ancestral forms. Evolution does not scrap ancestral anatomy and build each new complex structure from scratch; it co-opts existing structures and adapts them to new situations. If a terrestrial four-legged animal were to become adapted to an environment in which flight was advantageous, it might be best to grow an extra pair of limbs to serve as wings. However, evolution operates on the traits an organism already has. Thus, as birds and bats evolved from Earth-bound ancestors, their existing forelimbs took on new functions for flight.

3. *Adaptations are often compromises.* Each organism must do many different things. A blue-footed booby uses its webbed feet to swim as it dives into the ocean for prey, but these same feet make for clumsy travel on land.

4. *Chance, natural selection, and the environment interact.* Chance probably affects the genetic structure of populations to a greater extent than was once believed. For instance, when a storm blows insects hundreds of miles over an ocean to an island, the wind does not necessarily transport the specimens that are best suited to the new environment. And not all alleles fixed by genetic drift in the gene pool of a small population are better suited to the environment than alleles that are lost.

With all these constraints, we cannot expect evolution to craft perfect organisms. Natural selection operates on a "better than" basis. We can see evidence for evolution in the imperfections of the organisms it produces.

? Humans owe much of their physical versatility and athleticism to their flexible limbs and joints. But we are prone to sprains, torn ligaments, and dislocations. Why?

■ Adaptations are compromises: Structural reinforcement has been compromised as agility was selected for.

Chapter Review

Reviewing the Concepts

Darwin's Theory of Evolution (Introduction–13.6)

Adaptations are inherited characteristics that enhance an organism's ability to survive and reproduce in a particular environment. According to Darwin's theory of evolution, living species are descended from earlier life-forms that differed from present day organisms (**Introduction**).

Descent with modification is what Darwin called his theory, which explains that all of life is connected by common ancestry and that descendants have accumulated adaptations to changing environments over vast spans of time. Darwin's theory differed greatly from the long-held notion of a young Earth inhabited by unchanging species (**13.1**).

Natural selection (13.2):

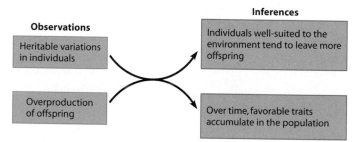

Observations
- Heritable variations in individuals
- Overproduction of offspring

Inferences
- Individuals well-suited to the environment tend to leave more offspring
- Over time, favorable traits accumulate in the population

Evidence of evolution. Natural selection has been observed in populations of birds, insects, and many other organisms (**13.3**). The fossil record reveals the historical sequence in which organisms have evolved and many fossils linking ancestral species with those living today (**13.4**). Further evidence for evolution comes from biogeography, comparative anatomy, and molecular biology. Homologous structures and DNA sequences provide evidence of evolutionary relationships (**13.5**).

Evolutionary trees are diagrams based on homologies that reflect the evolutionary relationships among groups of organisms (**13.6**).

The Evolution of Populations (13.7–13.10)

Populations evolve. Microevolution is a change in the relative frequencies of alleles in a population's gene pool (**13.7**).

Genetic variation is generated by mutation and sexual reproduction. Mutations are important in the adaptation of prokaryotes to the environment. In diploid organisms, the shuffling of alleles in sexual reproduction provides most variation (**13.8**).

The Hardy-Weinberg equilibrium states that the allele and genotype frequencies of a population will remain constant if the population is large, mating is random, and there is no mutation, gene flow, or natural selection. The Hardy-Weinberg equation calculates allele and genotype frequencies in a population (**13.9**). Public health scientists use the Hardy-Weinberg equation to estimate frequencies of disease-causing alleles (**13.10**).

Allele frequencies	$p + q = 1$
Genotype frequencies	$p^2 + 2pq + q^2 = 1$

Dominant homozygotes — Heterozygotes — Recessive homozygotes

Mechanisms of Microevolution (13.11–13.17)

Allele frequencies change due to natural selection (reproductive success of individuals best suited to the environment), genetic drift (change in a gene pool due to chance), and gene flow (movement of individuals or gametes between populations). The bottleneck effect and founder effect lead to genetic drift (**13.11**).

Fitness is the relative contribution an individual makes to the gene pool of the next generation. As a result of natural selection, favorable traits increase in a population (**13.12**).

Outcomes of natural selection (13.13):

Original population — Evolved population — Pressure of natural selection

Stabilizing selection — Directional selection — Disruptive selection

Sexual selection leads to the evolution of secondary sex characteristics, which can give individuals an advantage in mating (**13.14**).

Antibiotic resistance in bacteria illustrates directional selection resulting from excessive or incorrect use of antibiotics (**13.15**).

Preservation of variation. Diploidy preserves variation by "hiding" recessive alleles. Balancing selection may result from heterozygote advantage or frequency-dependent selection (**13.16**).

Perfect organisms? Natural selection can act only on available variation; anatomical structures result from modified ancestral forms; adaptations are often compromises; and chance, natural selection, and the environment interact (**13.17**).

Connecting the Concepts

1. Summarize the key points of Darwin's theory of descent with modification, including his proposed mechanism of evolution.

2. Complete this map describing potential causes of evolutionary change within populations.

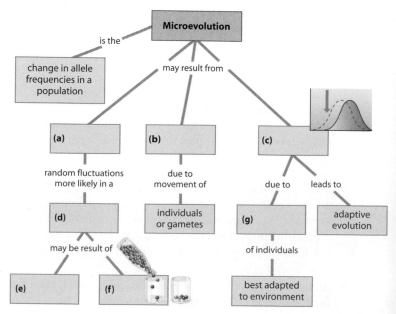

Microevolution — is the — change in allele frequencies in a population

may result from — (a) — (b) — (c)

(a) random fluctuations more likely in a — (d) — may be result of — (e) — (f)

(b) due to movement of — individuals or gametes

(c) due to — (g) — of individuals — best adapted to environment — leads to — adaptive evolution

Testing Your Knowledge

Multiple Choice

3. Which of the following did not influence Darwin as he synthesized the theory of evolution by natural selection?
   a. examples of artificial selection that produce large and relatively rapid changes in domesticated species
   b. Lyell's *Principles of Geology* on gradual geologic changes
   c. comparisons of fossils with living organisms
   d. the biogeographic distribution of organisms such as the unique species on the Galápagos Islands
   e. Mendel's paper describing the "laws of inheritance"

4. Natural selection is sometimes described as "survival of the fittest." Which of the following best measures an organism's fitness?
   a. how many fertile offspring it produces
   b. its mutation rate
   c. how strong it is when pitted against others of its species
   d. its ability to withstand environmental extremes
   e. how much food it is able to make or obtain

5. Mutations are rarely the cause of evolution in populations of plants and animals because
   a. they are often harmful and do not get passed on.
   b. they do not directly produce most of the genetic variation present in a diploid population.
   c. they occur very rarely.
   d. they are only passed on when they occur in cells that lead to gametes.
   e. of all of the above.

6. In an area of erratic rainfall, a biologist found that grass plants with alleles for curled leaves reproduced better in dry years, and plants with alleles for flat leaves reproduced better in wet years. This situation would tend to (*Explain your answer.*)
   a. cause genetic drift in the grass population.
   b. preserve genetic variation in the grass population.
   c. lead to stabilizing selection in the grass population.
   d. lead to uniformity in the grass population.
   e. cause gene flow in the grass population.

7. Which of the following pairs of structures is *least* likely to represent homology?
   a. the hemoglobin of a human and that of a baboon
   b. the mitochondria of a plant and that of an animal
   c. the wings of a bird and those of an insect
   d. the tail of a cat and that of an alligator
   e. the foreleg of a pig and the flipper of a whale

8. If an allele is recessive and lethal in homozygotes before they reproduce,
   a. the allele is present in the population at a frequency of 0.001.
   b. the allele will be removed from the population by natural selection in approximately 1,000 years.
   c. the allele will most likely remain in the population at a low frequency because it cannot be selected against in heterozygotes.
   d. the fitness of the homozygous recessive genotype is 0.
   e. both c and d are correct.

9. Darwin's claim that all life is descended from a common ancestor is best supported with evidence from
   a. the fossil record.
   b. molecular biology.
   c. evolutionary trees.
   d. comparative anatomy.
   e. comparative embryology.

10. In a population with two alleles, B and b, the allele frequency of b is 0.4. B is dominant to b. What is the frequency of individuals with the dominant phenotype if the population is in Hardy-Weinberg equilibrium?
    a. 0.16
    b. 0.36
    c. 0.48
    d. 0.84
    e. You cannot tell from this information.

11. Within a few weeks of treatment with the drug 3TC, a patient's HIV population consists entirely of 3TC-resistant viruses. How can this result best be explained?
    a. HIV can change its surface proteins and resist vaccines.
    b. The patient must have become reinfected with a resistant virus.
    c. A few drug-resistant viruses were present at the start of treatment, and natural selection increased their frequency.
    d. The drug caused the HIV genes to change.
    e. HIV began making drug-resistant versions of its enzymes in response to the drug.

Describing, Comparing, and Explaining

12. Write a paragraph briefly describing the kinds of evidence for evolution.

13. Sickle-cell disease is caused by a recessive allele. Roughly one out of every 400 African-Americans (0.25%) is afflicted with sickle-cell disease. Use the Hardy-Weinberg equation to calculate the percentage of African-Americans who are carriers of the sickle-cell allele. (*Hint:* $q^2 = 0.0025$.)

14. It seems logical that natural selection would work toward genetic uniformity; the genotypes that are most fit produce the most offspring, increasing the frequency of adaptive alleles and eliminating less adaptive alleles. Yet there remains a great deal of genetic variation within populations. Describe some of the factors that contribute to this variation.

Applying the Concepts

15. A population of snails is preyed upon by birds that break the snails open on rocks, eat the soft bodies, and leave the shells. The snails occur in both striped and unstriped forms. In one area, researchers counted both live snails and broken shells. Their data are summarized below:

	Striped	Unstriped	Total	Percent Striped
Living	264	296	560	47.1
Broken	486	377	863	56.3

Which snail form seems to be better adapted to this environment? Why? Predict how the frequencies of striped and unstriped snails might change in the future.

16. Advocates of "scientific creationism" and "intelligent design" lobby school districts for such things as a ban on teaching evolution, equal time in science classes to teach alternative versions of the origin and history of life, or disclaimers in textbooks stating that evolution is "just a theory." They argue that it is only fair to let students evaluate both evolution and the idea that all species were created by God as the Bible relates or that, because organisms are so complex and well adapted, they must have been created by an intelligent designer. Do you think that alternative views of evolution should be taught in science courses? Why or why not?

Answers to all questions can be found in Appendix 4.
For Practice Quizzes, BioFlix, MP3 Tutors, and Activities, go to www.mybiology.com.

14.1 The origin of species is the source of biological diversity

Concepts of Species

14.2 There are several ways to define a species
14.3 Reproductive barriers keep species separate

Mechanisms of Speciation

14.4 In allopatric speciation, geographic isolation leads to speciation
14.5 In sympatric speciation, speciation takes place without geographic isolation
14.6 Most plant species trace their origin to polyploid speciation
14.7 Reproductive barriers may evolve as populations diverge
14.8 Hybrid zones provide opportunities to study reproductive isolation
14.9 Peter and Rosemary Grant study the evolution of Darwin's finches
14.10 Adaptive radiation may occur when new opportunities arise
14.11 Speciation can occur rapidly or slowly

14 The Origin of Species

The Rise and Fall of Cichlids

They are so colorful and so diverse. There are algae, insect, and fish eaters, leaf biters, muck feeders, snail crushers, even scale scrapers who steal scales off the flanks of other fish. They are all colors of the rainbow, making them favorites of the aquarium trade (see above). Cichlids are found in many tropical lakes and rivers of Central America, Asia, and Africa. Until recently, there were more than 500 species of these small fish in Lake Victoria, the largest of the Great Lakes of East Africa (see map on the facing page). Where did they all come from? And why are they disappearing?

Scientists call the Lake Victoria cichlids—this physically, ecologically, and behaviorally diverse assemblage of closely related genera and species—a superflock. Their species number more than all the fish species in all the lakes and rivers of Europe combined. And if you add the more than 1,000 species in Lakes Victoria, Tanganyika, and Malawi, you have the biggest diversification of species of any animal group in one geographic region. And the species are young. Studies show that the cichlids of Lake Victoria diversified about 100,000 years ago. (As a comparative time reference, bony fish have been evolving on Earth for about 400 million years.)

How did so many cichlid species evolve so fast? There are several hypotheses. The jaw structure and teeth of cichlids vary widely, and these highly adaptable characteristics may have allowed ancestral species to specialize on different food sources, such as algae or snails or other fishes. Or perhaps the bright color patterns of cichlids may have led to species diversity as females selected mates of specific coloration. The separation of sub-populations by feeding preferences or by female mate choice could have reduced or elim-

The Evolution
of Biological
Diversity

UNIT FOUR

16 The Origin and Evolution
    of Microbial Life:
    Prokaryotes and Protists

17 Plants, Fungi, and The
    Colonization of Land

18 The Evolution of
    Invertebrate Diversity

19 The Evolution of
    Vertebrate Diversity

16

The Origin and Evolution of Microbial Life: *Prokaryotes and Protists*

Prokaryotes

16.1 Prokaryotes are diverse and widespread

16.2 Bacteria and archaea are the two main branches of prokaryotic evolution

16.3 Prokaryotes come in a variety of shapes

16.4 Various structural features contribute to the success of prokaryotes

16.5 Prokaryotes obtain nourishment in a variety of ways

16.6 Archaea thrive in extreme environments—and in other habitats

16.7 Bacteria include a diverse assemblage of prokaryotes

16.8 Some bacteria cause disease

16.9 Bacteria can be used as biological weapons

16.10 Prokaryotes help recycle chemicals and clean up the environment

Protists

16.11 Protists are an extremely diverse assortment of eukaryotes

16.12 Secondary endosymbiosis is the key to much of protist diversity

16.13 A tentative phylogeny of eukaryotes includes multiple clades of protists

16.14 Diplomonads and parabasalids have modified mitochondria

16.15 Euglenozoans have flagella with a unique internal structure

16.16 Alveolates have sacs beneath the plasma membrane

16.17 Stramenopiles have "hairy" and smooth flagella

16.18 Amoebozoans have lobe-shaped pseudopodia

16.19 Foraminiferans and radiolarians have threadlike pseudopodia

16.20 Red algae and green algae are the closest relatives of land plants

16.21 Multicellularity evolved several times in eukaryotes

How Ancient Bacteria Changed the World

Imagine visiting Earth some 3 billion years ago. It might have looked as illustrated above, a planet bristling with volcanoes spewing gases into the atmosphere and molten rock onto the surface. Life is already present—the "stepping stones" that dominate the shoreline, which are called stromatolites, have been built by thick mats of prokaryotes. (You learned about stromatolites in Module 15.1.) Greenish lawns of prokaryotes cover virtually every wet, sunlit surface on the planet. Animals that might graze the fields of prokaryotes have not yet evolved, and huge expanses of stromatolites are rising as prokaryotes multiply unchecked. Prokaryotes will continue to have the planet to themselves for perhaps another 800 million years. It's an alien world compared to the one we know now, and it's no place for an oxygen-breathing human. If we were to return half a billion years later, however, we would find a more hospitable atmosphere. By that time, photosynthetic prokaryotes had become so numerous that the gaseous oxygen (O_2) they similar process. The distinctive pattern of layers can be seen in fossils such as the one shown in the photo above.

The direct descendants of the photosynthetic prokaryotes that dominated Earth from 3 billion years ago to about 1 billion years ago are the cyanobacteria and other photosynthetic bacteria of today. They remain abundant in freshwater lakes and ponds and in shallow oceans, but they only form thick mats or mounds in environments that are inhospitable to most other life. Thus, great expanses of stromatolites are a thing of the past. Nevertheless, the grand, global legacy of ancient photosynthetic prokaryotes—the aerobic atmosphere—remains with us today. And the aerobic atmosphere is but one illustration of the profound effects that microscopic organisms can have on the environment.

produced was changing Earth's anaerobic atmosphere to an aerobic atmosphere. This change set the stage for the evolution of all other aerobic life.

Few traces of that ancient landscape remain, but Shark's Bay in western Australia offers a rare glimpse of the prokaryotic life that changed Earth's atmosphere. Living stromatolites still stand in the warm, shallow waters, giving scientists a chance to see how the structures are formed. The photosynthetic prokaryotes live on the surface of the stromatolite, where they are exposed to sunlight. The sticky coating of these organisms concentrates sand grains and other fine particles from the seawater. While a sediment layer accumulates, the prokaryotes keep migrating to the surface and growing over it. A layered mat builds up as this process is repeated over and over. In this way, large mounds form over thousands of years, hardening as their older sediment layers solidify and become rocklike structures composed of many layers of prokaryotes and sediment. During their long reign as Earth's dominant organisms, ancient prokaryotes built stromatolites by a

In this unit of chapters, we examine a small sample of the remarkable variety of species—now numbered in the millions—that arose from those early prokaryotes over the course of time. We focus most of our attention on the current diversity of life, but we also retrace evolutionary journeys that changed the face of the Earth, such as the colonization of land by plants and vertebrates and the emergence of *Homo sapiens*. We begin our exploration of life in this chapter with the prokaryotes, the simplest organisms, and the protists, an assortment of organisms so diverse that researchers are just beginning to decipher their evolutionary relationships. ■ ■ ■

16.1 Prokaryotes are diverse and widespread

Stromatolites reach an impressive size because the prokaryotes that construct them live in colonies consisting of trillions of individuals. Individual prokaryotes are extremely small. You can get an idea of the size of most prokaryotes from Figure 16.1, a colorized scanning electron micrograph of the point of a pin (purple) covered with numerous bacteria (orange). Most prokaryotic cells have diameters in the range of 1–5 μm, much smaller than most eukaryotic cells (typically 10–100 μm).

Despite their small size, prokaryotes have an immense impact on our world. They are found wherever there is life, including in and on the bodies of multicellular organisms. The collective biological mass (biomass) of prokaryotes is at least ten times that of all eukaryotes! More prokaryotes inhabit a handful of fertile soil than the total number of people who have ever lived. Prokaryotes also thrive in habitats too cold, too hot, too salty, too acidic, or too alkaline for any eukaryote. And scientists are just beginning to investigate the extensive prokaryotic diversity in the oceans.

Although prokaryotes are a constant presence in our environment, we hear most about the relatively few species that cause illnesses. Bacteria cause about half of all human diseases, including potentially fatal diseases such as plague and cholera. Strep throat and some ear infections, certain types of food poisoning, and the sexually transmitted diseases chlamydia, syphilis, and gonorrhea are also bacterial diseases. We focus on bacterial **pathogens,** disease-causing agents, in Module 16.8. In Module 16.9, you'll learn about the use of bacterial pathogens as biological weapons.

Far more common than harmful bacteria are those that are benign or beneficial. For example, each of us harbors several hundred species of bacteria in and on our bodies. Many of the bacteria that live on our skin perform helpful housekeeping functions such as decomposing dead skin cells. Some of our intestinal residents supply essential vitamins and enable us to obtain nutrition from food molecules that we can't otherwise digest. Bacteria also guard the body against pathogenic intruders. Prokaryotes in the soil help to decompose dead organisms and other organic waste material, returning vital chemical elements to the environment. If prokaryotic decomposers were to disappear, the chemical cycles that sustain life would halt, and all forms of eukaryotic life would also be doomed. In contrast, prokaryotic life would undoubtedly persist in the absence of eukaryotes, as it once did for billions of years. As you'll learn in Module 16.10, prokaryotes also serve vital roles in a wide array of human enterprises.

Figure 16.1
Bacteria on the point of a pin

Colorized SEM 650×

🎧 **MP3 Tutor** *Microbial Life*

? The number of bacterial cells that live in and on our bodies is greater than the number of cells that comprise the body. Why aren't we aware of these trillions of cells?

■ We can't see our own eukaryotic cells individually, and bacterial cells are much smaller than that. Also, our "companion" microbes are adapted for coexisting with us.

16.2 Bacteria and archaea are the two main branches of prokaryotic evolution

Prokaryotes have a cellular organization fundamentally different from that of eukaryotes, as we saw in Modules 4.3 and 4.4. Whereas eukaryotic cells have a membrane-enclosed nucleus and numerous other membrane-enclosed organelles, prokaryotic cells lack these structural features.

As we discussed in earlier chapters, however, there are two very different kinds of prokaryotes. Researchers first began comparing nucleotide sequences of prokaryotic genes in the 1970s, by studying a type of ribosomal RNA (rRNA) that is found in all prokaryotes and eukaryotes as a marker for evolutionary relationships. They concluded that many prokaryotes once classified as bacteria are actually more closely related to eukaryotes and belong in a domain of their own. Thus, prokaryotes are now classified in the domains **Bacteria** and **Archaea.** The name Archaea comes from the Greek *archaios* ("ancient").

In recent years, researchers have focused on DNA and have completely sequenced many bacterial and archaeal genomes (see Module 12.17). When compared with each other and with the genomes of eukaryotes, these genome sequences strongly support the three-domain view of life (see Module 15.19). Some genes of archaea are similar to bacterial genes and others to eukaryotic genes; still others seem unique to archaea.

A current hypothesis is that present-day archaea and eukaryotes evolved from a common ancestor (see Figure 15.19A). But as described in Module 15.19, tracing their evolution is complicated by gene transfer between prokaryotic lineages. Over hundreds of millions of years, prokaryotes have acquired genes from distantly related species, and they continue to do so today. As a result, significant portions of the genomes of many prokaryotes are mosaics of genes imported from other species.

Table 16.2 summarizes some of the main differences among the three domains. In addition to the rRNA sequences, several other differences involve the cellular machinery for gene expression. These include differences in RNA polymerases (the enzymes that catalyze the synthesis of RNA), in the presence of introns within genes, and in sensitivity to certain antibiotics that inhibit protein synthesis. Subtle differences between bacterial and archaeal ribosomes—in both rRNA and proteins—undoubtedly account for the insensitivity of archaea to these antibiotics.

Other differences between bacteria and archaea show up in their cell walls and membranes. Nearly all prokaryotes have a cell wall outside their plasma membrane. As in plants, the wall maintains cell shape and provides physical protection. Bacterial cell walls contain a unique material called **peptidoglycan,** a polymer of sugars cross-linked by short polypeptides. No archaea have true peptidoglycan. Furthermore, the lipids forming the backbone of plasma membranes differ between the two domains.

For most of the features listed in the table, archaea are actually more like eukaryotes than like bacteria. In fact, archaea have at least as much in common with eukaryotes as they do with bacteria. The main point here is that there are two very different kinds of prokaryotic organisms. We will discuss the diversity within these two groups after a look at some more general features of prokaryotes.

? As different as bacteria and archaea are, both groups are characterized by _____ cells, which lack nuclei and other membrane-enclosed organelles.

■ prokaryotic

TABLE 16.2	DIFFERENCES AMONG THE DOMAINS BACTERIA, ARCHAEA, AND EUKARYA		
Characteristic	Bacteria	Archaea	Eukarya
rRNA sequences	Some unique to bacteria	Some unique to archaea; some match eukaryotic sequences	Some unique to eukarya; some match archaea sequences
RNA polymerase	One kind; relatively small and simple	Several kinds; complex	Several kinds; complex
Introns	Rare	In some genes	Present
Response to antibiotics streptomycin and chloramphenicol	Growth inhibited	Growth not inhibited	Growth not inhibited
Peptidoglycan in cell wall	Present	Absent	Absent
Histones associated with DNA	Absent	Present in some species	Present

16.3 Prokaryotes come in a variety of shapes

Determining cell shape by microscopic examination is an important step in identifying prokaryotes. The micrographs below show three of the most common prokaryotic cell shapes. Spherical prokaryotic cells are called **cocci** (from the Greek word for "berries"). Cocci (singular, *coccus*) that occur in chains, like the ones in Figure 16.3A, are called streptococci (from the Greek *streptos,* twisted). The bacterium that causes strep throat in humans is a streptococcus. Other cocci occur in clusters; they are called staphylococci (from the Greek *staphyle,* cluster of grapes).

Figure 16.3B shows rod-shaped prokaryotes, which are called **bacilli** (singular, *bacillus*). Most bacilli occur singly, but the cells of some species occur in pairs (diplobacilli) and in chains (streptobacilli). The species shown here, which is common in fertile soil, exists as solitary cells.

A third prokaryotic cell shape is curved or spiral. Some bacteria in this category resemble commas and are called *vibrios.* Other bacteria and archaea have a helical shape, like a corkscrew. Helical prokaryotes that are relatively short and rigid are called *spirilla;* those with longer, more flexible cells are called *spirochetes* (Figure 16.3C). The bacterium that causes syphilis, for example, is a spirochete. Spirochetes include some giants by prokaryotic standards—cells 0.5 mm long (though very thin).

? How could a microscope help you distinguish the cocci that cause "staph" infections from those that cause "strep" throat?

■ It would show clusters of cells for staphylococcus and chains of cells for streptococcus.

Colorized SEM 12,000×

Figure 16.3A Cocci

Colorized SEM 9,000×

Figure 16.3B Bacilli

Colorized SEM 3,000×

Figure 16.3C Spirochete

16.4 Various structural features contribute to the success of prokaryotes

Most prokaryotes are unicellular, but they are able to carry out all of the functions of life within that single cell. In addition, prokaryotes thrive in a great variety of habitats. In this module, we discuss some of the structural and functional adaptations that contribute to the diversity and success of prokaryotes.

External Structures   One of the most important features of nearly all prokaryotic cells is their cell wall. The wall maintains cell shape, provides physical protection, and prevents the cell from bursting in a hypotonic environment (see Module 5.5). In a hypertonic environment, most prokaryotes lose water and shrink away from their wall. Severe water loss inhibits reproduction, which explains why salt can be used to preserve certain foods, such as pork and fish.

As mentioned in Module 16.2, the cell walls of archaea differ from those of bacteria. The cell walls of bacteria fall into two general types, which scientists can identify with a technique called the **gram stain** (Figure 16.4A). Gram-positive bacteria have simpler walls with a relatively thick layer of peptidoglycan. The walls of gram-negative bacteria stain differently. They have less peptidoglycan and are more complex, with an outer membrane that contains lipids bonded to carbohydrates.

Gram staining is a valuable identification tool in medicine. Among disease-causing bacteria, gram-negative species are generally more threatening than gram-positive species. The lipid molecules of the outer membrane of these bacteria are often toxic. The membrane also protects them against the body's defenses and impedes the entry of antibiotic drugs. The effectiveness of many antibiotics is due to their inhibition of cross-linking in the peptidoglycan cell wall. Such drugs can cripple many types of bacteria without adversely affecting human cells, which do not contain peptidoglycan.

The cell wall of many prokaryotes is covered by a capsule, a sticky layer of polysaccharides or protein. The capsule enables prokaryotes to adhere to their substrate or to other individuals in a colony. Capsules can also shield pathogenic prokaryotes from attacks by their host's immune system. The capsule surrounding the *Streptococcus* bacterium shown in Figure 16.4B enables it to attach to cells that line the human respiratory tract—in this image, a tonsil cell.

Some prokaryotes stick to their substrate or to one another by means of hairlike appendages called **pili** (singular, **pilus**). Pili show up clearly in the highly magnified micrograph in Figure 16.4C. Pili help prokaryotes stick to each other and to surfaces, such as rocks in flowing streams or the lining of human intestines. Specialized pili, called sex pili, link prokaryotes during conjugation, a process in which one cell transfers DNA to another (see Module 10.22).

Motility   Many bacteria and archaea are equipped with flagella, which enable them to move about. In response to chemical or physical signals in their environment, prokaryotes can move toward nutrients or other members of their species or away from a toxic substance. Flagella may be scattered over the entire cell surface or concentrated at one or both ends of the cell. Entirely different in structure from the flagellum of eukaryotic cells (described in Module 4.18), the prokaryotic flagellum is a naked protein structure that lacks microtubules. It is attached to the cell surface by a system of rotating rings anchored in the plasma membrane and cell wall. The rings give the flagellum a propeller-like rotary movement, as shown in Figure 16.4D, at the top of the next page. The flagellated organism in the photo is the bacterium *Proteus,* an especially fast swimmer.

Reproduction and Adaptation   Certainly a large part of the success of prokaryotes is their potential to reproduce quickly in a favorable environment. Dividing by binary fission, a single cell becomes 2 cells, which then become 4, 8, 16, and so on. While most prokaryotes produce a new generation within 1–3 hours, some species can produce a new generation in only 20 minutes under optimal conditions. If reproduction continued unchecked at this rate, a single prokaryote could give rise to a colony outweighing Earth in only three days! In reality, of course, prokaryotic reproduction is limited, as the cells eventually exhaust their nutrient supply, poison themselves with metabolic wastes, or are consumed by other organisms. Prokaryotes in nature also face competition from other microorganisms, many of which produce antibiotic chemicals that slow prokaryotic reproduction.

Figure 16.4A   Gram positive (purple) and gram negative (pink) bacteria

LM 780×

Capsule

Colorized TEM 50,000×

Figure 16.4B   Capsule

Pili

Colorized TEM 30,000×

Figure 16.4C   Pili

Figure 16.4D Prokaryotic flagella

Figure 16.4E An endospore within a cell of the anthrax bacterium

Figure 16.4F Infoldings of plasma membrane specialized for respiration in an aerobic prokaryote (left) and photosynthesis in a cyanobacterium (right)

Some prokaryotes are able to withstand harsh conditions. Certain bacteria, for example, can form specialized resistant cells when food is depleted or the environment has otherwise become inhospitable. **Figure 16.4E** shows an example of such an organism, *Bacillus anthracis*, the bacterium that produces a disease called anthrax in cattle, sheep, and humans. There are actually two cells here, one inside the other. The outer cell, which will later disintegrate, produced the specialized inner cell, called an **endospore.** The endospore, which has a thick, protective coat, dehydrates and becomes dormant. It can survive all sorts of trauma, including extreme heat or cold. When the endospore receives cues that the environmental conditions have improved, it absorbs water and resumes growth.

Some endospores can remain dormant for centuries. Not even boiling water kills most of these resistant cells, making it difficult to get rid of spores in a contaminated area. An island off the coast of Scotland that was used for anthrax testing in 1942 was finally declared safe 48 years later, after tons of formaldehyde were applied and huge amounts of top soil were removed. To sterilize laboratory equipment, microbiologists use an autoclave, a pressure cooker that kills endospores by heating to a temperature of 121°C (250°F) with high-pressure steam. The food-canning industry uses similar methods to kill endospores of dangerous bacteria such as *Clostridium botulinum*, the source of the potentially fatal disease botulism.

Internal Organization As seen in Module 4.3, the cells of prokaryotes are simpler than those of eukaryotes in both their internal structure and organization of their genome. However, some prokaryotic cells do have specialized membranes that perform metabolic functions. The left side of **Figure 16.4F**

shows an aerobic prokaryote with infoldings of the plasma membrane that are specialized to function in cellular respiration. The right side of the figure shows a cyanobacterium with thylakoid membranes that function in photosynthesis.

The genome of a prokaryote has on average only about one-thousandth as much DNA as a eukaryotic genome. The prokaryotic DNA usually forms a circular chromosome. Smaller rings of DNA, called plasmids, carry genes that may provide resistance to antibiotics, direct the metabolism of rarely encountered nutrients, or have other "contingency" functions. The ability of many prokaryotes to transfer genes within and even between species contributes to the growing problem of antibiotic resistance in disease-causing bacteria (see Module 13.15).

Prokaryotic ribosomes are slightly smaller than eukaryotic ribosomes and differ in their protein and RNA content. These differences are great enough that certain antibiotics bind to prokaryotic ribosomes and block protein synthesis but do not affect eukaryotic ribosomes. As a result, we can use these antibiotics to kill bacteria without harming ourselves.

Another feature that contributes to the success of prokaryotes is the diversity of ways in which they obtain their nourishment, which we consider in the next module.

Web Activity *Prokaryotic Cell Structure and Function*

? Why do microbiologists autoclave lab instruments and glassware, rather than simply boiling them?

■ To kill bacterial endospores, which can survive boiling water

16.5 Prokaryotes obtain nourishment in a variety of ways

When classifying diverse organisms, biologists often use the phrase "mode of nutrition" to describe how an organism obtains two main resources: energy and carbon. As a group, prokaryotes exhibit much more nutritional diversity than eukaryotes.

Source of Energy   As shown in Figure 16.5A, two sources of energy are used by prokaryotes. Like plants, prokaryotic *phototrophs* capture energy from sunlight. Prokaryotes called *chemotrophs* harness the energy stored in either organic molecules or inorganic chemicals such as hydrogen sulfide (H_2S), elemental sulfur (S), iron (Fe)-containing compounds, or ammonia (NH_3).

Source of Carbon   Organisms that make their own organic compounds from inorganic sources are autotrophic (see Module 7.1). **Autotrophs,** including plants and some prokaryotes and protists, obtain their carbon atoms from carbon dioxide (CO_2). Most prokaryotes, as well as animals, fungi, and some protists, are **heterotrophs,** meaning they obtain their carbon atoms from organic compounds.

Mode of Nutrition   The terms used to describe how a prokaryote obtains energy and carbon are combined to describe its mode of nutrition. **Photoautotrophs** harness sunlight for energy and use CO_2 for carbon. Cyanobacteria, such as the example shown in Figure 7.1D, are photoautotrophs. **Photoheterotrophs** obtain energy from sunlight but get their carbon atoms from organic sources. A group of bacteria called purple nonsulfur bacteria, which are found in anaerobic aquatic sediments, are examples of this nutritional type. **Chemoautotrophs** harvest energy from inorganic chemicals and use carbon from CO_2 to make organic molecules. This group includes sulfur bacteria that inhabit deep-sea vents (see the introduction to Chapter 34) and soil bacteria that are important to recycling nitrogen (see Module 37.21). **Chemoheterotrophs**, which acquire both energy and carbon from organic molecules, are by far the largest and most diverse group of prokaryotes. Almost any organic molecule is food for some species of chemoheterotrophic prokaryote.

Biofilms   Although prokaryotes may exist as single cells, many species live in surface-coating colonies called **biofilms.** A biofilm may include just one species, or it may consist of several different species. It forms when cells in a colony secrete signaling molecules that recruit nearby cells. Once the colony becomes sufficiently large, the cells produce proteins that stick them to the substrate and to each other. Channels in the biofilm allow nutrients to reach cells in the interior and wastes to leave. Biofilms are common among bacteria that cause disease in humans. For instance, a biofilm known as dental plaque (Figure 16.5B) can cause tooth decay. Ear infections and urinary tract infections may be caused by biofilms. Biofilms that form on catheters or replacement joints or heart valves can cause serious medical problems. On the other hand, biofilms are used to remove contaminants from water in sewage treatment plants (see Module 16.10).

Biofilms are common in all types of aquatic habitats—for example, on rocks in streams and rivers and on the surface of stagnant water. In complex biofilm communities found in the mud of the ocean floor, sulfate-consuming bacteria and methane-consuming archaea coexist in ball-shaped clumps. The bacteria appear to use the archaea's organic waste products and, in turn, produce compounds that facilitate methane consumption by the archaea. This partnership has global ramifications. Each year, these archaea consume an estimated 300 billion kilograms of methane, a major greenhouse gas (see Module 38.5).

SEM 2,000×

Figure 16.5B   Dental plaque, a biofilm that forms on teeth

Web Process of Science *What Are the Modes of Nutrition in Prokaryotes?*

? What term describes the mode of nutrition of stromatolite-building prokaryotes discussed in the chapter introduction?

Energy source

Carbon source	Light	Chemical
CO_2	Photoautotrophs	Chemoautotrophs
Organic compounds	Photoheterotrophs	Chemoheterotrophs

Figure 16.5A   Sources of energy and carbon in prokaryotic modes of nutrition

■ Photoautotroph

Archaea thrive in extreme environments—and in other habitats

Archaea are abundant in many habitats, including places where few other organisms can survive. The archaeal inhabitants of extreme environments have unusual proteins and other molecular adaptations that enable them to metabolize and reproduce effectively. Scientists are only beginning to learn about these adaptations.

A group of archaea called the **extreme halophiles** ("salt lovers") thrive in very salty places, such as the Great Salt Lake in Utah, the Dead Sea, and seawater-evaporating ponds used to produce salt. **Figure 16.6A** shows an aerial view of ponds of this sort next to San Francisco Bay. The colors of the ponds result from the dense growth of the archaea that thrive when the salinity of the water reaches 15–20%. (Before evaporation, seawater has a salt concentration of about 3%.) The purplish color of the ponds near the top of the photo is due to an archaean called *Halobacterium halobium*. A unique photosynthesizer, *H. halobium* lacks chlorophyll; it has a purple molecule called bacteriorhodopsin that traps solar energy.

Another group of archaea, the **extreme thermophiles** ("heat lovers"), thrive in very hot water; some even live near deep-ocean vents where temperatures are above 100°C, the boiling point of water at sea level! One such habitat is the Nevada geyser shown in **Figure 16.6B**. Other thermophiles thrive in acid. Many hot, acidic pools in Yellowstone National Park harbor such archaea, which give the pools a vivid greenish color. One of these organisms, *Sulfolobus*, can obtain energy by oxidizing sulfur or a compound of sulfur and iron; the mechanisms involved may be similar to those used billions of years ago by the first cells.

A third group of archaea, the **methanogens,** live in anaerobic environments and give off methane as a waste product. Many thrive in anaerobic mud at the bottom of lakes and swamps. You may have seen methane, also called marsh gas, bubbling up from a swamp. Great numbers of methanogens also inhabit the digestive tracts of animals. In humans, intestinal gas is largely the result of their metabolism. More importantly, methanogens aid digestion in cattle, deer, and other animals that depend heavily on cellulose for their nutrition. Unfortunately, these animals belch out large volumes of methane, contributing to the global release of this major greenhouse gas.

Accustomed to thinking of archaea as "extremophiles," scientists have been surprised to discover their abundance in more moderate environments, especially in the oceans. Archaea live at all depths, making up a substantial fraction of the prokaryotes in waters below 150 m and equaling the number of bacteria below 1,000 m. Archaea are thus one of the most abundant cell types in Earth's largest habitat.

Because bacteria have been the subject of most prokaryotic research throughout the history of microbiology, much more is known about them than about archaea. Now that the evolutionary and ecological importance of archaea has come into focus, we can expect research on this domain to turn up many more surprises about the history of life and the roles of microbes in ecosystems.

Figure 16.6A "Salt-loving" archaea, extreme halophiles, growing in seawater-evaporating ponds near San Francisco Bay

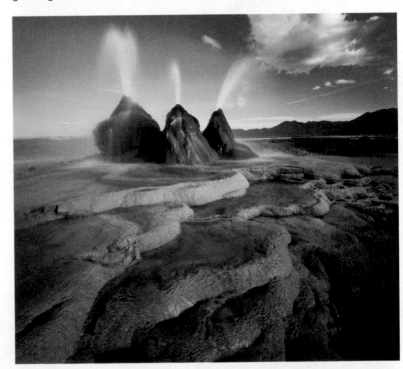

Figure 16.6B Orange and yellow colonies of "heat-loving" archaea, extreme thermophiles, growing in a Nevada geyser

? Some archaea are referred to as "extremophiles." Why?

■ Because they can thrive in extreme environments too hot, too salty, or too acidic for other organisms

Bacteria include a diverse assemblage of prokaryotes

In this module we sample some of the diversity of bacteria. Until the late 20th century, systematists based prokaryotic taxonomy on phenotypic criteria such as shape, motility, nutritional mode, and Gram staining. These criteria are still valuable in some contexts, such as the rapid identification of bacteria cultured from a patient's blood. But they do not reveal relationships. Although still a work in progress, molecular systematics is starting to unravel bacterial phylogeny.

Domain Bacteria is currently divided into nine groups, five of which are considered subgroups of a clade of gram-negative bacteria called **proteobacteria.** Members of the subgroup alpha proteobacteria include *Rhizobium* species, which live in nodules in the roots of legumes, where they fix atmospheric N_2 (see Module 32.13), and *Agrobacterium* species, which produce tumors in plants and are used by genetic engineers to carry foreign DNA into the genomes of crop plants (see Module 12.8).

Figure 16.7A *Thiomargarita namibiensis,* showing globules of sulfur wastes

The photosynthetic members of the subgroup gamma proteobacteria include sulfur bacteria that oxidize H_2S. The small greenish globules you see in **Figure 16.7A** are sulfur wastes. Other gamma proteobacteria include many species that inhabit animal intestines, such as *Salmonella,* one cause of food poisoning; *Vibrio cholerae,* which causes cholera; and *Escherichia coli,* a common resident of the intestines of humans and other mammals and a favorite research organism.

The delta proteobacteria include the slime-secreting myxobacteria, which form elaborate colonies. When the soil dries out or food is scarce, the cells congregate into a fruiting body that releases resistant spores. *Bdellovibrio* bacteria are delta proteobacteria that attack other bacteria. They charge their prey at up to 100 μm/sec (comparable to a human running 600 km/hr) and bore into the prey by spinning at 100 revolutions per second (**Figure 16.7B**).

The **chlamydias,** which live inside eukaryotic host cells, form a second bacterial group. *Chlamydia trachomatis* is a common cause of blindness in developing countries and also causes nongonococcal urethritis, the most common sexually transmitted disease in the United States.

Spirochetes are a group of helical bacteria (see Figure 16.3C) that spiral through their environment by means of rotating, internal filaments. Some spirochetes are notorious pathogens: *Treponema pallidum* causes syphilis, and *Borrelia burgdorferi* causes Lyme disease.

The group of **gram-positive bacteria** rivals the proteobacteria in diversity. One subgroup, the actinomycetes (from the Greek *mykes,* fungus, for which these bacteria were once mistaken), form colonies of branched chains of cells. Actinomycetes are very common in the soil, where they decompose organic matter. Soil-dwelling species in the genus *Streptomyces* (**Figure 16.7C**) are cultured by pharmaceutical companies as a source of many antibiotics, including streptomycin. Gram-positive bacteria also include many solitary species, such as *Bacillus anthracis* (see Figure 16.4E). *Staphylococcus* and *Streptococcus* are also gram-positive bacteria. Mycoplasmas are gram-positive bacteria that lack cell walls and are the tiniest of all known cells, with diameters as small as 0.1 μm, only about five times as large as a ribosome.

The **cyanobacteria** are the only prokaryotes with plant-like, oxygen-generating photosynthesis. Ancient cyanobacteria generated the stromatolites discussed in the chapter introduction and made the atmosphere aerobic. Today, both solitary and colonial cyanobacteria provide an enormous amount of food for freshwater and marine ecosystems. **Figure 16.7D** shows the cyanobacterium *Anabaena* which has specialized cells that convert nitrogen gas into a form usable by other organisms.

Web Activity *Diversity of Prokaryotes*

? Which group of bacteria uses H_2S as an electron source in its photosynthetic production of organic molecules?

■ Sulfur bacteria of the subgroup gamma proteobacteria

Figure 16.7B *Bdellovibrio bacteriovorus* (flagellated cell) attacking a larger bacterium

Figure 16.7C *Streptomyces,* the source of many antibiotics

Nitrogen-fixing cells

Photosynthetic cells

Figure 16.7D *Anabaena,* a filamentous cyanobacterium

All organisms, humans included, are almost constantly exposed to pathogenic bacteria. Most often, our body's defenses prevent pathogens from affecting us (see Chapter 24). Occasionally, however, a pathogen establishes itself in the body and causes illness. Even some of the bacteria that are normal residents of the human body can make us ill when our defenses have been weakened by poor nutrition or by a viral infection.

Most bacteria that cause illness do so by producing a poison—either an exotoxin or an endotoxin. **Exotoxins** are proteins secreted by bacterial cells and include some of the most powerful poisons known. For example, the exotoxin of *Clostridium tetani* produces muscle spasms, including "lockjaw," which prevents the mouth from opening. *Staphylococcus aureus*, shown in **Figure 16.8A**, produces several exotoxins. Although *S. aureus* is commonly found on the skin and in the nasal passages, if it enters the body through a wound, it can cause serious diseases. One of the exotoxins that *S. aureus* produces can cause layers of skin to slough off; another causes the potentially deadly toxic shock syndrome. Food may also be contaminated with *S. aureus* exotoxins, which are so potent that less than a microgram (3.5×10^{-8} ounce) causes vomiting and diarrhea.

Occasionally, bacterial species that are generally harmless acquire an exotoxin-producing gene through transfer from another species (see Module 10.22). *Escherichia coli*, a normally benign resident of our intestines, is an example. An exotoxin-producing strain of *E. coli* designated O157:H7 has caused a number of outbreaks of bloody diarrhea and hundreds of deaths. Although many cases are associated with contaminated ground beef, outbreaks have also been traced to fresh produce such as spinach and lettuce, as well as to other sources. The recently sequenced genome of *E. coli* O157:H7 shows that more than 20% of its genes are not found in the genome of a harmless *E. coli* strain.

Endotoxins are components of the outer membrane of gram-negative bacteria that are released when the cell dies or is digested by a defensive cell. All endotoxins induce the same general symptoms: fever, aches, and sometimes a dangerous drop in blood pressure (septic shock). An endotoxin of *Neisseria meningitidis* causes bacterial meningitis, a disease that can kill a healthy person in a matter of days, or even hours. Other examples of endotoxin-producing bacteria include the species of *Salmonella* that cause food poisoning and typhoid fever.

During the last century, improvements in sanitation in the developed world greatly reduced the incidence of bacterial diseases. The installation of water treatment and sewage systems continues to be a public health priority throughout the world. Medical advances, especially the development of antibiotics, have also helped to control bacterial diseases. However, many pathogenic bacteria have evolved resistance to widely used antibiotics, becoming newly dangerous (see Module 13.15).

Education is another powerful weapon for combating disease. For example, sexually active adults who understand the importance of condom use are more likely to protect themselves against sexually transmitted diseases such as nongonococcal urethritis (caused by a type of chlamydia), syphilis, and gonorrhea (beta proteobacteria). Another case in point is Lyme disease, currently the most widespread pest-carried disease in the United States. The disease is caused by *Borrelia burgdorferi*, a spirochete carried by ticks that live on deer and field mice. As shown in **Figure 16.8B**, the disease usually starts as a red rash shaped like a bull's-eye around a tick bite. Antibiotics can cure the disease if administered within about a month after exposure. If untreated, Lyme disease can cause debilitating arthritis, heart disease, and nervous disorders. The best prevention is public education about avoiding tick bites and the importance of seeking treatment if a rash develops.

While billions of dollars and countless hours of research have been devoted to disease prevention and cures, people also have developed methods of using pathogens to deliberately cause harm. We look at biological weapons in the next module.

Spirochete that causes Lyme disease

SEM 3,000×

Tick that carries the Lyme disease bacterium

"Bull's-eye" rash

Figure 16.8B Lyme disease, a bacterial disease transmitted by ticks

? Contrast exotoxins with endotoxins.

■ Exotoxins are proteins secreted by pathogenic bacteria; endotoxins are components of the outer membranes of pathogenic bacteria.

Figure 16.8A *Staphylococcus aureus*, an exotoxin producer

16.9 Bacteria can be used as biological weapons

In October 2001, endospores of *Bacillus anthracis*, the bacterium that causes anthrax, were found in envelopes mailed to members of the news media and the U.S. Senate (Figure 16.9A). Eighteen people developed cases of anthrax, and five died. Unfortunately, while these attacks were shocking, they were not unique. There is a long and ugly history of using biological agents as weapons, especially viruses and bacteria. *B. anthracis*, *Yersinia pestis* (the bacterium that causes plague), and the exotoxin of *Clostridium botulinum* are among the biological agents that are considered the highest-priority threats today.

B. anthracis forms hardy endospores (see Figure 16.4D) that are commonly found in the soil of agricultural regions, where large grazing animals can become infected. People who work in agriculture, leather tanning, or wool processing occasionally catch the cutaneous (skin) form of anthrax from infected animals. Cutaneous anthrax produces skin lesions and is relatively easy to treat. Inhalation anthrax, which affects the lungs, is the deadly form of the disease. "Weaponizing" anthrax involves manufacturing a preparation of endospores that disperses easily in the air, where the endospores will be inhaled by the target population. Endospores that enter the lungs germinate and the bacteria multiply, producing an exotoxin that eventually accumulates to lethal levels in the blood. *B. anthracis* can be controlled by certain antibiotics, including Ciprofloxacin, which was in huge demand during the 2001 crisis. But antibiotics only kill the bacteria—they can't eliminate the toxin already in the body. As a result, inhalation anthrax has a very high death rate. Researchers have recently made a great deal of progress toward developing antitoxins.

Plague conjures images of medieval epidemics, when people died by the thousands and corpses piled up in the streets. But plague is a modern disease as well. Bacteria that cause plague, *Y. pestis*, are carried by rodents in many parts of the world and are transmitted by fleas. People contract the disease when they are bitten by infected fleas. If diagnosed in time, plague can be treated by antibiotics. If the disease progresses, however, symptoms become strikingly gruesome. Egg-size

Figure 16.9B   Swellings (buboes) characteristic of the bubonic form of plague

swellings grow in the armpits, groin, and neck (Figure 16.9B), and black blotches appear where the bacteria proliferate in clots under the skin. If the bacteria spill into the bloodstream, death from the bacterial toxins is certain. As a weapon, though, pneumonic plague is the worst case scenario. In the pneumonic form of plague, *Y. pestis* infect cells in the lungs, becoming airborne as the disintegrating lung tissue is coughed out in droplets. As a result, pneumonic plague is easily transmitted from person to person and can become epidemic.

Unlike other biological agents, the weapon form of *C. botulinum* is the exotoxin it produces, botulinum, rather than the living microbes. Botulinum is the deadliest poison on earth. Thirty grams of pure toxin, a bit more than an ounce, could kill every person in the United States. Botulinum blocks transmission of the nerve signals that cause muscle contraction, resulting in paralysis of the muscles required for breathing. As a weapon, it would most likely be broadcast as an aerosol. An effective antitoxin is available, but existing methods of preparing it yield only small quantities. The U.S. government recently contracted with a biotechnology firm to develop mass production methods.

The United States has a long-standing bioweapons program. During World War II, the government established a research laboratory at Camp Detrick, Maryland, that is still in operation today. Fearing biological attack by the Soviets during the Cold War, the United States worked on developing its own arsenal of bioweapons as well as on defensive strategies. In 1969, however, the government abandoned its pursuit of offensive biological weapons and concentrated solely on defending against possible biological attacks. In 1975, the United States signed the Biological Weapons Convention, pledging never to develop or store biological weapons. Eventually, 103 nations joined the ban, although not all signatories have honored it.

Figure 16.9A   Cleaning up after an anthrax attack in October 2001

? Why is *Bacillus anthracis* an effective bioweapon?

■ It is easy to obtain from the soil and forms potentially deadly endospores that resist destruction and can be easily dispersed.

16.10 Prokaryotes help recycle chemicals and clean up the environment

Despite the attention they demand, pathogenic prokaryotes are in the minority. Far more common are prokaryotes that are vital to our well-being. All life depends on the cycling of chemical elements between organisms and the nonliving parts of our environment. As you'll learn in Chapter 37, prokaryotes are indispensable components of the chemical cycle that makes nitrogen available to plants and, in turn, to animals. Prokaryotes also participate in other chemical cycles through decomposition of organic wastes and dead organisms to inorganic chemicals.

The varied metabolic talents of prokaryotes also enable them to help us solve environmental problems through **bioremediation,** the use of organisms to remove pollutants from soil, air, or water. Prokaryotic decomposers are the mainstays of our sewage treatment facilities. Raw sewage is first passed through a series of screens and shredders, and solid matter settles out from the liquid waste. This solid matter, called sludge, is then gradually added to a culture of anaerobic prokaryotes, including both bacteria and archaea. The microbes decompose the organic matter in the sludge to material that can be used as landfill or fertilizer.

Liquid wastes are treated separately from the sludge. In Figure 16.10A, you can see a trickling filter system, one type of mechanism for treating liquid wastes. The long horizontal pipes rotate slowly, spraying liquid wastes through the air onto a thick bed of rocks, the filter. Biofilms of aerobic bacteria and fungi growing on the rocks remove much of the organic material dissolved in the waste. Outflow from the rock bed is sterilized and then released, usually into a river or ocean.

In Figure 16.10B, workers are spraying fertilizers on an oil-polluted beach in Alaska. The fertilizers stimulate the growth of "oil-eating" bacteria that occur naturally in the soil, in some cases speeding the natural breakdown process fivefold. Researchers are trying to genetically engineer bacteria to degrade oil even more efficiently.

Figure 16.10B   Treatment of an oil spill in Alaska

Bacteria may also help us clean up old mining sites. The water that drains from mines is highly acidic and is also laced with poisons—often compounds of arsenic, copper, zinc, and the heavy metals lead, mercury, and cadmium. Contamination of our soils and groundwater by these toxic substances poses a widespread threat, and cleaning up the mess can be extremely expensive. Prokaryotes may be able to help. Bacteria called *Thiobacillus* thrive in the acidic waters that drain from mines, accumulating metals from the mine waters. Unfortunately, *Thiobacillus* bacteria also add sulfuric acid to the water. If this problem is solved, perhaps through genetic engineering, *Thiobacillus* and other prokaryotes may help us overcome some serious environmental problems.

Some mining companies use microbes to extract valuable metals from low-grade ores. Bacteria assist in extracting over 30 billion kilograms of copper from copper sulfides each year. Using prokaryotes that can extract gold from ore, one factory in the African nation of Ghana processes 1 million kilograms of gold concentrate a day.

? What is bioremediation?

■ The use of organisms to clean up pollution

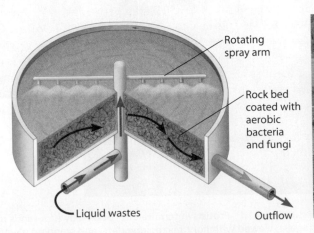

Rotating spray arm

Rock bed coated with aerobic bacteria and fungi

Liquid wastes

Outflow

Figure 16.10A   The trickling filter system at a sewage treatment plant

16.11 Protists are an extremely diverse assortment of eukaryotes

The photograph in **Figure 16.11A**—a drop of pond water viewed with the light microscope—illustrates a variety of **protists,** a diverse collection of mostly unicellular eukaryotes. Biologists used to classify all protists in a kingdom called Protista, but now it is thought that these organisms constitute multiple kingdoms within domain Eukarya. While our knowledge of the evolutionary relationships among these diverse groups remains incomplete, *protist* is still useful as a convenient term to refer to eukaryotes that are not plants, animals, or fungi.

Protists obtain their nutrition in a variety of ways. Some protists are autotrophic, producing their food by photosynthesis; these are called **algae** (another useful term that is not taxonomically meaningful). Others, informally called **protozoans** (from the Greek *protos*, first, and *zoion*, animal), are heterotrophic, eating bacteria and other protists. Some heterotrophic protists are fungus-like and obtain organic molecules by absorption. And some protists can be either heterotrophic or autotrophic, depending on availability of light and nutrients.

Protist habitats are also diverse. Like the sample shown in Figure 16.11A, most protists are aquatic, and they are found almost anywhere there is water, including moist terrestrial habitats, such as damp soil and leaf litter. Others inhabit the bodies of various host organisms. For example, **Figure 16.11B** shows some of the protists that live in the intestinal tract of termites. These protists are *endosymbionts*. **Symbiosis** is a close association between organisms of two or more species, and *endo*symbiosis refers to one species, called the endosymbiont, living *within* another. Termite endosymbionts digest the tough cellulose in the wood eaten by their host. Some of these protists even have endosymbionts of their own—prokaryotes that metabolize the cellulose.

As eukaryotes, protists are more complicated than any prokaryotes. Their cells have a membrane-enclosed nucleus (containing multiple chromosomes) and other organelles characteristic of eukaryotic cells. The flagella and cilia of protistan cells have a 9 + 2 pattern of microtubules, another typical eukaryotic trait (see Module 4.18).

Because most protists are unicellular, they are justifiably considered to be the simplest eukaryotes. However, the cells of many protists are among the most elaborate in the world. This level of cellular complexity is not really surprising, for each unicellular protist is a complete eukaryotic organism analogous to an entire animal or plant.

During the past 15 years, molecular and cellular studies have shaken the foundations of protistan taxonomy as much as they have that of the prokaryotes. The more intuitive groupings of protozoans and algae and fungus-like protists are phylogenetically meaningless, because the nutritional modes used to categorize them are spread across many different lineages. It is now clear that there are multiple clades of protists, with some lineages more closely related to plants, fungi, or animals than they are to other protists. Several protistan lineages appear to have arisen through secondary endosymbiosis, as you will learn in the next module.

? What is a general definition for protist?

■ A eukaryote that is not an animal, fungus, or plant

LM 275×

Figure 16.11A Protists in pond water

SEM 750×

LM 300×

Figure 16.11B Protists in termite gut covered by thousands of flagella, viewed with light microscope (left) and scanning electron microscope (right).

16.12 Secondary endosymbiosis is the key to much of protist diversity

As Module 16.11 indicates (and a quick look at Figure 16.13 on the next page will confirm), protists are a bewilderingly diverse group. What is the origin of this enormous diversity? To explain the current hypothesis, let's first review the endosymbiosis hypothesis for the origin of eukaryotic cells (see Module 4.16). According to that hypothesis, known as primary endosymbiosis, eukaryotic cells evolved when prokaryotes established residence within other, larger prokaryotes. The evidence for this hypothesis includes the structural and molecular similarities between prokaryotic cells and present-day mitochondria and chloroplasts. Mitochondria and chloroplasts even replicate their own DNA and reproduce by a process similar to that of prokaryotes.

Scientists think that heterotrophic eukaryotes evolved first; these had mitochondria but not chloroplasts. Autotrophic eukaryotes are thought to have arisen later from a lineage of heterotrophic eukaryotes descended from an individual that engulfed an autotrophic cyanobacterium (left side of **Figure 16.12**). If the cyanobacterium continued to function within its host cell, its photosynthesis would have provided a steady source of food for the heterotrophic host and thus given it a significant selective advantage. And because the cyanobacterium had its own DNA, it could reproduce to make multiple copies of itself within the host cell. In addition, cyanobacteria could be passed on when the host reproduced. Over time, the descendants of the original cyanobacterium evolved into chloroplasts. This chloroplast-bearing lineage of eukaryotes later diversified into green algae and red algae (see Module 16.20).

On subsequent occasions during eukaryotic evolution, green algae and red algae themselves became endosymbionts following ingestion by heterotrophic eukaryotes. Heterotrophic host cells enclosed the algal cells in food vacuoles, but the algae—or parts of them—survived and became cellular organelles. The presence of the endosymbionts, which also had the ability to replicate themselves, gave their hosts a selective advantage. This process, in which an autotrophic eukaryotic protist became endosymbiotic in a heterotrophic eukaryotic protist, is called **secondary endosymbiosis.**

Secondary endosymbiosis appears to be a major key to protist diversity. In green algae, shown across the top of Figure 16.12, secondary endosymbiosis gave rise to the Euglenozoans (see Module 16.15). Some members of this group are primarily autotrophic, but can become heterotrophic when sunlight is limited. Secondary endosymbiosis of red algae (bottom of Figure 16.12) led to nutritional diversity in dinoflagellates (see Module 16.16) and stramenopiles (see Module 16.17). Some species in these two groups are exclusively autotrophic; other species are exclusively heterotrophic. The dinoflagellates also include species that can obtain their food by either method. In apicomplexans (see Module 16.16), which are all parasitic, an organelle acquired by secondary endosymbiosis is vital to the protist's survival. Its function, however, is not known for certain.

? Distinguish between primary and secondary endosymbiosis.

■ In primary endosymbiosis, the endosymbiont is a prokaryote. In secondary endosymbiosis, the endosymbiont is a eukaryote.

Figure 16.12 A hypothesis of the origin of protistan diversity through endosymbiosis (mitochondria not shown)

16.13 A tentative phylogeny of eukaryotes includes multiple clades of protists

The classification of protists, like all scientific inquiries, remains a work in progress. **Figure 16.13** illustrates an abbreviated version of one hypothesis of the phylogeny of kingdoms Fungi, Animalia, and Plantae and the groups that were traditionally placed in kingdom Protista. Don't be overwhelmed by the complexity of the scheme. It simply shows that protists are an extremely diverse group that are difficult to categorize. Indeed, both in terms of number of species and number of living individuals, most eukaryotes are protists. Parts of Figure 16.13 are in dispute (dotted lines), but we present the phylogenetic tree as a means of providing a framework for the protistan groups that we will survey in the next several modules. Certainly, the names, boundaries, and placement of these clades will continue to change as the genomes of more protists are sequenced and compared.

? Why are protists especially important to biologists investigating the evolution of eukaryotic life?

■ Because the first eukaryotes were protists, and protists were ancestral to all other eukaryotes, including plants, fungi, animals, and modern protists

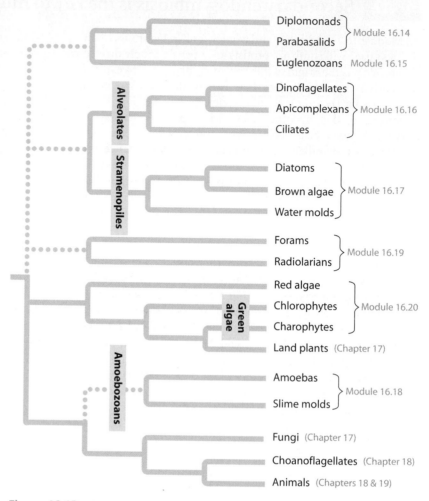

Figure 16.13 A tentative phylogeny of eukaryotes, with indication of the module or chapter in which each group is covered

16.14 Diplomonads and parabasalids have modified mitochondria

The **diplomonads** are heterotrophic protists that may represent the most ancient surviving lineage of eukaryotes. They have modified mitochondria with no DNA or electron transport chains. Most diplomonads are anaerobic.

An infamous example of a diplomonad is *Giardia intestinalis*, a common waterborne parasite that causes severe diarrhea. **Parasites** derive their nutrition from living hosts, which are harmed by the interaction. People most often pick up *Giardia* by drinking water contaminated with feces containing the parasite. For example, a swimmer in a lake or river might accidentally ingest water, or a hiker might drink contaminated water from a seemingly pristine stream. (Boiling the water first will kill *Giardia*.)

Parabasalids are heterotrophic protists that have modified mitochondria that generate some energy anaerobically. The termite endosymbionts shown in Module 16.11 are parabasalids. A common sexually transmitted parasite, *Trichomonas vaginalis* (**Figure 16.14**), also belongs to this group. An estimated

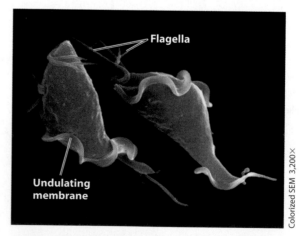

Figure 16.14 A parabasalid: *Trichomonas vaginalis*

5 million new infections by this parasite occur each year. *T. vaginalis* travels through the reproductive tract by moving its flagella and undulating part of its membrane. In women, the protists feed on white blood cells and bacteria living on the cells lining the vagina. *T. vaginalis* also infects the cells lining the male urethra, but limited availability of food results in very small population sizes. Consequently, males typically have no symptoms of infection, although they can repeatedly infect their female partners. The only treatment available is a drug called metronidazole. Disturbingly, drug resistance seems to be evolving in *T. vaginalis*, especially on college campuses.

? What characteristics do diplomonads and parabasalids have in common?

■ Both have modified mitochondria and generate energy mostly anaerobically.

16.15 Euglenozoans have flagella with a unique internal structure

The **euglenozoans** are a diverse clade of protists whose common feature is the presence of a crystalline rod of unknown function inside their flagella. Other characteristics give little clue that the organisms in this group are related. Euglenozoans include heterotrophs, photosynthetic autotrophs, and pathogenic parasites. In **Figure 16.15A**, the squiggly "worms" are cells of *Trypanosoma;* the red cells are human red blood cells. This trypanosome causes sleeping sickness, a potentially fatal disease spread by the African tsetse fly. *Euglena*, a common inhabitant of pond water, is a member of a different euglenozoan lineage (**Figure 16.15B**).

? How do the nutritional modes of diplomonads and euglenozoans differ?

■ Most diplomonads are anaerobic heterotrophs; euglenozoans exhibit all nutritional modes.

Colorized SEM 1,300×

Figure 16.15A
A euglenozoan: *Trypanosoma* (with blood cells)

Colorized SEM 1,300×

Figure 16.15B
A euglenozoan: *Euglena*

16.16 Alveolates have sacs beneath the plasma membrane

Dinoflagellates, apicomplexans, and ciliates form another clade of protists, the **alveolates,** whose identity is emerging from molecular systematics. Alveolates are characterized by membrane-enclosed sacs just beneath the plasma membrane. Researchers hypothesize that these sacs, called alveoli, help stabilize the cell surface or regulate water and ion content.

Dinoflagellates (**Figure 16.16A**) are very common components of marine and freshwater phytoplankton (microscopic autotrophs). Some reside within coral animals, providing much of the food for coral reef communities. Other dinoflagellates are heterotrophic. Dinoflagellate blooms—population explosions—sometimes cause warm coastal waters to turn pinkish orange, a phenomenon known as red tide. Toxins produced by some red-tide dinoflagellates have killed large numbers of fish. Humans who consume molluscs that have accumulated the toxins by feeding on dinoflagellates may be affected as well.

Ciliates are a large, varied group of alveolates, named for their use of cilia to move and feed. Nearly all ciliates are free-living, including the common freshwater protist *Paramecium* (see Figure 4.12B). Ciliates are unique in having two types of nuclei: a single, large macronucleus, which controls everyday activities, and multiple tiny micronuclei, which function in sexual reproduction. You can see the macronucleus, which resembles a string of beads running the length of the cell, in the trumpet-shaped ciliate *Stentor* (**Figure 16.16B**).

All **apicomplexans** are parasites of animals, and some cause serious human diseases. *Plasmodium*, which causes malaria, is one example of an apicomplexan.

? Where might autotrophic dinoflagellates be found?

■ Some are floating phytoplankton; others are symbionts within coral.

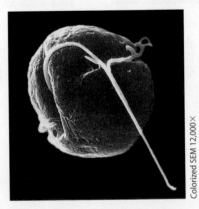

Colorized SEM 12,000×

Figure 16.16A *Gymnodinium*, a dinoflagellate that causes red tides

Cilia

Macronucleus

LM 86×

Figure 16.16B *Stentor*, a ciliate

16.17 Stramenopiles have "hairy" and smooth flagella

Stramenopiles (from the Latin *stramen*, straw, and *pilos*, hair) are protists named for their "hairy" flagellum, which has numerous hairlike projections. This flagellum is usually paired with a "smooth" flagellum. The clade is diverse, including both heterotrophs and autotrophs.

Water molds are fungus-like stramenopiles that typically decompose dead plants and animals in freshwater habitats (Figure 16.17A). Although they were long classified as fungi, molecular comparisons have revealed that water molds are more closely related to protists than to fungi. Parasitic water molds sometimes grow on the skin or gills of fish. Downy mildews, which are plant parasites, are another example of water molds. Late blight of potatoes, a disease caused by a downy mildew, led to a devastating famine in Ireland in the mid-1800s.

Figure 16.17A Water mold (the white threads decomposing an insect)

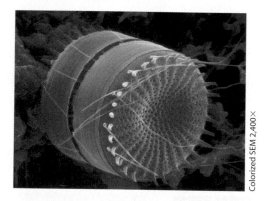

Colorized SEM 2,400×

Figure 16.17B Diatom, a unicellular alga

Diatoms are unicellular stramenopiles with a unique, glassy cell wall containing silica. They belong to the informal category called algae, which include all autotrophic protists (see Module 16.11). The cell wall of a diatom consists of two halves that fit together like the bottom and lid of a shoe box (Figure 16.17B). Both freshwater and marine environments are rich in diatoms, and the organic molecules these microscopic algae produce are a key source of food in all aquatic environments. Diatoms store their food reserves in the form of oil droplets. In addition to being a rich source of energy, oil makes the diatoms buoyant, which keeps them floating near the surface in the sunlight. Massive accumulations of fossilized diatoms make up thick sediments known as diatomaceous earth, which is mined for use as a filtering medium and as a grinding and polishing agent.

Brown algae are large, complex stramenopiles. Like diatoms, they are autotrophic. Brown algae owe their characteristic brown color to some of the pigments in their chloroplasts. All are multicellular, and most are marine. Brown algae include many of the species commonly called seaweeds. We use the word *seaweeds* here to refer to marine algae that have large multicellular bodies. (Some red and green algae are also referred to as seaweeds.) However, seaweeds lack the true stems, leaves, and roots found in most plants. Figure 16.17C shows an underwater bed of brown algae called **kelp** off the coast of California. Anchored to the seafloor by rootlike structures, kelp may grow to heights of 100 m. Fish, sea lions, sea otters, and gray whales regularly use these kelp "forests" as their feeding grounds.

Figure 16.17C Brown algae: a kelp "forest"

? Which stramenopiles are not autotrophic?

■ Water molds

16.18 Amoebozoans have lobe-shaped pseudopodia

Amoebas move and feed by means of **pseudopodia** (singular, *pseudopodium*), which are temporary extensions of the cell. Molecular systematics now indicates that amoebas are dispersed across many taxonomic groups. Members of the clade **amoebozoans,** including many species of free-living amoebas, some parasitic amoebas, and the slime molds, have lobe-shaped pseudopodia.

The amoeba in Figure 16.18A is ingesting a small protist. Its pseudopodia arch around the prey and will enclose it in a food vacuole (see Module 4.11). Free-living amoebas creep over rocks, sticks, or mud at the bottom of a pond or ocean. One species of parasitic amoeba causes amebic dysentery, a potentially fatal disease.

Figure 16.18A An amoeba ingesting a smaller protist

The yellow, branching growth on the dead log in **Figure 16.18B** is an amoebozoan called a **plasmodial slime mold.** These protists are common where there is moist, decaying organic matter and are often brightly pigmented. Although it is large and has many extensions, the organism in Figure 16.18B is not multicellular. Rather, it is a **plasmodium,** a single, multinucleate mass of cytoplasm undivided by plasma membranes. (Don't confuse this word with the apicomplexan *Plasmodium*, which causes malaria.) Because most of the nuclei go through mitosis at the same time, plasmodial slime molds are used to study molecular details of the cell cycle.

The plasmodium extends pseudopodia through soil and rotting logs, engulfing food by phagocytosis as it grows. Within the fine channels of the plasmodium, cytoplasm streams first one way and then the other in pulsing flows that probably help distribute nutrients and oxygen. When food and water are in short supply, the plasmodium stops growing and differentiates into reproductive structures (shown in the inset) that produce spores. When conditions become favorable, the spores release haploid cells that fuse to form a zygote, and the life cycle continues.

Cellular slime molds are also common on rotting logs and decaying organic matter. Most of the time, these organisms exist as solitary amoeboid cells. When food is scarce, the amoeboid cells swarm together, forming a slug-like aggregate that wanders around for a short time. Some of the cells then dry up and form a stalk supporting an asexual reproductive structure in which yet other cells develop into spores. The cellular slime mold *Dictyostelium* is a useful model for researchers studying the genetic mechanisms and chemical changes underlying cellular differentiation (**Figure 16.18C**).

Figure 16.18B   A plasmodial slime mold: *Physarum*

Figure 16.18C   A group of amoeboid cells (left) and reproductive structure of a cellular slime mold, *Dictyostelium*

15×

? Contrast the plasmodium of a plasmodial slime mold with the slug-like stage of a cellular slime mold.

■ A plasmodium is not multicellular, but is one cytoplasmic mass with many nuclei; the slug-like stage of a cellular slime mold consists of many cells.

16.19   Foraminiferans and radiolarians have threadlike pseudopodia

Like amoebozoans, **foraminiferans** (forams) and radiolarians are protists that move and feed by means of pseudopodia. However, they can be distinguished from amoebozoans morphologically by their threadlike (rather than lobe-shaped) pseudopodia (**Figure 16.19A**). Molecular studies have confirmed that forams and radiolarians are only distantly related to amoebozoans.

Forams are found both in the ocean and in fresh water. They have porous shells, called tests, composed of organic material hardened by calcium carbonate. The pseudopodia, which function in feeding and locomotion, extend through small pores in the test (inset of Figure 16.19A). Ninety percent of forams that have been identified are fossils. The fossilized tests, which are a component of sedimentary rock, are excellent markers for correlating the ages of rocks in different parts of the world.

Like forams, **radiolarians** produce a mineralized support structure, in this case an internal skeleton made of silica (**Figure 16.19B**). The cell is also surrounded by a test composed of organic material. Most species of radiolarians are marine. When they die, their hard parts, like those of forams, settle to the bottom of the ocean and become part of the sediments. In some areas, radiolarians are so abundant that sediments, known as radiolarian ooze, are hundreds of meters thick.

? What minerals compose foram tests and radiolarian skeletons?

■ Forams, calcium carbonate; radiolarians, silica

LM 525×

42×

Figure 16.19A   A foraminiferan (inset SEM shows a foram test)

Figure 16.19B A radiolarian skeleton

16.20 Red algae and green algae are the closest relatives of land plants

As you learned in Module 16.12, autotrophic eukaryotes are thought to have arisen by primary endosymbiosis of a cyanobacterium that evolved into chloroplasts. The descendants of this ancient protist evolved into red algae and green algae.

The warm coastal waters of the tropics are home to the majority of species of **red algae.** Their red color comes from an accessory pigment that masks the green of chlorophyll. Red algae are typically soft-bodied, but some have cell walls encrusted with hard, chalky deposits. Encrusted species, such as the one in Figure 16.20A, are common on coral reefs, and their hard parts are important in reef building. Other red algae are commercially important. Carrageenan, a gel that is used to stabilize many products, including yogurt, chocolate milk, and pudding, is derived from species of red algae. Sheets of a red alga known as nori are used to wrap sushi. Agar, a polysaccharide used to grow bacteria, also comes from red algae.

Green algae, which are named for their grass-green chloroplasts, are split into two groups, the chlorophytes and the charophytes (see the phylogenetic tree in Figure 16.13). As you'll learn in Chapter 17, charophytes are the closest living relatives of land plants. The micrographs in Figure 16.20B show two types of green algae. *Chlamydomonas* is a unicellular alga common in freshwater lakes and ponds. It is propelled through the water by two flagella. (Such cells are said to be biflagellated.) *Volvox* is a colonial green alga. Each *Volvox* colony is a hollow ball composed of hundreds or thousands of biflagellated cells. The large colonies shown here will eventually release the small daughter colonies within them. Some marine green algae are large and complex enough to qualify as seaweeds.

Most green algae have complex life cycles. The life cycle of *Ulva*, or sea lettuce (Figure 16.20C), follows a pattern called **alternation of generations,** in which a multicellular diploid (2n) form alternates with a multicellular haploid (n) form. Alternation of generations occurs in a number of multicellular algae and in all plants. Notice in the figure that multicellular haploid forms are called **gametophytes.** The gametophyte generation alternates with a diploid generation that features a multicellular diploid form called a **sporophyte.** In *Ulva*, the gametophyte and sporophyte organisms are identical in appearance; both look like the one in the photograph, although they differ in chromosome number. The haploid gametophyte produces gametes by mitosis, and fusion of the gametes begins the sporophyte generation. In turn, cells in the sporophyte undergo meiosis and produce haploid, flagellated spores. The life cycle is completed when a spore settles to the bottom of the ocean and develops into a gametophyte.

Web Process of Science *What Kinds of Protists Are Found in Various Habitats?*

? What were the probable origins of the chloroplasts of green, red, and brown algae?

■ A cyanobacterial endosymbiont in both green and red algae; a red algal endosymbiont in brown algae

Figure 16.20A A red alga: an encrusted type, on a coral reef

Figure 16.20B Green algae, colonial and unicellular (inset)

Volvox colonies

Chlamydomonas

LM 1,200×

LM 80×

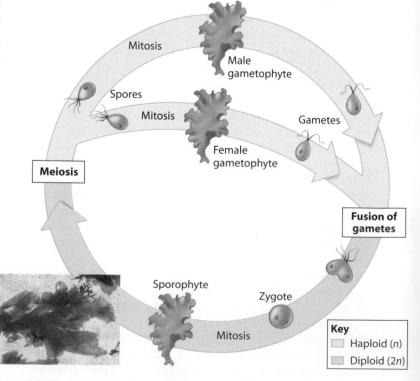

Mitosis

Male gametophyte

Spores

Mitosis

Gametes

Female gametophyte

Meiosis

Fusion of gametes

Sporophyte

Zygote

Mitosis

Key
Haploid (n)
Diploid (2n)

Figure 16.20C A multicellular green alga: *Ulva* (sea lettuce) and its life cycle

16.21 Multicellularity evolved several times in eukaryotes

Increased complexity often makes more variations possible. Thus, the origin of the eukaryotic cell led to an evolutionary radiation of new forms of life. As you saw in this chapter, unicellular protists, which are structurally complex eukaryotic cells, are much more diverse in form than the simpler prokaryotes. The evolution of multicellular bodies broke through another threshold in structural organization.

Multicellular organisms—seaweeds, plants, animals, and most fungi—are fundamentally different from unicellular ones. In a unicellular organism, all of life's activities occur within a single cell. In contrast, a multicellular organism has various specialized cells that perform different functions and are dependent on each other. For example, some cells give the organism its shape, while others make or procure food, transport materials, enable movement, or reproduce.

The most widely held view is that the organisms linking multicellular organisms to their unicellular ancestors were probably unicellular protists that lived as colonies, federations of independent cells sticking loosely together. Figure 16.21 suggests how a unicellular protist with flagellated cells may have formed colonies that eventually gave rise to multicellular organisms. ❶ An ancestral colony may have formed, as colonial protists do today, when a cell divided and its offspring remained attached to one another. ❷ Next, the cells in the colony may have become somewhat specialized and interdependent, with different cell types becoming more and more efficient at performing specific, limited tasks. ❸ Later on, additional specialization among the cells in the colony may have led to distinctions between sex cells (gametes) and nonreproductive cells (somatic cells).

We see specialization and cooperation among cells today in several colonial protists, such as the green alga *Volvox* in Figure 16.20B. *Volvox* produces gametes, which depend on somatic cells while developing. Cells in truly multicellular organisms, as we know them today, are specialized for many more nonreproductive functions, including feeding, waste disposal, gas exchange, and protection, to name a few. Evolution of the division of labor to this extent involved many additional steps in somatic cell specialization.

As you saw in Figure 16.13, at least three major lineages from the ancestral eukaryote led to multicellular forms: the stramenopile lineage led to brown algae, a currently unnamed lineage led to red algae, green algae, and land plants, and another lineage led to fungi and animals. In Chapter 18, you will meet the choanoflagellates, the protists that are the closest relatives of animals.

The oldest known fossils of multicellular eukaryotes are small multicellular algae that date from 1.2 billion years ago. For the next 600 million years or so, the fossil record remains somewhat scanty, but by about 600 million years ago, a variety of multicellular algae had evolved, along with some soft-bodied animals resembling corals, jellies, and worms.

A period of mass extinctions separated the Precambrian from the Paleozoic era, but multicellular life again flourished soon thereafter. By about 500 million years ago, diverse animals, fungi, and multicellular algae populated aquatic environments. All life was still aquatic.

Around 500 million years ago, the move onto land began, probably as certain green algae living along the edges of lakes gave rise to primitive plants. In the next chapter, we trace the long evolutionary movement of plants onto land and their diversification there. After that, we pick up the threads of animal evolution in Chapter 18.

> **?** In what way do multicellular organisms differ fundamentally from unicellular ones?

■ In unicellular organisms, all the functions of life are carried out within a single cell. Multicellular organisms have specialized cells that perform different functions.

Figure 16.21 A model for the evolution of a multicellular organism from a unicellular protist

Unicellular protist — *Colony* — *Early multicellular organism with specialized, interdependent cells* — *Later organism that produces gametes*

Labels: Locomotor cells; Food-synthesizing cells; Gamete; Somatic cells

Reviewing the Concepts

Prokaryotes (16.1–16.10)

Prokaryotes are the oldest life-forms and remain the most numerous and widespread organisms (**16.1**).

Domains Bacteria and Archaea are distinguished on the basis of nucleotide sequences and other molecular and cellular features (**16.2**). Prokaryotes may be shaped as spheres (cocci), rods (bacilli), and curves or spirals (**16.3**).

Structural features that help prokaryotes thrive virtually everywhere are protective cell walls, sticky capsules, pili that cling to surfaces, flagella that provide motility, and resistant endospores. Rapid growth contributes to success (**16.4**).

Nutritional modes of prokaryotes are diverse (**16.5**):

Nutritional Mode	Energy Source	Carbon Source
Photoautotroph	Sunlight	CO_2
Chemoautotroph	Inorganic chemicals	CO_2
Photoheterotroph	Sunlight	Organic compounds
Chemoheterotroph	Organic compounds	Organic compounds

Archaea are common in extreme environments, such as salt lakes, acidic hot springs, and deep-sea hydrothermal vents. They are also a major life-form in the ocean (**16.6**).

Bacteria are currently organized into several subgroups of proteobacteria, chlamydias, spirochetes, gram-positive bacteria, and cyanobacteria. Cyanobacteria photosynthesize in a plant-like way (**16.7**).

Pathogenic bacteria cause disease by producing exotoxins or endotoxins (**16.8**). Bacteria such as the species that cause anthrax and plague, and bacterial toxins such as botulinum can be used as biological weapons (**16.9**).

Bioremediation is the use of organisms to clean up pollution. Prokaryotes are decomposers in sewage treatment and can clean up oil spills and toxic mine wastes. Prokaryotes are vital to Earth's chemical cycles (**16.10**).

Protists (16.11–16.21)

Protists are a diverse collection of mostly unicellular eukaryotes that are found in a variety of aquatic or moist habitats. Molecular systematics is exploring protistan phylogeny (**16.11**).

Endosymbiosis of prokaryotic cells resulted in the evolution of eukaryotic cells containing mitochondria. Eukaryotic autotrophs arose by primary endosymbiosis of a heterotroph and cyanobacterium, leading to green algae and red algae. Secondary endosymbiosis of green algae by heterotrophic eukaryotes gave rise to the Euglenozoans. Secondary endosymbiosis of red algae by heterotrophic eukaryotes produced dinoflagellates, apicomplexans, and stramenopiles. Thus, protist diversity is largely the result of secondary endosymbiosis followed by the divergence of lineages (**16.12**).

Eukaryotic phylogeny, based on molecular systematics, has been proposed, but much of it is highly tentative. These organisms are very difficult to classify (**16.13**).

Diplomonads and parabasalids are mostly anaerobic protists that have modified mitochondria. The parasitic *Giardia* is a diplomonad. Termite endosymbionts and *Trichomonas vaginalis* are parabasalids (**16.14**).

Euglenozoans are a diverse clade of flagellated protists that includes trypanosomes (parasites that cause sleeping sickness) and *Euglena* (**16.15**).

Alveolates have membrane sacs under the plasma membrane. Dinoflagellates are unicellular algae; apicomplexans are parasites, such as *Plasmodium,* which causes malaria; ciliates use cilia to move and feed (**16.16**).

Stramenopiles are named for their "hairy" flagella. This clade includes fungus-like water molds, photosynthetic, unicellular diatoms, and brown algae—large, complex seaweeds. Kelp forms important marine habitats (**16.17**).

Amoebozoans include amoebas with lobe-shaped pseudopodia and slime molds. A plasmodial slime mold is a multinucleate plasmodium that forms reproductive structures under adverse conditions. Cellular slime molds have unicellular and multicellular stages (**16.18**).

Foraminiferans and radiolarians have threadlike pseudopodia. Forams have a calcium carbonate test and radiolarians have a skeleton composed of silica. The hard parts of both groups are a significant component of sediments wherever they occur (**16.19**).

Red and green algae are in the lineage that includes plants. Red algae contribute to coral reefs. Green algae may be unicellular, colonial, or multicellular. The life cycles of many algae involve the alternation of haploid gametophyte and diploid sporophyte generations (**16.20**).

Multicellularity evolved in several different lineages, probably by specialization of the cells of colonial protists. Multicellular life arose over a billion years ago (**16.21**).

Connecting the Concepts

1. Explain how each of the following characteristics contributes to the success of prokaryotes: cell wall, capsule, motility, rapid reproduction, endospores.

2. For each organism shown below, name the group it belongs to, and explain how the photo represents the group's characteristics.

(a)

(b)

(c)

(d)

Testing Your Knowledge

Multiple Choice

3. You set your time machine for 3 billion years ago and push the start button. When the dust clears, you look out the window. Which of the following describes what you would probably see?
   a. plants and animals very different from those alive today
   b. a cloud of gas and dust in space
   c. green scum in the water
   d. land and water sterile and devoid of life
   e. an endless expanse of red-hot molten rock

4. In terms of nutrition, autotrophs are to heterotrophs as
   a. kelp are to diatoms.
   b. archaea are to bacteria.
   c. slime molds are to algae.
   d. algae are to slime molds.
   e. pathogenic bacteria are to harmless bacteria.

5. The bacteria that cause tetanus can be killed only by prolonged heating at temperatures considerably above boiling. This suggests that tetanus bacteria
   a. have cell walls containing peptidoglycan.
   b. protect themselves by secreting antibiotics.
   c. secrete endotoxins.
   d. are autotrophic.
   e. produce endospores.

6. Glycolysis is the only metabolic pathway common to nearly all organisms. To scientists, this suggests that it
   a. evolved many times during the history of life.
   b. was first seen in early eukaryotes.
   c. appeared early in the history of life.
   d. must be very complex.
   e. appeared rather recently in the evolution of life.

7. A new organism has been discovered. Tests have revealed that it is unicellular, autotrophic, and has a cell wall that contains peptidoglycan. Based on this evidence, it should be classified as a(n)
   a. algae.
   b. archean.
   c. stramenopile.
   d. bacterium.
   e. apicomplexan.

8. Which pair of protists has support structures composed of silica?
   a. dinoflagellates and diatoms
   b. diatoms and radiolarians
   c. radiolarians and forams
   d. forams and diplomonads
   e. diplomonads and diatoms

9. Of the following groups, which is thought to have most recently shared a common ancestor with animals?
   a. red algae
   b. cellular slime molds
   c. brown algae
   d. dinoflagellates
   e. green algae

10. Which of the following groups is incorrectly paired with an example of that group?
    a. euglenozoans—trypanosome causing sleeping sickness
    b. alveolates—apicomplexan such as *Plasmodium*
    c. stramenopiles—brown algae
    d. amoebozoans—water mold
    e. diplomonads—*Giardia*

11. Which of the following prokaryotes is not pathogenic?
    a. *Chlamydia*
    b. *Rhizobium*
    c. *Streptococcus*
    d. *Salmonella*
    e. *Bacillus anthracis*

Describing, Comparing, and Explaining

12. How can antibiotics kill bacteria without harming the cells in our bodies?

13. Explain how protist diversity may have arisen through secondary endosymbiosis.

14. *Chlamydomonas* is a unicellular green alga. How does it differ from a photosynthetic bacterium, which is also single-celled? How does it differ from a protozoan, such as an amoeba? How does it differ from larger green algae, such as sea lettuce (*Ulva*)?

15. What characteristic distinguishes true multicellularity from colonies of cells?

Applying the Concepts

16. Imagine you are on a team designing a moon base that will be self-contained and self-sustaining. Once supplied with building materials, equipment, and organisms from Earth, the base will be expected to function indefinitely. One of the team members has suggested that everything sent to the base be sterilized so that no bacteria of any kind are present. Do you think this is a good idea? Predict some of the consequences of eliminating all bacteria from an environment.

17. The buildup of CO_2 in the atmosphere resulting from the burning of fossil fuels is regarded as a major contributor to global warming (see Module 7.13). Diatoms and other microscopic algae in the oceans counter this buildup by using large quantities of atmospheric CO_2 in photosynthesis, which requires small quantities of iron. Experts suspect that a shortage of iron may limit algal growth in the oceans. Some scientists have suggested that one way to reduce CO_2 buildup might be to fertilize the oceans with iron. The iron would stimulate algal growth and thus the removal of more CO_2 from the air. A single supertanker of iron dust, spread over a wide enough area, might reduce the atmospheric CO_2 level significantly. Do you think this approach would be worth a try? Why or why not?

Answers to all questions can be found in Appendix 4.

For Practice Quizzes, BioFlix, MP3 Tutors, and Activities, go to www.mybiology.com.

chapter 17

Plants, Fungi, and the Colonization of Land

Plant Evolution and Diversity

17.1 Plants have adaptations for life on land

🎧 17.2 Plant diversity reflects the evolutionary history of the plant kingdom

Alternation of Generations and Plant Life Cycles

🎧 17.3 Haploid and diploid generations alternate in plant life cycles

17.4 Mosses have a dominant gametophyte

17.5 Ferns, like most plants, have a dominant sporophyte

17.6 Seedless vascular plants dominated vast "coal forests"

17.7 A pine tree is a sporophyte with gametophytes in its cones

17.8 The flower is the centerpiece of angiosperm reproduction

17.9 The angiosperm plant is a sporophyte with gametophytes in its flowers

17.10 The structure of a fruit reflects its function in seed dispersal

17.11 Angiosperms sustain us—and add spice to our diets

17.12 Pollination by animals has influenced angiosperm evolution

17.13 Plant diversity is an irreplaceable resource

Fungi

17.14 Fungi absorb food after digesting it outside their bodies

17.15 Fungi produce spores in both asexual and sexual life cycles

17.16 Fungi are classified into five groups

17.17 Fungal groups differ in their life cycles and reproductive structures

17.18 Parasitic fungi harm plants and animals

17.19 Lichens consist of fungi living in close association with photosynthetic organisms

17.20 Some fungi have mutually beneficial relationships with ants

17.21 Fungi have enormous ecological benefits and practical uses

APPENDIX 1 Metric Conversion Table

Measurement	Unit and Abbreviation	Metric Equivalent	Approximate Metric-to-English Conversion Factor	Approximate English-to-Metric Conversion Factor
Length	1 kilometer (km)	= 1000 (10^3) meters	1 km = 0.6 mile	1 mile = 1.6 km
	1 meter (m)	= 100 (10^2) centimeters	1 m = 1.1 yards	1 yard = 0.9 m
		= 1000 millimeters	1 m = 3.3 feet	1 foot = 0.3 m
			1 m = 39.4 inches	
	1 centimeter (cm)	= 0.01 (10^{-2}) meter	1 cm = 0.4 inch	1 foot = 30.5 cm
				1 inch = 2.5 cm
	1 millimeter (mm)	= 0.001 (10^{-3}) meter	1 mm = 0.04 inch	
	1 micrometer (μm)	= 10^{-6} meter (10^{-3} mm)		
	1 nanometer (nm)	= 10^{-9} meter (10^{-3} μm)		
	1 angstrom (Å)	= 10^{-10} meter (10^{-4} μm)		
Area	1 hectare (ha)	= 10,000 square meters	1 ha = 2.5 acres	1 acre = 0.4 ha
	1 square meter (m^2)	= 10,000 square centimeters	1 m^2 = 1.2 square yards	1 square yard = 0.8 m^2
			1 m^2 = 10.8 square feet	1 square foot = 0.09 m^2
	1 square centimeter (cm^2)	= 100 square millimeters	1 cm^2 = 0.16 square inch	1 square inch = 6.5 cm^2
Mass	1 metric ton (t)	= 1000 kilograms	1 t = 1.1 tons	1 ton = 0.91 t
	1 kilogram (kg)	= 1000 grams	1 kg = 2.2 pounds	1 pound = 0.45 kg
	1 gram (g)	= 1000 milligrams	1 g = 0.04 ounce	1 ounce = 28.35 g
			1 g = 15.4 grains	
	1 milligram (mg)	= 10^{-3} gram	1 mg = 0.02 grain	
	1 microgram (mg)	= 10^{-6} gram		
Volume (Solids)	1 cubic meter (m^3)	= 1,000,000 cubic centimeters	1 m^3 = 1.3 cubic yards	1 cubic yard = 0.8 m^3
			1 m^3 = 35.3 cubic feet	1 cubic feet = 0.03 m^3
	1 cubic centimeter (cm^3 or cc)	= 10^{-6} cubic meter	1 cm^3 = 0.06 cubic inch	1 cubic inch = 16.4 cm^3
	1 cubic millimeter (mm^3)	= 10^{-9} cubic meter (10^{-3} cubic centimeter)		
Volume (Liquids and Gases)	1 kiloliter (kL or kl)	= 1000 liters	1 kL = 264.2 gallons	1 gallon = 3.79 L
	1 liter (L)	= 1000 milliliters	1 L = 0.26 gallon	1 quart = 0.95 L
			1 L = 1.06 quarts	
	1 milliliter (mL or ml)	= 10^{-3} liter	1 mL = 0.03 fluid ounce	1 quart = 946 mL
		= 1 cubic centimeter	1 mL = approx. $\frac{1}{4}$ teaspoon	1 pint = 473 mL
			1 mL = approx. 15–16 drops	1 fluid ounce = 29.6 mL
				1 teaspoon = approx. 5 mL
Volume (Liquids and Gases)	1 microliter (ml or mL)	= 10^{-6} liter (10^{-3} milliliters)		
Time	1 second (s)	= $\frac{1}{60}$ minute		
	1 millisecond (ms)	= 10^{-3} second		
Temperature	Degrees Celsius (°C)		°F = $\frac{9}{5}$ °C − 32	°C = $\frac{5}{9}$(°F − 32)

APPENDIX 2 The Periodic Table

Groups: Elements in a vertical column have the same number of electrons in their valence (outer) shell and thus have similar chemical properties.

Period: Each horizontal row contains elements with the same total number of electron shells. Across each period, elements are ordered by increasing atomic number.

Noble gases are elements with full valence shells and thus do not react readily with other elements.

Noble gases →

Transition elements

Metals
Metalloids
Nonmetals

Period Number	Group 1A	Group 2A	3B	4B	5B	6B	7B	8B	8B	8B	1B	2B	13 Group 3A	14 Group 4A	15 Group 5A	16 Group 6A	17 Group 7A	18 Group 8A
1	H 1.008																	He 4.003
2	Li 6.941	Be 9.012											B 10.81	C 12.01	N 14.01	O 16.00	F 19.00	Ne 20.18
3	Na 22.99	Mg 24.31											Al 26.98	Si 28.09	P 30.97	S 32.07	Cl 35.45	Ar 39.95
4	K 39.10	Ca 40.08	Sc 44.96	Ti 47.87	V 50.94	Cr 52.00	Mn 54.94	Fe 55.85	Co 58.93	Ni 58.69	Cu 63.55	Zn 65.41	Ga 69.72	Ge 72.64	As 74.92	Se 78.96	Br 79.90	Kr 83.80
5	Rb 85.47	Sr 87.62	Y 88.91	Zr 91.22	Nb 92.91	Mo 95.94	Tc (98)	Ru 101.1	Rh 102.9	Pd 106.4	Ag 107.9	Cd 112.4	In 114.8	Sn 118.7	Sb 121.8	Te 127.6	I 126.9	Xe 131.3
6	Cs 132.9	Ba 137.3	La 138.9	Hf 178.5	Ta 180.9	W 183.8	Re 186.2	Os 190.2	Ir 192.2	Pt 195.1	Au 197.0	Hg 200.6	Tl 204.4	Pb 207.2	Bi 209.0	Po (209)	At (210)	Rn (222)
7	Fr (223)	Ra (226)	Ac (227)	Rf (261)	Db (262)	Sg (266)	Bh (264)	Hs (269)	Mt (268)	Ds (271)	— (272)	— (285)	— (284)	— (289)	— (288)			

Atomic numbers (row 4): 19 K, 20 Ca, 21 Sc, 22 Ti, 23 V, 24 Cr, 25 Mn, 26 Fe, 27 Co, 28 Ni, 29 Cu, 30 Zn, 31 Ga, 32 Ge, 33 As, 34 Se, 35 Br, 36 Kr.
(row 5): 37, 38, 39, 40, 41, 42, 43, 44, 45, 46, 47, 48, 49, 50, 51, 52, 53, 54.
(row 6): 55, 56, 57, 72, 73, 74, 75, 76, 77, 78, 79, 80, 81, 82, 83, 84, 85, 86.
(row 7): 87, 88, 89, 104, 105, 106, 107, 108, 109, 110, 111, 112, 113, 114, 115.

*Lanthanides

58 Ce 140.1	59 Pr 140.9	60 Nd 144.2	61 Pm (145)	62 Sm 150.4	63 Eu 152.0	64 Gd 157.3	65 Tb 158.9	66 Dy 162.5	67 Ho 164.9	68 Er 167.3	69 Tm 168.9	70 Yb 173.0	71 Lu 175.0

†Actinides

90 Th 232.0	91 Pa 231.0	92 U 238.0	93 Np (237)	94 Pu (244)	95 Am (243)	96 Cm (247)	97 Bk (247)	98 Cf (251)	99 Es 252	100 Fm 257	101 Md 258	102 No 259	103 Lr 260

Atomic number (number of protons) → 6
Element symbol (see table above) → C
Atomic mass (number of protons plus number of neutrons averaged over all isotopes) → 12.01

Name	Symbol											
Actinium	Ac	Cesium	Cs	Hafnium	Hf	Mercury	Hg	Protactinium	Pa	Tellurium	Te
Aluminum	Al	Chlorine	Cl	Hassium	Hs	Molybdenum	Mo	Radium	Ra	Terbium	Tb
Americium	Am	Chromium	Cr	Helium	He	Neodymium	Nd	Radon	Rn	Thallium	Ti
Antimony	Sb	Cobalt	Co	Holmium	Ho	Neon	Ne	Rhenium	Re	Thorium	Th
Argon	Ar	Copper	Cu	Hydrogen	H	Neptunium	Np	Rhodium	Rh	Thulium	Tm
Arsenic	As	Curium	Cm	Indium	In	Nickel	Ni	Rubidium	Rb	Tin	Sn
Astatine	At	Darmstadtium	Ds	Iodine	I	Niobium	Nb	Ruthenium	Ru	Titanium	Ti
Barlium	Ba	Dubnium	Db	Iridium	Ir	Nitrogen	N	Rutherfordium	Rf	Tungsten	W
Berkelium	Bk	Dysprosium	Dy	Iron	Fe	Nobelium	No	Samarium	Sm	Uranium	U
Beryllium	Be	Einsteinium	Es	Krypton	Kr	Osmium	Os	Scandium	Sc	Vanadium	V
Bismuth	Bi	Erbium	Er	Lanthanum	La	Oxygen	O	Seaborgium	Sg	Xenon	Xe
Bohrium	Bh	Europium	Eu	Lawrencium	Lr	Palladium	Pd	Selenium	Se	Ytterbium	Yb
Boron	B	Fermium	Fm	Lead	Pb	Phosphorous	P	Silicon	Si	Yttrium	Y
Bromine	Br	Fluorine	F	Lithium	Li	Platinum	Pt	Silver	Ag	Zinc	Zn
Cadmium	Cd	Francium	Fr	Lutetium	Lu	Plutonium	Pu	Sodium	Na	Zirconium	Zr
Calcium	Ca	Gadolinium	Gd	Magnesium	Mg	Polonium	Po	Strontium	Sr		
Californium	Cf	Gallium	Ga	Manganese	Mn	Potassium	K	Sulfur	S		
Carbon	C	Germanium	Ge	Meitnerium	Mt	Praseodymium	Pr	Tantalum	Ta		
Cerium	Ce	Gold	Au	Mendelevium	Md	Promethium	Pm	Technetium	Tc		

APPENDIX 3 The Amino Acids of Proteins

HYDROPHOBIC (Nonpolar)

GLYCINE (Gly) ALANINE (Ala) VALINE (Val) LEUCINE (Leu) ISOLEUCINE (Ile)

METHIONINE (Met) PHENYLALANINE (Phe) TRYPTOPHAN (Trp) PROLINE (Pro)

HYDROPHILIC (polar or charged)

SERINE (Ser) THREONINE (Thr) CYSTEINE (Cys) TYROSINE (Tyr) ASPARAGINE (Asn) GLUTAMINE (Gln)

Acidic

Basic

ASPARTIC ACID (Asp) GLUTAMIC ACID (Glu) LYSINE (Lys) ARGININE (Arg) HISTIDINE (His)

Chapter 1

1. The vertical scale of biology refers to the hierarchy of biological organization: from molecules to organelles, cells, tissues, organs, organ systems, organisms, populations, communities, ecosystems, and biosphere. At each level, emergent properties arise from the interaction and organization of component parts. The horizontal scale of biology refers to the incredible diversity of living organisms, past and present, including the 1.8 million species that have been named so far, which can be grouped into three domains—Bacteria, Archaea, and Eukarya—and divided among numerous kingdoms.

2. a. life; b. evolution; c. natural selection; d. unity of life; e. three domains (or numerous kingdoms; 1.8 million species)

3. d **4.** c **5.** e (You may have been tempted to choose b, the molecular level. However, protists may have chemical communication or interactions with other protists. No protists, however, have organs.) **6.** d **7.** c **8.** b **9.** d

10. Both energy and chemical nutrients are passed through an ecosystem from producers to consumers to decomposers. But energy enters an ecosystem as sunlight and leaves as heat. Chemical nutrients are recycled from the abiotic soil or atmosphere through plants, consumers, and decomposers and returned to the air, soil, and water.

11. Darwin described how natural selection operates in populations whose individuals have varied traits that are inherited. When natural selection favors the reproductive success of certain individuals in a population more than others, it changes the proportions of heritable variations in the population, gradually adapting a population to its environment.

12. In pursuit of answers to questions about nature, a scientist uses a logical thought process involving the key elements: observations about natural phenomena, questions derived from observations, hypotheses posed as tentative explanations of observations, logical predictions of the outcome of tests if the hypotheses are true, and actual tests of hypotheses. Scientific research is not a rigid method because a scientist must adapt these key components to the set of conditions particular to each study. Intuition, chance, and luck are also part of science.

13. Technology is the application of scientific knowledge. For example, the use of solar power to run a calculator or heat a home is an application of our knowledge, derived by the scientific process, of the nature of light as a type of energy and how light energy can be converted to other forms of energy. Another example is the use of pieces of DNA removed from bacteria to insert new genes into crop plants. This process, often called genetic engineering, stems from decades of scientific research on the structure and function of DNA from many kinds of organisms.

14. Natural selection screens heritable variations by favoring the reproductive success of some individuals over others. These individuals pass more genes to the next generation than individuals that are not favored. As a result, the genetic makeup of a population changes. The change results from a screening (editing) of individuals (and consequently their genes), not from the creation of new genes or new individuals.

15. a. Hypothesis: Giving rewards to mice will improve their learning. Prediction: If mice are rewarded with food, they will learn to run a maze faster.
    b. The control group was the mice that were not rewarded. Without them, it would be impossible to know if the mice that were rewarded decreased their time running the maze only because of practice.
    c. Both groups of mice should be about the same age. Both experiments should be run at the same time of day and under the same conditions.
    d. Yes, the data show that the rewarded mice began to run the maze faster by day 3, and improved their performance (ran faster than the control mice) each day thereafter.

16. The researcher needed to compare the number of attacks on artificial king snakes with attacks on artificial brown snakes. It may be that there were simply more predators in the coral snake areas or that the predators were hungrier than the predators in the other areas. The experiment needed a control and proper data analysis.

17. If these cell division control genes are involved in producing the larger tomato, they may have similar effects if transferred to other fruits or vegetables. Cancer is a result of uncontrolled cell division. One could see if there are similarities between the tomato genes and any human genes that could be related to human development or disease. The control of cell division is a fundamental process in growth, repair, and asexual reproduction—all important topics in biology.

18. Virtually any news report or magazine contains stories that are mainly about biology or at least have biological connections. How about biological connections in advertisements?

Chapter 2

1. a. protons; b. neutrons; c. electrons; d. different isotopes; e. covalent bonds; f. ionic bonds; g. polar covalent bonds; h. hydrogen bonding

2.

```
                    ┌─────────────┐
                    │    Water    │
                    └─────────────┘
              is a      has    readily
                               forms
   ┌──────────────┐      ┌─────────────────┐
   │polar molecule│      │ hydrogen bonds  │
   └──────────────┘      └─────────────────┘
       contributes  contributes
           to           to      weak attractions
                                    between
            ┌──────────────────┐
            │ life-supporting  │    ┌──────────────┐ ┌──────────────┐
            │   properties     │    │ positively   │ │ negatively   │
            └──────────────────┘    │ charged H    │ │ charged O    │
      polarity                      └──────────────┘ └──────────────┘
      makes a    hydrogen    breaking and
                bonds make  forming hydrogen
                               bonds
  ┌──────────┐ ┌──────────┐ ┌──────────┐ ┌──────────────┐
  │versatile │ │liquid    │ │  ice     │ │help moderate │
  │ solvent  │ │water     │ │ floats   │ │ temperature  │
  └──────────┘ │cohesive  │ └──────────┘ └──────────────┘
               └──────────┘
```

3. c 4. b 5. c 6. e 7. a (It needs to share 2 more electrons for a full outer shell of 8.) 8. a 9. c 10. d 11. F (Only salt and water are compounds; carbon is an element.) 12. F (The smallest particle of an element is an atom.) 13. T 14. T 15. F (Water molecules in ice are farther apart.) 16. T 17. F (Most acid precipitation results from burning fossil fuels.) 18. T

19. For a diagram, see Figure 2.10. Water molecules form hydrogen bonds because they are polar. Their slightly negative O atoms are attracted to the slightly positive H atoms of neighboring molecules. The unique properties of water that result from hydrogen bonding are cohesion, adhesion, surface tension, the ability to absorb and store large amounts of heat, a solid form (ice) that is less dense than liquid water, and solvent properties.

20. First: Because increasing the temperature of water (the average speed of its molecules) requires breaking hydrogen bonds, a process that uses heat, a large amount of heat can be added to water before the water's temperature starts to rise. Conversely, when the surrounding temperature falls, new hydrogen bonds form in water, with the release of heat that slows the cooling process. Second: When the body becomes overheated, water evaporating from its surface decreases the body's temperature (evaporative cooling) because the hotter water molecules leave.

21. A covalent bond forms when atoms complete their outer shells by sharing electrons. Atoms can also complete their outer shells by gaining or losing electrons. This leaves the atoms as ions, with $+$ and $-$ charges. The oppositely charged ions are attracted to each other, forming an ionic bond.

22. An acid is a compound that donates hydrogen ions (H^+) to a solution. A base is a compound that accepts hydrogen ions and removes them from solution. Acidity is described by the pH scale, which measures H^+ concentration on a scale of 0 (most acidic) to 14 (most basic).

23. Fluorine needs 1 electron for a full outer shell of 8, and if potassium loses 1 electron, its outer shell will have 8. Potassium will lose an electron (becoming a $+$ ion), and fluorine will pick it up (becoming a $-$ ion). The ions will form an ionic bond.

24. Give a mouse sugar or oxygen gas containing a radioactive isotope of oxygen. See whether the carbon dioxide it exhales is radioactive.

25. The elements in a row all have the same number of electron shells. In a column, all the elements have the same number of electrons in their outer shell.

26. Some issues and questions to consider: Which is less expensive, power from nuclear power plants or power from fossil fuel plants? Does the price of electricity reflect its actual cost, including environmental costs? Which would be more harmful: the environmental effects of acid rain and global warming from fossil fuel power plants or the effects of nuclear wastes and potential nuclear accidents? Do you favor development of nuclear energy or fossil fuel power plants? Which would you prefer to have near you? Do your answers to these last two questions differ? If so, why?

Chapter 3

1. Carbon forms four covalent bonds, either with other carbon atoms, producing chains or rings of various lengths and shapes, or with other atoms, such as characteristic chemical groups that confer specific properties on a molecule. This is the basis for the incredible diversity of organic compounds. Organisms can link a small number of monomers into different arrangements to produce a huge variety of polymers.

2. a. glucose; b. energy storage; c. cellulose; d. fats; e. cell membrane component; f. steroids; g. amino group; h. carboxyl group; i. R group; j. enzyme; k. structural protein; l. movement; m. hemoglobin; n. defense; o. phosphate group; p. nitrogenous base; q. ribose or deoxyribose; r. DNA; s. code for proteins

3. d (The second kind of molecule is a polymer of the first.) 4. c 5. d 6. c 7. a 8. b 9. e 10. d

11. Fats (triglycerides)—store energy. Phospholipids—are major components of membranes. Steroids—one kind, cholesterol, is a component of cell membranes; other kinds function as hormones.

12. Weak bonds that stabilize the three-dimensional structure of a protein are disrupted, and the protein unfolds. Function depends on shape, so if the protein is the wrong shape, it won't function properly.

13. Proteins are made of 20 amino acids arranged in many different sequences into chains of many different lengths. Genes, defined stretches of DNA, dictate the amino acid sequences of proteins in the cell.

14. Proteins function as enzymes to catalyze chemical reactions. They also function in structure, contraction, transport,

defense, signaling, signal reception, and storage of amino acids (see Module 3.11).

15. The sequence of nucleotides in DNA is transcribed into a sequence of nucleotides in RNA, which determines the sequence of amino acids that will be used to build a polypeptide. Proteins mediate all the activities of a cell; thus, by coding for proteins, DNA controls the functions of a cell.

16. This is a hydrolysis reaction, which consumes water. It is essentially the reverse of the diagram in Figure 3.5, except note that fructose has a different shape than glucose.

17. Circle NH_2, an amino group; COOH, a carboxyl group; and OH, a hydroxyl group on the R group. This is an amino acid, a monomer of proteins. The OH group makes it a polar amino acid.

18. Some issues and questions to consider: How will you choose your test subjects? How many subjects should you have? Will you give them all vitamin C, or just some of them? What criteria will you use to divide the test subjects into groups? What is a control group? Should the subjects know whether they are getting vitamin C or not? Should the experimenters who are giving out the drug and measuring the severity of cold symptoms know which of the subjects are getting vitamin C? What is a double-blind study? If there is a difference between your groups, can you be sure it can be attributed to vitamin C dosing?

19. a. A: at about 37°C; B: at about 78°C.
    b. A: from humans (human body temperature is about 37°C; B: from thermophilic bacteria.
    c. Above 40°C, the human enzyme denatures and loses its shape and thus its function. The increased thermal energy disrupts the weak bonds that maintain secondary and tertiary structure in an enzyme.

20. Silicon has four electrons in its outer electron shell, as does carbon. One would predict that silicon could thus form complex molecules by binding with four partners. Neon has a filled outer shell and is nonreactive. Sulfur can only form two covalent bonds and thus would not have the versatility of carbon or silicon.

Chapter 4

1. a. nucleus; b. nucleolus; c. ribosomes; d. Golgi apparatus; e. plasma membrane; f. mitochondrion; g. cytoskeleton; h. peroxisome; i. centriole; j. lysosome; k. rough endoplasmic reticulum; l. smooth endoplasmic reticulum. For functions, see Table 4.23.

2. flagellum or cilia (in some cells), lysosome, centriole (involved with microtubule formation)

3. chloroplast, central vacuole, cell wall

4. d 5. c (Small cells have a greater ratio of surface area to volume.) 6. b 7. d 8. e 9. a 10. c 11. b 12. d 13. c 14. d

15. DNA as genetic material, ribosomes, plasma membrane

16. Tight junctions form leakproof sheets of cells. Anchoring junctions link cells to each other but allow materials to pass

between them; they form strong sheets of cells. Gap junctions are channels that allow flow from cell to cell.

17. Both process energy. A chloroplast converts light energy to chemical energy (sugar molecules). A mitochondrion converts chemical energy (food molecules) to another form of chemical energy (ATP).

18. Different conditions and conflicting processes can occur simultaneously within separate, membrane-enclosed compartments. Also, there is increased area for membrane-attached enzymes that carry out metabolic processes.

19. Cilia may propel a cell through its environment or sweep a fluid environment past the cell.

20. A protein inside the ER is packaged inside transport vesicles that bud off the ER and then join to the Golgi apparatus. A transport vesicle containing the finished protein product then buds off the Golgi and travels to and joins with the plasma membrane, expelling the protein from the cell.

21. Part true, part false. Both animal and plant cells have mitochondria.

22. The plasma membrane is a phospholipid bilayer with the hydrophilic heads facing the aqueous environment on both sides and the hydrophobic fatty acid tails mingling in the center of the membrane. Proteins are embedded in and attached to this membrane. Microfilaments form a three-dimensional network just inside the plasma membrane. The extracellular matrix outside the membrane is composed largely of glycoproteins, which may be attached to membrane proteins called integrins. Integrins can transmit information from the ECM to microfilaments on the other side of the membrane.

23. Cell 1: $S = 1,256 \ \mu m^2$; $V = 4,187 \ \mu m^3$; $S/V = 0.3$. Cell 2: $S = 5,024 \ \mu m^2$; $V = 33,493 \ \mu m^3$; $S/V = 0.15$. The smaller cell has a larger surface area relative to volume for absorbing food and oxygen and excreting waste. Small cells thus perform these activities more efficiently.

24. Individuals with PCD have nonfunctional cilia and flagella due to a lack of dynein motor proteins. This defect would also mean that the cilia involved in left-right pattern formation in the embryo would not be able to set up the fluid flow that initiates the normal arrangement of organs.

25. A single layer of phospholipids surrounding the oil droplet would have their hydrophobic fatty acid tails associated with the hydrophobic oil and their hydrophilic heads facing the aqueous environment of the cell outside the droplet.

Hydrophobic tails

Oil droplet

Hydrophilic head of phospholipid

26. Some issues and questions to consider: Were the cells the patient's property, a gift, or just surplus? Was he asked to donate the cells? Was he informed about how the cells might be used? Is it important to ask permission or inform the patient in such a case? How much did the researchers modify the cells? What did they have to do to them to sell the product? Do the researchers and the university have a right to make money from patient's cells? Is the fact that they saved the patient's life a factor? Does the patient have the right to sell his cells? Would he have been able to sell the cells without the researchers' help?

Chapter 5

1. a. active transport; b. concentration gradient; c. small nonpolar molecules; d. facilitated diffusion; e. transport proteins

2. a. enzyme; b. active site of enzyme; c. substrate; d. substrate in active site; induced fit strains substrate bonds; e. substrate converted to products; f. product molecules released; enzyme is ready for next catalytic cycle

3. b 4. d 5. e 6. c (Only active transport can move solute against a concentration gradient.) 7. d 8. b

9. Aquaporins are water transport channels that allow for very rapid diffusion of water through a cell membrane. They are found in cells that have high water-transport needs, such as blood cells, kidney cells, and plant cells.

10. Energy is neither created nor destroyed but can be transferred and transformed. Plants transform the energy of sunlight into chemical energy stored in organic molecules. Almost all organisms rely on the products of photosynthesis for the source of their energy. In every energy transfer or transformation, disorder increases as some energy is lost to the random motion of heat.

11. The work of cells falls into three main categories: mechanical, chemical, and transport. ATP provides the energy for cellular work, usually by transferring a phosphate group to a protein (movement and transport) or a substrate (chemical).

12. Energy is stored in the chemical bonds of organic molecules. The barrier of E_A prevents these molecules from spontaneously breaking down and releasing that energy. When a substrate fits into an enzyme's active site with an induced fit, its bonds may be strained and thus easier to break, or the active site may orient two substrates in such a way as to facilitate the reaction.

13. Cell membranes are composed of a lipid bilayer with embedded proteins. The bilayer creates the hydrophobic boundary between cells and their surroundings (or between organelles and the cytoplasm). The proteins perform the many functions of membranes, such as enzyme action, transport, attachment, and signaling.

14. Inhibitors that are toxins or poisons irreversibly inhibit key cellular enzymes. Inhibitors that are designed as drugs are beneficial if they interfere with the enzymes of bacterial or viral invaders or cancer cells. Cells use feedback inhibition

of enzymes in metabolic pathways as important mechanisms that conserve resources.

15. Heating, pickling, and salting denature enzymes, changing their shapes so they do not fit substrates. Freezing decreases the kinetic energy of molecules, so they lack energy of activation, even in the presence of enzymes.

16. a. The more enzyme present, the faster the rate of reaction, because it is more likely that enzyme and substrate molecules will meet.

b. The more substrate present, the faster the reaction, for the same reason, but only up to a point. An enzyme molecule can work only so fast; once it is saturated (working at top speed), more substrate does not increase the rate.

17. The black curve on the left would correspond to the stomach enzyme pepsin, which has a lower optimal pH as is found in the stomach; the red curve on the right would correspond to trypsin, which has a higher optimal pH. The curve for a lysosomal enzyme should have an optimal pH at 4.5.

18. Some issues and questions to consider: Does a woman have a right to work in an unsafe environment, even if it may put her child at risk? What are the rights of the child? Does the company have the right to "protect" women who are not pregnant? Is the company trying to protect the mother and child or protect itself from a potential lawsuit? Who is responsible for protecting employees and their children? The employees? The company? The government?

Chapter 6

1. a. glycolysis; b. citric acid cycle; c. oxidative phosphorylation; d. oxygen; e. electron transport chain; f. CO_2 and H_2O

2. e 3. c (NAD^+ and FAD, which are recycled by electron transport, are limited.) 4. e 5. d 6. c 7. b (at the same time NADH is oxidized to NAD^+) 8. a

9. Glycolysis is considered the most ancient because it occurs in all living cells and doesn't require oxygen or membrane-enclosed organelles.

10. Oxygen picks up electrons from the oxidation of glucose at the end of the electron transport chain. Carbon dioxide results from the oxidation of glucose. It is released in the grooming of pyruvate and the citric acid cycle.

11. In lactic acid fermentation (in muscle cells), pyruvate is reduced by NADH to form lactate, and NAD^+ is recycled. In alcohol fermentation, pyruvate is broken down to CO_2 and ethanol as NADH is oxidized to NAD^+. Both types of fermentation allow glycolysis to continue to produce 2 ATP/glucose by recycling NAD^+.

12. As carbohydrates are broken down in glycolysis and the grooming of pyruvate, glycerol can be made from G3P and fatty acids from acetyl CoA. Amino groups, containing N atoms, must be supplied to various intermediates of glycolysis and the citric acid cycle to produce amino acids.

13. 100 kcal per day is 700 kcal per week. On the basis of Table 6.4, walking 3 mph would require $\frac{700}{245}$ = about 2.8 hr; swimming, 1.7 hr; running, 0.7 hr.

14. NAD^+ and FAD are not used up but are recycled. NAD^+ and FAD are recycled between the electron transport chain and glycolysis or the citric acid cycle. We need a small additional supply to replace those that are damaged.

15. a. No, this shows the blue color getting more intense. The reaction decolorizes the blue dye.
    b. No, this shows the dye being decolorized, but it also shows the three mixtures with different initial color intensities. The intensities should have started out the same, since all mixtures used the same concentration of dye.
    c. Correct. The mixtures all start out the same, and then the ones with more succinate (reactant) decolorize faster. The mixture with the highest concentration of succinate decolorizes the fastest.

16. The presence of ATP synthase enzymes in prokaryotic plasma membranes and the inner membrane of mitochondria provides support for the hypothesis of endosymbiosis—that mitochondria evolved from an engulfed prokaryote that used aerobic respiration (see Module 4.16).

17. Some issues and questions to consider: Is your customer aware of the danger? Do you have an obligation to protect the customer, even against her wishes? Does your employer have the right to dismiss you for informing the customer? For refusing to serve the customer? Could you or the restaurant later be held liable for injury to the fetus? Or is the mother responsible for willfully disregarding warnings about drinking?

Chapter 7

1. a. electron transport chain; b. ATP synthase; c. thylakoid space (higher H^+ concentration); d. stroma; e. ATP

2. In chemiosmosis in mitochondria: a. Electrons come from food molecules. b. Electrons get their energy from the chemical energy of bonds in organic molecules. c. Electrons are passed to oxygen, which picks up H^+ and forms water.

   In chemiosmosis in chloroplasts: a. Electrons come from splitting of water. b. Light energy excites the electrons. c. Electrons flow from water to the reaction center chlorophyll in photosystem II to the reaction center chlorophyll in photosystem I to NADPH.

   In both processes: d. Energy released by redox reactions in the electron transport chain is used to transport H^+ across a membrane. The flow of H^+ down its concentration gradient back through ATP synthase drives the phosphorylation of ADP to make ATP.

3. a. light energy; b. light reactions; c. Calvin cycle; d. O_2 released; e. electron transport chain; f. NADPH; g. ATP; h. 3-PGA is reduced

4. d 5. c 6. c 7. b 8. a 9. e 10. c (NADPH and ATP from the light reactions are used by the Calvin cycle.) 11. d 12. e

13. Light reactions: light and water are inputs; ATP, NADPH, and O_2, are outputs. Calvin cycle: CO_2, ATP, and NADPH are inputs; G3P, ADP, and $NADP^+$ are outputs.

14. Plants can break down the sugar for energy in cellular respiration or use the sugar as a raw material for making other organic molecules. Excess sugar is stored as starch.

15. Some issues and questions to consider: What are the risks that we take and costs we must pay if global warming continues? How certain do we have to be that warming is caused by human activities before we act? What can we do to reduce CO_2 emissions? What are the risks and costs if we reduce CO_2 emissions and greenhouse warming turns out not to be a real threat? Is it possible that the costs and sacrifices of reducing CO_2 emissions might actually improve our lifestyle?

16. Some issues and questions to consider: How much land would be required for large-scale conversion to biomass energy? Would different power plants have to be built? How do the benefits of energy plantations (habitat for wildlife, reduced erosion, diversification for farmers) compare with the benefits of fossil fuel harvesting? Is there a difference in net output of CO_2 between production and use of fossil fuels and production and use of biomass energy? Which one offers a more long-term solution to energy needs?

Chapter 8

1.

	Mitosis	Meiosis
Number of chromosomal duplications	*1*	*1*
Number of cell divisions	*1*	*2*
Number of daughter cells produced	*2*	*4*
Number of chromosomes in daughter cells	*Diploid* (2n)	*Haploid* (n)
How chromosomes line up during metaphase	*Singly*	*In tetrads (metaphase I), then singly (metaphase II)*
Genetic relationship of daughter cells to parent cell	*Genetically identical*	*Genetically unique*
Functions performed in the human body	*Growth, development, repair*	*Production of gametes*

2. c 3. a 4. b 5. c 6. e (A diploid cell would have an even number of chromosomes; the odd number suggests that meiosis I has been completed. Sister chromatids are together only in prophase and metaphase of meiosis II.)
7. c 8. b 9. c 10. b 11. d

12. Various orientations of chromosomes at metaphase I of meiosis lead to different combinations of chromosomes in gametes. Crossing over during prophase I results in an exchange of chromosome segments and new combinations of genes. Random fertilization of eggs by sperm further increases possibilities for variation in offspring.

13. Interphase (for example, third column from left in micrograph, third cell from top): Growth; metabolic activity; DNA synthesis. Prophase (for example, second column, cell at bottom): Chromosomes shorten and thicken; mitotic spindle forms. Metaphase (for example, first column, middle cell): Chromosomes line up on a plane going through the cell's equator. Anaphase (for example, third column, second cell from top): Sister chromatids separate and move to the poles of the cell. Telophase (for example, fourth column, fourth complete cell from top): Daughter nuclei form around chromosomes; cytokinesis usually occurs.

14. In culture, normal cells usually divide only when they are in contact with a surface but not touching other cells on all sides (the cells usually grow to form only a single layer). The density-dependent inhibition of cell division apparently results from local depletion of substances called growth factors. Growth factors are proteins secreted by certain cells that stimulate other cells to divide; they act via signal transduction pathways to signal the cell cycle control system of the affected cell to proceed past its checkpoints. The cell cycle control systems of cancer cells do not function properly. Cancer cells generally do not require externally supplied growth factors to complete the cell cycle, and they divide indefinitely (in contrast to normal mammalian cells, which stop dividing after 20–50 generations)—two reasons why they are relatively easy to grow in the lab. Furthermore, cancer cells can often grow without contacting a solid surface, making it possible to culture them in suspension in a liquid medium.

15. A ring of microfilaments pinches an animal cell in two, a process called cleavage. In a plant cell, membranous vesicles form a disk called the cell plate at the midline of the parent cell, cell plate membranes fuse with the plasma membrane, and a cell wall grows in the space, separating the daughter cells.

16. See Figures 8.21A and 8.21B.

17. a. No. For this to happen, the chromosomes of the two gametes that fused would have to represent, together, a complete set of the donor's maternal chromosomes (the ones that originally came from the donor's mother) and a complete set of the donor's paternal chromosomes (from the donor's father). It is much more likely that the zygote would be missing one or more maternal chromosomes and would have an excess of paternal chromosomes, or vice versa.
   b. Correct. Consider what would have to happen to produce a zygote genetically identical to the gamete donor: The zygote would have to have a complete set of the donor's maternal chromosomes and a complete set of the donor's paternal chromosomes. The first gamete in this union could contain any mixture of maternal and paternal chromosomes, but once that first gamete was "chosen," the second one would have to have one particular combination of chromosomes—the combination that supplies whatever the first gamete did not supply. So, for example, if the first three chromosomes of the first gamete were maternal, maternal, and paternal, the first three of the second gamete would have to be paternal, paternal, and maternal. The chance that all 23 chromosome pairs would be complementary in this way is only one in 22^3 (that is, one in 8,388,608). Because of independent assortment, it is much more likely that the zygote would have an unpredictable combination of chromosomes from the donor's father and mother.
   c. No. First, the zygote could not be genetically identical to the gamete donor (see b). Second, the zygote could not be identical to either of the gamete donor's parents because the donor only has half the genetic material of each of his or her parents. For example, even if the zygote were formed by two gametes containing only paternal chromosomes, the combined set of chromosomes could not be identical to that of the donor's father because it would still be missing half of the father's chromosomes.
   d. No. See answer c.

18. Some possible hypotheses: The replication of the DNA of the bacterial chromosome takes less time than the replication of the DNA in a eukaryotic cell. The time required for a growing bacterium to roughly double its cytoplasm is much less than for a eukaryotic cell. Bacteria

have a cell cycle control system much simpler than that of eukaryotes.

19. $1 \text{ cm}^3 = 1{,}000 \text{ mm}^3$, so $5{,}000 \text{ mm}^3$ of blood contain $5{,}000 \times 1{,}000 \times 5{,}000{,}000 = 25{,}000{,}000{,}000{,}000$, or 2.5×10^{13}, red blood cells. The $\frac{1}{120}$ of the cells that are replaced each day $= 2.5 \times 10^{13}/120 = 2.1 \times 10^{11}$ cells. There are $24 \times 60 \times 60 = 86{,}400$ seconds in a day. Therefore, the number of cells replaced each second $= 2.1 \times 10^{11}/86{,}400 =$ about 2×10^6, or 2 million. Thus, about 2 million cell divisions must occur each second to replace red blood cells that are lost.

20. Each chromosome is on its own in mitosis; chromosome replication and the separation of sister chromatids occur independently for each horse or donkey chromosome. Therefore, mitotic divisions, starting with the zygote, are not impaired.

    In meiosis, however, homologous chromosomes must pair in prophase I. This process of synapsis cannot occur properly because horse and donkey chromosomes do not match in number or content.

21. Some issues and questions to consider: Could it be that less money is spent on prevention because effective prevention is so much cheaper? Or because prevention has been tried, and it does not work well? Are lifestyle changes the kind of measures that could benefit from a shift in resources? Is prevention an individual matter of avoiding exposure or a social matter of preventing exposure? How might the answer to this question shape prevention policy? If more money were devoted to prevention, how could it be used to encourage you or others to make lifestyle changes? Would prevention work better for younger or older people? Might older people, already exposed to cancer-causing agents, actually be harmed by a shift of resources to prevention?

Chapter 9

1. a. alleles; b. loci; c. homozygous; d. dominant; e. recessive; f. incomplete dominance

2. c 3. d 4. d (Neither parent is ruby-eyed, but some offspring are, so it is recessive. Different ratios among male and female offspring show that it is sex-linked.) 5. a 6. e

7. Genes on the single X chromosome in males are always expressed because there are no corresponding genes on the Y chromosome to mask them. A male needs only one recessive color blindness allele (from his mother) to show the trait; a female must inherit the allele from both parents, which is less likely.

8. See Figure 9.18A. The parental gametes are *WS* and *ws*. Recombinant gametes are *Ws* and *wS*, produced by crossing over.

9. Height appears to be a quantitative trait resulting from polygenic inheritance, like human skin color. See Module 9.14.

10. The trait of freckles is dominant, so Tim and Jan must both be heterozygous. There is a $\frac{3}{4}$ chance that they will produce a child with freckles and a $\frac{1}{4}$ chance that they will produce

a child without freckles. The probability that the next two children will have freckles is $\frac{3}{4} \times \frac{3}{4} = \frac{9}{16}$.

11. As in problem 10, both Tim and Jan are heterozygous, and Mike is homozygous recessive. The probability of the next child having freckles is $\frac{3}{4}$. The probability of the next child having a straight hairline is $\frac{1}{4}$. The probability that the next child will have freckles and a straight hairline is $\frac{3}{4} \times \frac{1}{4} = \frac{3}{16}$.

12. The genotype of the black short-haired parent rabbit is *BBSS*. The genotype of the brown long-haired parent rabbit is *bbss*. The F1 rabbits will all be black and short-haired, *BbSs*. The F$_2$ rabbits will be $\frac{9}{16}$ black short-haired, $\frac{3}{16}$ black long-haired, $\frac{3}{16}$ brown short-haired, and $\frac{1}{16}$ brown long-haired.

13. If the genes are not linked, the proportions among the offspring will be 25% gray red, 25% gray purple, 25% black red, 25% black purple. The actual percentages show that the genes are linked. The recombination frequency is 6%.

14. The recombination frequencies are: black dumpy 36%, purple dumpy 41%, and black purple 6% (see problem 13). Since these recombination frequencies reflect distances between the genes, the sequence must be purple-black-dumpy (or dumpy-black-purple).

15. $\frac{1}{4}$ will be boys suffering from hemophilia, and $\frac{1}{4}$ will be female carriers. (The mother is a heterozygous carrier, and the father is normal.)

16. For a woman to be color-blind, she must inherit X chromosomes bearing the color blindness allele from both parents. Her father has only one X chromosome, which he passes on to all his daughters, so he must be color-blind. A male need only inherit the color blindness allele from a carrier mother; both his parents are usually phenotypically normal.

17. Start out by breeding the cat to get a population to work with. If the curl allele is recessive, two curl cats can have only curl kittens. If the allele is dominant, curl cats can have "normal" kittens. If the curl allele is sex-linked, ratios will differ in male and female offspring of some crosses. If the curl allele is autosomal, the same ratios will be seen among males and females. Once you have established that the curl allele is dominant and autosomal, you can determine if a particular curl cat is true-breeding (homozygous) by doing a testcross with a normal cat. If the curl cat is homozygous, all offspring of the testcross will be curl; if heterozygous, half of the offspring will be curl and half normal.

Chapter 10

1. a. nucleotides; b. transcription; c. RNA polymerase; d. mRNA; e. rRNA; f. tRNA; g. translation; h. ribosomes; i. amino acids

2. e (Only the phage DNA enters a host cell; lambda DNA determines both DNA and protein.) 3. e 4. b 5. c

6. Ingredients: original DNA, nucleotides, several enzymes and other proteins, including DNA polymerase and DNA ligase. Steps: Original DNA strands separate at a specific

site (origin of replication), nucleotides line up along each strand according to base-pairing rules, DNA polymerase links the nucleotides to form new strands. New nucleotides are added only to the 3′ end of a growing strand. One new strand is made in one continuous piece; the other new strand is made in a series of short pieces that are then joined by DNA ligase. Product: two identical DNA molecules, each with one old strand and one new strand.

7. A gene is the polynucleotide sequence with information for making one polypeptide. Each codon—a triplet of bases in DNA or RNA—codes for one amino acid. Transcription occurs when RNA polymerase produces RNA using one strand of DNA as a template. In prokaryotic cells, the RNA transcript may immediately serve as mRNA. In eukaryotic cells, the RNA is processed: A cap and tail are added, and RNA splicing removes introns and links exons together to form a continuous coding sequence. A ribosome is the site of translation, or polypeptide synthesis, and tRNA molecules serve as interpreters of the genetic code. Each tRNA molecule has an amino acid attached at one end and a three-base anticodon at the other end. Beginning at the start codon, mRNA moves relative to the ribosome a codon at a time. A tRNA with a complementary anticodon pairs with each codon, adding its amino acid to the polypeptide chain. The amino acids are linked by peptide bonds. Translation stops at a stop codon, and the finished polypeptide is released. The polypeptide folds to form a functional protein, sometimes in combination with other polypeptides.

8.

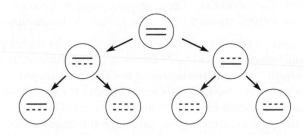

9. mRNA: GAUGCGAUCCGCUAACUGA. Amino acids: Met-Arg-Ser-Ala-Asn.

10. Some issues and questions to consider: Is it fair to issue a patent for a gene or gene product that occurs naturally in every human being? Or should a patent be issued only for something new that is invented rather than found? Suppose another scientist slightly modifies the gene or protein. How different does the gene or protein have to be to avoid patent infringement? Might patents encourage secrecy and interfere with the free flow of scientific information? What are the benefits to the holder of a patent? When research discoveries cannot be patented, what are the scientists' incentives for doing the research? What are the incentives for the institution or company that is providing financial support?

Chapter 11

1. a. proto-oncogene; b. repressor (or activator); c. cancer; d. operator; e. X inactivation; f. transcription factors; g. alternative RNA splicing

2. b (Different genes are active in different kinds of cells.) 3. c 4. b 5. a 6. b 7. e 8. b

9. A mutation in a single gene can influence the actions of many other genes if the mutated gene is a control gene, such as a homeotic gene. A single control gene may encode a protein that affects (activates or represses) the expression of a number of other genes. In addition, some of the affected genes may themselves be control genes that in turn affect other batteries of genes. Cascades of gene expression are common in embryonic development.

10. a. If the mutated repressor could still bind to the operator on the DNA, it would continuously repress the operon; enzymes for lactose utilization would not be made, whether or not lactose was present.
    b. The lac genes would continue to be transcribed and the enzymes made, whether or not lactose was present.
    c. Same predicted result as for b.
    d. RNA polymerase would not be able to transcribe the genes; no proteins would be made, whether or not lactose was present.

11. The protein to which dioxin binds in the cell is probably a transcription factor that regulates multiple genes (see Module 11.6). If the binding of dioxin influences the activity of this transcription factor (either activating or inactivating it), dioxin could thereby affect multiple genes and thus have a variety of effects on the body. The differing effects in different animals might be explained by differing genetic details in the different species. It would be extremely difficult to demonstrate conclusively that dioxin exposure was the cause of illness in a particular individual, even if dioxin had been shown to be present in the person's tissues. However, if you had detailed information about how dioxin affects patterns of gene expression in humans and were able to show dioxin-specific abnormal patterns in the patient (perhaps using DNA microarrays; see Module 11.11), you might be able to establish a strong link between dioxin and the illness.

Chapter 12

1. a. PCR; b. restriction enzymes; c. gel electrophoresis; d. nucleic acid probe; e. cloning; f. genomic library

2. d 3. c 4. b 5. c (Bacteria lack the RNA-splicing machinery needed to delete eukaryotic introns.) 6. b 7. d

8. Isolate plasmids from E. coli. Cut the plasmids and the human DNA containing the HGH gene with restriction enzyme to produce molecules with sticky ends. Join the plasmids and the fragments of human DNA with ligase. Allow E. coli to take up recombinant plasmids. Bacteria will then replicate plasmids and multiply, producing clones of bacterial cells. Identify a clone carrying and expressing the HGH gene using a nucleic

acid probe. Grow large amounts of the bacteria and extract and purify HGH from the culture.

9. Medicine: Genes can be used to engineer viruses for vaccines, to produce transgenic lab animals for AIDS research, or for research related to human gene therapy. Proteins can be hormones, enzymes, blood-clotting factor, or the starting material for making vaccines. Agriculture: Foreign genes can be inserted into plant cells or animal eggs to produce transgenic crop plants or farm animals or inserted into viruses for making animal vaccines. Animal growth hormones are examples of agriculturally useful proteins that can be made using recombinant DNA technology.

10. She could start with DNA isolated from liver cells (the entire genome) and carry out the procedure outlined in Module 12.1 to produce a collection of recombinant bacterial clones, each carrying a small piece of liver cell DNA. To find the clone with the desired gene, she could then make a probe of radioactive RNA with a nucleotide sequence complementary to part of the gene: GACCUGACUGU. This probe would bind to the gene, labeling it and identifying the clone that carries it. Alternatively, the biochemist could start with mRNA isolated from liver cells and use it as a template to make DNA (using reverse transcriptase). Cloning this DNA rather than the entire genome would yield a smaller library of genes to be screened—only those active in liver cells. Furthermore, the genes would lack introns, making the desired gene easier to manipulate after isolation.

11. Determining the nucleotide sequences is just the first step. Once researchers have written out the DNA "book," they will have to try to figure out what it means—what the nucleotide sequences code for and how they work.

12. Some issues and questions to consider: What are some of the unknowns in recombinant DNA experiments? Do we know enough to anticipate and deal with possible unforeseen and negative consequences? Do we want this kind of power over evolution? Who should make these decisions? If scientists doing the research were to make the decisions about guidelines, what factors might shape their judgment? What might shape the judgment of business executives in the decision-making process? Does the public have a right to a voice in the direction of scientific research? Does the public know enough about biology to get involved in this decision-making process? Who represents "the public," anyway?

13. Some issues and questions to consider: What kinds of impact will gene therapy have on the individuals who are treated? On society? Who will decide what patients and diseases will be treated? What costs will be involved, and who will pay them? How do we draw the line between treating disorders and "improving" the human species?

14. Some issues and questions to consider: Should genetic testing be mandatory or voluntary? Under what circumstances? Why might employers and insurance companies be interested in genetic data? Since genetic characteristics differ among ethnic groups and between the sexes, might such information be used to discriminate? Which of these questions do you think is most important? Which issues are likely to be the most serious in the future?

Chapter 13

1. The two major components of Darwin's theory of descent with modification are that all life has descended from a common ancestral form as a result of natural selection. Individuals in a population have hereditary variations. The overproduction of offspring in the face of limited resources leads to a struggle for existence. Individuals that are well-suited to their environment tend to leave more offspring than other individuals, leading to the gradual accumulation of adaptations to the local environment in the population.

2. a. genetic drift; b. gene flow; c. natural selection; d. small population; e. founder effect; f. bottleneck effect; g. unequal reproductive success

3. e 4. a 5. e 6. b (Erratic rainfall and unequal reproductive success would ensure that a mixture of both forms remained in the population.) 7. c 8. e 9. b (All of these provide evidence of evolution, but DNA and the universal genetic code are best able to connect all of life's diverse forms through common ancestry.) 10. d 11. c

12. Your paragraph should include such evidence as fossils and the fossil record, biogeography, comparative anatomy, comparative embryology, DNA and protein comparisons, artificial selection, and examples of natural selection.

13. If $q^2 = 0.0025$, then $q = 0.05$. Since $p + q = 1, p = 1 - q = 0.95$. The proportion of heterozygotes is $2pq = 2 \times 0.95 \times 0.05 = 0.095$. About 9.5% of African-Americans are carriers.

14. Genetic variation is retained in a population by diploidy and balanced selection. Recessive alleles are hidden from selection when in the heterozygote; thus, less adaptive or even harmful alleles are maintained in the gene pool and are available should environmental conditions change. Both heterozygote advantage and frequency-dependent selection tend to maintain alternate alleles in a population.

15. The unstriped snails appear to be better adapted. Striped snails make up 47% of the living population but 56% of the broken shells. Assuming that all the broken shells result from the meals of birds, we would predict that bird predation would reduce the frequency of striped snails and the frequency of unstriped individuals would increase.

16. Some issues and questions to consider: Who should decide curriculum, scientific experts in a field or members of the community? Are these alternative versions scientific ideas? Who judges what is scientific? If it is fairer to consider alternatives, should the door be open to all alternatives? Are constitutional issues (separation of church and state) involved here? Can a teacher be compelled to teach an idea he or she disagrees with? Should a student be required to learn an idea he or she thinks is wrong?

Chapter 14

1. a. Allopatric speciation: Reproductive barriers may evolve between these two geographically separated populations as a by-product of the genetic changes associated with each population's adaptation to its own environment or caused by genetic drift or mutation.

   b. Sympatric speciation: Some change, perhaps in resource use or female mate choice, may lead to a reproductive barrier that isolates the gene pools of these two populations, which are not separated geographically. If speciation occurred by polyploidy (common in plants but unusual in animals), then the new species is instantly isolated from the parent species.

2. a. hybrid zone
   b. reinforcement
   c. fusion
   d. stability
   e. strengthened
   f. weakened or eliminated

3. c 4. b 5. b 6. d 7. c 8. b 9. c 10. a 11. e 12. e

13. Different physical appearance may indicate different species or just differences within a species. Isolated populations may or may not be able to interbreed. Organisms that reproduce only asexually and fossil organisms do not have the potential to interbreed and produce fertile offspring; therefore, the biological species concept does not apply to them.

14. There is more chance for gene flow between populations on a mainland and nearby island. This interbreeding would make it more difficult for reproductive isolation to develop and separate the two populations.

15. *Punctuated equilibria* refers to a common pattern seen in the fossil record, in which most species diverge relatively quickly as they arise from an ancestral species and then remain fairly unchanged for the rest of their existence as a species.

16. Microevolution is the change in the gene pool of a population from one generation to the next. Speciation is the origin of a new species when a population becomes reproductively isolated from its parent species.

17. A broad hypothesis would be that cultivated American cotton arose from a sequence of hybridization, mistakes in cell division, and self-fertilization. We can divide this broad statement into at least three testable hypotheses. *Hypothesis 1:* The first step in the origin of cultivated American cotton was hybridization between a wild American cotton plant (with 13 pairs of small chromosomes) and an Old World cotton plant (with 13 pairs of large chromosomes). If this hypothesis is correct, we would predict that the hybrid offspring would have 13 small chromosomes and 13 large chromosomes. *Hypothesis 2:* The second step in the origin of cultivated American cotton was a failure of cell division in the hybrid offspring, such that all chromosomes are duplicated (now 26 small and 26 large). If this hypothesis is true, we would expect the resulting gametes to each have 13 large chromosomes and 13 small chromosomes.

Hypothesis 3: The third step in the origin of cultivated American cotton was self-fertilization of these gametes. If this hypothesis is true, we would expect the outcome of self-fertilization to be a hybrid plant with 52 chromosomes: 13 pairs of large ones and 13 pairs of small ones. This is the genetic makeup of cultivated American cotton.

18. By decreasing the ability of females to distinguish males of their own species, the polluted turbid waters have increased the frequency of mating between members of species that had been reproductively isolated from one another. As the number of hybrid fish increase, the parent species' gene pools may fuse, resulting in a loss of the two separate parent species and the formation of a new hybrid species. Future speciation events in Lake Victoria cichlids are now less likely to occur because females are less able to base mate choice on male breeding color. Reducing the pollution in the lake may help reverse this trend.

19. Some issues and questions to consider: The rationale behind protecting all endangered groups is the desire to preserve genetic diversity. Each species, subspecies, and hybrid group may represent a unique mix of genes. Studies of the degree of genetic distinctiveness of a subspecies or hybrid group may help decision makers if cost is an issue. If the species as a whole is not at risk, it seems appropriate to determine how distinctive the gene pool of a subspecies or hybrid group is before assigning it a lower priority for saving. Questions for society in general are: What is the value of any particular species and its genetically distinct subgroups? And how far are we willing (should we be willing) to go to preserve a genetically distinct group of organisms? How should the costs of preserving genetic diversity compare with the costs of other public projects?

Chapter 15

1. a. Abiotic synthesis of organic molecules using chemicals in atmosphere and lightning or other source of energy (or around deep-sea vents)
   b. Polymerization of monomers, perhaps on hot rocks
   c. Enclosure within a lipid membrane, which maintains distinct internal environment
   d. Beginnings of heredity as RNA molecules may have replicated themselves. Natural selection could act on protobionts that enclosed self-replicating RNA.

2. a. phylogenetic tree; b. homologies; c. morphology; d. analogies; e. outgroup; f. shared derived characters

3. c 4. b 5. e 6. c 7. e 8. a 9. d 10. b

11. Microevolution is the change in the gene pool of a population from one generation to the next. Macroevolution involves the pattern of evolutionary changes over large time spans and includes the origin of new groups and evolutionary novelties, as well as mass extinctions.

12. The latter are more likely to be closely related, since even small genetic changes can produce divergent

physical appearances. But if genes have diverged greatly, it implies that lineages have been separate for some time, and the similar appearances may be analogous, not homologous.

13. Complex structures can evolve by the gradual refinement of earlier versions of those structures, all of which served a useful function in the ancestor.

14. Where and when in a developing embryo that key developmental genes are expressed can greatly alter body geography and structures. Regulating gene expression allows these genes to continue to be expressed in some areas, turned off in other areas, and expressed at different times during development.

15. The ribosomal RNA genes, which code for the RNA parts of ribosomes, have evolved so slowly that homologies between even distantly related organisms can still be detected. Analysis of other homologous genes is also used.

16. 22,920 years old, a result of four half-life reductions

17.

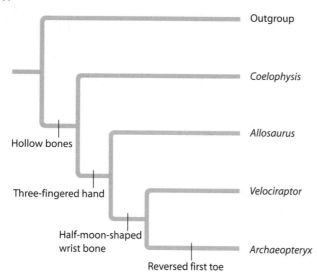

18. Some issues and questions to consider: Whereas previous mass extinctions have resulted from catastrophic events, such as asteroid collisions or volcanism, the current mass extinction is the result of human-caused environmental alteration. Mass extinctions can reduce complex ecological communities to much simpler ones. It can take millions of years for diversity to recover from a mass extinction. Do we have any ethical responsibility to preserve other species? By disrupting ecological communities throughout the world, a sixth mass extinction would have great consequences for all species alive today—including humans.

Chapter 16

1. Cell wall: maintains cell shape, provides physical protection, prevents cell from bursting in a hypotonic environment

   Capsule: enables cell to stick to substrate or to other individuals in a colony; shields pathogens from host's defensive cells

Motility: responds to chemical or physical signals in the environment that lead to nutrients or other members of their species and away from toxic substances

Rapid reproduction: colonizes favorable environment rapidly

Endospores: withstands harsh conditions

2. (a) Amoebozoan: has lobe-shaped pseudopodia

   (b) Ciliate: cilia visible on wide end of cell

   (c) Green alga: chloroplasts visible

   (d) Either a radiolarian or foraminiferan: threadlike pseudopodia

3. c 4. d (Algae are autotrophs; slime molds are heterotrophs.)
   5. e 6. c 7. d 8. b 9. b 10. d 11. b

12. Antibiotics target structures or processes that differ in bacteria and eukaryotic cells. Some antibiotics interfere with cross-linking in peptidoglycan; other antibiotics inhibit prokaryotic ribosomes.

13. Small, free-living prokaryotes were probably engulfed by a larger cell and took up residence inside. A symbiotic relationship developed between the host cell and engulfed cells, which became mitochondria. By a similar process, heterotrophic eukaryotic cells engulfed cyanobacteria, which became chloroplasts. Lineages of these autotrophic cells then diverged into several groups of protists.

14. *Chlamydomonas* is a eukaryotic cell, much more complex than a prokaryotic bacterium. It is autotrophic, while amoebas are heterotrophic. It is unicellular, unlike multicellular sea lettuce.

15. Multicellular organisms have a greater extent of cellular specialization and more interdependence of cells. New organisms are produced from a single cell, either an egg or an asexual spore.

16. Not a good idea; all life depends on bacteria. You could predict that eliminating all bacteria from an environment would result in a buildup of toxic wastes and dead organisms (both of which bacteria decompose), a shutdown of all chemical cycling, and the consequent death of all organisms.

17. Some issues and questions to consider: Could we determine beforehand whether the iron would really have the desired effect? How? Would the "fertilization" need to be repeated? Could it be a cure for the problem, or would it merely treat the symptoms? Might the iron treatment have side effects? What might they be?

Chapter 17

1. a. bryophytes; b. ferns and relatives; c. gymnosperms; d. angiosperms; 1. lignin-hardened vascular tissue; 2. seeds that protect and disperse embryos; 3. flowers that enclose gametophyte generation; fruits

2. A. This is a cloud of pollen being released from a pollen cone of a pine tree. The pine tree is the sporophyte generation. Sporangia in ovulate and pollen cones produce spores by meiosis. In ovulate cones, spores develop into the female gametophyte in the ovule. In pollen cones, spores produce

millions of the male gametophytes—the pollen grains. Pollination followed by fertilization produces a sporophyte embryo that is protected within the seed.

B. This is a cloud of haploid spores produced by a puffball fungus. Each spore may germinate to produce a haploid mycelium. Haploid hyphae of different mating types will fuse, creating a heterokaryotic mycelium, which is the feeding structure. Eventually, another puffball may develop, in which nuclei fuse in reproductive cells called basidia. Meiosis will produce spores that will be released, as shown in the photo.

3. b 4. c (It is the only gametophyte among the possible answers.) 5. a 6. e 7. b 8. e 9. c 10. d

11. The alga is surrounded and supported by water, and it has no supporting tissues, vascular system, or special adaptations for obtaining or conserving water. Its whole body is photosynthetic, and its gametes and embryos are dispersed into the water. The seed plant has lignified vascular tissues that support it against gravity and carry food and water and organs that absorb water and minerals (roots), provide support (stems and roots), and photosynthesize (leaves and stems). It is covered by a waterproof cuticle and has stomata for gas exchange. Its sperm are carried by pollen grains, and embryos develop on the parent plant and are then protected and provided for by seeds.

12. Animals carry pollen from flower to flower and thus help fertilize eggs. They also disperse seeds by consuming fruit or carrying fruit that clings to their fur. In return, they get food (nectar, pollen, fruit).

13. Plants are autotrophs; they have chlorophyll and make their own food by photosynthesis. Fungi are heterotrophs that digest food externally and absorb nutrient molecules. There are also many structural differences; for example, the threadlike fungal mycelium is different from the plant body, and their cell walls are made of different substances. Plants evolved from green algae, fungi from a unicellular, flagellated, protistan ancestor. Evidence indicates that fungi are more closely related to animals than to plants.

14. Antibiotics probably kill off bacteria that compete with fungi for food. Similarly, bad tastes and odors deter animals that eat or compete with fungi. Those fungi that produce antibiotics and bad-smelling and bad-tasting chemicals would survive and reproduce more successfully than fungi unable to inhibit competitors. Animals that could recognize the smells and tastes also would survive and reproduce better than their competitors. Thus, natural selection would favor fungi that produce the chemicals and, to some extent, the competitors deterred by them.

15. Moss gametophytes, the dominant stage in the moss life cycle, are haploid plants. The diploid (sporophyte) generation is dominant in most other plants. Recessive mutations are not expressed in a diploid organism unless both homologous chromosomes carry the mutation. In haploid organisms, recessive mutations are apparent in the phenotype of the organism because haploid organisms have only one set of chromosomes. Some factors to consider in designing

your experiment: What are the advantages/disadvantages of performing the experiment in the laboratory? In the field? What variables would be important to control? How many potted plants should you use? At what distances from the radiation source should you place them? What would serve as a control group for the experiment? What age of plants should you use?

16. Some issues and questions to consider: What are the other functions of forestland? How are other uses affected by logging? Must all the trees in an area be clear-cut? Should a particular area have multiple uses, or should different areas be used for different purposes? How much timber do we need? Could we conserve and recycle more? Are government-managed forests subsidizing private industry? Should we protect habitats as well as species? Does the rate of regrowth of trees match the rate of harvest? Will the ancient forests grow back? How do we balance conservation of the owl with the need for jobs and a productive economy?

Chapter 18

1. Sponges: sessile, saclike body with pores, suspension feeder; sponges

   Cnidarians: radial symmetry, gastrovascular cavity, cnidocytes, polyp or medusa body form; hydras, sea anemones, jellies, corals

   Flatworms: bilateral symmetry, gastrovascular cavity, no body cavity; free-living planarians, flukes, tapeworms

   Nematodes: pseudocoelom, covered with cuticle, complete digestive tract, ubiquitous, free-living and parasitic; roundworms, heartworms, hookworms, trichinosis worms

   Molluscs: muscular foot, mantle, visceral mass, circulatory system, many with shells, radula in some; snails and slugs, bivalves, cephalopods (squids and octopuses)

   Annelids: segmented worms, closed circulatory system, many organs repeated in each segment; earthworms, polychaetes, leeches

   Arthropods: exoskeleton, jointed appendages, segmentation, open circulatory system; chelicerates (spiders), crustaceans (lobsters, crabs), millipedes and centipedes, insects

   Echinoderms: radial symmetry as adult, water vascular system with tube feet, endoskeleton, spiny skin; sea stars, sea urchins

   Chordates: notochord; dorsal, hollow nerve cord; pharyngeal slits; post-anal tail; tunicates, lancelets, hagfish, and all the vertebrates (lampreys, sharks, ray-finned fishes, lobefins, amphibians, reptiles (including birds), mammals

2. c 3. d 4. a (The invertebrates include all animals except the vertebrates.) 5. d 6. c 7. i 8. f 9. e 10. c 11. a 12. d 13. h 14. b 15. g

16. The gastrovascular cavity of a flatworm is an incomplete digestive tract; the worm takes in food and expels waste through the same opening. An earthworm has a complete digestive tract; food travels one way, and different areas

are specialized for different functions. The flatworm's body is solid and unsegmented. The earthworm has a coelom, allowing its internal organs to grow and move independently of its outer body wall. Fluid in the coelom cushions internal organs, acts as a skeleton, and aids circulation. Segmentation of the earthworm, including its coelom, allows for greater flexibility and mobility.

17. Cnidarians and most adult echinoderms are radially symmetrical, while most other animals, such as arthropods and chordates, are bilaterally symmetrical. Most radially symmetrical animals stay in one spot or float passively. Most bilateral animals are more active and move headfirst through their environment.

18. For example, the legs of a horseshoe crab are used for walking, while the antennae of a grasshopper have a sensory function. Some appendages on the abdomen of a lobster are used for swimming, while the scorpion catches prey with its pincers. (Note that the scorpion stinger and insect wings are not considered jointed appendages.)

19. Both trees agree on the early branching of eumetazoans into two groups based on body symmetry and the number of cell layers formed in gastrulation. Both trees recognize deuterostomes as a clade of bilaterians. In the morphological tree, protostomes are a second clade of bilaterians. The molecular tree distinguishes two clades within the protosomes, lophotrochozoans and ecdysozoans.

20. Important characteristics include symmetry, the presence and type of body cavity, segmentation, type of digestive tract, type of skeleton, and appendages.

21. Some issues and questions to consider: How does the decline of the reefs relate to agriculture? Deforestation? Overfishing? Rapid population growth? What value are the reefs to the local people? What is the value of reefs as a world biological resource? What might be the consequences if the reefs disappear? What is likely to make the situation worse? What is likely to improve the situation? In what ways might developed countries contribute to this problem? In what ways might developed countries be able to help the local people preserve the reefs? How might developed countries benefit from helping?

Chapter 19

1. a. brain; b. head; c. vertebral column; d. jaws; e. lungs or lung derivatives; f. lobed fins; g. legs; h. amniotic egg; i. milk

2. a. Primates: limber shoulder and hip joints, mobile digits of hands and feet, flexible thumb and big toe, short snout, and eyes set close together
   b. Hominoids: larger brains relative to body size than other primates, lack tails, more flexible behavior. (Along with other anthropoids, hominoids have an opposable thumb.)
   c. Hominids: bipedalism, larger brains, reduced sexual dimorphism, shorter jaws, flatter faces, language, symbolic thought, manufacture and use of complex tools, longer period of parental care. (Note that these traits appeared at various times in hominid evolution.)

3. c 4. c 5. e 6. b 7. b 8. c 9. c 10. a 11. b

12. Amphibians have four limbs adapted for locomotion on land, a skeletal structure that supports the body in a non-buoyant medium, and lungs. However, most amphibians are tied to water because they obtain some of their oxygen through thin, moist skin and they require water for fertilization and development. Reptiles are completely adapted to life on land. They have amniotic eggs that contain food and water for the developing embryo and a shell to protect it from dehydration. Reptiles are covered by waterproof scales that enable them to resist dehydration (more efficient lungs eliminate the need for gas exchange through the skin).

13. Fossil evidence supports the evolution of birds from a small, bipedal, feathered dinosaur, which was probably endothermic. The last common ancestor that birds and mammals shared was the ancestral amniote. The four-chambered hearts of birds and mammals must have evolved independently.

14. Several primate characteristics make it easy for us to make and use tools—mobile digits, opposable fingers and thumb, and great sensitivity of touch. Primates also have forward-facing eyes, which enhances depth perception and eye-hand coordination, and a relatively large brain.

15. Hominoids include all apes (gibbons, orangutans, gorillas, chimpanzees, and humans). Hominids include the species on the human evolutionary branch, more closely related to humans than to chimpanzees.

16. UV radiation is most intense in tropical regions and decreases farther north. Skin pigmentation is darkest in people indigenous to tropical regions and much lighter in northern latitudes. Scientists hypothesize that depigmentation was an adaptation to permit sufficient exposure to UV radiation, which catalyzes the production of vitamin D, a vitamin that permits the calcium absorption needed for both maternal and fetal bones. Dark pigmentation is hypothesized to protect against degradation of folate, a vitamin essential to normal embryonic development.

17. The paleontologists who discovered Tiktaalik hypothesized the existence of transitional forms between fishlike tetrapods such as *Pandericthyes* and tetrapod-like fish such as *Acanthostega*. From the available evidence, they knew the time periods when fishlike tetrapods and tetrapod-like fish lived. From the rocks in which the fossils had been found, they knew the geographic region and the type of habitat these creatures occupied. With this knowledge, they predicted the type of rock formation where transitional fossils might be found.

18. Our intelligence and culture—accumulated and transmitted knowledge, beliefs, arts, and products—have enabled us to overcome our physical limitations and alter the environment to fit our needs and desires.

19. Most anthropologists think that humans and chimpanzees diverged from a common ancestor 5–7 million years ago. Primate fossils 4–8 million years old might help us understand how the human lineage first evolved.

Chapter 20

1. a. epithelial tissue; b. connective tissue; c. smooth muscle tissue; d. connective tissue; e. epithelial tissue

   The structure of the specialized cells in each type of tissue fits their function. For example, columnar epithelial cells are specialized for absorption and secretion; the fibers and cells of connective tissue provide support and connect the tissues. The hierarchy from cell to tissue to organ is evident in this diagram. The functional properties of a tissue or organ emerge from the structural organization and coordination of its component parts. The many projections of the lining of the small intestine greatly increase the surface area for absorption of nutrients.

2. b 3. c 4. a 5. d (Expelling salt opposes the increase in blood salt concentration, thereby maintaining a constant internal environment.) 6. d 7. c 8. a 9. d 10. a 11. c 12. b 13. d 14. b

15. Stratified squamous epithelium consists of many cell layers. The outer cells are flattened, filled with the protein keratin, and dead, providing a protective, waterproof covering for the body. Neurons are cells with long branches that conduct signals to other cells, making multiple connections in the brain. Simple squamous epithelium is a single, thin layer of cells that allows for diffusion of gases across the lining of the lung. Bone cells are surrounded by a matrix that consists of fibers and mineral salts, forming a hard protective covering around the brain.

16. The surfaces of the intestine, urinary system, and lungs are highly folded and divided, increasing their surface area for exchange. These surfaces interface with many blood capillaries. Smaller creatures have a greater surface-to-volume ratio, and their cells are closer to the surface, enabling direct exchange between cells and the outside environment.

17. Some issues and questions to consider: Should a doctor's prescription be required for a whole-body CT scan? Should such scans be available only to those who can pay for them? Are CT scan machines calibrated so that they expose children or small adults to less radiation? Have there been research studies to test the effect of repeated exposures to radiation from CT scans? Whose responsibility is it to perform such studies and then publicize the results?

Chapter 21

1. a. mouth—ingests food; b. salivary glands—produce saliva; c. liver—produces bile and processes nutrient-laden blood from intestines; d. gall bladder—stores bile; e. pancreas—produces digestive enzymes and bicarbonate; f. rectum—storage of feces before elimination; g. oral cavity—where food is chewed, moistened, and formed into a bolus; h. pharynx—site of openings into esophagus and trachea; i. esophagus—transports bolus to stomach by peristalsis; j. stomach—food storage, mixes food with acid, begins digestion of proteins; k. small intestine—digestion and absorption; l. large intestine—absorption of water, compacts feces; m. anus—elimination of feces

2. a. fuel, chemical energy; b. raw materials, monomers; c. essential nutrients; d. overnourishment or obesity; e. vitamins and minerals; f. essential amino acids; g. malnourishment

3. e 4. c 5. b 6. d 7. e

8. You ingest the sandwich one bite at a time. In the oral cavity, chewing begins mechanical digestion, and salivary amylase action on starch begins chemical digestion. When you swallow, food passes through the pharynx and esophagus to the stomach. Mechanical and chemical digestion continue in the stomach, where HCl in gastric juice breaks apart food cells and pepsin begins protein digestion. In the small intestine, enzymes from the pancreas and intestinal wall break down starch, protein, and nucleic acids to monomers. Bile from the liver and gallbladder emulsifies fat droplets for attack by enzymes. Most nutrients are absorbed into the bloodstream through the walls of the small intestine. Fats travel through lymph. In the large intestine, water is absorbed from undigested material, and feces are produced and eliminated.

9. Our craving for fatty foods may have evolved from the feast-and-famine existence of our ancestors. Natural selection may have favored individuals who gorged on and stored high-energy molecules, as they were more likely to survive famines.

10. a. 58%
    b. Based on a 2,000-Calorie diet, this product would supply about 9.5% of daily Calories, and it supplies 10% of vitamin A and calcium. If all food consumed supplied a similar quantity, the daily requirement for these two nutrients would be met.
    c. The 8 g of saturated fat in this product represent 40% of the daily value. Thus, the daily value must be 20 g (8/0.4 = 20). This represents 180 Calories from saturated fat.

11. Sodas, chips, crackers, and cookies provide many calories (high energy) but few vitamins, minerals, proteins, or other nutrients. Unprocessed, fresh foods such as fruits and vegetables are considered nutrient-dense—they provide substantial amounts of vitamins, minerals, and other nutrients, and relatively few calories.

12. Some issues and questions to consider: What are the roles of family, school, advertising, media, and government in providing nutritional information? How might the available information be improved? What types of scientific studies form the foundation of various nutritional claims?

13. Some issues and questions to consider: In wealthy countries, what are the factors that make it difficult for some people to get enough food? In your community, what types of help exist to feed hungry people? Think of two recent food crises in other countries and what caused them. Did other countries or international organizations provide aid? Which ones, and how did they help? Did that aid address the underlying causes of malnutrition and starvation in the stricken area or only provide temporary relief? How might that aid be changed to offer more permanent solutions to food shortages?

Chapter 22

1. a. respiratory surface; b. circulatory system; c. lungs; d. hemoglobin; e. cellular respiration; f. negative pressure breathing; g. O_2

2. a. nasal cavity; b. pharynx; c. larynx; d. trachea; e. right lung; f. bronchus; g. bronchiole; h. diaphragm

3. c 4. b 5. d 6. a 7. e 8. d 9. c

10. Advantages of breathing air: It has a higher concentration of O_2 than water and is easier to move over the respiratory surface. Disadvantage of breathing air: It dries out the respiratory surface; living cells on the respiratory surface must remain moist.

11. Nasal cavity, pharynx, larynx, trachea, bronchus, bronchiole, alveolus, through wall of alveolus into blood vessel, blood plasma, into red blood cell, attaches to hemoglobin, carried by blood through heart, blood vessel in muscle, dropped off by hemoglobin, out of red blood cell, into blood plasma, through capillary wall, through interstitial fluid, and into muscle cell.

12. Both these effects of carbon monoxide interfere with cellular respiration and the production of ATP. By binding more tightly to hemoglobin, CO would decrease the amount of O_2 picked up in the lungs and delivered to body cells. Without sufficient O_2 to act as the final electron acceptor, cellular respiration would slow. And by blocking electron flow in the electron transport chain, cellular respiration and ATP production would cease. Without ATP, cellular work stops and cells and organisms die.

13. Llama hemoglobin has a higher affinity for O_2 than does human hemoglobin. The dissociation curve shows that its hemoglobin becomes saturated with O_2 at the lower PO_2 of the high altitudes to which llamas are adapted. At that PO_2, human hemoglobin is only 80% saturated.

14. Insects have a tracheal system for gas exchange. In order to provide O_2 to all the body cells in such a huge moth, the tracheal tubes would have to be wider (to provide enough ventilation across larger distances) and very extensive (to service large flight muscles and other tissues), thus presenting problems of water loss and increased weight. Both the tracheal system and the weight of the exoskeleton would limit the size of insects.

15. Some issues and questions to consider: Would a total ban on advertising decrease the number of cigarette smokers? If cigarettes are legal, can the right of cigarette manufacturers to advertise their product be restricted in this manner? Have similar bans on advertising of other legal, but potentially deadly products (such as alcohol) been tried? How have they worked? Do health concerns outweigh commercial concerns? If cigarettes are so bad, should they be declared illegal?

Chapter 23

1. a. capillaries of head, chest, and arms; b. aorta; c. pulmonary artery; d. capillaries of left lung; e. pulmonary vein; f. left atrium; g. left ventricle; h. aorta; i. capillaries of abdominal region and legs; j. inferior vena cava; k. right ventricle; l. right atrium; m. pulmonary vein; n. capillaries of right lung; o. pulmonary artery; p. superior vena cava

   See text Figure 23.3A for numbers and red vessels.

2. b 3. d (The second sound is the closing of the semilunar valves as the ventricles relax.) 4. c 5. c 6. a 7. e 8. b 9. a

10. Pulmonary vein, left atrium, left ventricle, aorta, artery, arteriole, body tissue capillary bed, venule, vein, vena cava, right atrium, right ventricle, pulmonary artery, capillary bed in lung, pulmonary vein

11. Capillaries are very numerous, producing a large surface area for exchange close to body cells. The capillary wall is only one epithelial cell thick. Clefts between epithelial cells allow fluid with small solutes to move out at the arteriole end and back in at the venous end of the capillary.

12. a. Plasma (the straw-colored fluid) would contain water, inorganic salts (ions such as sodium, potassium, calcium, magnesium, chloride, and bicarbonate), plasma proteins such as fibrinogen and immunoglobulins (antibodies), and substances transported by blood, such as nutrients (for example, glucose, amino acids, vitamins), waste products of metabolism, respiratory gases (O_2 and CO_2), and hormones. b. The red portion would contain erythrocytes (red blood cells), leukocytes (white blood cells—basophils, eosinophils, neutrophils, lymphocytes, and monocytes), and platelets.

13. Oxygen content is reduced as oxygen-poor blood returning to the right ventricle from the systemic circuit mixes with oxygen-rich blood of the left ventricle.

14. Proteins are important solutes in blood, accounting for much of the osmotic pressure that draws fluid back into the blood. If protein concentration is reduced, the inward pull of osmotic pressure will fail to balance the outward push of blood pressure. The net pressure at the arterial end of a capillary forces fluid out into the interstitial fluid. Net pressure at the venous end is not great enough to draw fluid back in.

15. Some issues and questions to consider: Is it ethical to have a child in order to save the life of another? Is it right to conceive a child as a means to an end—to produce a tissue or organ? Is this a less acceptable reason than most reasons parents have for bearing children? Do parents even need a reason for conceiving a child? Do parents have the right to make decisions like this for their young children? How will the donor (and recipient) feel about this when the donor is old enough to know what happened?

16. With a three-chambered heart, there is some mixing of oxygen-rich blood returning from the lungs with oxygen-poor blood returning from the systemic circulation. Thus, the blood of a dinosaur might not have supplied enough O_2 to support the higher metabolism and strong cardiac muscle contractions needed to generate such a high systolic blood pressure. Also, with a single ventricle pumping simultaneously to both pulmonary and systemic circuits, the blood pumped to the lungs would be at such a high pressure that it would damage the lungs.

Chapter 24

1. a. innate immunity; b. acquired immunity; c. B cells;
   d. T cells; e. antibodies; f. helper T cells

2. e 3. b 4. b 5. d 6. a 7. b 8. f 9. d 10. e 11. a 12. g 13. c

14. AIDS is mainly transmitted in blood and semen. It enters the body through slight wounds during sexual contact or via needles contaminated with infected blood. AIDS is deadly because it infects helper T cells, crippling both the humoral and cell-mediated immune responses and leaving the body vulnerable to other infections. The most effective way to avoid HIV transmission is to prevent contact with bodily fluids by practicing safe sex and avoiding intravenous drugs.

15. Inflammation is triggered by tissue injury. Damaged cells release histamine and other chemicals, which cause nearby blood vessels to dilate and become leakier. Blood plasma leaves vessels, and phagocytes are attracted to the site of injury. An increase in blood flow, fluid accumulation, and increased cell population cause redness, heat, and swelling. Inflammation disinfects and cleans the area and curtails the spread of infection from the injured area. Inflammation is considered part of the innate immune response because similar defenses are presented in response to any infection.

16. One hypothesis is that your roommate's previous bee stings caused her to become sensitized to the allergens in bee venom. During sensitization, antibodies to allergens attach to receptor proteins on mast cells. During this sensitization stage, she would not have experienced allergy symptoms. When she was exposed to the bee venom again at a later time, the bee venom allergens bound to the mast cells, which triggered her allergic reaction.

17. Some issues and questions to consider: There is no correct answer to this question. Possible directions include the idea that if the donor felt strongly about the process, then his or her wishes should be respected. The opposite direction would be that the next of kin should be able to approve or deny the procedure. Other considerations may be appropriate, including religious beliefs.

18. Some issues and questions to consider: How important is it to protect students from AIDS? Is this a function of schools? Do schools serve other such "noneducational" purposes? Should parents or citizens' and church groups—on either side of the issue—have a say in this, or is it a matter between the school and the student? Does the distribution of condoms condone or sanction sexual activity or promiscuity? Is a school legally liable if a school-issued condom fails to protect a student? Are there alternative measures, such as education, that might be as effective for slowing the spread of AIDS?

Chapter 25

1. a. thermoregulation; b. osmoregulation; c. excretion;
   d. ectotherm; e.-g. ammonia, urea, uric acid; h. behavioral responses; i. environment

2. a. filtration: water; NaCl, HCO_3^-, H^+, urea, glucose, amino acids, some drugs; b. reabsorption: nutrients, NaCl, water, HCO_3^-, urea; c. secretion: some drugs and toxins, H^+, K^+; d. excretion: urine containing water, urea, and excess ions

3. c 4. a 5. e 6. d 7. c 8. c, a 9. b 10. c 11. c 12. c

13. b 14. d 15. b 16. a

17. In salt water, the fish loses water by osmosis. It drinks salt water and disposes of salts through its gills. Its kidneys conserve water and excrete excess ions. In fresh water, it gains water by osmosis. Its kidneys excrete a lot of dilute urine. Its gills take up salt, and some ions are ingested with food.

18. Yes. Ectotherms that live in very stable environments, such as tropical seas or deep oceans, have stable body temperatures. And terrestrial ectotherms can maintain relatively stable temperatures by behavioral means.

19. a. An endotherm would produce more nitrogenous wastes because it must eat more food to maintain its higher metabolic rate.
    b. A carnivore, because it eats more protein and thus produces more breakdown products of protein digestion—nitrogenous wastes.

20. You could take it back to the laboratory and measure its body temperature under different ambient temperatures.

21. A countercurrent heat exchange in the birds' legs reduces the loss of heat from the body. You would expect the temperature of blood flowing back to the body from the legs to be only slightly cooler than the blood flowing from the body to the legs.

22. Some issues and questions to consider: Could drug use endanger the safety of the employee or others? Is drug testing relevant to jobs where safety is not a factor? Is drug testing an invasion of privacy, interfering in the private life of an employee? Is an employer justified in banning drug use off the job if it does not affect safety or ability to do the job? Do the same criteria apply to employers requiring the test? Could an employer use a drug test to regulate other employee behavior that is legal, such as smoking?

23. Some issues and questions to consider: Should human organs be sold? If the donor is poor, he or she may also not be in the best of health. What are the health risks to the donor? Will the recipient be assured of buying a healthy organ? How much does the organ broker make from this transaction? Both parties in such a transaction are probably fairly desperate. Should regulations be in place when people may not be able to make reasoned decisions? Or do people have a right to sell parts of their bodies, just as they can now sell other possessions or their labor?

Chapter 26

1–8. Pineal gland: 5, f
     Testes: 3, d
     Parathyroid gland: 7, g
     Adrenal medulla: 2, c
     Hypothalamus: 8, h
     Pancreas: 4, a
     Anterior pituitary: 6, b
     Thyroid gland: 1, e

9. d 10. e 11. a 12. b (Negative feedback: When thyroxine increases, it inhibits TSH, which reduces thyroxine secretion.) 13. d

14. The hypothalamus secretes releasing hormones and inhibiting hormones, which are carried by the blood to the anterior pituitary. In response to these signals from the hypothalamus, the anterior pituitary increases or decreases its secretion of a variety of hormones that directly affect body activities or influence other glands. Neurosecretory cells that extend from the hypothalamus into the posterior pituitary secrete hormones that are stored in the posterior pituitary until they are released into the blood.

15. Only cells with the proper receptors will respond to a hormone. For a steroid hormone, the presence (or absence) and types of receptor proteins inside the cell determine the hormone's effect. For a nonsteroid hormone, the types of receptors on the cell's plasma membrane are key, and the proteins of the signal transduction pathway may have different effects inside different cells.

16. a. No. Blood sugar level goes too low. Diabetes would tend to make the blood sugar level go too high after a meal.
    b. No. Insulin is working, as seen by the homeostatic blood sugar response to feeding.
    c. Correct. Without glucagon, exercise and fasting lower blood sugar, the cells cannot mobilize any sugar reserves, and their blood sugar level drops. Insulin (which lowers blood sugar) has no effect.
    d. No. If this were true, blood sugar level would increase too much after a meal.

17. If cells within a male embryo do not secrete testosterone at the proper time during development, the embryo will develop into a female despite being genetically male.

Chapter 27

1. A. FSH; B. estrogen; C. LH; D. progesterone; P. menstruation; Q. growth of follicle; R. ovulation; S. development of corpus luteum.

   If pregnancy occurs, the embryo produces human chorionic gonadotrophin (HCG), which maintains the corpus luteum, keeping levels of estrogen and progesterone high.

2. c 3. c (The outer layer in a gastrula is the ectoderm; of the choices given, only the brain develops from ectoderm.)
   4. a 5. d 6. e 7. g 8. d 9. h 10. f 11. a 12. b 13. c

14. Both produce haploid gametes. Spermatogenesis produces four small sperm; oogenesis produces one large ovum. In humans, the ovary contains all the primary oocytes at birth, while testes can keep making primary spermatocytes throughout life. Oogenesis is not complete until fertilization, but sperm mature without eggs.

15. The extraembryonic membranes provide a moist environment for the embryos of terrestrial vertebrates and enable the embryos to absorb food and oxygen and dispose of wastes. Such membranes are not needed when an embryo is surrounded by water, as are those of fishes and amphibians.

16. The nerve cells may follow chemical trails to the muscle cells and identify and attach to them by means of specific surface proteins.

17. The researcher might find out whether chemicals from the notochord stimulate the nearby ectoderm to become the neural tube, a process called induction. Transplanted notochord tissue might cause ectoderm anywhere in the embryo to become neural tissue. Control: Transplant non-notochord tissue under the ectoderm of the belly area.

18. Some issues and questions to consider: What characteristics might parents like to select for? If parents had the right to choose embryos based on these characteristics, what are some of the possible benefits? What are potential pitfalls? Could an imbalance of the population result?

Chapter 28

1. a. sensory receptor; b. sensory neuron; c. synapse; d. spinal cord; e. interneuron; f. motor neuron; g. effector cell; h. CNS; i. PNS

2. b 3. a 4. Both a and c would prevent action potentials from occurring; b could actually increase the generation of action potentials.

5. At the point where the action potential is triggered, sodium ions rush into the neuron. They diffuse laterally and cause sodium gates to open in the adjacent part of the membrane, triggering another action potential. The moving wave of action potentials, each triggering the next, is a moving nerve signal. Behind the action potential, sodium gates are temporarily inactivated, so the action potential can only go forward. At a synapse, the transmitting cell releases a chemical neurotransmitter, which binds to receptors on the receiving cell and may trigger a nerve signal in the receiving cell.

6. The results show the cumulative effect of all incoming signals on neuron D. Comparing experiments 1 and 2, we see that the more nerve signals D receives from C, the more it sends; C is excitatory. Because neuron A is not varied here, its action is unknown; it may be either excitatory or mildly inhibitory. Comparing experiments 2 and 3, we see that neuron B must release a strongly inhibitory neurotransmitter, because when B is transmitting, D stops.

7. Some issues and questions to consider: Some people might be against the use of embryonic stem cells for any disorder. This may be related to religious or moral beliefs. Potentially, some people may not be aware of the source of these stem cells and may be against their use because they believe that the cells come from elective abortions. Other people may agree with the use of stem cell research because of the potential to cure diseases that are currently fatal. Some people who may have a neutral opinion on the issue might be swayed by the thought of a loved one who might be helped by stem cell therapy.

8. Some issues and questions to consider: What is the role of alcohol in crime? What are its effects on families and in the workplace? In what ways is the individual responsible

for alcohol abuse? The family? Society? Who is affected by alcohol abuse? How effective are treatment and punishment in curbing alcohol abuse? Who pays for alcohol abuse and consequent treatment or punishment? Is it possible to enjoy alcohol without abusing it?

Chapter 29

1. a. mechanoreceptors; b. chemoreceptors; c. electricity, magnetism, light; d. hair cells; e. photoreceptors

2. d (He could hear the tuning fork against his skull, so the cochlea, nerve, and brain are OK. Apparently, sounds are not being transmitted to the cochlea; therefore, the bones are the problem.) **3.** b **4.** a **5.** b **6.** e **7.** a

8. Louder sounds create pressure waves with greater amplitude, moving hair cells more and generating a greater frequency of action potentials. Different pitches affect different parts of the basilar membrane; different hair cells stimulate different sensory neurons that transmit action potentials to different parts of the brain.

9. Sensation is the detection of stimuli (light) by the photoreceptors of the retina and transmission of action potentials to the brain. Perception is the interpretation of these nerve signals—sorting out the patterns of light and dark and determining their meaning.

10. Taste is used to sample food and determine its quality. Smell is used for many functions—communication of territories (scent marking), navigation (salmon), mate location (moths), sensing danger (predators, fires), and finding food.

11. Some possible hypotheses: Paired sensory receptors enable an animal to determine the direction from which stimuli come. Paired receptors enable comparison of the intensity of stimuli on either side. Paired receptors enable comparison of slightly different images seen by the eyes or sounds heard by the ears (thus enabling the brain to perceive depth and distance).

12. Do the turtles hear the surf? Plug the ears of some turtles and not others. If turtles without earplugs head for the water and turtles with earplugs get lost, they probably hear the ocean. Or do they smell the water? Plug their nostrils and follow the same process.

13. Some issues and questions to consider: Assuming that the sound is loud enough to impair hearing, how long an exposure is necessary for this to occur? Does exposure have to occur all at once, or is damage cumulative? Who is responsible, concert promoters or listeners? Should there be regulations regarding sound exposure at concerts (as there are for job-related noise)? Are young people sufficiently mature and aware to heed such warnings?

Chapter 30

1. a. skeleton; b. muscles; c. exoskeleton; d. sarcomeres; e. bone and cartilage

2. c **3.** d **4.** a (Water supports aquatic animals, reducing the effects of gravity.) **5.** c **6.** d **7.** e **8.** d **9.** a (Each neuron controls a smaller number of muscle fibers.) **10.** e

11. Advantages of an insect exoskeleton include strength, good protection for the body, flexibility at joints, and protection from water loss. The major disadvantage is that the exoskeleton must be shed periodically as the insect grows, leaving the insect temporarily weak and vulnerable.

12. The bird's wings are airfoils, with convex upper surfaces and flat or concave lower surfaces. As the wings beat, air passing over them travels farther than air beneath. Air molecules above the wings are more spread out, lowering pressure. Higher pressure beneath the wings pushes them up.

13. Calcium is needed for healthy bone development. It strengthens bones and makes them less susceptible to stress fractures.

14. Action potentials from the brain travel down the spinal cord and along a motor neuron to the muscle. The neuron releases a neurotransmitter, which triggers action potentials in a muscle fiber membrane. These action potentials initiate the release of calcium ions from the ER of the cell. Calcium enables myosin heads of the thick filaments to bind with actin of the thin filaments. ATP provides energy for the movement of myosin heads, which causes the thick and thin filaments to slide along one another, shortening the muscle fiber. The shortening of muscle fibers pulls on bones, bending the arm. If more motor units are activated, the contraction is stronger.

15. The fundamental vertebrate body plan includes an axial skeleton (skull, backbone, and rib cage) and an appendicular skeleton (bones of the appendages). Species vary in the numbers of vertebrae and the numbers of different types of vertebrae they possess. For example, pythons have no cervical vertebrae. Mammals (almost) all have seven cervical vertebrae, but may have different numbers of other types. For example, human coccygeal vertebrae are small and fused together, but horses and other animals with long tails have many coccygeal vertebrae. Limb bones have been modified into a variety of appendages, such as wings, fins, and limbs. Snakes have no appendages.

16. Chemical A would work better, because acetylcholine triggers contraction. Blocking it would prevent contraction. Chemical B would actually increase contraction, because Ca^{2+} allows contraction to occur.

17. Circular muscles in the earthworm body wall decrease the diameter of each segment, squeezing internal fluid and lengthening the segment. Longitudinal muscles shorten and thicken each segment. Different parts of the earthworm can lengthen while others shorten, producing a crawling motion. The whole roundworm body moves at once because of a lack of segmentation. The body can only shorten or bend, not lengthen, because of a lack of circular muscles. Roundworms simply thrash from side to side.

18. Calcium ions move the regulatory protein tropomyosin out of the way so myosin heads can bind to actin, resulting in muscle contraction. ATP causes the myosin heads of the thick filaments to detach from the thin filaments (Figure 30.9B, step 1). If there is no ATP present, the myosin heads remain attached to the thin filaments, and the muscle fiber remains fixed in position.

19. Some issues and questions to consider: Are the places where you live, work, or attend class accessible to a person in a wheelchair? If you were in a wheelchair, would you have trouble with doors, stairs, drinking fountains, toilet facilities, and eating facilities? What kinds of transportation would be available to you, and how convenient would they be? What activities would you have to forgo? How might your disability alter your relationships with your friends and family? How well would you manage on your own?

Chapter 31

1. Here is one possible concept map:

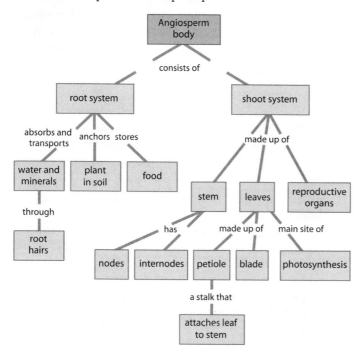

2. d (The vascular cambium forms to the outside of the primary xylem. The secondary xylem forms between primary xylem and the vascular cambium. The secondary phloem and primary phloem are outside the vascular cambium.)
   3. b **4.** e **5.** e **6.** f **7.** b **8.** e **9.** a **10.** c **11.** d

12. Bees deposit the pollen on the stigma of a carpel, and a pollen tube grows to the ovary at the base of the carpel. Sperm travel down the pollen tube and fertilize egg cells in ovules. The ovules grow into seeds, and the ovary grows into the flesh of the fruit (actually, in an apple, just the core). As the seeds mature, the fruit ripens and falls (or is picked).

13. Bulbs, root sprouts, and runners are all examples of asexual reproduction. Asexual reproduction is less wasteful and costly than sexual reproduction and less hazardous for young plants. The primary disadvantage of asexual reproduction is that it produces genetically identical offspring, decreasing genetic variability that can help a species survive times of environmental change.

14. Tomato: fruit (ripened ovary); celery stalk: leaf stalk (petiole); peanut: seed (ovule); strawberry: fruit (ripened ovary); lettuce: leaf blades; artichoke: terminal bud; beet: root

15. Modern methods of plant breeding and propagation have increased crop yields but have decreased genetic variability, so plants have become more vulnerable to epidemics. Primitive varieties of crop plants could contribute to gene banks and be used for breeding new strains.

16. Some issues and questions to consider: Why are the forests being cut when preserving them is more beneficial in the long run? Why can't the developing nations create new forest products themselves? Should developing and developed nations share in the profits from the forest? What incentive is there for a company to create a new product if it can't keep the profits? What about companies paying an exploration fee for exclusive rights to take plants from a certain area? What about a contract for the developing nation to get a percentage of the profits from new products? Are there reasons to preserve the forest other than profits and beneficial new products?

Chapter 32

1. a. roots; b. xylem; c. sugar source; d. phloem; e. transpiration; f. sugar sink

2. d **3.** d **4.** e **5.** b

6. If the plant starts to dry out, K^+ is pumped out of the guard cells. Water follows by osmosis, the guard cells become flaccid, and the stomata close. This prevents wilting, but it keeps leaves from taking in carbon dioxide, needed for photosynthesis.

7. Hypothesis: The hydrogen ions in acid precipitation displace positively charged nutrient ions from negatively charged clay particles. Test: In the laboratory, place equal amounts and types of soil in separate filters. The pore size of the filter must not allow any undissolved soil particles to pass through. Spray (to simulate rain) soil samples in the filters with solutions of different pH (for example, pH 5, 6, 7, 8, 9). Determine the concentration of nutrient ions in the solutions. (The only variable in the solutions should be the hydrogen ion concentration. Ideally, the solutions would contain no dissolved nutrient ions.) Collect fluid that drips through soil samples and filters. Determine the hydrogen ion concentration and the nutrient ion concentration in each sample of fluid. Prediction: If the hypothesis is correct, the fluid collected from the soil samples exposed to pH lower than 5.6 (acid rain) will contain the highest concentration of positively charged nutrient ions.

8. Hypothesis: When fixed nitrogen levels increase to a certain level in the soil, it slows the metabolism of (or otherwise harms or kills) the nitrogen-fixing bacteria that provide usable nitrogen to the crops. Test: Expose cultures of nitrogen-fixing bacteria (symbiotic and nonsymbiotic ones found in soil) to solutions of different concentrations of fixed nitrogen (that is, NO_3^- and NH_4^+). Determine the concentrations of nitrogen-fixing enzymes produced by the surviving bacteria in each sample. Prediction: If your hypothesis is correct, and the fixed nitrogen concentration is high enough to cause

harm in some of the samples, you would expect the enzyme concentration to be measurably lower in samples whose fixed nitrogen concentration is above the level that causes harm.

9. The hypothesis is supported if transpiration varies with light intensity when humidity and temperature are about the same. These conditions are seen at two places in the table; at hours 11 and 12, recordings for temperature and humidity are about the same, but light intensity increased markedly from 11 to 12, as did the transpiration rate. The recordings made at hours 3 and 4 show the same effects. Also, the recordings made at hours 1 and 2 generally support the hypothesis. Here, both temperature and humidity decreased, so you might expect the transpiration rate to stay about the same or perhaps increase because the temperature decrease is small; however, the transpiration rate dropped, as did the light intensity.

10. Some issues and questions to consider: How were the farmers assigned or sold "rights" to the water? How is the price established when a farmer buys or sells water rights? Is there enough water for everyone who "owns" it? What kinds of crops are these farmers growing? What will the water be used for in the city? Are there other users with no rights, such as wildlife? Is any effort being made to curb urban growth and conserve water? Should millions of people be living in what is essentially a desert? What are the reasons for farming desert land?

Chapter 33

1. a. auxin; b. gibberellin; c. auxin; d. cytokinin; e. auxin; f. ethylene; g. gibberellin; h. abscisic acid

2. b 3. c (A short-day plant requires a long night. The 13-hour night of answer c is the only uninterrupted night longer than 12 hours.) 4. b 5. a 6. d 7. b 8. b 9. f 10. e 11. d 12. a 13. b 14. g 15. c

16. Fruit produces ethylene gas, which triggers the ripening and aging of the fruit. Ventilation prevents a buildup of ethylene and delays its effects.

17. The terminal bud produces auxins, which counter the effects of cytokinins from the roots and inhibit the growth of axillary buds. If the terminal bud is removed, the cytokinins predominate, and lateral growth occurs at the axillary buds.

18. The red wavelengths in the room's lights quickly convert the phytochrome in the mums to the P_{fr} form, which inhibits flowering in a long-night plant. The mums will not flower unless Jon can rig up some far-red lights. Exposure to a burst of far-red light would convert the phytochrome to the P_r form, allowing flowering to occur.

19. The biologist could remove leaves at different stages of being eaten to see how long it takes for changes to occur in nearby leaves. The "hormone" could be captured in an agar block, as in the phototropism experiments in Module 33.1, and applied to an undamaged plant. Another experiment would be to block "hormone" movement out of a damaged leaf or into a nearby leaf.

20. The results illustrated in the graph generally support the hypothesis; measured by chlorophyll fluorescence, greater leaf damage occurred in air with no isoprene than in air with isoprene. The experimenters exposed leaves to N_2 to prevent the leaves themselves from emitting isoprene. By doing so, they were able to control the amount of isoprene in the air to which the leaves were exposed.

21. Some issues and questions to consider: Is the hormone safe for human consumption? What are its effects in the environment? Could its production produce impurities or wastes that might be harmful? What kinds of tests need to be done to demonstrate its safety? How much does it cost to make and use? Are the benefits worth the costs and risks? Is it worth using an artificial chemical on food simply to improve its appearance?

A scientist could seek answers by studying the stability of the hormone in a variety of laboratory simulations of natural conditions. The toxicity of the hormone, the materials used to produce it, and its breakdown products could be determined in laboratory tests.

Chapter 34

1. a. The shape of Earth results in uneven heating, such that the tropics are warm and polar regions are cold.
   b. The seasonal differences of winter and summer in temperate and polar regions are produced as Earth tips toward or away from the sun during its orbit around the sun.
   c. Intense solar radiation in the tropics evaporates moisture; warm air rises, cools, and drops its moisture as rain; air circulates, cools, and drops around 30°N and S, warming as it descends and evaporating moisture from land, which creates arid regions.

2. a. All three areas have plenty of sunlight and nutrients.
   b. The addition of nitrogen or phosphorus "fertilizes" the algae living in ponds and lakes, leading to explosive population growth. (These nutrients are typically in short supply in aquatic ecosystems.) The effects are harmful to the ecosystem. Algae cover the surface, reducing light penetration. When the algae die, bacterial decomposition of the large amount of biomass can deplete the oxygen available in the pond or lake, which may adversely affect the animal community.

3. f 4. g 5. d 6. a 7. c 8. b 9. e 10. a 11. e 12. d 13. a 14. c 15. b 16. e

17. Tropical rain forests have a warm, moist climate, with favorable growing conditions year-round. The diverse plant growth provides various habitats for other organisms.

18. After identifying your biome by looking at the map in Figure 34.8, review Module 34.5 on climate and the module that describes your biome (Modules 34.9–34.16).

19. a. desert; b. grassland; c. tropical forest; d. temperate forest; e. coniferous forest; f. arctic tundra. Areas of

overlap have to do with seasonal variations in temperature and precipitation.

20. Through convergent evolution, these unrelated animals adapted in similar ways to similar environments—temperate grasslands and savanna.

21. Some issues and questions to consider: What reasons are there for protecting areas like this? Is a public refuge or reserve the only way to protect species and habitats? Is there some way to protect organisms without confiscating land? Does protection take precedence over property rights? Would the prairie have been better off without the publicity? Should there be state or federal laws to protect endangered plants on private land? Should there be laws to protect endangered habitats, like this patch of prairie?

Chapter 35

1.

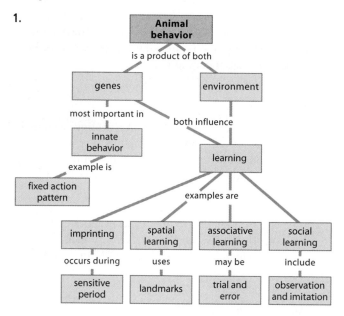

2. Your concept map should include: a. proximate questions; b. ultimate questions; c. mating behavior; d. communication/signals; e. agonistic behaviors; f. altruism

3. d 4. c 5. d 6. a

7. Main advantage: Flies do not live long. Innate behaviors can be performed the first time without learning, enabling flies to find food, mates, etc., without practice. Main disadvantage: Innate behaviors are rigid; flies cannot learn to adapt to specific situations.

8. In a stressful environment, for example, where predators are abundant, rats that behave cautiously are more likely to survive long enough to reproduce.

9. Courtship behaviors reduce aggression between potential mates and confirm their species, sex, and physical condition. Environmental changes such as rainfall, temperature, and day length probably lead frogs to start calling, so these would be the proximate causes. The

ultimate cause relates to evolution. Fitness (reproductive success) is enhanced for frogs that engage in courtship behaviors.

10. a. Yes. The experimenter found that 5 m provided the most food for the least energy because the total flight height (number of drops × height per drop) was the lowest. Crows appear to be using an optimal foraging strategy.
    b. An experiment could measure the average drop height for juvenile and adult birds, or it could trace individual birds during a time span from juvenile to adult and see if their drop height changed.

11. One likely hypothesis is that the helper is closely related to one or both of the birds in the mated pair. Because closely related birds share relatively many genes, the helper bird is indirectly enhancing its own fitness by helping its relatives raise their young. (In other words, this behavior evolved by kin selection.) The easiest way to test the hypothesis would be to determine the relatedness of the birds by comparing tissue samples using molecular methods such as those described in Module 15.18. If birds are closely related, their DNA and proteins should be more similar than those of more distantly related or unrelated birds.

12. Identical twins are genetically the same, so any differences between them are due to environment. Thus, the study of identical twins enables researchers to sort out the effects of "nature" and "nurture" on human behavior. The data suggest that many aspects of human behavior are inborn. Some people find these studies disturbing because they seem to leave less room for free will and self-improvement than we would like. Results of such studies may be carelessly cited in support of a particular social agenda.

13. Animals are used in experiments for various reasons. A particular species of animal may have features that make it well suited to answer an important biological question. Squids, for example, have a giant nerve fiber that made possible the discovery of how all nerve cells function. Animal experiments play a major role in medical research. Many vaccines that protect humans against deadly diseases, as well as drugs that can cure diseases, have been developed using animal experiments. Animals also benefit, as vaccines and drugs are developed for combating their own pathogens. Some researchers point out that the number of animals used in research is a small fraction of those killed as strays by animal shelters and a minuscule fraction of those killed for human food. They also maintain that modern research facilities are models of responsible and considerate treatment of animals. Whether or not this is true, the possibility that at least some kinds of animals used in research suffer physical pain as a result, and perhaps mental anguish as well, raises serious ethical issues. Some questions to consider: What are some medical treatments or products that have undergone testing in animals? Have you benefited from any of them? Are there alternatives to using animals in experiments?

Would alternatives put humans at risk? Are all kinds of animal experiments equally valuable? In your opinion, what kinds of experiments are acceptable, and what kinds are unnecessary? What kinds of treatment are humane, and what kinds are inhumane?

Chapter 36

1. a. The x-axis is time; the y-axis is the number of individuals (N). The blue curve represents exponential growth; red is logistic growth.
   b. $G = rN$
   c. Carrying capacity of the environment (K).
   d. In exponential growth, population growth continues to increase as the population size increases. In logistic growth, the population grows fastest when the population is about $\frac{1}{2}$ the carrying capacity—when N is large enough so that rN produces a large increase, but the expression $(K - N)/K$ has not yet slowed growth as much as it will as N gets closer to K.
   e. Exponential growth curve, although the worldwide growth rate is slowing.

2. a. Birth rate is blue line; death rate is red line.
   b. I. Both birth and death rates are high. II. Birth rate remains high; death rate decreases, perhaps as a result of increased sanitation and health care. III. Birth rate declines, often coupled with increased opportunities for women and access to birth control; death rates are low. IV. Both birth and death rates are low.
   c. I and IV
   d. II, when death rate has fallen but birth rate remains high

3. a 4. c 5. e 6. c 7. b 8. d

9. Food and resource limitation, such as food or nesting sites; accumulation of toxic wastes; disease; increase in predation; stress responses, such as seen in some rodents

10. Survivorship is the fraction of individuals in a given age interval that survive to the next interval. It is a measure of the probability of surviving at any given age. A survivorship curve shows the fraction of individuals in a population surviving at each age interval during the life span. Oysters produce large numbers of offspring, most of which die young, with a few living a full life span. Few humans die young; most live out a full life span and die of old age. Squirrels have approximately constant mortality and about an equal chance of surviving at all ages.

11. Clumped is the most common dispersion pattern, usually associated with unevenly distributed resources or social grouping. Uniform dispersion may be related to territories or inhibitory interactions between plants. A random dispersion is least common and may occur when other factors do not influence the distribution of organisms.

12. 10% of the animals in the second capture were marked. Knowing that 50 animals were initially marked, and assuming that 10% of the whole population is marked, then the population is estimated to be 500. The equation for the mark-recapture method is:

$$N = \frac{\text{Number marked in first catch} \times \text{total second catch}}{\text{recaptured marked individuals}}$$

13. An animal that has been trapped before may be wary of the traps or, having learned that traps contain food, may have deliberately returned for more. This would cause estimates to be either higher or lower, respectively, than actual population numbers.

14. Populations with K-selected life history traits tend to live in fairly stable environments held near carrying capacity by density-dependent limiting factors. They reproduce later and have fewer offspring than species with r-selected traits. Their lower reproductive rate makes it hard for them to recover from human-caused disruption of their habitat. We would expect species with K-selected life histories to have a Type I survivorship curve (see Module 36.3).

15. The largest population segment, the baby boomers, is currently in the workforce in their peak earning years, paying into the Social Security system. However, they are approaching the end of their contributing years, and the smaller working numbers following them will provide less money, driving the fund into a deficit.

16. Some issues and questions to consider: How does population growth in developing countries relate to food supply, pollution, and the use of natural resources such as fossil fuels? How are these things affected by population growth in developed countries? Which of these factors are most critical to our survival? Are they affected more by the growth of developing or developed countries? What will happen as developing countries become more developed? Will it be possible for everyone to live at the level of the developed world?

Chapter 37

1. a. energy flow; b. chemical cycling; c. solar energy; d. producers; e. abiotic reservoirs; f. trophic levels (food chain or web)

2.

Interspecific interaction	Effect on species 1	Effect on species 2	Example (other answers possible)
Predation	+	−	Crocodile/fish
Competition	−	−	Squirrel/black bear
Herbivory	+	−	Hippo/grasses
Parasites and pathogens	+	−	Heartworm/dog; *Salmonella*/human
Mutualism	+	+	Hippo/microbes in hippo stomach

(Many other examples possible)

3. e 4. d 5. c 6. c 7. c

8. Plants benefit by having their seeds distributed away from the parent. Animals benefit when the seed contains food, for example, in fleshy fruits.

9. Cultural eutrophication is excessive fertilization of bodies of water from agricultural or suburban runoff that results in blooms of cyanobacteria and algae. Respiration from these organisms and their decomposers depletes oxygen levels, leading to fish kills.

10. The abiotic reservoir of the first three nutrients is the soil. Carbon is available as carbon dioxide in the atmosphere.

11. These animals are secondary or tertiary consumers, at the top of the production pyramid. Stepwise energy loss means not much energy is left for them; thus, they are rare and require large territories in which to hunt.

12. Chemicals with a gaseous form in the atmosphere, such as carbon and nitrogen, have a global biogeochemical cycle.

13. Nitrogen fixation of atmospheric N_2 into ammonium; decomposition of detritus into ammonium; nitrification of ammonium into nitrate; denitrification (by denitrifiers) of nitrates into N_2

14. Hypothesis: The kangaroo rat is a keystone species in the desert. (Apparently, herbivory by the rats kept the one plant from outcompeting the others; removing the rats reduced plant diversity.) Additional supporting evidence: Observations of the rats preferentially eating dominant plants; finding that the dominant plant recovers from herbivore damage faster

15. Some issues and questions to consider: What relationships (predators, competitors, parasites) might exist in the mussels' native habitat that are altered in the Great Lakes? How might the mussels compete with Great Lakes organisms? Might the Great Lakes species adapt in some way? Might the mussels adapt? Could possible solutions present problems of their own?

Chapter 38

1. endangered and threatened species; b. restoration ecology; c. bioremediation and augmentation; d. zoned reserves; e. critical habitat needs

2. c 3. d 4. a 5. e 6. b 7. d 8. a

9. Genetic, species, and ecosystem diversity. As populations become smaller, genetic diversity is usually reduced. Genetic biodiversity is also threatened when local populations of a species become extinct owing to habitat destruction or other assaults or when entire species are lost. Many human activities have led to the extinction of species. The greatest threats include habitat loss, introduced species, and overexploitation. Species extinction may alter the structure of whole communities. Pollution and other widespread disruptions may lead to the loss of entire ecosystems.

10. Carbon dioxide and several other gases in the atmosphere absorb infrared radiation and thus slow the escape of heat from Earth. This is called the greenhouse effect. The greenhouse effect is beneficial to life on Earth; without CO_2 in the atmosphere, the temperature at the surface of Earth would be much colder and less hospitable for life.

11. Fossil fuel consumption, industry, and agriculture are increasing the quantity of greenhouse gases—such as CO_2, methane, and nitrous oxide—in the atmosphere. These gases are trapping more heat and raising atmospheric temperatures. Increases of 2–5°C are projected over the next century. Logging and the clearing of forests for farming contribute to global warming by reducing the uptake of CO_2 by plants (and adding CO_2 to the air when trees are burned). Global warming is having numerous effects already, including melting polar ice, permafrost, and glaciers, shifting patterns of precipitation, causing spring temperatures to arrive earlier, and reducing the number of cold days and nights. Future consequences include rising sea levels and the extinction of many plants and animals. Global warming is an international problem; air and climate do not recognize international boundaries. Greenhouse gases are primarily produced by industrialized nations. Cooperation and commitment to less use of fossil fuels and to reduce deforestation will be necessary if the problem of global warming is to be solved.

12. These birds might be affected by pesticides while in their wintering grounds in Central and South America, where such chemicals may still be in use. The birds are also affected by deforestation throughout their range.

13. About 1.8 million species have been named and described. Assume that 80% of all living things (not just plants and animals) live in tropical rain forests. This means that there are 1.44 million species there. If half the species survive, this means that 0.72 million species will be extinct in 100 years, or 7,400 per year. This means that 19+ species will disappear per day, or almost one per hour. If there are 30 million species on Earth, 24 million live in the tropics, and 12 million will disappear in the next century. This is 120,000 per year, 329 per day, or 14 per hour.

14. Some issues and questions to consider: How does the use of fossil fuels affect the environment? What about oil spills? Disruption of wildlife habitat for construction of oil fields and pipelines? Burning of fossil fuels and possible climate change and flooding from global warming? Pollution of lakes and destruction of property by acid precipitation? Health effects of polluted air on humans? How are we paying for these "side effects" of fossil fuel use? In taxes? In health insurance premiums? Do we pay a nonfinancial price in terms of poorer health and quality of life? Could oil companies be required to pick up the tab for environmental effects of fossil fuel use? Could these costs be covered by an oil tax? How would this change the price of oil? How would a change in the price of oil change our pattern of energy use, our lifestyle, and our environment?

15. Data on carbon emissions can be found at a number of websites, including the United Nations Statistics Division (http://unstats.un.org/unsd/default.htm) and the World Resources Institute (http://www.wri.org/climate/). The per capita rank of the United States and Canada are generally very high, along with other developed nations. Transportation and energy use are the major contributors to the carbon

footprint. Any actions you can take to reduce these will help. For example, if you have a car, you can try to minimize the number of miles you drive by consolidating errands into fewer trips and using an alternative means of transportation (public transportation, walking, biking, etc) whenever possible. To reduce energy consumption, be aware of the energy you use—turn off lights, disconnect electronics that draw power when on standby, do laundry in cold water, for example. Websites such as http://www.ucsusa.org/ (Union of Concerned Scientists) and http://climatecrisis.net offer simple suggestions such as changing to energy-efficient light-bulbs. A Web search will turn up plenty of sites.

16. Some issues and questions to consider: How do population growth, resource consumption, pollution, and reduction in biodiversity relate to sustainability? How do poverty, economic growth and development, and political issues relate to sustainability? Why might developed and developing nations take different views of a sustainable society? What would life be like in a sustainable society? Have any steps toward sustainability been taken in your community? What are the obstacles to sustainability in your community? What steps have you taken toward a sustainable lifestyle? How old will you be in 2030? What do you think life will be like then?

	BioFlix	MP3 Tutors	Web Activities	Web Process of Science	Discovery Channel Videos	GraphIt!/You Decide
Chapter 1 *Biology: Exploring Life*		The Process of Science (1.7)	The Levels of Life Card Game (1.1); Classification Schemes (1.5)	How Do Environmental Changes Affect a Population? (1.6); How Does Acid Precipitation Affect Trees? (1.8)	Antibiotic Resistance (1.10)	GraphIt!: An Introduction to Graphing (1.8)
Chapter 2 *The Chemical Basis of Life*		The Properties of Water (2.11)	Structure of the Atomic Nucleus (2.4); Electron Arrangement (2.6); Build an Atom (2.6); Ionic Bonds (2.7); Covalent Bonds (2.8); Nonpolar and Polar Molecules (2.9); Water's Polarity and Hydrogen Bonding (2.10); Cohesion of Water (2.11); Acids, Bases, and pH (2.15)	How Are Space Rocks Analyzed for Signs of Life? (2.1); How Does Acid Precipitation Affect Trees? (2.16)	Early Life (2.17)	
Chapter 3 *The Molecules of Cells*		Protein Structure and Function (3.13); DNA Structure (3.16)	Diversity of Carbon-Based Molecules (3.1); Functional Groups (3.2); Making and Breaking Polymers (3.3); Models of Glucose (3.4); Carbohydrates (3.7); Lipids (3.9); Protein Functions (3.11); Protein Structure (3.14); Nucleic Acid Structure (3.16)	Connection: What Factors Determine the Effectiveness of Drugs? (3.16)		You Decide: Low-Fat or Low-Carb Diets—Which is Healthier? (3.6)

Chapter				
Chapter 4 *A Tour of the Cell*	Tour of an Animal Cell (4.4)	Cell Organelles (4.4)	Metric System Review (4.1)	Connection: What is the Size and Scale of Our World? 4.1
	Tour of a Plant Cell (4.4)		Prokaryotic Cell Structure and Function (4.3)	Cells (4.1)
			Overview of Protein Synthesis (4.9)	
			The Endomembrane System (4.13)	
			Build a Chloroplast and a Mitochondrion (4.15)	
			Cilia and Flagella (4.18)	
			Cell Junctions (4.21)	
			Review: Animal Cell Structure and Function (4.23)	
			Review: Plant Cell Structure and Function	
Chapter 5 *The Working Cell*		Basic Energy Concepts (5.10)	Membrane Structure (5.1)	How Do Cells Communicate with Each Other? (5.1)
			Signal Transduction (5.1)	How Does Osmosis Affect Cells? (5.5)
			Selective Permeability of Membranes (5.1)	How Is the Rate of Enzyme Catalysis Measured? (5.15)
			Diffusion (5.3)	
			Osmosis and Water Balance in Cells (5.5)	
			Facilitated Diffusion (5.6)	
			Active Transport (5.8)	
			Exocytosis and Endocytosis (5.9)	
			Energy Transformations (5.10)	
			Chemical Reactions and ATP (5.12)	
			The Structure of ATP (5.13)	
			How Enzymes Function (5.15)	

(Continued)

	BioFlix	MP3 Tutors	Web Activities	Web Process of Science	Discovery Channel Videos	GraphIt!/You Decide
Chapter 6 *How Cells Harvest Chemical Energy*	Cellular Respiration (6.6)	Cellular Respiration Part 1: Glycolysis (6.7) Cellular Respiration Part 2: Citric Acid and Electron Transport Chain (6.9)	Build a Chemical Cycling System (6.1) Overview of Cellular Respiration (6.6) Glycolysis (6.7) The Citric Acid (Krebs) Cycle (6.9) Electron Transport and Chemiosmosis (6.10) Fermentation (6.13)	How is the Rate of Cellular Respiration Measured? (6.12)	Tasty Bacteria (6.13)	
Chapter 7 *Photosynthesis: Using Light to Make Food*	Photosynthesis (7.2)	Photosynthesis (7.5)	The Sites of Photosynthesis (7.2) Overview of Photosynthesis (7.5) Light Energy and Pigments (7.6) The Light Reactions (7.9) The Calvin Cycle (7.10) Photosynthesis in Dry Climates (7.12)	How Does Paper Chromatography Separate Plant Pigments? (7.6) How is the Rate of Photosynthesis Measured? (7.11)	Space Plants (7.11) Early Life (7.13)	
Chapter 8 *The Cellular Basis of Reproduction and Inheritance*	Mitosis (8.5) Meiosis (8.14)	Mitosis (8.5) Meiosis (8.14) Mitosis-Meiosis Comparison (8.15)	The Cell Cycle (8.5) Mitosis and Cytokinesis Video (8.7) Asexual and Sexual Life Cycles (8.13) Origins of Genetic Variation (8.18)	How Much Time Do Cells Spend in Each Phase of Mitosis? (8.6) How is Crossing Over Measured in the Fungus *Sordaria*? (8.18)	Fighting Cancer (8.1) Cells (8.2)	
Chapter 9 *Patterns of Inheritance*		Chromosomal Basis of Inheritance (9.16)	Monohybrid Cross (9.3) Dihybrid Cross (9.6) Gregor's Garden (9.7) Incomplete Dominance (9.11) Linked Genes and Crossing Over (9.19) Sex-Linked Genes (9.21)	How is the Chi-Square Test Used in Genetic Analysis? (9.21)	Colored Cotton (9.2)	

Chapter 10 Molecular Biology of the Gene	Protein Synthesis (10.6)	DNA to RNA to Protein (10.6)	The Hershey-Chase Experiment (10.1); Phage T2 Reproductive Cycle (10.1); DNA and RNA Structure (10.3); DNA Double Helix (10.3); DNA Replication (10.5); Transcription (10.9); Translation (10.14); Phage Lysogenic and Lytic Cycles (10.17); Simplified Reproductive Cycle of a DNA Virus (10.18); Retrovirus (HIV Reproductive Cycle) (10.20)	What is the Correct Model for DNA Replication? (10.4); How Are Nutritional Mutations Identified? (10.6); How Do You Diagnose a Genetic Disorder? (10.16); Why Do AIDS Rates Differ Across the United States? (10.19); What Causes Infections in AIDS Patients? (10.20); How Can Antibiotic-Resistant Plasmids (10.23) Transform E. coli?	Emerging Diseases (10.19)	
Chapter 11 How Genes Are Controlled		Control of Gene Expression (11.9)	The *lac* Operon in *E. coli* (11.1); Gene Regulation in Eukaryotes (11.8); Review: Gene Regulation in Eukaryotes (11.9); Development of Head-Tail Polarity (11.10); Signal Transduction Pathway (11.12); Connection: Causes of Cancer (11.21)	How Do You Design a Gene Expression System? (11.5); How Can the "Head" Gene be Regulated to Alter Development? (11.10)	Cloning (11.16); Fighting Cancer (11.18)	You Decide: Do Cell Phones Cause Brain Cancer? (11.21)

APPENDIX 5

Student Media Activities

A-31

	BioFlix	MP3 Tutors	Web Activities	Web Process of Science	Discovery Channel Videos	GraphIt!/You Decide
Chapter 12 *DNA Technology and Genomics*		DNA Technology (12.1)	Connection: Applications of DNA Technology (12.1) Cloning a Gene in Bacteria (12.2) Restriction Enzymes (12.2) Connection: DNA Technology and Golden Rice (12.8) Gel Electrophoresis of DNA (12.13) Analyzing DNA Fragments Using Gel Electrophoresis (12.14) Connection: DNA Fingerprinting (12.15)	How Can Antibiotic-Resistant Plasmids Transform *E. coli*? (12.1) How Can Gel Electrophoresis Be Used to Analyze DNA? (12.13)	Transgenics (12.8) DNA Forensics (12.11)	
Chapter 13 *How Populations Evolve*		Natural Selection (13.2)	Darwin and the Galápagos Islands (13.1) The Voyage of the *Beagle*: Darwin's Trip Around the World (13.1) Reconstructing Forelimbs (13.5) Genetic Variation from Sexual Recombination (13.8) Causes of Microevolution (13.11)	How Do Environmental Changes Affect a Population? (13.2) How Can Frequency of Alleles Be Calculated? (13.9) What Are the Patterns of Antibiotic Resistance? (13.15)	Charles Darwin (13.1) Antibiotic Resistance (13.15)	You Decide: What Can We Do About Antibiotic-Resistant Bacteria? (13.15)
Chapter 14 *The Origin of Species*		Speciation (14.1)	Polyploid Plants (14.6) Exploring Speciation on Islands (14.10)	How Do New Species Arise By Genetic Isolation? (14.5)		

Chapter 15 *Tracing Evolutionary History*		The History of Life (15.4) A Scrolling Geologic Record (15.6) Paedomorphosis: Morphing Chimps and Humans (15.11) Mechanisms of Macroevolution (15.12) Classification Schemes (15.19)	How Might Conditions on Early Earth Have Created Life? (15.2) How is Phylogeny Determined Using Protein Comparisons? (15.17)	Mass Extinction (15.9)
Chapter 16 *The Origin and Evolution of Microbial Life: Prokaryotes and Protists*	Microbial Life (16.1)	Prokaryotic Cell Structure and Function (16.4) Diversity of Prokaryotes (16.7)	What Are the Modes of Nutrition in Prokaryotes? (16.5) What Kinds of Protists Are Found in Various Habitats? (16.20)	Bacteria (16.1) Tasty Bacteria (16.1) Early Life (16.6) Antibiotic Resistance (16.8)
Chapter 17 *Plants, Fungi, and the Colonization of Land*	Evolution of Plants (17.2) Alternation of Generations (17.3)	Terrestrial Adaptations of Plants (17.1) Highlights of Plant Phylogeny (17.2) Moss Life Cycle (17.4) Fern Life Cycle (17.5) Pine Life Cycle (17.7) Angiosperm Life Cycle (17.9) Connection: Madagascar and the Biodiversity Crisis (17.13) Fungal Reproduction and Nutrition (17.17) Fungal Life Cycles (17.17)	What Are the Different Stages of a Fern Life Cycle? (17.5) How Does the Fungus *Pilobolus* Succeed as a Decomposer? (17.14)	Plant Pollination (17.12) Trees (17.14) Leafcutter Ants (17.20) Fungi (17.21)

(Continued)

	BioFlix	MP3 Tutors	Web Activities	Web Process of Science	Discovery Channel Videos	GraphIt!/You Decide
Chapter 18 *The Evolution of Invertebrate Diversity*			Characteristics of Invertebrates (18.13) Characteristics of Chordates (18.14) Animal Phylogenetic Tree (18.15)	How Are Insect Species Identified? (18.12) How Do Molecular Data Fit Traditional Phylogenies? (18.15)	Invertebrates (18.5) Leafcutter Ants (18.12)	
Chapter 19 *The Evolution of Vertebrate Diversity*		Human Evolution (19.11)	Characteristics of Chordates (19.8) Primate Diversity (19.10) Human Evolution (19.15)	How Does Bone Structure Shed Light on the Origin of Birds? (19.7)	Introduced Species (19.18)	
Chapter 20 *Unifying Concepts of Animal Structure and Function*		Animal Structure (20.1)	Correlating Structure and Function of Cells (20.1) The Levels of Life Card Game (20.1) Epithelial Tissue (20.4) Connective Tissue (20.5) Muscle Tissue (20.6) Nervous Tissue (20.7) Overview of Animal Tissue (20.7) Regulation: Negative and Positive Feedback (20.15)		An Introduction to the Human Body (20.1)	
Chapter 21 *Nutrition and Digestion*		The Human Digestive System (21.4)	Digestive System Function (21.10)	What Role Does Amylase Play in Digestion? (21.10)	Nutrition (21.21)	You Decide: Is Ephedra Safe and Effective? (21.22)
Chapter 22 *Gas Exchange*		Human Respiration (22.6)	The Human Respiratory System (22.6) Transport of Respiratory Gases (22.11)			You Decide: Is Second-Hand Smoke Dangerous? (22.7)

Chapter 23 *Circulation*	The Human Circulatory System (23.3)	Mammalian Cardiovascular System Structure (23.3); Path of Blood Flow in Mammals (23.3); Mammalian Cardiovascular System Function (23.8)	How Is Cardiovascular Fitness Measured? (23.9)	Blood (23.12)
Chapter 24 *The Immune System*	The Human Immune System (24.5)	Immune Responses (24.12); HIV Reproductive Cycle (24.13)	What Causes Infections in AIDS Patients? (24.13); Why Do AIDS Rates Differ Across the U.S.? (24.13)	Vaccines (24.4); Fighting Cancer (24.5)
Chapter 25 *Control of Body Temperature and Water Balance*	Kidney Function (25.6)	Structure of the Human Excretory System (25.6); Nephron Function (25.8); Control of Water Reabsorption (25.8)	How Does Temperature Affect Metabolic Rate in *Daphnia*? (25.3); What Affects Urine Production? (25.8)	
Chapter 26 *Hormones and the Endocrine System*	Homeostasis and the Endocrine System (26.1)	Overview of Cell Signaling (26.2); Nonsteroid Hormone Action (26.2); Steroid Hormone Action (26.2); Human Endocrine Glands and Hormones (26.10)	How Do Thyroxine and TSH Affect Metabolism? (26.5)	The Endocrine System (26.3)
Chapter 27 *Reproduction and Embryonic Development*	Spermatogenesis and Oogenesis (27.5); The Female Reproductive Cycle (27.6); Embryonic Development (27.10)	Reproductive System of the Human Male (27.4); Reproductive System of the Human Female (27.6); Sea Urchin Development Video (27.11); Frog Development Video (27.12)	Connection: What Might Obstruct the Male Urethra? (27.4); What Determines Cell Differentiation in the Sea Urchin? (27.13)	

(Continued)

	BioFlix	MP3 Tutors	Web Activities	Web Process of Science	Discovery Channel Videos	GraphIt!/You Decide
Chapter 28 *Nervous Systems*	How Neurons Work (28.4)	Neurons and Electrical Potentials (28.2) The Human Brain (28.15)	Neuron Structure (28.2) Nerve Signals: Action Potentials (28.5) Neuron Communication (28.6)	What Triggers Nerve Impulses? (28.4)	Teen Brains (28.15)	
Chapter 29 *The Senses*		Sensory Receptors (29.2)	Structure and Function of the Eye (29.8)			
Chapter 30 *How Animals Move*		Muscle (30.7)	The Human Skeleton (30.3) Skeletal Muscle Structure (30.8) Muscle Contraction (30.9)	How Do Electrical Stimuli Affect Muscle Contraction? (30.10)	Muscles and Bones (30.7)	
Chapter 31 *Plant Structure, Reproduction, and Development*	Tour of a Plant Cell (31.6)	From Flower to Fruit (31.9)	Root, Stem, and Leaf Sections (31.5) Primary and Secondary Growth (31.8) Angiosperm Life Cycle (31.10) Seed and Fruit Development (31.12)	How Are Trees Identified by Their Leaves? (31.3) What Are the Functions of Monocot Tissues? (31.5) What Tells Desert Seeds When to Germinate? (31.13)	Colored Cotton (31.1) Plant Pollination (31.10)	
Chapter 32 *Plant Nutrition and Transport*	Transpiration (32.3)	Transpiration (32.3)	Transpiration (32.4) Transport in Phloem (32.5) Absorption of Nutrients from Soil (32.8) Connection: Genetic Engineering of Golden Rice (32.11)	How is the Rate of Transpiration Calculated? (32.3) Connection: How Does Acid Precipitation Affect Mineral Deficiency? (32.8)		GraphIt!: Global Soil Degradation (32.9)
Chapter 33 *Control Systems in Plants*			Leaf Abscission (33.7) Flowering Lab (33.12)	What Plant Hormones Affect Organ Formation? (33.2)		

Chapter 34 *The Biosphere: An Introduction to Earth's Diverse Environments*	Ecological Hierarchy (34.1)	Connection: DDT and the Environment (34.2) Adaptations to Biotic and Abiotic Factors (34.4) Aquatic Biomes (34.7) Terrestrial Biomes (34.16)	How Do Abiotic Factors Affect Distribution of Organisms? (34.3)		
Chapter 35 *Behavioral Adaptations to the Environment*		Honeybee Waggle Dance (35.13)	How Can Sow Bug Responses to Environments Be Tested? (35.7)	Novelty Gene (35.23)	
Chapter 36 *Population Ecology*		Techniques for Estimating Population Density and Size (36.2) Investigating Survivorship Curves (36.3) Human Population Growth (36.9) Analyzing Age-Structure Diagrams (36.9)			GraphIt!: Age Pyramids and Population Growth (36.9)
Chapter 37 *Communities and Ecosystems*	Energy Flow in Ecosystems (37.16)	Interspecific Interactions (37.2) Food Webs (37.9) Primary Succession (37.12) Energy Flow and Chemical Cycling (37.14) Energy Pyramids (37.17) The Carbon Cycle (37.19) The Nitrogen Cycle (37.21) Water Pollution from Nitrates (37.21)	How Are Impacts on Community Diversity Measured? (37.1) How Do Temperature and Light Affect Primary Production? (37.15)	Leafcutter Ants (37.4) Rain Forests (37.9) Trees (37.14) Space Plants (37.19)	GraphIt!: Species Area Effect and Island Geography (37.10) GraphIt!: Animal Food Production Efficiency and Food Policy (37.17)

(Continued)

BioFlix	MP3 Tutors	Web Activities	Web Process of Science	Discovery Channel Videos	GraphIt!/You Decide
Chapter 38 *Conservation Biology*	Global Warming (38.5)	Connection: Madagascar and the Biodiversity Crisis (38.1)	How Are Potential Restoration Sites Analyzed? (38.14)	Introduced Species (38.3)	GraphIt!: Forestation Change (38.3)
		Connection: Fire Ants: An Invasive Species (38.3)			GraphIt!: Global Fisheries and Overfishing (38.3)
		Connection: DDT and the Environment (38.4)			GraphIt!: Global Fresh Water Resources (38.3)
		Connection: The Greenhouse Effect (38.6)			GraphIt!: Atmospheric CO_2 and Temperature Changes (38.6)
		Conservation Biology Review (38.15)			You Decide: Does Human Activity Cause Global Warming? (38.2)
					You Decide: Can We Prevent Species Extinction? (38.11)

Photo Credits

Front matter: xxii top Anup Shah/Photolibrary. **bottom** Mitch Ranger/Workbook Stock/Jupiter Images. **xxiii** Y. Kito/Image Quest 3-D. **xxiv** Getty Images. **xxv** Andoni Canela/agefotostock. **xxvi left** David Mack/SPL/Photo Researchers, Inc. **right** Lee Jae Won/Reuters. **xxvii** Wolfgang Kaehler/CORBIS. **xxviii** Joe Tucciarone/Photo Researchers, Inc. **xxix left** Peter Titmuss/Alamy. **right** Jez Tryner/Image Quest Marine. **xxx** Columbia/Marvel/Picture Desk, Inc./Kobal Collection. **xxxi left** Robert Holmes/CORBIS. **right** Andrew Syred/Photo Researchers, Inc. **xxxii** Michael Breuer/agefotostock. **xxxiii** ullstein-Nill/Peter Arnold Inc. **xxxiv** Mavis Yorks. **xxxv** Garry Weare/Lonely Planet Images. **xxxvii** Belinda Wright/Photolibrary.

Unit Openers: Unit 1 Dr. Torsten Wittmann/SPL/Photo Researchers, Inc. **Unit 2** Michael Clutson/SPL/Photo Researchers, Inc. **Unit 3** Louie Psihoyos/CORBIS. **Unit 4** Reinhard Dirscheri/Visuals Unlimited/Getty Images. **Unit 5** Pete Oxford/Nature Picture Library. **Unit 6** Purestock/Getty Images. **Unit 7** J & C Sohns/age fotostock.

Chapter 1: Chapter Opener 1 Peter Blackwell/npl/Minden Pictures. **Chapter Opener 2** Roger De La Harpe/Photolibrary. **Chapter Opener 3** Anup Shah/Photolibrary. **1.1 top** NASA/Goddard Space Flight Center. **1.1 center** Dan Guravich/CORBIS. **1.1 bottom** CORBIS. **1.2** Shin Yoshino/Minden Pictures. **1.3** (eukaryotic cell) Don W. Fawcett/Visuals Unlimited. **1.3** (prokaryotic cell) S. C. Holt/Biological Photo Service. **1.4B** (1) Image State/International Stock Photography Ltd. (2) Joe McDonald/CORBIS. (3) Frans Lanting/Minden Pictures. (4) Michael DeYoung/CORBIS. (5) Kim Taylor and Jane Burton/Dorling Kindersley. (6) Frans Lanting/Minden Pictures. (7) Fred Bavendam/Minden Pictures. **1.5A** National Museum of Natural History, Smithsonian Institution. **1.5B top left** Oliver Meckes/Nicole Ottawa/Photo Researchers. **1.5B top center** D. P. Wilson/Photo Researchers. **1.5B top right** Michael & Patricia Fogden/Minden Pictures. **1.5B bottom left** Ralph Robinson/Visuals Unlimited. **1.5B bottom center** Frank Young/Papilio/CORBIS. **1.5B bottom right** Michael and Patricia Fogden/CORBIS. **1.6A** Courtesy Department of Library Services, American Museum of Natural History. **1.6C left** Frans Lanting/Minden Pictures. **1.6C right** Fred Felleman/Stone/Getty Images. **1.8B** E. R. Degginger/Photo Researchers. **1.8C** Breck P. Kent. **1.8D left** David Pfennig. **1.8D right** David Pfennig. **Chapter Review** Shin Yoshino/Minden Pictures.

Chapter 2: Chapter Opener 1 Mark Moffett/Minden Pictures. **Chapter Opener 2** Martin Dohrn/BBC Natural History Unit. **Chapter Opener 3** Martin Dohrn/BBC Natural History Unit. **2.2A** Ivan Polunin/Bruce Coleman, Inc. **2.2B** Kristin Piljay. **2.3** Chip Clark. **2.5A** CC Studio/Photo Researchers, Inc. **2.5B** W. E. Klunk and C. A. Mathis, University of Pittsburgh. **2.11** Bernard Photo Productions/Animals Animals/Earth Scenes. **2.12** Jose Luis Pelaeq, Inc./CORBIS. **2.13B** BIOS Klein & Hubert/Peter Arnold, Inc. **2.16** P. J. Wagner/Photo Access/Taxi/Getty Images, Inc. **2.17** NASA.

Chapter 3: Chapter Opener 1 Mitch Ranger/Workbook Stock/Jupiter Images. **Chapter Opener 2** Peter Dean/Getty Images. **3.2 top** Stockbyte/Getty Images. **3.2 bottom** John Downer/Taxi/Getty Images. **3.4A** Scott Camazine/Photo Researchers. **3.6** Kristin Piljay. **3.7 top & bottom** Biophoto Associates/Photo Researchers. **3.7 center** Courtesy of Dr. L. M. Beidler. **3.8A** Tony Hamblin/Frank Lane Picture Agency/CORBIS. **3.10** Mike Neveux Photography. **3.11** Cancan Chu/Getty Images Sport. **3.14** Denny Allen/Getty Images. **3.15** Courtesy of the Archives, California Institute of Technology.

Chapter 4: Chapter Opener 1 James King-Holmes/Photo Researchers, Inc. **Chapter Opener 2** Tina Carvalho/Visuals Unlimited. **Chapter Opener 3** ISM/Phototake. **4.1A** Leica Microsystems Inc. **4.1B** Dennis Kunkel/Phototake. **4.1C** Dennis Kunkel/Phototake. **4.1D** Microworks Color/Phototake. **4.1E** M. I. Walker/Photo Researchers, Inc. **4.1F** Dr. Torsten Wittmann/Photo Researchers, Inc. **4.3** S. C. Holt, University of Texas Health Center/Biological Photo Service. **4.6** Courtesy of Richard Rodewald/Biological Photo Service. **4.7** D. W. Fawcett/Photo Researchers, Inc. **4.9A** R. Bolender, D. Fawcett/Photo Researchers. **4.10** Don Fawcett/Visuals Unlimited. **4.12A** Biophoto Associates/Photo Researchers, Inc. **4.12B** Roland Birke/Peter Arnold, Inc. **4.14** Nicolae Simionescu. **4.15** Courtesy of W. P. Wergin and E. H. Newcomb, University of Wisconsin/BPS **4.17 left** Dr. Frank Solomon. **4.17 center** Mark S. Ladinsky and J. Richard McIntosh, University of Colorado. **4.17 right** Dr. Mary Osborn. **4.18A** Science Photo Library/Photo Researchers, Inc. **4.18B** Biophoto Associates/Photo Researchers. **4.18C** W. L. Dentler/Biological Photo Service. **4.19** Bjorn Afzelius.

Chapter 5: Chapter Opener 1 Y. Kito/Image Quest 3-D. **Chapter Opener 2** Peter Herring/Image Quest 3-D. **Chapter Opener 3** Edith Widder/Ocean Research & Conservation Association. **5.2** Peter B. Armstrong. **5.7** Reuters. **5.9 top** Michael Abbey/Visuals Unlimited. **5.9 center** D. W. Fawcett/Science Source/Photo Researchers, Inc. **5.9 bottom** M. M. Perry and A. B. Gilbert, *J. Cell Sci.* (1979) 39: 257. Copyright 1979 The Company of Biologists Ltd. **5.10A** Dennis Curran/Photolibrary. **5.10B** Alain McGlaughlin, Pearson Benjamin Cummings. **5.10C** Scott Markewitz/Getty Images.

Chapter 6: Chapter Opener 1 Joe Sohm/Chromosohm/The Stock Connection. **Chapter Opener 2** Getty Images. **Chapter Opener 3** Duomo/CORBIS. **6.2** BananaStock/Jupiter Images. **6.13C** Charles O'Rear/CORBIS. **6.15** Simon Smith/Dorling Kindersley. **6.16** Gerry Ellis/Minden Pictures.

Chapter 7: Chapter Opener 1 James King-Holmes/Photo Researchers, Inc. **Chapter Opener 2** Martin Bond/Photo Researchers, Inc. **7.1A** Theresa DeSalis/Peter Arnold, Inc. **7.1B** EyeWire/Photodisc/Getty Images. **7.1C** Jeff Rotman/Nature Picture Library. **7.1D** Susan M. Barns, Ph.D. **7.2 top** Graham Kent. **7.2 bottom** Courtesy of W. P. Wergin and E. H. Newcomb, University of Wisconsin/BPS. **7.3A** Runk/Schoenberger/Grant Heilman Photography, Inc. **7.6B** Adamsmith/Taxi/Getty Images. **7.7A** Christine L. Case/Skyline College. **7.13A** Doug Martin/Photo Researchers, Inc. **7.14A** Stella Johnson. **7.14B** NASA.

Chapter 8: Chapter Opener 1 Greg Vaughn/Pacific Stock. **Chapter Opener 2** Andoni Canela/age fotostock. **Chapter Opener 3** National Tropical Botanical Garden. **8.1A** Biophoto Associates/Photo Researchers, Inc. **8.1B** Bob Thomas/Photographers Choice/Getty Images. **8.3B** Lee D. Simon/Photo Researchers, Inc. **8.4A** Andrew S. Bajer. **8.4B** Biophoto/Photo Researchers, Inc. **8.6** Conly L. Rieder, Ph.D. **8.7A** David M. Phillips/Visuals Unlimited. **8.7B** Eldon H. Newcomb. **8.11A left** Garcia/photocuisine/CORBIS. **8.11A center** Joseph F. Gennaro Jr./Photo Researchers, Inc. **8.11A right** Brian Capon. **8.11B** Biophoto/Science Source/Photo Researchers, Inc. **8.11C** Biophoto/Science Source/Photo Researchers, Inc. **8.17B left** F. Schussler/Getty Images. **8.17B right** Chris Collins/Bettmann/CORBIS. **8.18A** Cabisco/Visuals Unlimited. **8.19 left** Veronique Burger/Phanie Agency/Photo Researchers, Inc. **8.19 right** CNRI/SPL/Photo Researchers, Inc. **8.20A** CNRI/Science Photo Library/Photo Researchers, Inc. **8.20B** Lauren Shear/Photo Researchers, Inc. **Chapter Review** Carolina Biological Supply/Phototake.

Chapter 9: Chapter Opener 1 Jon Gordon/Getty Images. **Chapter Opener 2** Dorling Kindersley. **9.2A** Hulton Archive/Getty Images, Inc. **9.8A top left** CORBIS. **9.8A top right** Miep van Damm/Masterfile Stock Image Library. **9.8A center left** PhotoDisc/Getty Images. **9.8A center right** PhotoDisc/Getty Images. **9.9B** Michael Ciesielski Photography. **9.10A** Science Source/CNRI/SPL/Photo Researchers, Inc. **9.10B** Eric J. Simon. **9.10B inset** Stone/Getty Images. **9.13** Bill Longcore/Photo Researchers. **9.15** Eric J. Simon. **9.20A** Andrew Syred/Photo Researchers,

cio Robles Gil/Sierra Madre/Minden Pictures. **26.5A** NMSB/Custom Medical Stock Photo, Inc. **26.10** Jonathan Blair/CORBIS. **26.11** CORBIS.

Chapter 27: Chapter Opener 1 Brooks Kraft/Sygma. **Chapter Opener 2** Annie Griffiths Belt/CORBIS. **27.1** David Wrobel. **27.2A** Adam Reitzel, John R. Finnerty, Boston University **27.2B** Hans Pfletschinger/Peter Arnold, Inc. **27.2C** John Cancalosi/Nature Picture Library. **27.3B** C. Edelman/La Vilette/Photo Researchers, Inc. **27.8** Gusto/Photo Researchers, Inc. **27.9A** D. Phillips/Photo Researchers, Inc. **27.12A** Cabisco/Visuals Unlimited. **27.12C** Thomas Poole, SUNY Health Science Center. **27.12D** G.I. Bernard/Photo Researchers, Inc. **27.13A left** David Barlow. **27.13A right** David Barlow/BBC Photo Library. **27.16A** Lennart Nilsson/A Child is Born, Dell Publishing. **27.16B** Lennart Nilsson/A Child is Born, Dell Publishing. **27.16C** Lennart Nilsson/A Child is Born, Dell Publishing. **27.16D** Lennart Nilsson/Albert Bonniers Forlag AB. **27.16E** Eric J. Simon.

Chapter 28: Chapter Opener 1 Lester Lefkowitz/CORBIS. **Chapter Opener 2** AP Wide World Photos. **28.2** Manfred Kage/Peter Arnold, Inc. **28.7** Edwin R. Lewis, University of California at Berkeley. **28.9** Steve Gorton/Dorling Kindersley and PhotoDisc/Getty Images, Inc. **28.17A** From H. Damasio, et al., "The return of Phineas Cage: Clues about the brain from a famous patient." *Science,* 264:1102–1105, 1994. Department of Neurology and Image Analysis Facility, University of Iowa. **28.17B** Dana Boatman & John Freeman, Johns Hopkins School of Medicine. **28.21A** WDCN/Univ. College London/Photo Researchers, Inc. **28.21B** Jonathan Nourak/Stone/Getty Images. **28.21C** Douglas Graham/Roll Call/Sygma/CORBIS.

Chapter 29: Chapter Opener 1 Jim Watt/Pacific Stock. **Chapter Opener 2** F. Graner/WILDLIFE/Peter Arnold. **Chapter Opener 3** ullstein-Nill/Peter Arnold Inc. **29.3C** Dr. R.A. Steinbrecht. **29.3D** Joe McDonald/Animals Animals Earth Scenes. **29.7A** Tom Adams/Visuals Unlimited. **29.7B** Thomas Eisner, Cornell University. **29.9A** CORBIS. **29.9B** CORBIS.

Chapter 30: Chapter Opener Juniors Bildarchiv/age fotostock. **30.1A** David B. Fleetham/Visuals Unlimited. **30.1B** Dave Watts/NHPA/Photo Researchers, Inc. **30.1C** Arco Digital Images/Wegner/Jupiter Images. **30.1E** Stephen J. Krasemann/DRK Photo. **30.2A** Dwight Kuhn. **30.2B** Piotr Naskrecki/Minden Pictures. **30.2C** Carlos Villoch/Image Quest 3-D. **30.2D left** Darrell Gulin/CORBIS. **30.2D right** Kaj R. Svensson/Photo Researchers, Inc. **30.5A** Jochen Tack Alamy. **30.5B left** Professor P. Motta, Department of Anatomy, University lá Sapienzá Rome/Photo Researchers, Inc. **30.5B right** P. Motta/Photo Researchers, Inc. **30.8** Professor Clara Franzini-Armstrong. **30.11** Whit Richardson/Aurora Photos.

Chapter 31: Chapter Opener 1 Steve Sillett. **Chapter Opener 2** Michael Hutchinson/Nature Picture Library. **Chapter Opener 3** Henk Wallays/Photographer's Direct. **31.1** D. Cavagnaro/Visuals Unlimited. **31.4A** Eric Simon. **31.4B top** Dorling Kindersley. **31.4B right** Grant Heilman Photography, Inc. **31.4B bottom** Nigel Cattlin/Photo Researchers Inc. **31.4C top** Scott Camazine/Photo Researchers, Inc. **31.4C bottom** CORBIS. **31.6B** Dwight Kuhn/Dwight R. Kuhn Photography. **31.6C** Graham Kent. **31.6D left** Graham Kent. **31.6D right** Bruce Iverson, Photomicrography. **31.6E** R. Kessel-Shih/Visuals Unlimited. **31.6F** Visuals Unlimited. **31.7C** Ed Reschke. **31.8B** Runk/Schoenberger/Grant Heilman Photography. **31.12A** W. H. Hodge/Peter Arnold, Inc. **31.14A** Kevin Schafer Photography. **31.14B** Frank Balthis. **31.14C** Mountain Light Photography, Inc. **31.14D** Francois Gohier/Photo Researchers. **31.14E** Rosenfeld Images Ltd/Photo Researchers, Inc. **31.15** David Welling/Nature Picture Library.

Chapter 32: Chapter Opener 1 Mavis Yorks. **Chapter Opener 2** Kayte Deioma/Photographer's Direct. **Chapter Opener 3** Common Ground Collective. **32.1B** Chris Falkenstein/Photodisc/Getty Images. **32.2A** Brian Capon. **32.5A** Ray F. Evert. **32.5C** M. H. Zimmermann. **32.7A** Grant Heilman Photography. **32.7B** Nigel Cattlin/Holt Studios International Ltd. **32.7C** Paul Rapson/Photo Researchers, Inc. **32.8A** Agricultural Research Service/USDA. **32.9A** Runk/Schoenberger/Grant Heilman Photography. **32.9B** Kevin Horan/Stone/Getty Images. **32.10** Ralf-Finn Hestoft/CORBIS. **32.11** Louisiana State University Press. **32.13A** R. L. Peterson/Biological Photo Service. **32.13B** Breck P. Kent/Animals Animals Earth ~nes. **32.13C** E. H. Newcomb and S. R. Tandon/BPS. **32.14A** Clay

Perry/Photolibrary. **32.14B** Kevin Schafer/CORBIS. **32.14C** Jim Strawser/Grant Heilman Photography **32.14D** Fritz Polking/Frank Lane Picture Agency/CORBIS **32.14E** Fabio Colombini/Animals Animals

Chapter 33: Chapter Opener 1 D. Hurst/Alamy Images. **Chapter Opener 2** CORBIS. **Chapter Opener 3** Michael Pohuski/Botanica/Jupiter Images. **33.1A** Dorling Kindersley. **33.3A** David Newman/Visuals Unlimited. **33.4** Chandoha Photography. **33.5A** Alan Crozier. **33.5B** Fred Jensen. **33.6** Charles Krebs/CORBIS. **33.7A** Runk/Schoenberg/Grant Heilman Photography. **33.7B** Ed Reschke. **33.8** Stockbyte/Getty Images. **33.9A** Michael Evans. **33.9B** Scott Camazine/Photo Researchers, Inc. **33.10** Malcolm B. Wilkins, University of Glasgow, Glasgow, Scotland, U.K. **33.13** James Aronovsky. **33.14B** Barbara Baker. **33.15** Mary De Chirico.

Chapter 34: Chapter Opener 1 Garry Weare/Lonely Planet Images. **Chapter Opener 2** Verena Tunnicliffe. **Chapter Opener 3** AP Photo/Ifremer, A. Fifis. **Chapter Opener 4** Tom Kornack. **34.2A** Rich Reid/NGS Image Collection. **34.2B** Alfred Eisenstaedt/Time Life Pictures/Getty Images. **34.3A** Peter Batson/Imagequest Marine. **34.3B** Richard Kolar/Animals Animals. **34.4** CORBIS. **34.6B** Digital Vision/Getty Images. **34.6C** SOC/Imagequest Marine. **34.6D** James Randklev/Image Bank/Getty Images. **34.7A** Jay Dickman/CORBIS. **34.7B** David Muench/CORBIS. **34.9** Frans Lanting/Minden Pictures. **34.10** Wolfgang Kaehler/CORBIS. **34.11** Dennis Frates/Workbook Stock/Jupiter Images. **34.12** John D. Cunningham/Visuals Unlimited. **34.13** Jake Rajs/Stone/Getty Images, Inc. **34.14** Kennan Ward/CORBIS. **34.15** Steve Terrill/CORBIS. **34.16** Darrell Gulin/CORBIS.

Chapter 35: Chapter Opener 1 Lowell L. Getz and Lisa Davis. **Chapter Opener 2** John R. MacGregor/Peter Arnold, Inc. **Chapter Opener 3** Zuoxin Wang, Ph.D., Florida State University. **35.2B** Theo Allofs/Danita Delimont. **35.5A** Thomas McAvoy/Time & Life Pictures/Getty Images. **35.5B** Frank Lane Picture Agency/CORBIS. **35.6A** Ruth Cole/Animals Animals. **35.6B** Star Banner, Doug Engle/AP Photo. **35.7A** George Grall/National Geographic Image Collection. **35.8** Jonathan Blair/Woodfin Camp. **35.9** Harry Engels/Animals Animals Earth Scenes. **35.10** Richard Wrangham, Harvard University. **35.10 inset** Alissa Crandall/CORBIS. **35.11A** Clive Bromhall/OSF/Animals Animals. **35.11B** Bernd Heinrich/University of Vermont. **35.12A** Jose B. Ruiz/Nature Picture Library. **35.12B** Michael Hutchinson/Nature Picture Library. **35.13A** J. P. Varin/Jacana/Photo Researchers, Inc. **35.14A** Georgette Douwma/ImageState/Jupiter Images. **35.14C** Carol Walker/Nature Picture Library. **35.15** Fred Bavendam/Minden Pictures. **35.16B** W. Mike Howell. **35.18A** Wolfgang Kaehler/CORBIS. **35.18B** C & M Denis-Huot/Peter Arnold, Inc. **35.19** Gordon Wiltsie/AlpenImage Ltd. **35.20** Renne Lynn. **35.21A** Ken Regan/Camera 5. **35.21B** Frans B. M. De Waal. **35.22A** Stephen Kraseman/Peter Arnold, Inc. **35.22B** Jennifer Jarvis. **35.23A** Ted S. Warren/AP Photo. **35.23B** Lisa O'Connor/ZUMA/CORBIS.

Chapter 36: Chapter Opener 1 Franz Pagot/Alamy. **Chapter Opener 2** Euan Denholm/Reuters/CORBIS. **Chapter Opener 3** Trygve Bolstad/Peter Arnold Inc. **36.2A** Fred Bavendam/Minden Pictures. **36.2B** Frans Lanting/Minden Pictures. **36.2C** Ross M. Horowitz/Iconica/Getty Images. **36.4B** Roy Corral/CORBIS. **36.5A** Tom Bean/CORBIS. **36.5B** B. Borrell Casals/Frank Lane Picture Agency/CORBIS. **36.5C** Tom Bean/CORBIS. **36.6** Alan Carey/Photo Researchers, Inc. **36.11A left** Peter Ginter. **36.11A right** Peter Menzel. **36.11B** SASI Group, University of Sheffield.

Chapter 37: Chapter Opener 1 Frans Lanting/Minden Pictures. **Chapter Opener 2** Doug Allan/Nature Picture Library. **Chapter Opener 3** Jonathan and Angela/Getty Images. **37.3A** Doug Backlund. **37.3B** Terry Sohl, South Dakota Birds. **37.4** Jurgen Freund/Nature Picture Library. **37.5A** Thomas Gula/Visuals Unlimited. **37.5B** Mark Moffett/Minden Pictures. **37.6** Lawrence E. Gilbert/Biological Photo Service. **37.7** Joel Sartore/Photolibrary. **37.11B** William E. Townsend/Photo Researchers, Inc. **37.11C** Aletta Yniguez, National Center for Coral Reef Research (NCORE). **37.11D** Reinhard Dirscherl/Alamy. **37.13B** Embassy of Australia. **37.22A** Hubbard Brook Research Foundation. **37.22B** USDA Forest Service. **37.23A** Richard Siemens. **37.23B** David Schindler.

Chapter 38: Chapter Opener 1 Belinda Wright/Photolibrary. **Chapter Opener 2** altrendo nature/Getty Images. **Chapter Opener 3** Steve Winter/National Geographic Image Collection. **38.1** Scott Camazine/Photo Researchers, Inc. **38.2A** Rickey Rogers/Reuters/CORBIS. **38.2B** Fred Davendam/Minden Pictures. **38.3A** Michael Fodgen/Animals Animals/Earth Scenes. **38.3B** Michel Gunther/Peter Arnold, Inc. **38.5A** NASA Goddard Institute for Space Studies. **38.5B left** T. J. Hileman, Glacier National Park Archives. **38.5B center** Carl Key, USGS. **38.5B right** Blase Reardon, USGS. **38.7A** Justin Sullivan/Getty Images. **38.7B** Tom Murphy/WWI/Peter Arnold, Inc. **38.8A** William Osborn/Nature Picture Library. **38.8B** Paul McCormick/Getty Images. **38.9A** Gary Braasch/CORBIS. **38.9B** T. Davis/Photo Researchers, Inc. **38.9C** Tim Thompson/CORBIS. **38.10A** Yann Arthus-Bertrand/CORBIS. **38.10B** Calvin Larsen/Photo Researchers, Inc. **38.10C** Alan Sirulnikoff/SPL/Photo Researchers, Inc. **38.11B** Mark Conlin/Planet Earth Pictures. **38.12B** Frans Lanting/Minden Pictures. **38.13B** NPS Photo. **38.13C** Tim Davis/CORBIS. **38.14B** South Florida Water Management District (WPB). **38.15** Heinrich van den Berg/Getty Images.

Illustration and Text Credits

The following figures are adapted from Elaine N. Marieb, *Human Anatomy and Physiology,* 5th ed. Copyright © 2001 Pearson Education, Inc., publishing as Pearson Benjamin Cummings: **4.4A, 4.6, 4.9A,** and **EOC UN4.3.**

The following figures are adapted from Elaine N. Marieb, *Human Anatomy and Physiology,* 4th ed. Copyright © 1998 Pearson Education, Inc., publishing as Pearson Benjamin Cummings: **22.10, 22.12, 25.8, 27.3A, 27.3C, 27.4B, 27.17B, 29.9A, 29.9B, 30.4**

The following figures are adapted from Gerard J. Tortora, Berdell R. Funke, and Christine L. Case, *Microbiology: An Introduction,* 9th ed. Copyright © 2007 Pearson Education, Inc., publishing as Pearson Benjamin Cummings: **16.10A, 24.8B,** and **Table 27.7.**

The following figures are adapted from Lawrence G. Mitchell, John A. Mutchmor, and Warren D. Dolphin, *Zoology.* Copyright © 1988 Pearson Education, Inc., publishing as Pearson Benjamin Cummings: **18.1B, 18.14B, 21.10B, 25.5, 30.2E,** and **35.7C.**

Chapter 1: 1.8E Data in graph based on D. W. Pfennig et al. 2001. Frequency-dependent Batesian mimicry. *Nature* 410: 323.

Chapter 2: Chapter 2 introduction Adapted from an interview in Neil Campbell and Jane Reece, *Biology,* 6th ed. Copyright © 2002 Pearson Education, Inc., publishing as Pearson Benjamin Cummings.

Chapter 3: Figure 3.13A Adapted from D. W. Heinz, W. A. Baase, F. W. Dahlquist, B. W. Matthews, 1993. How amino-acid insertions are allowed in an alpha-helix of T4 lysozyme. *Nature* 361: 561. **Unnumbered figure, page 44** Illustration, Irving Geis. Image from Irving Geis Collection, Howard Hughes Medical Institute. Rights owned by HHMI. Reprinted by permission. Not to be reproduced without permission. **Module 3.15: Talking About Science** Adapted from an interview in Neil Campbell *Biology,* 1st Copyright © 1987 Pearson Education, Inc., publishing as Pearson Benjamin Cummings.

Chapter 5: Module 5.7: Talking About Science Adapted from an interview in Neil Campbell and Jane Reece, *Biology,* 7th ed. Copyright © 2005 Pearson Education, Inc., publishing as Pearson Benjamin Cummings.

Chapter 6: Table 6.4 Data from C. M. Taylor and G. M. McLeod, *Rose's Laboratory Handbook for Dietetics,* 5th ed. (New York: Macmillan, 1949), p. 18; J. V. G. A. Durnin and R. Passmore, *Energy and Protein Requirements in FAO/WHO Technical Report* No. 522, 1973; W. D. McArdle, F. I. Katch, and V. L. Katch, *Exercise Physiology* (Philadelphia, PA: Lea & Feibiger, 1981); R. Passmore and J. V. G. A. Durnin, *Physiological Reviews* vol. 35, pp. 801–840 (1955).

Chapter 7: 7.8B Adapted from Richard and David Walker. *Energy, Plants and Man,* fig. 4.1, p. 69. Sheffield: University of Sheffield. Courtesy of Richard Walker (http://www.oxygraphics.co.uk/. **Module 7.14: Talking About Science** Adapted from an interview in Neil Campbell, Jane Reece, and Lawrence Mitchell, *Biology,* 5th ed. Copyright © 1999 Pearson Education, Inc., publishing as Pearson Benjamin Cummings.

Chapter 9: 9.13 Adapted from *Introduction to Genetic Analysis,* 4th ed. by Suzuki, Griffiths, Miller, and Lewontin. Copyright © 1976, 1981, 1986, 1989, 1993, 1996 by W. H. Freeman and Company. Used with permission.

Chapter 11: 11.3 Adapted from C. K. Mathews and K. E. van Holde, *Biochemistry,* 2nd ed. Copyright © 1996 Pearson Education, Inc., publishing as Pearson Benjamin Cummings. **11.14** Adapted from W. H. Becker, *The World of the Cell,* p. 592. Copyright © 1986 Pearson Education, Inc., publishing as Pearson Benjamin Cummings. **Table 11.21** Data from *American Cancer Society. Cancer Facts & Figures 2007.* Atlanta: American Cancer Society, 2007.

Chapter 13: 13.14a Adapted from J. G. M. Thewissen et al. 2001. Skeletons of terrestrial cetaceans and the relationship of whales to artiodactyls. *Nature* 413:277–281, fig. 2a. **13.14b** Adapted from P. D. Gingerich et al. 2001. Origin of whales from early artiodactyls: Hands and feet of eocene protocetidae from Pakistan. *Science* 293: 2239–2242, fig. 3. **13.14c and d** Adapted from C. de Muizon. 2001. Walking with whales, *Nature* 413: 259–260, fig. 1.

Chapter 14: 14.7A Adapted from D. M. B. Dodd, *Evolution,* vol. 11, pp. 1308–1311. Reprinted by permission of the Society for the Study of Evolution. **Module 14.9: Talking About Science** Adapted from an interview in Neil Campbell and Jane Reece, *Biology,* 6th ed. Copyright © 2002 Pearson Education, Inc., publishing as Pearson Benjamin Cummings.

Chapter 15: Module 15.2: Talking About Science Adapted from an interview in Neil Campbell, *Biology,* 2nd ed. Copyright © 1990 Pearson Education, Inc. publishing as Pearson Benjamin Cummings. **15.7A** Map adapted from http://geology.er.usgs.gov/eastern/plates.html. **15.7D** Adapted from W. K. Purves and G. H. Orians, *Life: The Science of Biology,* 2nd ed., fig. 16.5c, p. 1180 (New York: Sinauer Associates, 1987.) Used with permission. **15.10** Adapted from Hickman, Roberts, and Larson. 1997, *Zoology,* 10/e, Wm. C. Brown, fig. 31.1. **15.12** Adapted from M. Strickberger. 1990. *Evolution.* Boston: Jones & Bartlett. **15.18** Adapted from B. Korber et al., June 9, 2000. Timing the ancestor of the HIV-1 pandemic strains. *Science* 288: 1789–1796, fig. 1b. **15.19A** Adapted from S. Blair Hedges. The origin and evolution of model organisms. *Nature Reviews Genetics* 3: 838–848, fig. 1, p. 840. **15.19B** Adapted from M. C. Rivera and J. A. Lake. 2004. The ring of life provides evidence for a genome fusion origin of eukaryotes. *Nature* 431: 152–155, fig. 3.

Chapter 16: CO16 Artist: Peter Sawyer © NMNH Smithsonian Institution. **16.12** From Archibald and Keeling, "Recycled Plastids," *Trends in Genetics,* Vol. 18, No. 11, 2002. Copyright © 2002, with permission from Elsevier.

Chapter 17: Table 17.13 Adapted from Randy Moore et al., *Botany,* 2nd ed. Dubuque, IA: Brown, 1998, Table 2.2, p. 37.

Chapter 18: Module 18.16: Talking About Science Adapted from an interview in Neil Campbell and Jane Reece, *Biology,* 8th ed. Copyright © 2008 Pearson Education, Inc., publishing as Pearson Benjamin Cummings.

Chapter 19: 19.4A Adapted from B. Holmes. Sept. 9, 2006. Meet your ancestor—the fish that crawled. *New Scientist,* 2568: 35–39. By permission of *New Scientist* magazine. **19.4B** From C. Zimmer. *At the Water's Edge.* Free Press, Simon & Schuster, p. 90. Copyright © 1999 by Carl Zimmer. Reprinted by permission of the author. **19.11** Drawn from photos of fossils: *O. tugenensis* photo in Michael Balter. Early hominid sows division, *ScienceNow,* Feb. 22, 2001, © 2001 American Association for the Advancement of Science. *A. ramidus kadabba* photo by Timothy White, 1999/Brill Atlanta. *A. anamensis, A. garhi,* and *H. neanderthalensis* adapted from *The Human Evolution Coloring Book. K. platyops* drawn from photo in Meave Leakey et al., New hominid genus from eastern Africa shows diverse middle Pliocene lineages, *Nature,* March 22, 2001, 410: 433. *P. boisei* drawn from a photo by David Bill. *H. ergaster* drawn from a photo at www.inhandmuseum.com. *S. tchadensis* drawn from a photo in Michel Brunet et al., A new hominid from the Upper Miocene of Chad, Central Africa, *Nature,* July 11, 2002, 418: 147, fig. 1b. **19.14** Adapted from D. Jones. Nov. 11, 2006. Blueprint for a Neanderthal, *New Scientist,* Issue

2577. By permission of *New Scientist* magazine. **19.15** Adapted from L. Luca Cavalli-Sforza and M. W. Feldman. 2003. The application of molecular genetic approaches to the study of human evolution. *Nature Genetics* 33: 266–275, fig. 3.

Chapter 21: 21.4 Adapted from R.A. Rhoads and R. G. Pflanzer. 1996. *Human Physiology,* 3/e., p. 666, fig. 22–1. Copyright 1996 Saunders. **21.17** Adapted from Murray W. Nabors, *Introduction to Botany.* Copyright © 2004 Pearson Education, Inc., publishing as Pearson Benjamin Cummings. **Table 21.18A** Data from RDA Subcommittee, *Recommended Dietary Allowances* (Washington, D. C.: National Academy Press, 1989); M. E. Shils and V. R. Young, *Modern Nutrition in Health and Disease* (Philadelphia, PA: Lea & Feibiger, 1988). **Table 21.18B** Data from (1) M. E. Shils, "Magnesium," in M. E. Shils and V. R. Young, eds. *Modern Nutrition in Health and Disease* (Philadelphia, PA: Lea & Feibiger, 1988); (2) V. F. Fairbanks and E. Beutler, "Iron" [same as 1]; (3) N. W. Solomons, "Zinc and Copper" [same as 1]; (4) RDA Subcommittee, *Recommended Dietary Allowances* (Washington, D. C.: National Academy Press, 1989); (5) E. J. Underwood, *Trace Elements in Human and Animal Nutrition* (New York: Academic Press, 1977).

Chapter 22: 22.11 Illustration, Irving Geis. Image from Irving Geis Collection. Howard Hughes Medical Institute. Rights owned by HHMI. Reprinted by permission. Not to be reproduced without permission.

Chapter 26: 26.8 Data from C. J. Bryne, D. F. Saxton et al., *Laboratory Tests: Implications for Nursing Care,* 2nd ed. Copyright © 1986 Pearson Education, Inc., publishing as Pearson Benjamin Cummings.

Chapter 27: 27.4C Adapted from Robert Crooks and Karla Baur, *Our Sexuality,* 5th ed. Copyright © 1993 Pearson Education, Inc., publishing as Pearson Benjamin Cummings. **27.14B** Adapted from an illustration by William McGinnis, UCSD. **Table 27.8** Data from R. Hatcher et al., *Contraceptive Technology: 1990–1992,* p. 134 (New York: Irvington, 1990).

Chapter 28: 28.6 Adapted from Becker, Kleinsmith, and Hardin, *The World of the Cell,* 6th ed. Copyright © 2006 Pearson Education, Inc., publishing as Pearson Benjamin Cummings.

Chapter 30: 30.12 Adapted from J. L. Andersen, et al. 2000. Muscles, Genes, and Athletic Performance. *Scientific American,* September, 2000, p. 49. Copyright 2000 Scientific American, Inc.

Chapter 33: Module 33.13: Talking About Science Adapted from an interview in Neil Campbell and Jane Reece, *Biology,* 6th ed. Copyright © 2002 Pearson Education, Inc., publishing as Pearson Benjamin Cummings. **33.14A** Adapted from Edward Farmer, "Plant Biology: New Fatty Acid-based Signals: A Lesson from the Plant World," *Science* 276: 912 (1997). Reprinted with permission from AAAS. **Module 33.15: Talking About Science** Adapted from an interview in Neil Campbell, *Biology,* 4th ed. Copyright © 1996 Pearson Education, Inc., publishing as Pearson Benjamin Cummings.

Chapter 34: Module 34.2 Text quotation from Rachel Carson, *Silent Spring* (New York: Houghton Mifflin, 1962). **34.8** Adapted from Heinrich Walter and Siegmar-Walter Breckle. 2003. *Walter's Vegetation of the Earth,* fig. 16, p. 36. Springer-Verlag, © 2003.

Chapter 35: 35.5B Courtesy of Masakazu Konishi. **35.8 (top)** Adapted from *Animal Navigation,* p. 109, by Talbot H. Waterman. Copyright © 1989 by Scientific American Books, Inc. Used with permission by W. H. Freeman and Company. **35.12C and D** Graphs from N. B. Davies. Prey selection and social behaviour in wagtails (Aves: Motacillidae). *Journal of Animal Ecology* 46: 37–57. Reprinted by permission of Blackwell Publishing Ltd. **35.14B** From Judith W. McIntyre, drawings by Anne Olson, *The Common Loon: Spirit of Northern Lakes,* p. 97 (University of Minnesota Press, 1988). Copyright © 1988 by University of Minnesota Press. Reprinted by permission. **35.16A** Map adapted from W. M. Howell et al. 1980. Abnormal expression of secondary sex characters in a population of mosquitofish, *Gambusia affinis holbrooki, Copeia* Vol. 1980, No. 4 (Dec. 5, 1980), pp. 676–681. Reprinted by permission of ASIH. **Module 35.21: Talking About Science** Adapted from an interview in Neil Campbell, *Biology,* 3rd ed. Copyright © 1993 Pearson Education, Inc., publishing as Pearson Benjamin Cummings.

Chapter 36: Table 36.3 Data from Center for Health Statistics, 2003 CDC. **36.5A** Data courtesy of J. N. M. Smith and P. Arcese. **36.5C** Data courtesy of P. Arcese and J. N. M. Smith. **36.8** Data from Fisheries and Oceans, Canada, 1999. **Table 36.9** Data from United Nations, the World at Six Billion, 2007. **36.9A** Data from United Nations, the World at Six Billion, 2007. **36.9B** Data from Population Reference Bureau, 2000 and U.S. Census Bureau International Data Base, 2003. **36.9C and 36.10** Data from U.S. Census Bureau, International Data Base. **36.11B** Adapted from information at phtbb.org/natural/footprint.

Chapter 37: 37.9 From Robert Leo Smith, *Ecology and Field Biology,* 4th ed. Copyright © 1990 by Robert Leo Smith. Reprinted by permission of Addison Wesley Longman, Inc. **37.13A** Source: www.dest.gov.au/ archive/Science/pmsec/14meet/rcd1.html. **37.22C** From G. E. Likens et al., "Effects of Forest Cutting and Herbicide Treatment on Nutrient Budgets in the Hubbard Brook Watershed Ecosystem," *Ecological Monographs,* vol. 50, pp. 22–32 (1966). Copyright © 1966 by The Ecological Society of America. Reprinted by permission. **Module 37.23: Talking About Science** Adapted from an interview with Neil Campbell and Jane Reece, *Biology,* 6th ed. Copyright © 2002 Pearson Education, Inc., publishing as Benjamin Cummings.

Chapter 38: 38.5A From "Global Temperature Change," J. Hansen et al., *PNAS,* Sept. 26, 2006, Vol. 103, No. 39. Copyright 2006 National Academy of Sciences, U.S.A. Reprinted by permission. **38.6A** From Climate Change 2007: *The Physical Science Basis,* Intergovernmental Panel on Climate Change. Reprinted by permission of IPCC, c/o World Meteorological Organization. **38.11A** From N. Myers et al., "Biodiversity hotspots for conservation priorities," *Nature,* Vol. 403, p. 853, 2/24/2000. Copyright © 2000 Nature Publishing, Inc. Used with permission. **38.12A** Adapted from W. Purves and G. Orians, *Life: The Science of Biology,* 5th ed., fig. 55.23, p. 1239. Coypright © 1998 by Sinauer and W. H. Freeman & Company. Reprinted by permission. **38.13A** Reprinted by permission of Yellowstone to Yukon Conservation Initiative.

Glossary

A

abiotic factor (ā'-bī-ot'-ik) A nonliving component of an ecosystem, such as air, water, or temperature.

abiotic reservoir The part of an ecosystem where a chemical, such as carbon or nitrogen, accumulates or is stockpiled outside of living organisms.

ABO blood groups Genetically determined classes of human blood that are based on the presence or absence of carbohydrates A and B on the surface of red blood cells. The ABO blood group phenotypes, also called blood types, are A, B, AB, and O.

abscisic acid (ABA) (ab-sis'-ik) A plant hormone that inhibits cell division and promotes dormancy; interacts with gibberellins in regulating seed germination.

absorption The uptake of small nutrient molecules by an organism's own body; the third main stage of food processing, following digestion.

accommodation The automatic changes made by the eye as it focuses on nearby objects.

acetyl CoA (acetyl coenzyme A) The entry compound for the citric acid cycle in cellular respiration; formed from a fragment of pyruvate attached to a coenzyme.

acetylcholine (as'-uh-til-kō'-lēn) A nitrogen-containing neurotransmitter. Among other effects, it slows the heart rate and makes skeletal muscles contract.

achondroplasia (uh-kon'-druh-plā'-zhuh) A form of human dwarfism caused by a single dominant allele; the homozygous condition is lethal.

acid A substance that increases the hydrogen ion concentration in a solution.

acid precipitation Rain, snow, or fog with a pH below 5.6.

acquired immunity The kind of defense that is mediated by B lymphocytes (B cells) and T lymphocytes (T cells). It exhibits specificity, memory, and self-nonself recognition.

acrosome (ak'-ruh-som) A membrane-enclosed sac at the tip of a sperm; contains enzymes that help the sperm penetrate an egg.

actin A globular protein that links into chains, two of which twist helically around each other, forming microfilaments in muscle cells.

action potential A self-propagating change in the voltage across the plasma membrane of a neuron; a nerve signal.

activator A protein that switches on a gene or group of genes.

active immunity Immunity conferred by recovering from an infectious disease or by receiving a vaccine.

active site The part of an enzyme molecule where a substrate molecule attaches (by means of weak chemical bonds); typically, a pocket or groove on the enzyme's surface.

active transport The movement of a substance across a biological membrane against its concentration gradient, aided by specific transport proteins and requiring input of energy (often as ATP).

adaptation An inherited characteristic that enhances an organism's ability to survive and reproduce in a particular environment.

adaptive radiation Period of evolutionary change in which groups of organisms form many new species whose adaptations allow them to fill new or vacant ecological roles in their communities.

adenine (A) (ad'-uh-nēn) A double-ring nitrogenous base found in DNA and RNA.

adenosine triphosphate (ATP) Main energy source for cells.

adhesion The attraction between different kinds of molecules.

adipose tissue A type of connective tissue whose cells contain fat.

adrenal cortex (uh-drē'-nul) The outer portion of an adrenal gland, controlled by ACTH from the anterior pituitary; secretes hormones called glucocorticoids and mineralocorticoids.

adrenal gland One of a pair of endocrine glands, located atop each kidney in mammals, composed of an outer cortex and a central medulla.

adrenal medulla (uh-drē'-nul muh-dul'-uh) The central portion of an adrenal gland, controlled by nerve signals; secretes the fight-or-flight hormones epinephrine and norepinephrine.

adrenocorticotropic hormone (ACTH) (uh-drē'-nō-cōr'-ti-kō-trop'-ik) A protein hormone secreted by the anterior pituitary that stimulates the adrenal cortex to secrete corticosteroids.

adult stem cell A cell present in adult tissues that generates replacements for nondividing differentiated cells.

age structure The relative number of individuals of each age in a population.

agonistic behavior (a'-gō-nis'-tik) Confrontational behavior involving a contest waged by threats, displays, or actual combat, which settles disputes over limited resources, such as food or mates.

AIDS Acquired immunodeficiency syndrome; the late stages of HIV infection, characterized by a reduced number of T cells and the appearance of characteristic opportunistic infections.

alcohol fermentation The conversion of pyruvate from glycolysis to carbon dioxide and ethyl alcohol.

alga (al'-guh) (plural, **algae**) A protist that produces its food by photosynthesis.

alimentary canal (al'-uh-men'-tuh-rē) A digestive tract consisting of a tube running between a mouth and an anus.

allantois (al'-an-tō'-is) In animals, an extraembryonic membrane that develops from the yolk sac; helps dispose of the embryo's nitrogenous wastes and forms part of the umbilical cord in mammals.

allele (uh-lē'-ul) An alternative version of a gene.

allergen (al'-er-jen) An antigen that causes an allergy.

allergy A disorder of the immune system caused by an abnormal sensitivity to an antigen. Symptoms are triggered by histamines released from mast cells.

allopatric speciation The formation of new species in populations that are geographically isolated from one another.

alpha helix (al'-fuh hē'-liks) The spiral shape resulting from the coiling of a polypeptide in a protein's secondary structure.

alternation of generations A life cycle in which there is both a multicellular diploid form, the sporophyte, and a multicellular haploid form, the gametophyte; a characteristic of plants and multicellular green algae.

alternative RNA splicing A type of regulation at the RNA-processing level in which different mRNA molecules are produced from the same primary transcript, depending on which RNA segments are treated as exons and which as introns.

altruism (al'-trū-iz-um) Behavior that reduces an individual's fitness while increasing the fitness of another individual.

alveolates A clade of protists that includes dinoflagellates, apicomplexans, and ciliates.

alveolus (al-vē'-oh-lus) (plural, **alveoli**) One of millions of tiny dead-end sacs within the vertebrate lungs where gas exchange occurs.

Alzheimer's disease (AD) An age-related dementia (mental deterioration) characterized by confusion, memory loss, and other symptoms.

amine (uh-mēn') An organic compound with one or more amino groups.

amino acid (uh-mēn'-ō) An organic molecule containing a carboxyl group and an amino group; serves as the monomer of proteins.

amino group In an organic molecule, a functional group consisting of a nitrogen atom bonded to two hydrogen atoms.

ammonia A small and very toxic nitrogenous waste produced by metabolism.

amniocentesis (am′-nē-ō-sen-tē′-sis) A technique for diagnosing genetic defects while a fetus is in the uterus. A sample of amniotic fluid, obtained by a needle inserted into the amnion, is analyzed for telltale chemicals and defective fetal cells.

amnion (am′-nē-on) In vertebrate animals, the extraembryonic membrane that encloses the fluid-filled amniotic sac containing the embryo.

amniote Member of a clade of tetrapods that have an amniotic egg containing specialized membranes that protect the embryo. Amniotes include mammals and birds and other reptiles.

amniotic egg (am′-nē-ot′-ik) A shelled egg in which an embryo develops within a fluid-filled amniotic sac and is nourished by yolk; produced by reptiles, birds, and egg-laying mammals, it enables them to complete their life cycles on dry land.

amoeba (uh-mē′-buh) Protist that moves and feeds by means of pseudopodia.

amoebocyte (uh-mē′-buh-sīt) An amoeba-like cell that moves by pseudopodia, found in most animals; depending on the species, may digest and distribute food, dispose of wastes, form skeletal fibers, fight infections, and change into other cell types.

amoebozoan A member of a clade of protists that includes amoebas and slime molds and is characterized by lobe-shaped pseudopodia.

amphibian Member of the tetrapod class Amphibia. Amphibians include frogs, toads, and salamanders.

amygdala (uh-mig′-duh-la) An integrative center of the cerebrum; functionally the part of the limbic system that seems to label information to be remembered.

anabolic steroid (an′-uh-bol′-ik stār′-oyd) A synthetic variant of the male hormone testosterone that mimics some of its effects.

analogy The similarity between two species that is due to convergent evolution rather than to descent from a common ancestor with the same trait.

anaphase The fourth stage of mitosis, beginning when sister chromatids separate from each other and ending when a complete set of daughter chromosomes arrives at each of the two poles of the cell.

anaphylactic shock (an′-uh-fi-lak′-tik) A potentially fatal allergic reaction caused by extreme sensitivity to an allergen; involves an abrupt dilation of blood vessels and a sharp drop in blood pressure.

anatomy The study of the structure of an organism.

anchorage dependence The requirement that to divide, a cell must be attached to a solid surface.

androgen (an′-drō-jen) A steroid sex hormone secreted by the gonads that promotes the development and maintenance of the male reproductive system and male body features.

anemia (uh-nē′-me-ah) A condition in which an abnormally low amount of hemoglobin or a low number of red blood cells results in the body cells receiving too little oxygen.

angiosperm (an′-jē-ō-sperm) A flowering plant, which forms seeds inside a protective chamber called an ovary.

annelid (uh-nel′-id) A segmented worm. Annelids include earthworms, polychaetes, and leeches.

annual A plant that completes its life cycle in a single year or growing season.

antagonistic hormones Two hormones that have opposite effects.

anterior Pertaining to the front, or head, of a bilaterally symmetrical animal.

anterior pituitary (puh-tū′-uh-tār-ē) An endocrine gland, adjacent to the hypothalamus and the posterior pituitary, that synthesizes several hormones, including some that control the activity of other endocrine glands.

anther A sac in which pollen grains develop, located at the tip of a flower's stamen.

anthropoid (an′-thruh-poyd) A member of a primate group made up of the apes (gibbons, orangutans, gorillas, chimpanzees, bonobos, and humans) and monkeys.

antibody (an′-tih-bod′-ē) A protein dissolved in blood plasma that attaches to a specific kind of antigen and helps counter its effects.

anticodon (an′-tī-kō′-don) On a tRNA molecule, a specific sequence of three nucleotides that is complementary to a codon triplet on mRNA.

antidiuretic hormone (ADH) (an′-tē-dī′-yū-ret′-ik) A hormone made by the hypothalamus and secreted by the posterior pituitary that promotes water retention by the kidneys.

antigen (an′-tuh-jen) A foreign (nonself) molecule that elicits an acquired immune response.

antigen receptor A transmembrane version of an antibody molecule that B cells and T cells use to recognize specific antigens; also called a membrane antibody.

antigen-binding site A region of the antibody molecule responsible for the antibody's recognition and binding function.

antigenic determinant A region on the surface of an antigen molecule to which an antibody binds.

antigen-presenting cell (APC) One of a family of white blood cells (for example, a macrophage) that ingests a foreign substance or a microbe and attaches antigenic portions of the ingested material to its own surface, thereby displaying the antigens to a helper T cell.

antihistamine (an′-tē-his′-tuh-mēn) A drug that interferes with the action of histamine, providing temporary relief from an allergic reaction.

anus The opening through which undigested materials are expelled.

aorta (ā-or′-tuh) An artery that conveys blood directly from the left ventricle of the heart to other arteries.

aphotic zone (ā-fō′-tik) The region of an aquatic ecosystem beneath the photic zone, where light does not penetrate enough for photosynthesis to take place.

apical dominance (ā′-pik-ul) In a plant, the hormonal inhibition of axillary buds by a terminal bud.

apical meristem (ā′-pik-ul mer′-uh-stem) A meristem at the tip of a plant root or in the terminal or axillary bud of a shoot.

apicomplexan (ap′-ē-kom-pleks′-un) A member of a protistan group of parasitic alveolates, some of which cause human diseases.

appendicular skeleton (ap′-en-dik′-yū-ler) Components of the skeletal system that support the fins of a fish or the arms and legs of a land vertebrate: cartilage and bones of the shoulder girdle, pelvic girdle, and forelimbs and hind limbs. *See also* axial skeleton.

appendix (uh-pen′-dix) A small, fingerlike extension of the vertebrate cecum; contains a mass of white blood cells that contribute to immunity.

aquaporin A transport protein in the plasma membrane of some plant or animal cells that facilitates the diffusion of water across the membrane (osmosis).

aqueous humor (ā′-kwē-us hyū′-mer) Plasma-like liquid in the space between the lens and the cornea in the vertebrate eye; helps maintain the shape of the eye, supplies nutrients and oxygen to its tissues, and disposes of its wastes.

aqueous solution (ā′-kwā-us) A solution in which water is the solvent.

arachnid A member of a major arthropod group (chelicerates) that includes spiders, scorpions, ticks, and mites.

Archaea (ar′-kē-uh) One of two prokaryotic domains of life, the other being Bacteria.

arteriole (ar-ter′-ē-ōl) A vessel that conveys blood between an artery and a capillary bed.

artery A vessel that carries blood away from the heart to other parts of the body.

arthropod (ar′-thrō-pod) A member of the most diverse phylum in the animal kingdom. Arthropods include the horseshoe crab, arachnids (for example, spiders, ticks, scorpions, and mites), crustaceans (for example, crayfish, lobsters, crabs, and barnacles), millipedes, centipedes, and insects. Arthropods are characterized by a chitinous exoskeleton, molting, jointed appendages, and a body formed of distinct groups of segments.

artificial selection The selective breeding of domesticated plants and animals to promote the occurrence of desirable traits.

ascomycete *See* sac fungus.

asexual reproduction The creation of offspring by a single parent, without the participation of sperm and egg.

assisted reproductive technology (ART) Procedure that involves surgically removing eggs from a woman's ovaries, fertilizing them, and then returning them to the woman's body. *See also* in vitro fertilization.

associative learning Learning that a particular stimulus or response is linked to a reward or punishment; includes classical conditioning and trial-and-error learning.

astigmatism (uh-stig'-muh-tizm) Blurred vision caused by a misshapen lens or cornea.

atherosclerosis (ath'-uh-rō'-skluh-rō'-sis) A cardiovascular disease in which fatty deposits called plaques develop on the inner walls of the arteries, narrowing their inner diameters.

atom The small unit of matter that retains the properties of an element.

atomic mass The approximate total mass of an atom; also called atomic weight. Given as a whole number, the atomic mass approximately equals the mass number.

atomic number The number of protons in each atom of a particular element.

ATP synthase A cluster of several membrane proteins that function in chemiosmosis with adjacent electron transport chains, using the energy of a hydrogen ion concentration gradient to make ATP.

atrium (ā'-trē-um) (plural, **atria**) A heart chamber that receives blood from the veins.

auditory canal Part of the vertebrate outer ear that channels sound waves from the pinna or outer body surface to the eardrum.

australopith (os-trā'-lō-pith) The first hominids; scavenger-gatherer-hunters who lived on African savannas between about 4.4 million years ago and 1.5 million years ago.

autoimmune disease An immunological disorder in which the immune system attacks the body's own molecules.

autonomic nervous system (ot'-ō-nom'-ik) The component of the vertebrate peripheral nervous system that regulates the internal environment; made up of sympathetic and parasympathetic subdivisions.

autosome A chromosome not directly involved in determining the sex of an organism; in mammals, for example, any chromosome other than X or Y.

autotroph (ot'-ō-trōf) An organism that makes its own food (often by photosynthesis), thereby sustaining itself without eating other organisms or their molecules. Plants, algae, and numerous bacteria are autotrophs.

auxin (ok'-sin) A plant hormone, indoleacetic acid or a related compound, whose chief effect is to promote seedling elongation.

AV (atrioventricular) node A region of specialized heart muscle tissue between the left and right atria where electrical impulses are delayed for about 0.1 second before spreading to both ventricles and causing them to contract.

axial skeleton (ak'-sē-ul) Components of the skeletal system that support the central trunk of the body: the skull, backbone, and rib cage in a vertebrate. *See also* appendicular skeleton.

axillary bud (ak'-sil-ār-ē) An embryonic shoot present in the angle formed by a leaf and stem.

axon (ak'-son) A neuron fiber that conducts signals to another neuron or to an effector cell.

B

B cell A type of lymphocyte that matures in the bone marrow and later produces antibodies; responsible for the humoral immune response. *See also* T cell.

bacillus (buh-sil'-us) (plural, **bacilli**) A rod-shaped prokaryotic cell.

Bacteria One of two prokaryotic domains of life, the other being Archaea.

bacteriophage (bak-tēr'-ē-ō-fāj) A virus that infects bacteria; also called a phage.

balancing selection Natural selection that maintains stable frequencies of two or more phenotypic forms in a population.

ball-and-socket joint A joint that allows rotation and movement in several planes. Examples in humans are the hip and shoulder joints.

bark All the tissues external to the vascular cambium in a plant that is growing in thickness. Bark is made up of secondary phloem, cork cambium, and cork.

Barr body A dense body formed from a deactivated X chromosome found in the nuclei of female mammalian cells.

basal body (ba'-sul) A eukaryotic cell organelle consisting of a 9 + 0 arrangement of microtubule triplets; may organize the microtubule assembly of a cilium or flagellum; structurally identical to a centriole.

basal metabolic rate (BMR) The number of kilocalories a resting animal requires to fuel its essential body processes for a given time.

basal nuclei (bā'-sul nū'-klē-ī) Clusters of nerve cell bodies located deep within the cerebrum that are important in motor coordination.

base A substance that decreases the hydrogen ion (H) concentration in a solution.

basidiomycete *See* club fungus.

basilar membrane The floor of the middle canal of the inner ear.

behavior Individually, an action carried out by the muscles or glands under control of the nervous system in response to a stimulus; collectively, the sum of an animal's responses to external and internal stimuli.

behavioral ecology The scientific field concerned with behavior in an evolutionary context.

benign tumor An abnormal mass of cells that remains at its original site in the body.

benthic realm A seafloor, or the bottom of a freshwater lake, pond, river, or stream.

biennial A plant that completes its life cycle in two years.

bilateral symmetry An arrangement of body parts such that an organism can be divided equally by a single cut passing longitudinally through it. A bilaterally symmetrical organism has mirror-image right and left sides.

bilaterian Member of the clade of animals Bilateria exhibiting bilateral symmetry.

bile A mixture of substances that is produced by the liver and stored in the gallbladder; it emulsifies fats and aids in their digestion.

binary fission A means of asexual reproduction in which a parent organism, often a single cell, divides into two individuals of about equal size.

binomial A two-part, latinized name of a species; for example, *Homo sapiens*.

biodiversity The variety of living things, encompassing genetic diversity, species diversity, and ecosystem diversity.

biodiversity crisis The current rapid decline in the variety of life on Earth, largely due to the effects of human culture.

biodiversity hot spot A small geographic area with an exceptional concentration of endangered and threatened species, especially endemic species (those found nowhere else).

biofilm A surface-coating colony of prokaryotes that engage in metabolic cooperation.

biogenic amine A neurotransmitter derived from an amino acid.

biogeochemical cycle Any of the various chemical circuits that involve both biotic and abiotic components of an ecosystem.

biogeography The study of past and present distribution of organisms.

biological clock An internal timekeeper that controls an organism's biological rhythms; marks time with or without environmental cues, but often requires signals from the environment to remain tuned to an appropriate period. *See also* circadian rhythm.

biological control The intentional release of a natural enemy to attack a pest population.

biological magnification The accumulation of persistent chemicals in the living tissues of consumers in food chains.

biological species concept Definition of a species as a population or groups of populations whose members have the potential to interbreed in nature and produce viable, fertile offspring, but do not produce viable, fertile offspring with members of other such populations.

biology The scientific study of life.

biomass The amount, or mass, of organic material in an ecosystem.

biome (bī'-ōm) Major types of ecological associations that occupy broad geographic regions of land or water and are characterized by organisms adapted to the particular environments.

bioremediation The use of living organisms to detoxify and restore polluted and degraded ecosystems.

biosphere The entire portion of Earth inhabited by life; the sum of all the planet's ecosystems.

biotechnology The use of living organisms (often microbes) to perform useful tasks; today, usually involves DNA technology.

biotic factor (bī-o'-tik) A living component of a biological community; an organism, or a factor pertaining to one or more organisms.

bipolar disorder Depressive mental illness characterized by swings of mood from high to low; also called manic-depressive disorder.

birth control pill A chemical contraceptive that inhibits ovulation, retards follicular development, or alters a woman's cervical mucus to prevent sperm from entering the uterus.

bivalve A member of a group of molluscs that includes clams, mussels, scallops, and oysters.

blastocoel (blas'-tuh-sēl) In a developing animal, a central, fluid-filled cavity in a blastula.

blastocyst (blas'-tō-sist) A mammalian embryo (equivalent to an amphibian blastula) made up of a hollow ball of cells that results from cleavage and that implants in the mother's endometrium.

blastula (blas'-tyū-luh) An embryonic stage that marks the end of cleavage during animal development; a hollow ball of cells in many species.

blood A type of connective tissue with a fluid matrix called plasma in which blood cells are suspended.

blood pressure The force that blood exerts against the walls of blood vessels.

blood-brain barrier A system of capillaries in the brain that restricts passage of most substances into the brain, thereby preventing large fluctuations in the brain's environment.

body cavity A fluid-containing space between the digestive tract and the body wall.

bolus A lubricated ball of chewed food.

bone A type of connective tissue consisting of living cells held in a rigid matrix of collagen fibers embedded in calcium salts.

bottleneck effect Genetic drift resulting from a drastic reduction in population size; typically, the surviving population is no longer genetically representative of the original population.

Bowman's capsule A cup-shaped swelling at the receiving end of a nephron in the vertebrate kidney; collects the filtrate from the blood.

brain The part of the central nervous system involved in regulating and controlling bodily activity and interpreting information from the senses transmitted through the nervous system.

brainstem A functional unit of the vertebrate brain, composed of the midbrain, the medulla oblongata, and the pons; serves mainly as a sensory filter, selecting which information reaches higher brain centers.

breathing Ventilation of the lungs through alternating inhalation and exhalation.

breathing control center A brain center that directs the activity of organs involved in breathing.

bronchiole (bron'-kē-ōl) A thin breathing tube that branches from a bronchus within a lung.

bronchus (bron'-kus) (plural, **bronchi**) One of a pair of breathing tubes that branch from the trachea into the lungs.

brown alga One of a group of marine, multicellular, autotrophic protists belonging to the stramenopile clade; the most common and largest type of seaweed. Brown algae include the kelps.

bryophyte (brī'-uh-fīt) One of a group of plants that lack xylem and phloem; a nonvascular plant. Bryophytes include mosses, liverworts, and hornworts.

budding A means of asexual reproduction whereby a new individual developed from an outgrowth of a parent splits off and lives independently.

buffer A chemical substance that resists changes in pH by accepting hydrogen ions from or donating hydrogen ions to solutions.

bulbourethral gland (bul'-bō-yū-rē'-thrul) One of a pair of glands near the base of the penis in the human male that secrete fluid that lubricates and neutralizes acids in the urethra during sexual arousal.

bulk feeder An animal that eats relatively large pieces of food.

C

C_3 plant A plant that uses the Calvin cycle for the initial steps that incorporate CO_2 into organic material, forming a three-carbon compound as the first stable intermediate.

C_4 plant A plant that prefaces the Calvin cycle with reactions that incorporate CO_2 into four-carbon compounds, the end product of which supplies CO_2 for the Calvin cycle.

calcitonin (kal'-sih-tōn'-in) A peptide hormone secreted by the thyroid gland that lowers the blood calcium level.

Calvin cycle The second of two stages of photosynthesis; a cyclic series of chemical reactions that occur in the stroma of a chloroplast, using the carbon in CO_2 and the ATP and NADPH produced by the light reactions to make the energy-rich sugar molecule G3P.

CAM plant A plant that uses an adaptation for photosynthesis in arid conditions in which carbon dioxide entering open stomata during the night is converted to organic acids, which release CO_2 for the Calvin cycle during the day, when stomata are closed.

capillary (kap'-il-er-ē) A microscopic blood vessel that conveys blood between an arteriole and a venule; enables the exchange of nutrients and dissolved gases between the blood and interstitial fluid.

capillary bed One of the networks of capillaries that infiltrate every organ and tissue in the body.

capsid The protein shell that encloses a viral genome. It may be rod-shaped, polyhedral, or more complex in shape.

carbohydrate (kar'-bō-hī'-drāt) Member of the class of biological molecules consisting of simple single-monomer sugars (monosaccharides), two-monomer sugars (disaccharides), and other multiunit sugars (polysaccharides).

carbon fixation The incorporation of carbon from atmospheric CO_2 into the carbon in organic compounds. During photosynthesis in a C_3 plant, carbon is fixed into a three-carbon sugar as it enters the Calvin cycle. In C_4 and CAM plants, carbon is fixed into a four-carbon sugar.

carbon skeleton The chain of carbon atoms that forms the structural backbone of an organic molecule.

carbonyl group (kar'-buh-nēl') In an organic molecule, a functional group consisting of a carbon atom linked by a double bond to an oxygen atom.

carboxyl group (kar'-bok-sil) In an organic molecule, a functional group consisting of an oxygen atom double-bonded to a carbon atom that is also bonded to a hydroxyl group.

carboxylic acid An organic compound containing a carboxyl group.

carcinogen (kar-sin'-uh-jin) A cancer-causing agent, either high-energy radiation (such as X-rays or UV light) or a chemical.

carcinoma (kar'-sih-nō'-muh) Cancer that originates in the coverings of the body, such as skin or the lining of the intestinal tract.

cardiac cycle (kar'-dē-ak) The alternating contractions and relaxations of the heart.

cardiac muscle Striated muscle that forms the contractile tissue of the heart.

cardiac output The volume of blood pumped per minute by each ventricle of the heart.

cardiovascular disease (kar'-dē-ō-vas'-kyū-ler) Diseases of the heart and blood vessels.

cardiovascular system A closed circulatory system with a heart and branching network of arteries, capillaries, and veins.

carnivore An animal that mainly eats other animals.

carpel (kar'-pul) The female part of a flower, consisting of a stalk with an ovary at the base and a stigma, which traps pollen, at the tip.

carrier An individual who is heterozygous for a recessively inherited disorder and who therefore does not show symptoms of that disorder but who may pass on the recessive allele to offspring.

carrying capacity In a population, the number of individuals that an environment can sustain.

cartilage (kar'-ti-lij) A flexible connective tissue consisting of living cells and collagenous fibers embedded in a rubbery matrix.

Casparian strip (kas-par'-ē-un) A waxy barrier in the walls of endodermal cells in a plant root that prevents water and ions from entering the xylem without crossing one or more cell membranes.

cation exchange A process in which positively charged minerals are made available to a plant when hydrogen ions in the soil displace mineral ions from the clay particles.

cecum (sē'-kum) (plural, **ceca**) A blind outpocket at the beginning of the large intestine.

cell A basic unit of living matter separated from its environment by a plasma membrane; the fundamental structural unit of life.

cell body The part of a cell, such as a neuron, that houses the nucleus.

cell cycle An ordered sequence of events (including interphase and the mitotic phase) that extends from the time a eukaryotic cell is first formed from a dividing parent cell until its own division into two cells.

cell cycle control system A cyclically operating set of proteins that triggers and coordinates events in the eukaryotic cell cycle.

cell division The reproduction of a cell.

cell plate A double membrane across the midline of a dividing plant cell, between which the new cell wall forms during cytokinesis.

cell theory The theory that all living things are composed of cells and that all cells come from other cells.

cell wall A protective layer external to the plasma membrane in plant cells, bacteria, fungi, and some protists; protects the cell and helps maintain its shape.

cell-mediated immune response The type of specific immunity brought about by T cells; fights body cells infected with pathogens. *See also* humoral immune response.

cellular metabolism (muh-tab'-uh-lizm) The chemical activities of cells.

cellular respiration The aerobic harvesting of energy from food molecules; the energy-releasing chemical breakdown of food molecules, such as glucose, and the storage of potential energy in a form that cells can use to perform work; involves glycolysis, the citric acid cycle, and oxidative phosphorylation (the electron transport chain and chemiosmosis).

cellular respiration The aerobic harvesting of energy from food molecules; the breakdown of organic molecules, such as glucose, for the production of ATP; involves glycolysis, the citric acid cycle, and oxidative phosphorylation (the electron transport chain and chemiosmosis).

cellular slime mold A type of protist that has unicellular amoeboid cells and aggregated reproductive bodies in its life cycle; members of amoebozoan clade.

cellulose (sel'-yū-lōs) A large polysaccharide composed of many glucose monomers linked into cable-like fibrils that provide structural support in plant cell walls.

centipede A carnivorous terrestrial arthropod that has one pair of long legs for each of its numerous body segments, with the front pair modified as poison claws.

central canal The narrow cavity in the center of the spinal cord that is continuous with the fluid-filled ventricles of the brain.

central nervous system (CNS) The integration and command center of the nervous system; the brain and, in vertebrates, the spinal cord.

central vacuole (vak'-yū-ōl) A membrane-enclosed sac occupying most of the interior of a mature plant cell, having diverse roles in reproduction, growth, and development.

centralization The presence of a central nervous system (CNS) distinct from a peripheral nervous system.

centriole (sen'-trē-ōl) A structure in an animal cell composed of cylinders of microtubule triplets arranged in a 9 and 0 pattern. An animal usually has a centrosome with a pair of centrioles involved in cell division.

centromere (sen'-trō-mēr) The region of a duplicated chromosome where two sister chromatids are joined and where spindle microtubules attach during mitosis and meiosis. The centromere divides at the onset of anaphase during mitosis and anaphase II during meiosis.

centrosome (sen'-trō-sōm) Material in the cytoplasm of a eukaryotic cell that gives rise to microtubules; important in mitosis and meiosis; also called microtubule-organizing center.

cephalization (sef'-uh-luh-zā'-shun) The concentration of a nervous system at the anterior (head) end.

cephalopod A member of a group of molluscs that includes squids and octopuses.

cerebellum (sār'-ruh-bel'-um) Part of the vertebrate hindbrain; mainly a planning center that interacts closely with the cerebrum in coordinating body movement.

cerebral cortex (suh-rē'-brul kor'-teks) A folded sheet of gray matter forming the surface of the cerebrum. In humans, it contains integrating centers for higher brain functions such as reasoning, speech, language, and imagination.

cerebral hemisphere The right or left half of the vertebrate cerebrum.

cerebrospinal fluid (suh-rē'-brō-spī'-nul) Blood-derived fluid that surrounds, protects against infection, nourishes, and cushions the brain and spinal cord.

cerebrum (suh-rē'-brum) The largest, most sophisticated, and most dominant part of the vertebrate forebrain, made up of right and left cerebral hemispheres.

cervix (ser'-viks) The neck of the uterus, which opens into the vagina.

chaparral (shap'-uh-ral') A biome dominated by spiny evergreen shrubs adapted to periodic drought and fires; found where cold ocean currents circulate offshore, creating mild, rainy winters and long, hot, dry summers.

character A heritable feature that varies among individuals within a population, such as flower color in pea plants.

charophyte (kār'-uh-fīt) A member of the green algal group that are considered the closest relatives of land plants.

chelicerate A lineage of arthropods that includes horseshoe crabs, scorpions, ticks, and spiders.

chemical bond An attraction between two atoms resulting from a sharing of outer-shell electrons or the presence of opposite charges on the atoms. The bonded atoms gain complete outer electron shells.

chemical cycling The use and reuse of chemical elements such as carbon within an ecosystem.

chemical energy Energy available in molecules for release in a chemical reaction; a form of potential energy.

chemical reaction The making and breaking of chemical bonds, leading to changes in the composition of matter.

chemiosmosis (kem'-ē-oz-mō'-sis) Energy-coupling mechanics that uses the energy of hydrogen ion (H^+) gradients across membranes to phosphorylate ADP; powers most ATP synthesis in cells.

chemoautotroph An organism that obtains both energy and carbon from inorganic chemicals. A chemoautotroph makes its own organic compounds from CO_2 without using light energy.

chemoreceptor (kē'-mō-rē-sep'-ter) A sensor (sensory receptor) that detects chemical changes within the body or a specific kind of molecule in the external environment.

chiasma (kī-az'-muh) (plural, **chiasmata**) The microscopically visible site where crossing over has occurred between chromatids of homologous chromosomes during prophase I of meiosis.

chitin A structural polysaccharide found in many fungal cell walls and in the exoskeletons of arthropods.

chlamydia A group of bacteria that live inside eukaryotic host cells. Includes human pathogens that cause blindness and nongonococcal urethritis, a common sexually transmitted disease.

chlorophyll A green pigment located within the chloroplasts of plants, algae, and certain prokaryotes. Chlorophyll *a* can participate directly in the light reactions, which convert solar energy to chemical energy.

chloroplast (klōr'-rō-plast) An organelle found in plants and photosynthetic protists that absorbs sunlight and uses it to drive the synthesis of organic molecules (sugars) from carbon dioxide and water.

choanocyte (kō-an'-uh-sīt) A flagellated feeding cell found in sponges. Also called a collar cell, it has a collar-like ring that traps food particles around the base of its flagellum.

cholesterol (k-les'-tuh-rol) A steroid that is an important component of animal cell membranes and that acts as a precursor molecule for the synthesis of other steroids such as hormones.

chondrichthyan Member of the class Chondrichthyes, vertebrates with skeletons made mostly of cartilage, such as sharks and rays.

Chordate (kōr'-date) Member of the phylum Chordata, animals that at some point during their development have a dorsal hollow nerve cord, a notochord, pharyngeal slits, and a post-anal tail. Chordates include lancelets, tunicates, and vertebrates.

chorion (kō'r-ē-on) In animals, the outermost extraembryonic membrane, which becomes the mammalian embryo's part of the placenta.

chorionic villus (kōr'-ē-on'-ik vil'-us) An outgrowth of the chorion, containing embryonic blood vessels. As part of the placenta, chorionic villi absorb nutrients and oxygen from, and pass wastes into, the mother's bloodstream.

chorionic villus sampling (CVS) A technique for diagnosing genetic defects while the fetus is in an early development stage within the uterus. A small sample of the fetal portion of the placenta is removed and analyzed.

choroid (kōr'-oyd) A thin, pigmented layer in the vertebrate eye, surrounded by the sclera. The iris is part of the choroid.

chromatin (krō'-muh-tin) The complex of DNA and proteins that constitutes eukaryotic chromosomes; often used to refer to the diffuse, very extended form taken by chromosomes when a cell is not dividing.

chromosome (krō'-muh-sōm) A threadlike, gene-carrying structure found in the nucleus of a eukaryotic cell and most visible during mitosis and meiosis; also, the main gene-carrying structure of a prokaryotic cell. Chromosomes consist of chromatin, a combination of DNA and protein.

chromosome theory of inheritance A basic principle in biology stating that genes are located on chromosomes and that the behavior of chromosomes during meiosis accounts for inheritance patterns.

chyme (kīm) The mixture of partially digested food and digestive juices formed in the stomach.

chytrid Member of a group of fungi that are mostly aquatic and have flagellated spores. They probably represent the most primitive fungal lineage.

cilia A short cellular appendage specialized for locomotion formed from a core of nine outer doublet microtubules and two single microtubules covered by the cell's plasma membrane.

ciliate (sil'-ē-it) A type of protist that moves and feeds by means of cilia. Ciliates belong to the alveolate clade.

circadian rhythm (ser-kā'-dē-un) In an organism, a biological cycle of about 24 hours that is controlled by a biological clock, usually under the influence of environmental cues; a pattern of activity that is repeated daily. *See also* biological clock.

circulatory system The organ system that transports materials such as nutrients, O_2, and hormones to body cells and transports CO_2 and other wastes from body cells.

citric acid cycle The metabolic cycle fueled by acetyl CoA formed after glycolysis in cellular respiration. Chemical reactions in the citric acid cycle complete the metabolic breakdown of glucose molecules to carbon dioxide. The cycle occurs in the matrix of mitochondria and supplies most of the NADH molecules that carry energy to the electron transport chains. The second major stage of cellular respiration.

clade A group of species that includes an ancestral species and all its descendants.

cladistics (kluh-dis'-tiks) An approach to systematics in which common descent is the primary criterion used to classify organisms by placing them into groups called clades.

class In classification, the taxonomic category above order.

cleavage (klē'-vij) (1) Cytokinesis in animal cells and in some protists, characterized by pinching in of the plasma membrane. (2) In animal development, the succession of rapid cell divisions without cell growth that converts the animal zygote into a ball of cells.

cleavage furrow The first sign of cytokinesis during cell division in an animal cell; a shallow groove in the cell surface near the old metaphase plate.

clitoris An organ in the female that engorges with blood and becomes erect during sexual arousal.

clonal selection (klōn'-ul) The production of a lineage of genetically identical cells that recognize and attack the specific antigen that stimulated their proliferation. Clonal selection is the mechanism that underlies the immune system's specificity and memory of antigens.

clone As a verb, to produce genetically identical copies of a cell, organism, or DNA molecule. As a noun, the collection of cells, organisms, or molecules resulting from cloning; *also* (colloquially), a single organism that is genetically identical to another because it arose from the cloning of a somatic cell.

closed circulatory system A circulatory system in which blood is confined to vessels and is kept separate from the interstitial fluid.

club fungus Member of a group of fungi characterized by club-shaped, spore-producing structures called basidia.

clumped Describing a dispersion pattern in which individuals are aggregated in patches.

cnidarian (nī-dār'-ē-un) An animal characterized by cnidocytes, radial symmetry, a gastrovascular cavity, and a polyp and medusa body form. Cnidarians include the hydras, jellyfishes, sea anemones, corals, and related animals.

cnidocyte (nī'-duh-sīt) A specialized cell for which the phylum Cnidaria is named; consists of a capsule containing a fine coiled thread, which, when discharged, functions in defense and prey capture.

coccus (kok'-us) (plural, **cocci**) A spherical prokaryotic cell.

cochlea (kok'-lē-uh) A coiled tube in the inner ear of birds and mammals that contains the hearing organ, the organ of Corti.

codominant Inheritance pattern in which a heterozygote expresses the distinct trait of both alleles.

codon (kō'-don) A three-nucleotide sequence in mRNA that specifies a particular amino acid or polypeptide termination signal; the basic unit of the genetic code.

coelom (sē'-lom) A body cavity completely lined with mesoderm.

coenzyme An organic molecule serving as a cofactor. Most vitamins function as coenzymes in important metabolic reactions.

coevolution Evolutionary change in which adaptations in one species act as a selective force on a second species, inducing adaptations that in turn act as a selective force on the first species; mutual influence on the evolution of two different interacting species.

cofactor A nonprotein molecule or ion that is required for the proper functioning of an enzyme. *See also* coenzyme.

cognition The process carried out by an animal's nervous system, which includes perceiving, storing, integrating, and using information obtained by its sensory receptors.

cognitive map A representation within the nervous system of spatial relations among objects in an animal's environment.

cohesion (kō-hē'-zhun) The binding together of like molecules, often by hydrogen bonds.

collecting duct A tube in the vertebrate kidney that concentrates urine while conveying it to the renal pelvis.

collenchyma cell (kō-len'-kim-uh) In plants, a cell with a thick primary wall and no secondary wall, functioning mainly in supporting growing parts.

colon (kō´-lun) Large intestine; the tubular portion of the vertebrate alimentary tract between the small intestine and the anus; functions mainly in water absorption and the formation of feces.

communication Animal behavior including transmission of, reception of, and response to signals.

community An assemblage of all the organisms living together and potentially interacting in a particular area.

companion cell In a plant, a cell connected to a sieve-tube member whose nucleus and ribosomes provide proteins for the sieve-tube member.

competitive inhibitor A substance that reduces the activity of an enzyme by binding to the enzyme's active site in place of the substrate. A competitive inhibitor's structure mimics that of the enzyme's substrate.

complement system A family of innate defensive blood proteins that cooperate with other components of the vertebrate defense system to protect against microbes; can enhance phagocytosis, directly lyse pathogens, and amplify the inflammatory response.

complementary DNA (cDNA) A DNA molecule made *in vitro* using mRNA as a template and the enzyme reverse transcriptase. A cDNA molecule therefore corresponds to a gene but lacks the introns present in the DNA of the genome.

complete digestive tract A digestive tube with two openings, a mouth and an anus.

complete dominance A type of inheritance in which the phenotypes of the heterozygote and dominant homozygote are indistinguishable.

complete metamorphosis (met´-uh-mōr´-fuh-sis) A type of development in certain insects in which development from larva to adult is achieved by multiple molts that are followed by a pupal stage. While encased in its pupa, the body rebuilds from clusters of embryonic cells that have been held in reserve. The adult emerges from the pupa.

compost Decomposing organic material that can be used to add nutrients to soil.

compound A substance containing two or more elements in a fixed ratio. For example, table salt (NaCl) consists of one atom of the element sodium (Na) for every atom of chlorine (Cl).

compound eye The photoreceptor in many invertebrates; made up of many tiny light detectors, each of which detects light from a tiny portion of the field of view.

concentration gradient An increase or decrease in the density of a chemical substance in an area. Cells often maintain concentration gradients of ions across their membranes. When a gradient exists, substances tend to move from where they are more concentrated to where they are less concentrated.

conception The fertilization of the egg by a sperm cell in humans.

cone (1) In vertebrates, a photoreceptor cell in the retina, stimulated by bright light and enabling color vision. (2) In conifers, a reproductive structure bearing pollen or ovules.

coniferous forest A biome characterized by conifers, cone-bearing evergreen trees.

conjugation The union (mating) of two bacterial cells or protist cells and the transfer of DNA between the two cells.

connective tissue Tissue consisting of a sparse population of cells held in an abundant extracellular matrix, which they produce.

conservation biology A goal-oriented science that endeavors to sustain biological diversity.

consumer An organism that obtains its food by eating plants or by eating animals that have eaten plants.

continental drift A change in the position of continents resulting from the incessant slow movement of the plates of Earth's crust on the underlying molten mantle.

continental shelf The submerged part of a continent.

contraception The deliberate prevention of pregnancy.

controlled experiment A component of the process of science whereby a scientist carries out two parallel tests, an experimental test and a control test. The experimental test differs from the control by one factor, the variable.

convergent evolution Adaptive change resulting in nonhomologous (analogous) similarities among organisms. Species from different evolutionary lineages come to resemble each as a result of living in very similar environments.

copulation Sexual intercourse, usually necessary for internal fertilization to occur.

cork cambium Meristematic tissue that produces cork cells during secondary growth of a plant.

cork The outermost protective layer of a plant's bark, produced by the cork cambium.

cornea (kor´-nē-uh) The transparent frontal portion of the sclera, which admits light into the vertebrate eye.

corpus callosum (kor´-pus kuh-lō´-sum) The thick band of nerve fibers that connect the right and left cerebral hemispheres in placental mammals, enabling the hemispheres to process information together.

corpus luteum (kor´-pus lū´-tē-um) A small body of endocrine tissue that develops from an ovarian follicle after ovulation; secretes progesterone and estrogen during pregnancy.

cortex In plants, the ground tissue system of a root, made up mostly of parenchyma cells, which store food and absorb minerals that have passed through the epidermis. *See also* adrenal cortex; cerebral cortex; renal cortex.

corticosteroid A family of hormones synthesized and secreted by the adrenal cortex, consisting of the mineralocorticoids and glucocorticoids.

cotyledon (kot´-uh-lē´-don) The first leaf that appears on an embryo of a flowering plant; a seed leaf. Monocot embryos have one cotyledon; dicot embryos have two.

countercurrent exchange The transfer of a substance or heat between two fluids flowing in opposite directions.

countercurrent heat exchange Parallel blood vessels that convey warm and cold blood in opposite directions, maximizing heat transfer to the cold blood.

covalent bond (ko-vā´-lent) An attraction between atoms that share one or more pairs of outer-shell electrons; symbolized by a single line between the atoms.

cranial nerve A nerve that leaves the brain and innervates an organ of the head or upper body.

craniate A chordate with a head.

crista (kris´-tuh) (plural, **cristae**) An infolding of the inner membrane of a mitochondrion in which is embedded the electron transport chain and the enzyme catalyzing the synthesis of ATP.

crop A pouchlike organ in a digestive tract where food is softened and may be stored temporarily.

cross A mating of two sexually reproducing individuals; often used to describe a genetics experiment involving a controlled mating.

cross-fertilization The fusion of sperm and egg derived from two different individuals.

crossing over The exchange of segments between chromatids of homologous chromosomes during synapsis in prophase I of meiosis; also, the exchange of segments between DNA molecules in prokaryotes.

crustacean A member of a major arthropod group that includes lobsters, crayfish, crabs, shrimps, and barnacles.

cuticle (kyū´-tuh-kul) (1) In animals, a tough, nonliving outer layer of the skin. (2) In plants, a waxy coating on the surface of stems and leaves that helps retain water.

cyanobacteria (sī-an´-ō-bak-tēr´-ē-uh) Photoautotrophic prokaryotes with plantlike, oxygen-generating photosynthesis.

cystic fibrosis (sis´-tik fī-brō´-sis) A genetic disease that occurs in people with two copies of a certain recessive allele; characterized by an excessive secretion of mucus and vulnerability to infection; fatal if untreated.

cytokinesis (sī-tō-kuh-nē-sis) The division of the cytoplasm to form two separate daughter cells. Cytokinesis usually occurs during telophase of mitosis. Mitosis and cytokinesis make up the mitotic (M) phase of the cell cycle.

cytokinin (sī-tō-kī´-nin) One of a family of plant hormones that promotes cell division, retards aging in flowers and fruits, and may interact antagonistically with auxins in regulating plant growth and development.

cytoplasm (sī-tō-plaz′-um) Everything inside a cell between the plasma membrane and the nucleus; consists of a semifluid medium and organelles.

cytosine (C) (sī′-tuh-sin) A single-ring nitrogenous base found in DNA and RNA.

cytoskeleton A network of protein fibers in the cytoplasm of a eukaryotic cell; includes microfilaments, intermediate filaments, and microtubules.

cytotoxic T cell (sī′-tō-tok′-sik) A type of lymphocyte that attacks body cells infected with pathogens.

D

decomposer Prokaryotes and fungi that secrete enzymes that digest nutrients from organic material and convert them into inorganic forms.

decomposition The breakdown of organic materials into inorganic ones.

dehydration reaction (dē-hī-drā′-shun) A chemical process in which two molecules become covalently bonded to each other with the removal of a water molecule. Also called condensation.

dehydrogenase (dē′-hī-droj′-uh-nās) An enzyme that catalyzes a chemical reaction during which one or more hydrogen atoms are removed from a molecule.

deletion The loss of one or more nucleotides from a gene by mutation; the loss of a fragment of a chromosome.

demographic transition A shift from zero population growth in which birth rates and death rates are high to zero population growth characterized instead by low birth and death rates.

denaturation (dē-nā′-chur-ā′-shun) A process in which a protein unravels, losing its specific structure and hence function; can be caused by changes in pH or salt concentration or by high temperature. Also refers to the separation of the two strands of the DNA double helix, caused by similar factors.

dendrite (den′-drīt) A neuron fiber that conveys signals from its tip inward, toward the rest of the neuron; in a motor neuron, one of several short, branched extensions that convey nerve signals toward the cell body.

density-dependent Referring to a decline in birth rates or a rise in death rates in response to an increase in the number of individuals living in a designated area.

density-dependent inhibition The arrest of cell division that occurs when cells grown in a laboratory dish touch one another.

deoxyribonucleic acid (DNA) (dē-ok′-sē-rī′-bō-nū-klā′-ik) A double-stranded helical nucleic acid molecule consisting of nucleotide monomers with deoxyribose sugar and the nitrogenous bases adenine (A), cytosine (C), guanine (G), and thymine (T). Capable of replicating, is an organism's genetic material. *See also* gene.

dermal tissue system The outer protective covering of plants.

desert A biome characterized by organisms adapted to sparse rainfall (less than 30 cm per year) and rapid evaporation.

desertification The conversion of semi-arid regions to desert.

determinate growth Termination of growth after reaching a certain size, as in most animals. *See also* indeterminate growth.

detritivore (duh-trī′-tuh-vor) An organism that consumes organic wastes and dead organisms.

detritus (duh-trī′-tus) Dead organic matter.

deuterostome (dū-ter′-ō-stōm) An animal with a coelom that forms from hollow outgrowths of the digestive tube of the early embryo. The deuterostomes include the echinoderms and the chordates.

diabetes mellitus (dī′-uh-bē′-tis me-lī′-tis) A human hormonal disease in which body cells cannot absorb enough glucose from the blood and become energy starved; body fats and proteins are then consumed for their energy. Type 1 (insulin-dependent) diabetes results when the pancreas does not produce insulin; type 2 (non-insulin-dependent) diabetes results when body cells fail to respond to insulin.

dialysis (dī-al′-uh-sis) Separation and disposal of metabolic wastes from the blood by mechanical means; an artificial method of performing the functions of the kidneys.

diaphragm (dī′-uh-fram) The sheet of muscle separating the chest cavity from the abdominal cavity in mammals. Its contraction expands the chest cavity, and its relaxation reduces it.

diastole (dī-as′-tō-lē) The stage of the heart cycle in which the heart muscle is relaxed, allowing the chambers to fill with blood. *See also* systole.

diatom (dī′-uh-tom) A unicellular, autotrophic protist that belongs to the stramenopile clade. Diatoms possess a unique, glassy cell wall containing silica.

dicot (dī′-kot) A term traditionally used to refer to flowering plants that have two embryonic seed leaves, or cotyledons.

differentiation The specialization in the structure and function of cells that occurs during the development of an organism; results from selective activation and deactivation of the cells' genes.

diffusion The spontaneous tendency of a substance to move down its concentration gradient from where it is more concentrated to where it is less concentrated.

digestion The mechanical and chemical breakdown of food into molecules small enough for the body to absorb; the second main stage of food processing in animals.

digestive system The organ system involved in ingestion and digestion of food, absorption of nutrients, and elimination of wastes.

dihybrid cross (dī′-hī′-brid) An experimental mating of individuals differing at two genetic loci.

dinoflagellate (dī′-nō-flaj′-uh-let) A member of a group of protists belonging to the alveolate clade. Dinoflagellates are common components of marine and freshwater phytoplankton.

diploid cell In an organism that reproduces sexually, a cell containing two homologous sets of chromosomes, one set inherited from each parent; a 2n cell.

diplomonad A member of a group of heterotrophic protists that have modified mitochondria. The group diplomonads includes the waterborne parasite *Giardia*.

directional selection Natural selection in which individuals at one end of the phenotypic range survive and reproduce more successfully than do other individuals.

disaccharide (dī-sak′-uh-rīd) A sugar molecule consisting of two monosaccharides linked by a dehydration reaction.

dispersion pattern The manner in which individuals in a population are spaced within their area. Three types of dispersion patterns are clumped (individuals are aggregated in patches), uniform (individuals are evenly distributed), and random (unpredictable distribution).

disruptive selection Natural selection in which individuals on both extremes of a phenotypic range are favored over intermediate phenotypes.

distal tubule In the vertebrate kidney, the portion of a nephron that helps refine filtrate and empties it into a collecting duct.

disturbance In ecology, a force that changes a biological community and usually removes organisms from it.

DNA fingerprinting *See* DNA profiling.

DNA ligase (lī′-gās) An enzyme, essential for DNA replication, that catalyzes the covalent bonding of adjacent DNA strands; used in genetic engineering to paste a specific piece of DNA containing a gene of interest into a bacterial plasmid or other vector.

DNA microarray A glass slide carrying thousands of different kinds of single-stranded DNA fragments arranged in an array (grid). A DNA microarray is used to detect and measure the expression of thousands of genes at one time. Tiny amounts of a large number of single-stranded DNA fragments representing different genes are fixed to the glass slide. These fragments, ideally representing all the genes of an organism, are tested for hybridization with various samples of cDNA molecules.

DNA polymerase (puh-lim′-er-ās) An enzyme that assembles DNA nucleotides into polynucleotides using a preexisting strand of DNA as a template.

DNA profiling A procedure that analyzes DNA fragments to determine whether they come from a specific individual.

DNA technology Methods used to study and/or manipulate DNA, including recombinant DNA technology.

doldrums (dol'-drums) An area of calm or very light winds near the equator, caused by rising warm air.

domain A taxonomic category above the kingdom level. The three domains of life are Archaea, Bacteria, and Eukarya.

dominance hierarchy The ranking of individuals within a group, based on social interactions; usually maintained by agonistic behavior.

dominant allele The allele that determines the phenotype of a gene when the individual is heterozygous for that gene.

dorsal Pertaining to the back of a bilaterally symmetrical animal.

dorsal, hollow nerve cord One of the four hallmarks of chordates, a tube that forms on the dorsal side of the body, above the notochord.

double bond A type of covalent bond in which two atoms share two pairs of electrons; symbolized by a pair of lines between the bonded atoms.

double circulation Circulation with separate pulmonary and systemic circuits, in which blood passes through the heart after completing each circuit; ensures vigorous blood flow to all organs.

double fertilization In flowering plants, the formation of both a zygote and a cell with a triploid nucleus, which develops into the endosperm.

double helix The form of native DNA, referring to its two adjacent polynucleotide strands wound into a spiral shape.

Down syndrome A human genetic disorder resulting from the presence of an extra chromosome 21; characterized by heart and respiratory defects and varying degrees of mental retardation.

Duchenne muscular dystrophy (duh-shen' dis'-truh-fē) A human genetic disease caused by a sex-linked recessive allele; characterized by progressive weakening and a loss of muscle tissue.

duodenum (dū-ō-dē'-num) The first portion of the vertebrate small intestine after the stomach, where chyme from the stomach mixes with bile and digestive enzymes.

duplication Repetition of part of a chromosome resulting from fusion with a fragment from a homologous chromosome; can result from an error in meiosis or from mutagenesis.

E

eardrum A sheet of connective tissue separating the outer ear from the middle ear that vibrates when stimulated by sound waves and passes the waves to the middle ear.

echinoderm (uh-kī'-nō-derm) Member of a phylum of slow-moving or sessile marine animals characterized by a rough or spiny skin, a water vascular system, an endoskeleton, and radial symmetry in adults. Echinoderms include sea stars, sea urchins, and sand dollars.

ecological footprint A method of using multiple constraints, including food, fuel, water, housing, and waste deposits, to estimate the human carrying capacity of the Earth.

ecological niche (nich) The role of a species in its community; the sum total of a species use of the biotic and abiotic resources of its environment.

ecological species concept A definition of species in terms of ecological roles (niches).

ecological succession The process of biological community change resulting from disturbance; transition in the species composition of a biological community, often following a flood, fire, or volcanic eruption. *See also* primary succession; secondary succession.

ecology The scientific study of how organisms interact with their environments.

ecosystem (ē'-kō-sis-tem) All the organisms in a given area, along with the nonliving (abiotic) factors with which they interact; a biological community and its physical environment.

ectoderm (ek'-tō-derm) The outer layer of three embryonic cell layers in a gastrula; forms the skin of the gastrula and gives rise to the epidermis and nervous system in the adult.

ectopic pregnancy (ek-top'-ik) The implantation and development of an embryo outside the uterus.

ectotherm (ek'-tō-therm) An animal that warms itself mainly by absorbing heat from its surroundings.

ectothermic Referring to organisms that do not produce enough metabolic heat to have much effect on body temperature. *See also* ectotherm.

effector cell A cell capable of carrying out some action in response to a command from the nervous system.

egg The female gamete; when unfertilized, also called an ovum.

ejaculation (ih-jak'-yū-lā'-shun) Discharge of semen from the penis.

ejaculatory duct The short section of the ejaculatory route in mammals formed by the convergence of the vas deferens and a duct from the seminal vesicle. The ejaculatory duct transports sperm from the vas deferens to the urethra.

electromagnetic receptor A sensor (sensory receptor) that detects energy of different wavelengths, such as electricity, magnetism, and light.

electromagnetic spectrum The entire spectrum of radiation ranging in wavelength from less than a nanometer to more than a kilometer.

electron A subatomic particle with a single negative electrical charge. One or more electrons move around the nucleus of an atom.

electron microscope (EM) An instrument that focuses an electron beam through, or onto the surface of, a specimen. An electron microscope achieves a hundredfold greater resolution than a light microscope.

electron shell An energy level representing the distance of an electron from the nucleus of an atom.

electron transport chain A series of electron carrier molecules that shuttle electrons during the redox reactions that release energy used to make ATP; located in the inner membrane of mitochondria, the thylakoid membranes of chloroplasts, and the plasma membranes of prokaryotes.

electronegativity The attraction of a given atom for the electrons of a covalent bond.

element A substance that cannot be broken down to other substances by chemical means.

elimination The passing of undigested material out of the digestive compartment; the fourth and final stage of food processing in animals.

embryo (em'-brē-ō) A developing stage of a multicellular organism. In humans, the stage in the development of offspring from the first division of the zygote until body structures begin to appear, about the ninth week of gestation.

embryo sac The female gametophyte contained in the ovule of a flowering plant.

embryonic stem cell (ES cell) Cell in the early animal embryo that differentiates during development to give rise to all the different kinds of specialized cells in the body.

embryophyte Another name for land plants, recognizing that land plants share the common derived trait of multicellular, dependent embryos.

emergent properties New properties that emerge with each step upward in the hierarchy of life, owing to the arrangement and interactions of parts as complexity increases.

emerging virus A virus that has appeared suddenly or has recently come to the attention of medical scientists.

endangered species As defined in the U.S. Endangered Species Act, a species that is in danger of extinction throughout all or a significant portion of its range.

endemic species A species whose distribution is limited to a specific geographic area.

endergonic reaction (en'-der-gon'-ik) An energy-requiring chemical reaction, which yields products with more potential energy than the reactants. The amount of energy stored in the products equals the difference between the potential energy in the reactants and that in the products.

endocrine gland (en'-dō-krin) A ductless gland that synthesizes hormone molecules and secretes them directly into the bloodstream.

endocrine system The organ system consisting of ductless glands that secrete hormones and the molecular receptors on or in target cells that respond to the hormones; cooperates with the nervous system in regulating body functions and maintaining homeostasis.

endocytosis (en′-dō-sī-tō′-sis) Cellular uptake of molecules or particles via formation of new vesicles from the plasma membrane.

endoderm (en′-dō-derm) The innermost of three embryonic cell layers in a gastrula; forms the archenteron in the gastrula and gives rise to the innermost linings of the digestive tract and other hollow organs in the adult.

endodermis The innermost layer (a one-cell-thick cylinder) of the cortex of a plant root; forms a selective barrier determining which substances pass from the cortex into the vascular tissue.

endomembrane system A network of membranes inside and around a eukaryotic cell, related either through direct physical contact or by the transfer of membranous vesicles.

endometrium (en′-dō-mē′-trē-um) The inner lining of the uterus in mammals, richly supplied with blood vessels that provide the maternal part of the placenta and nourish the developing embryo.

endoplasmic reticulum (ER) An extensive membranous network in a eukaryotic cell, continuous with the outer nuclear membrane and composed of ribosome-studded (rough) and ribosome-free (smooth) regions. *See also* rough ER; smooth ER.

endorphin (en-dōr′-fin) A pain-inhibiting hormone produced by the brain and anterior pituitary; also serves as a neurotransmitter.

endoskeleton A hard skeleton located within the soft tissues of an animal; includes spicules of sponges, the hard plates of echinoderms, and the cartilage and bony skeletons of vertebrates.

endosperm In flowering plants, a nutrient-rich mass formed by the union of a sperm cell with two polar nuclei during double fertilization; provides nourishment to the developing embryo in the seed.

endospore A thick-coated, protective cell produced within a bacterial cell; endospore becomes dormant and is able to survive harsh environmental conditions.

endosymbiosis (en′-dō-sim′-bē-ō-sis) A process by which the mitochondria and chloroplasts of eukaryotic cells probably evolved from symbiotic associations between small prokaryotic cells living inside larger cells.

endotherm An animal that derives most of its body heat from its own metabolism.

endothermic Referring to animals that use heat generated by metabolism to maintain a warm, steady body temperature. *See also* endotherm.

endotoxin A poisonous component of the outer membrane of gram-negative bacteria that is released only when the bacteria die.

energy The capacity to perform work, or to rearrange matter.

energy coupling In cellular metabolism, the use of energy released from an exergonic reaction to drive an endergonic reaction.

energy flow The passage of energy through the components of an ecosystem.

energy of activation (E_A) The amount of energy that reactants must absorb before a chemical reaction will start.

enhancer A eukaryotic DNA sequence that helps stimulate the transcription of a gene at some distance from it. An enhancer functions by means of a transcription factor called an activator, which binds to it and then to the rest of the transcription apparatus. *See* silencer.

enteric division Part of the autonomic nervous system consisting of complex networks of neurons in the digestive tract, pancreas, and gallbladder.

entropy (en′-truh-pē) A measure of disorder. One form of disorder is heat, which is random molecular motion.

enzyme (en′-zīm) A protein (or RNA molecule) that serves as a biological catalyst, changing the rate of a chemical reaction without itself being changed into a different molecule in the process.

epidermis (ep′-uh-der′-mis) (1) In animals, the living layer or layers of cells forming the protective covering, or outer skin.

(2) In plants, the tissue system forming the protective outer covering of leaves, young stems, and young roots.

epididymis (ep′-uh-did′-uh-mus) A long coiled tube into which sperm pass from the testis and are stored until mature and ejaculated.

epinephrine (ep′-uh-nef′-rin) An amine hormone (also called adrenaline) secreted by the adrenal medulla that prepares body organs for action (fight or flight); also serves as a neurotransmitter.

epithelial tissue (ep′-uh-thē′-lē-ul) A sheet of tightly packed cells lining organs, body cavities, and external surfaces; also called epithelium.

epithelium (plural, epithelia) Epithelial tissue.

erythrocyte (eh-rith′-rō-sīt) A blood cell containing hemoglobin, which transports O_2. Also called red blood cell.

erythropoietin (EPO) A hormone that stimulates the production of erythrocytes. It is secreted by the kidney when tissues of the body do not receive enough oxygen.

esophagus (eh-sof′-uh-gus) The channel that conducts food by peristalsis, usually from the pharynx to the stomach.

essential amino acid An amino acid that an animal cannot synthesize itself and must obtain from food. Eight amino acids are essential for the human adult.

essential element In plants, a chemical element required for the plant to complete its life cycle (to grow from a seed and produce another generation of seeds).

essential fatty acid An unsaturated fatty acid that animals need but cannot make.

essential nutrient A substance that an organism must absorb in preassembled form because it cannot be synthesized from any other material. In humans, there are essential vitamins, minerals, amino acids, and fatty acids.

estrogen (es′-trō-jen) One of several chemically similar steroid hormones secreted by the gonads; maintains the female reproductive system and promotes the development of female body features.

estuary (es′-chū-ār-ē) The area where a freshwater stream or river merges with the ocean.

ethylene A gas that functions as a hormone in plants, triggering aging responses such as fruit ripening and leaf drop.

eudicot (yū-dē-kot) A group consisting of the vast majority of flowering plants that have two embryonic seed leaves, or cotyledons.

euglenozoan A member of a diverse clade of flagellated protists that includes trypanosomes and *Euglena*.

Eukarya The domain that includes all eukaryotic organisms.

eukaryotic cell (yū-kār-ē-ot′-ik) A type of cell that has a membrane-enclosed nucleus and other membrane-enclosed organelles. All organisms except bacteria and archaea are composed of eukaryotic cells.

eumetazoan Member of the clade of "true animals," the animals with true tissues (all animals except sponges).

eustachian tube (yū-stā′-shun) An air passage between the middle ear and throat of vertebrates that equalizes air pressure on either side of the eardrum.

eutherian (yū-thēr′-ē-un) Placental mammal; mammal whose young complete their embryonic development within the uterus, joined to the mother by the placenta.

"evo-devo" The research field that combines evolutionary biology with developmental biology.

evolution Descent with modification; the idea that living species are descendants of ancestral species that were different from present-day ones; also the genetic changes in a population over generations.

evolutionary tree A branching diagram that reflects a hypothesis about evolutionary relationships among groups of organisms.

excretion (ek-skrē′-shun) The disposal of nitrogen-containing metabolic wastes.

excretory system (ek′-skruh-tōr-ē) The organ system that disposes of nitrogen-containing waste products of cellular metabolism.

exergonic reaction (ek′-ser-gon′-ik) An energy-releasing chemical reaction in which the reactants contain more potential energy than the products. The reaction releases an amount of energy equal to the difference in potential energy between the reactants and the products.

exocytosis (ek′-sō-sī-tō′-sis) The movement of materials out of the cytoplasm of a cell by the fusion of vesicles with the plasma membrane.

exon (ek′-son) In eukaryotes, a coding portion of a gene. *See* intron.

exoskeleton A hard, external skeleton that protects an animal and provides points of attachment for muscles.

exotoxin A poisonous protein secreted by certain bacteria.

exponential growth model A mathematical description of idealized, unregulated population growth.

external fertilization The fusion of gametes that parents have discharged into the environment.

extinction The irrevocable loss of a species.

extracellular matrix (ECM) A substance in which the cells of an animal tissue are embedded; consists of protein and polysaccharides.

extraembryonic membranes Four membranes (the yolk sac, amnion, chorion, and allantois) that form a life-support system for the developing embryo of a reptile, bird, or mammal.

extreme halophile A microorganism that lives in a highly saline environment, such as the Great Salt Lake or the Dead Sea.

extreme thermophile A microorganism that thrives in a hot environment (often 60–80°C).

eye cup The simplest type of photoreceptor, a cluster of photo-receptor cells shaded by a cuplike cluster of pigmented cells; detects light intensity and direction.

F

F factor A piece of DNA that can exist as a bacterial plasmid. The F factor carries genes for making sex pili and other structures needed for conjugation, as well as a site where DNA replication can start. F stands for fertility.

F₁ generation The offspring of two parental (P generation) individuals; F_1 stands for first filial.

F₂ generation The offspring of the F_1 generation; F_2 stands for second filial.

facilitated diffusion The passage of a substance through a specific transport protein across a biological membrane down its concentration gradient.

facultative anaerobe (fak′-ul-tā′-tiv an′-uh-rōb) An organism that makes ATP by aerobic respiration if oxygen is present, but that switches to fermentation when oxygen is absent.

family In classification, the taxonomic category above genus.

farsightedness An inability to focus on close objects; occurs when the eyeball is shorter than normal and the focal point of the lens is behind the retina. Also called hyperopia.

fat A large lipid molecule made from an alcohol called glycerol and three fatty acids; a triglyceride. Most fats function as energy-storage molecules.

feces The wastes of the digestive tract.

feedback inhibition A method of metabolic control in which a product of a metabolic pathway acts as an inhibitor of an enzyme within that pathway.

fertilization The union of the nucleus of a sperm cell with the nucleus of an egg cell, producing a zygote.

fertilizer Compounds given to plants to promote their growth.

fetus (fē′-tus) A developing human from the ninth week of gestation until birth; has all the major structures of an adult.

fiber (1) In animals, an elongate, supportive thread in the matrix of connective tissue; an extension of a neuron; a muscle cell. (2) In plants, a long, slender sclerenchyma cell that usually occurs in a bundle.

fibrin (fī′-brin) The activated form of the blood-clotting protein fibrinogen, which aggregates into threads that form the fabric of a blood clot.

fibrinogen (fī′-brin′-uh-jen) The plasma protein that is activated to form a clot when a blood vessel is injured.

fibrous connective tissue A dense tissue with large numbers of collagenous fibers organized into parallel bundles. This is the dominant tissue in tendons and ligaments.

filtrate Fluid extracted by the excretory system from the blood or body cavity. The excretory system produces urine from the filtrate after extracting valuable solutes from it and concentrating it.

filtration In the vertebrate kidney, the extraction of water and small solutes, including metabolic wastes, from the blood by the nephrons.

first law of thermodynamics The principle of conservation of energy. Energy can be transferred and transformed, but it cannot be created or destroyed.

fission A means of asexual reproduction whereby a parent separates into two or more genetically identical individuals of about equal size.

fitness The contribution an individual makes to the gene pool of the next generation relative to the contribution of other individuals in the population.

fixed action pattern (FAP) A genetically programmed, virtually unchangeable behavioral sequence performed in response to a certain stimulus.

flagellum (fluh-jel′-um) (plural, **flagella**) A long cellular appendage specialized for locomotion. The flagella of prokaryotes and eukaryotes differ in both structure and function. Like cilia, eukaryotic flagella have a 9 + 2 arrangement of microtubules covered by the cell's plasma membrane.

flatworm A member of the phylum Platyhelminthes.

fluid feeder An animal that lives by sucking nutrient-rich fluids from another living organism.

fluid mosaic A description of membrane structure, depicting a cellular membrane as a mosaic of diverse protein molecules embedded in a fluid bilayer made of phospholipid molecules.

fluke One of a group of parasitic flatworms.

follicle (fol′-uh-kul) A cluster of cells that surround, protect, and nourish a developing egg cell in the ovary; also secretes estrogen.

food chain A sequence of food transfers from producers through one to four levels of consumers in an ecosystem.

food web A network of interconnecting food chains.

food-conducting cell A specialized, living plant cell with thin primary walls; arranged end to end, such cells collectively form phloem tissue. Also called sieve-tube member.

foot In an invertebrate animal, a structure used for locomotion or attachment, such as the muscular organ extending from the ventral side of a mollusc.

foraging Behavior used in recognizing, searching for, capturing, and consuming food.

foraminiferan (foram) A protist that moves and feeds by means of threadlike pseudopodia and has porous shells composed of calcium carbonate.

forebrain One of three ancestral and embryonic regions of the vertebrate brain; develops into the thalamus, hypothalamus, and cerebrum.

forensics The scientific analysis of evidence for crime scene and other legal proceedings. Also referred to as forensic science.

fossil fuel An energy-containing deposit of organic material formed from the remains of ancient organisms.

fossil record The chronicle of evolution over millions of years of geologic time engraved in the order in which fossils appear in rock strata.

fossils A preserved remnant or impression of an organism that lived in the past.

founder effect Genetic drift that occurs when a few individuals become isolated from a larger population, with the result that the composition of the new population's gene pool is not reflective of that of the original population.

fovea (fō′-vē-uh) An eye's center of focus and the place on the retina where photoreceptors are highly concentrated.

fragmentation A means of asexual reproduction whereby a single parent breaks into parts that regenerate into whole new individuals.

free-living flatworm One of a group of nonparasitic flatworms.

frequency-dependent selection A decline in the reproductive success of individuals that have a phenotype that has become too common in a population.

fruit A ripened, thickened ovary of a flower, which protects developing seeds and aids in their dispersal.

functional group An assemblage of atoms commonly attached to the carbon skeletons of organic molecules and usually involved in chemical reactions.

Fungi (fun′-jē) The kingdom that contains the fungi.

fungus (plural, **fungi**) A heterotrophic eukaryote that digests its food externally and absorbs the resulting small nutrient molecules. Most fungi consist of a netlike mass of filaments called hyphae. Molds, mushrooms, and yeasts are examples of fungi.

G

gallbladder An organ that stores bile and releases it as needed into the small intestine.

gametangium (gam′-uh-tan′-jē-um) (plural, **gametangia**) A reproductive organ that houses and protects the gametes of a plant.

gamete (gam′-ēt) A sex cell; a haploid egg or sperm. The union of two gametes of opposite sex (fertilization) produces a zygote.

gametogenesis The creation of gametes within the gonads.

gametophyte (guh-mē′-tō-fīt) The multicellular haploid form in the life cycle of organisms undergoing alternation of generations; mitotically produces haploid gametes that unite and grow into the sporophyte generation.

ganglion (gang′-glē-un) (plural, **ganglia**) A cluster (functional group) of nerve cell bodies in a centralized nervous system.

gas exchange The exchange of O_2 and CO_2 between an organism and its environment. An aerobic organism takes up O_2 and gives off CO_2.

gastric juice The collection of fluids (mucus, enzymes, and acid) secreted by the stomach.

gastrin A digestive hormone that stimulates the secretion of gastric juice.

gastropod A member of the largest group of molluscs, including snails and slugs.

gastrovascular cavity A digestive compartment with a single opening, the mouth; may function in circulation, body support, waste disposal, and gas exchange, as well as digestion.

gastrula (gas′-trū-luh) The embryonic stage resulting from gastrulation in animal development. Most animals have a gastrula made up of three layers of cells: ectoderm, endoderm, and mesoderm.

gastrulation (gas′-trū-lā′-shun) The phase of embryonic development that transforms the blastula into a gastrula. Gastrulation adds more cells to the embryo and sorts the cells into distinct cell layers.

gel electrophoresis (jel′ ē-lek′-trō-fōr-ē′-sis) A technique for separating and purifying macromolecules, either DNAs or proteins. A mixture of the macromolecules is placed on a gel between a positively charged electrode and a negatively charged one. Negative charges on the molecules are attracted to the positive electrode, and the molecules migrate toward that electrode. The molecules separate in the gel according to their rates of migration, which is mostly determined by their size.

gene A discrete unit of hereditary information consisting of a specific nucleotide sequence in DNA (or RNA, in some viruses). Most of the genes of a eukaryote are located in its chromosomal DNA; a few are carried by the DNA of mitochondria and chloroplasts.

gene cloning The production of multiple copies of a gene.

gene expression The process whereby genetic information flows from genes to proteins; the flow of genetic information from the genotype to the phenotype.

gene flow The transfer of alleles from one population to another, as a result of the movement of individuals or their gametes.

gene pool All the alleles for all the genes in a population.

gene therapy A treatment for a disease in which the patient's defective gene is supplemented or altered.

genetic code The set of rules that dictates the correspondence between RNA codons in an mRNA molecule and amino acids in protein.

genetic drift A change in the gene pool of a population due to chance; effects of genetic drift are most pronounced in small populations.

genetic engineering The direct manipulation of genes for practical purposes.

genetic recombination The production, by crossing over and/or independent assortment of chromosomes during meiosis, of offspring with allele combinations different from those in the parents. The term may also be used more specifically to mean the production by crossing over of eukaryotic or prokaryotic chromosomes with gene combinations different from those in the original chromosomes.

genetically modified (GM) organism An organism that has acquired one or more genes by artificial means. If the gene is from another species, the organism is also known as a transgenic organism.

genital herpes A sexually transmitted disease caused by the herpes simplex virus type 2.

genome (jē′-nōm) A complete (haploid) set of an organism's genes; an organism's genetic material.

genomic library (juh-nō′-mik) A set of DNA segments representing an organism's entire genome; each segment is usually carried by a plasmid or phage.

genomics The study of whole sets of genes and their interactions.

genotype (jē′-nō-tīp) The genetic makeup of an organism.

genus (jē′-nus) (plural, **genera**) In classification, the taxonomic category above species; the first part of a species' binomial; for example, *Homo*.

geologic record A time scale established by geologists that divides Earth's history into time periods, grouped into three eons—Archaean, Proterozoic, and Phanerozoic—and further subdivided into eras, periods, and epochs.

germinate To start developing or growing.

gestation (jes-tā′-shun) Pregnancy; the state of carrying developing young within the female reproductive tract.

gibberellin (jib′-uh-rel′-in) One of a family of plant hormones that triggers the germination of seeds and interacts with auxins in regulating growth and fruit development.

gill An extension of the body surface of an aquatic animal, specialized for gas exchange and/or suspension feeding.

gizzard A pouch-like organ in a digestive tract where food is mechanically ground.

glans The rounded, highly sensitive head of the clitoris in females and penis in males.

glia A supporting cell that is essential for the structural integrity and normal functioning of the nervous system.

global warming A slow but steady rise in Earth's surface temperature, caused by increasing concentrations of greenhouse gases (such as CO_2 and CH_4) in the atmosphere.

glomeromycete Member of a group of fungi characterized by a distinct branching form of mycorrhizae (symbiotic relationships with plant roots) called arbuscules.

glomerulus (glō-mer′-ū-lus) (plural, **glomeruli**) In the vertebrate kidney, the part of a nephron consisting of the capillaries that are surrounded by Bowman's capsule; together, a glomerulus and Bowman's capsule produce the filtrate from the blood.

glucagon (glū′-kuh-gon) A peptide hormone, secreted by the islets of Langerhaus in the pancreas, that raises the level of glucose in the blood.

glucocorticoid (glū′-kuh-kor′-tih-koyd) A corticosteroid hormone secreted by the adrenal cortex that increases the blood glucose level and helps maintain the body's response to long-term stress.

glycogen (glī′-kō-jen) An extensively branched polysaccharide of many glucose monomers; serves as an energy-storage molecule in liver and muscle cells; the animal equivalent of starch.

glycolysis (glī-kol′-uh-sis) The multistep chemical breakdown of a molecule of glucose into two molecules of pyruvate; the first stage of cellular respiration in all organisms; occurs in the cytoplasmic fluid.

glycoprotein (glī'-kō-prō'-tēn) A macromolecule consisting of one or more polypeptides linked to short chains of sugars.

goiter An enlargement of the thyroid gland resulting from a dietary iodine deficiency.

Golgi apparatus (gol'-jē) An organelle in eukaryotic cells consisting of stacks of membranous sacs that modify, store, and ship products of the endoplasmic reticulum.

gonad A sex organ in an animal; an ovary or testis.

gram stain Microbiology technique to identify the cell wall composition of bacteria. Results categorize bacteria as gram-positive or gram-negative.

gram-positive bacteria Diverse group of bacteria with a cell wall that is structurally less complex and contains more peptidoglycan than that of gram-negative bacteria. Gram-positive bacteria are usually less toxic than gram-negative bacteria.

granum (gran'-um) (plural, **grana**) A stack of hollow disks formed of thylakoid membrane in a chloroplast. Grana are the sites where light energy is trapped by chlorophyll and converted to chemical energy during the light reactions of photosynthesis.

gravitropism (grav'-uh-trō'-pizm) A plant's growth response to gravity.

gray matter Regions of dendrites and clusters of nerve cell bodies within the CNS.

green alga A member of a group of photosynthetic protists that includes chlorophytes and charophyceans, the closest living relatives of land plants. Green algae include unicellular, colonial, and multicellular species.

greenhouse effect The warming of the atmosphere caused by CO_2, CH_4, and other gases that absorb infrared radiation and slow its escape from Earth's surface.

ground tissue system A tissue of mostly parenchyma cells that makes up the bulk of a young plant and is continuous throughout its body. The ground tissue system fills the space between the epidermis and the vascular tissue system.

growth factor A protein secreted by certain body cells that stimulates other cells to divide.

growth hormone (GH) A protein hormone secreted by the anterior pituitary that promotes development and growth and stimulates metabolism.

guanine (G) (gwa'-nēn) A double-ring nitrogenous base found in DNA and RNA.

guard cell A specialized epidermal cell in plants that regulates the size of a stoma, allowing gas exchange between the surrounding air and the photosynthetic cells in the leaf.

gymnosperm (jim'-nō-sperm) A naked-seed plant. Its seed is said to be naked because it is not enclosed in an ovary.

H

habitat A place where an organism lives; an environment situation in which an organism lives.

habituation Learning not to respond to a repeated stimulus that conveys little or no information.

hair cell A type of mechanoreceptor that detects sound waves and other forms of movement in air or water.

haploid cell In the life cycle of an organism that reproduces sexually, a cell containing a single set of chromosomes; an *n* cell.

Hardy-Weinberg equilibrium The principle that the shuffling of genes that occurs during sexual reproduction by itself cannot change the overall genetic makeup of a population.

heart A muscular pump that propels a circulatory fluid (blood) through vessels to the body.

heart attack The damage or death of cardiac muscle cells and the resulting failure of the heart to deliver enough blood to the body.

heart murmur A hissing sound that most often results from blood squirting backward through a leaky valve in the heart.

heart rate The frequency of heart contraction.

heartwood In the center of trees, the darkened, older layers of secondary xylem made up of cells that no longer transport water and are clogged with resins. *See also* sapwood.

heat Thermal energy; the amount of energy associated with the movement of the atoms and molecules in a body of matter. Heat is energy in its most random form.

helper T cell A type of lymphocyte that helps activate other types of T cells and may help stimulate B cells to produce antibodies.

hemoglobin (hē'-mō-glō'-bin) An iron-containing protein in red blood cells that reversibly binds O_2 and transports it to body tissues.

hemophilia (hē'-mō-fil'-ē-uh) A human genetic disease caused by a sex-linked recessive allele; characterized by excessive bleeding following injury.

hepatic portal vein A blood vessel that conveys nutrient-laden blood from capillaries surrounding the intestine directly to the liver.

herbivore An animal that eats only plants or algae. *See also* carnivore; omnivore.

herbivory Consumption of plant parts or algae by an animal.

hermaphroditism (her-maf'-rō-dī-tizm) A condition in which an individual has both female and male gonads and functions as both a male and female in sexual reproduction by producing both sperm and eggs.

heterokaryotic stage A fungal life cycle stage that contains two genetically different nuclei in the same cell.

heterotroph (het'-er-ō-trōf) An organism that cannot make its own organic food molecules and must obtain them by consuming other organisms or their organic products; a consumer or a decomposer in a food chain.

heterozygote advantage Greater reproductive success of heterozygous individuals compared to homozygotes; tends to preserve variation in gene pools.

heterozygous (het'-er-ō-zī'-gus) Having two different alleles for a given gene.

high-density lipoprotein (HDL) A cholesterol-carrying particle in the blood, made up of cholesterol and other lipids surrounded by a single layer of phospholipids in which proteins are embedded. An HDL particle carries less cholesterol than a related lipoprotein, LDL, and may be correlated with a decreased risk of blood vessel blockage.

hindbrain One of three ancestral and embryonic regions of the vertebrate brain; develops into the medulla oblongata, pons, and cerebellum.

hinge joint A joint that allows movement in only one plane. In humans, examples include the elbow and knee.

hippocampus (hip'-uh-kam'-pus) An integrative center of the cerebrum; functionally, the part of the limbic system that plays a central role in memory and learning.

histamine (his'-tuh-mēn) A chemical alarm signal released by injured cells of vertebrates that causes blood vessels to dilate during an inflammatory response.

histone (his'-tōn) A small protein molecule associated with DNA and important in DNA packing in the eukaryotic chromosome.

HIV Human immunodeficiency virus, the retrovirus that attacks the human immune system and causes AIDS.

homeobox (hō'-mē-ō-boks') A 180-nucleotide sequence within a homeotic gene and some other developmental genes.

homeostasis (hō'-mē-ō-stā'-sis) The steady state of body functioning; a state of equilibrium characterized by a dynamic interplay between outside forces that tend to change an organism's internal environment and the internal control mechanisms that oppose such changes.

homeotic gene (hō'-mē-ot'-ik) A master control gene that determines the identity of a body structure of a developing organism, presumably by controlling the developmental fate of groups of cells. (In plants, such genes are called organ identity genes.)

hominid (hah'-mi-nid) A species on the human branch of the evolutionary tree; a member of the family Hominidae, including *Homo sapiens* and our ancestors.

homologous chromosomes (hō-mol'-uh-gus) The two chromosomes that make up a matched pair in a diploid cell. Homologous chromosomes are of the same length, centromere position, and staining pattern and possess genes for the same characteristics at corresponding loci. One homologous chromosome is inherited from the organism's father, the other from the mother.

homologous structures Structures in different species that are similar because of common ancestry.

homology Similarity in characteristics resulting from a shared ancestry.

homozygous (hō′-mō-zī′-gus) Having two identical alleles for a given gene.

horizontal gene transfer The transfer of genes from one genome to another through mechanisms such as transposable elements, plasmid exchange, viral activity, and perhaps, fusions of different organisms.

hormone (1) In animals, a regulatory chemical that travels in the blood from its production site, usually an endocrine gland, to other sites, where target cells respond to the regulatory signal. (2) In plants, a chemical that is produced in one part of the plant that travels to another part, where it coordinates certain plant activities.

horseshoe crab A bottom-dwelling marine chelicerate, a member of the phylum Arthropoda.

human chorionic gonadotropin (HCG) (kōr′-ē-on′-ik gon′-uh-dō-trō′-pin) A hormone secreted by the chorion that maintains the corpus luteum of the ovary during the first three months of pregnancy.

Human Genome Project (HGP) An international collaborative effort to map and sequence the DNA of the entire human genome.

humoral immune response The type of specific immunity brought about by antibody-producing B cells; fights bacteria and viruses in body fluids. *See also* cell-mediated immune response.

humus (hyū′-mus) Decomposing organic material found in topsoil.

Huntington's disease A human genetic disease caused by a dominant allele; characterized by uncontrollable body movements and degeneration of the nervous system; usually fatal 10–20 years after the onset of symptoms.

hybrid The offspring of parents of two different species or of two different varieties of one species; the offspring of two parents that differ in one or more inherited traits; an individual that is heterozygous for one or more pairs of genes.

hybrid zone A geographic region in which members of different species meet and mate, producing at least some hybrid offspring.

hydrocarbon A chemical compound composed only of the elements carbon and hydrogen.

hydrogen bond A type of weak chemical bond formed when the partially positive hydrogen atom participating in a polar covalent bond in one molecule is attracted to the partially negative atom participating in a polar covalent bond in another molecule (or in another part of the same macromolecule).

hydrolysis (hī-drol′-uh-sis) A chemical process in which polymers are broken down by the chemical addition of water molecules to the bonds linking their monomers; an essential part of digestion.

hydrophilic (hī′-drō-fil′-ik) "Water-loving"; pertaining to polar, or charged, molecules (or parts of molecules) that are soluble in water.

hydrophobic (hī′-drō-fō′-bik) "Water-fearing"; pertaining to nonpolar molecules (or parts of molecules) that do not dissolve in water.

hydrostatic skeleton A skeletal system composed of fluid held under pressure in a closed body compartment; the main skeleton of most cnidarians, flatworms, nematodes, and annelids.

hydroxyl group (hī-drok′-sil) In an organic molecule, a functional group consisting of a hydrogen atom bonded to an oxygen atom.

hypertension Abnormally high blood pressure; a persistent blood pressure above 140/90.

hypertonic solution In comparing two solutions, the one with the greater concentration of solutes; cells in such a solution will lose water to their surroundings.

hypha (hī′-fuh) (plural, **hyphae**) One of many filaments making up the body of a fungus.

hypoglycemia (hī′-pō-glī-sē′-mē-uh) An abnormally low level of glucose in the blood that results when the pancreas secretes too much insulin into the blood.

hypothalamus (hī-pō-thal′-uh-mus) The master control center of the system, located in the ventral portion of the vertebrate forebrain. The hypothalamus functions in maintaining homeostasis, especially in coordinating the endocrine and nervous systems; secretes hormones of the posterior pituitary and releasing hormones that regulate the anterior pituitary.

hypothesis (hī-poth′-uh-sis) (plural, **hypotheses**) A tentative explanation a scientist proposes for a specific phenomenon that has been observed.

hypotonic solution In comparing two solutions, the one with the lower concentration of solutes; cells in such a solution will take up water from their surroundings.

I

immune system An animal body's system of defenses against agents that cause disease.

immunodeficiency disease An immunological disorder in which the immune system lacks one or more components, making the body susceptible to infectious agents that would ordinarily not be pathogenic.

imperfect fungus A fungus with no known sexual stage.

impotence The inability to maintain an erection; also called erectile dysfunction.

imprinting Learning that is limited to a specific critical period in an animal's life and that is generally irreversible.

in vitro fertilization (IVF) (vē′-tro) Uniting sperm and egg in a laboratory container, followed by the placement of a resulting early embryo in the mother's uterus.

inbreeding Mating between close relatives.

inclusive fitness An individual's success at perpetuating its genes by producing its own offspring and by helping close relatives to produce offspring.

incomplete dominance A type of inheritance in which the phenotype of a heterozygote (*Aa*) is intermediate between the phenotypes of the two types of homozygotes (*AA* and *aa*).

incomplete metamorphosis A type of development in certain insects in which development from larva to adult is achieved by multiple molts, but without forming a pupa.

indeterminate growth Growth that continues throughout life, as in most plants. *See also* determinate growth.

induced fit The change in shape of the active site of an enzyme, induced by entry of the substrate so that it binds more snugly to the substrate.

induction During embryonic development, the influence of one group of cells on another group of cells.

inferior vena cava (vē′-nuh kā′-vuh) A large vein that returns O_2-poor blood to the heart from the lower, or posterior, part of the body. *See also* superior vena cava.

infertility The inability to conceive after one year of regular, unprotected intercourse.

inflammatory response An innate body defense in vertebrates caused by a release of histamine and other chemical alarm signals that trigger increased blood flow, a local increase in white blood cells, and fluid leakage from the blood. The resulting inflammatory response includes redness, heat, and swelling in the affected tissues.

ingestion The act of eating; the first main stage of food processing in animals.

ingroup In a cladistic study of evolutionary relationships among taxa of organisms, the group of taxa that is actually being analyzed. *See also* outgroup.

inhibiting hormone A kind of hormone released from the hypothalamus that makes the anterior pituitary stop secreting hormone.

innate behavior Behavior that is under strong genetic control and is performed in virtually the same way by all members of a species.

innate immunity The kind of immunity that is present in an animal before exposure to pathogens and is effective from the time of birth. Innate immune defenses include barriers, phagocytic cells, antimicrobial proteins, the inflammatory response, and natural killer cells.

inner ear One of three main regions of the vertebrate ear; includes the cochlea, organ of Corti, and semicircular canals.

insulin A protein hormone, secreted by the islets of Langerhans in the pancreas, that lowers the level of glucose in the blood.

integration The interpretation of sensory signals within neural processing centers of the central nervous system.

integrins A transmembrane protein that interconnects the extracellular matrix and the cytoskeleton.

integumentary system (in-teg′-yū-men′-ter-ē) The organ system consisting of the skin and its derivatives, such as hair and nails in mammals; helps protect the body from drying out, mechanical injury, and infection.

interferon (in′-ter-fēr′-on) An innate defensive protein produced by virus-infected vertebrate cells and capable of helping other cells resist viruses.

intermediate One of the compounds that form between the initial reactant and the final product in a metabolic pathway, such as between glucose and pyruvate in glycolysis.

intermediate filament An intermediate-sized protein fiber that is one of the three main kinds of fibers making up the cytoskeleton of eukaryotic cells. Intermediate filaments are ropelike, made of fibrous proteins.

intermembrane space One of the two fluid-filled internal compartments of the mitochondrion. The intermembrane space is the narrow region between the inner and outer membranes.

internal fertilization Reproduction in which sperm are typically deposited in or near the female reproductive tract and fertilization occurs within the tract.

interneuron (in′-ter-nūr′-on) A nerve cell, entirely within the central nervous system, that integrates sensory signals and may relay command signals to motor neurons.

internode The portion of a plant stem between two nodes.

interphase The period in the eukaryotic cell cycle when the cell is not actually dividing. Interphase constitutes the majority of the time spent in the cell cycle. *See also* mitotic phase.

interspecific competition Competition between individuals or populations of two or more species requiring a limited resource.

interspecific interactions Relationships among individuals of different species in a community.

interstitial fluid (in′-ter-stish′-ul) An aqueous solution that surrounds body cells and through which materials pass back and forth between the blood and the body tissues.

intertidal zone (in′-ter-tīd′-ul) A shallow zone where the waters of an estuary or ocean meet land.

intestine The region of a digestive tract located between the gizzard or stomach and the anus and where chemical digestion and nutrient absorption usually occur.

intron (in′-tron) In eukaryotes, a nonexpressed (noncoding) portion of a gene that is excised from the RNA transcript. *See* exon.

invasive species Non-native species that spread beyond the original point of introduction and cause environmental or economic damage.

inversion A change in a chromosome resulting from reattachment of a chromosome fragment to the original chromosome, but in a reverse direction. Mutagens and errors during meiosis can cause inversions.

invertebrate An animal that lacks a backbone.

ion (ī-on) An atom that has gained or lost one or more electrons, thus acquiring a charge.

ionic bond (ī-on′-ik) A chemical bond resulting from the attraction between oppositely charged ions.

iris The colored part of the vertebrate eye, formed by the anterior portion of the choroid.

isomers (ī′-sō-mers) Organic compounds with the same molecular formula but different structures and, therefore, different properties.

isotonic solution (ī-sō-ton′-ik) A solution having the same solute concentration as nother solution, thus having no effect on passage of water in or out of the cell.

isotope (ī′-sō-tōp) A variant form of an atom. Isotopes of an element have the same number of protons but different numbers of neutrons.

K

karyotype (kār′-ē-ō-tīp) A display of micrographs of the metaphase chromosomes of a cell, arranged by size and centromere position.

keystone species A species that is not usually abundant in a community yet exerts strong control on community structure by the nature of its ecological role or niche.

kilocalorie (kcal) A quantity of heat equal to 1,000 calories. Used to measure the energy content of food, it is usually called a "Calorie."

kin selection The natural selection that favors altruistic behavior by enhancing reproductive success of relatives.

kinesis (kuh-nē′-sis) Random movement in response to a stimulus.

kinetic energy (kuh-net′-ik) The energy of motion; the energy of a mass of matter that is moving. Moving matter does work by imparting motion to other matter.

kingdom In classification, the broad taxonomic category above phylum.

***K*-selection** The concept that in certain (*K*-selected) populations, life history is centered around producing relatively few offspring that have a good chance of survival.

L

labia majora (lā′-bē-uh muh-jor′-uh) A pair of outer thickened folds of skin that protect the female genital region.

labia minora (lā′-bē-uh mi-nor′-uh) A pair of inner folds of skin, bordering and protecting the female genital region.

labor A series of strong, rhythmic contractions of the uterus that expel a baby out of the uterus and vagina during childbirth.

lactic acid fermentation The conversion of pyruvate to lactate with no release of carbon dioxide.

lancelet One of a group of invertebrate chordates.

landscape Several different ecosystems linked by exchanges of energy, materials, and organisms.

landscape ecology The application of ecological principles to the study of the structure and dynamics of a collection of ecosystems; the scientific study of the biodiversity of interacting ecosystems.

large intestine *See* colon.

larva (lar′-vuh) (plural, **larvae**) A free-living, sexually immature form in some animal life cycles that may differ from the adult in morphology, nutrition, and habitat.

larynx (lar′-inks) The voice box, containing the vocal cords.

lateral line system A row of sensory organs along each side of a fish's body. Sensitive to changes in water pressure, it enables a fish to detect minor vibrations in the water.

lateral meristem A meristem that thickens the roots and shoots of woody plants. The vascular cambium and cork cambium are lateral meristems.

lateralization The phenomenon in which the two hemispheres of the brain become specialized for different functions.

law of independent assortment A general rule in inheritance that when gametes form during meiosis, each pair of alleles for a particular characteristic segregate independently of other pairs; also known as Mendel's second law of inheritance.

law of segregation A general rule in inheritance that individuals have two alleles for each gene and that when gametes form by meiosis, the two alleles separate, each resulting gamete ending up with only one allele of each gene; also known as Mendel's first law of inheritance.

leaf The main site of photosynthesis in a plant; consists of a flattened blade and a stalk (petiole) that joins the leaf to the stem.

learning Modification of behavior as a result of specific experiences.

leech A member of one of the three large groups of annelids. *See* annelid.

lens The structure in an eye that focuses light rays onto the retina.

leukemia (lū-kī′-mē-ah) A type of cancer of the blood-forming tissues, characterized by an excessive production of white blood cells and an abnormally high number of them in the blood; cancer of the bone marrow cells that produce leukocytes.

leukocyte (lū´-kō-sīt) A blood cell that functions in defending the body against infections and cancer cells. Also called white blood cell.

lichen (lī´-ken) A close association between a fungus and an alga or between a fungus and a cyanobacterium, some of which are known to be beneficial to both partners.

life cycle The entire sequence of stages in the life of an organism, from the adults of one generation to the adults of the next.

life history The series of events from birth through reproduction to death.

life table A listing of survivals and deaths in a population in a particular time period and predictions of how long, on average, an individual of a given age will live.

ligament A type of fibrous connective tissue that joins bones together at joints.

light microscope (LM) An optical instrument with lenses that refract (bend) visible light to magnify images and project them into a viewer's eye or onto photographic film.

light reactions The first of two stages in photosynthesis; the steps in which solar energy is absorbed and converted to chemical energy in the form of ATP and NADPH. The light reactions power the sugar-producing Calvin cycle but produce no sugar themselves.

lignin A chemical that hardens the cell walls of plants.

limbic system (lim´-bik) A functional unit of several integrating and relay centers located deep in the human forebrain; interacts with the cerebral cortex in creating emotions and storing memories.

limiting factors Environmental factors that restrict population growth.

linked genes Genes located near each other on the same chromosome that tend to be inherited together.

lipid An organic compound consisting mainly of carbon and hydrogen atoms linked by nonpolar convalent bonds, making the compound mostly hydrophobic. Lipids include fats, phospholipids, and steroids and are insoluble in water.

liver The largest organ in the vertebrate body. The liver performs diverse functions, such as producing bile, preparing nitrogenous wastes for disposal, and detoxifying poisonous chemicals in the blood.

lobe-fin A bony fish with strong, muscular fins supported by bones.

local regulator A chemical messenger that is secreted into the interstitial fluid and causes changes in cells very near the point of secretion. Neurotransmitters are local regulators.

locomotion Active movement from place to place.

locus (plural, **loci**) The particular site where a gene is found on a chromosome. Homologous chromosomes have corresponding gene loci.

logistic growth model A mathematical description of idealized population growth that is restricted by limiting factors.

long-day plant A plant that flowers in late spring or early summer, when day length is long. Long-day plants actually flower in response to a short night (and so are sometimes called short-night plants).

long-term memory The ability to hold, associate, and recall information over one's life.

loop of Henle (hen´-lē) In the vertebrate kidney, the portion of a nephron that helps concentrate the filtrate while conveying it between a proximal tubule and a distal tubule.

loose connective tissue The most widespread connective tissue in the vertebrate body. It binds epithelia to underlying tissues and functions as packing material, holding organs in place.

low-density lipoprotein (LDL) A cholesterol-carrying particle in the blood, made up of cholesterol and other lipids surrounded by a single layer of phospholipids in which proteins are embedded. An LDL particle carries more cholesterol than a related lipoprotein, HDL, and high LDL levels in the blood correlate with a tendency to develop blocked blood vessels and heart disease.

lung An infolded respiratory surface of terrestrial vertebrates that connects to the atmosphere by narrow tubes.

lymph A colorless fluid, derived from interstitial fluid, that circulates in the lymphatic sytem.

lymphatic system (lim-fat´-ik) The vertebrate organ system through which lymph circulates; includes lymph vessels, lymph nodes, and the spleen. The lymphatic system helps remove toxins and pathogens from the blood and interstitial fluid and returns fluid and solutes from the interstitial fluid to the circulatory system.

lymphocyte (lim´-fuh-sīt) A type of white blood cell that is chiefly responsible for the acquired immune response; found mostly in the lymphatic system. *See* B cell; T cell.

lymphoma (lim-fō´-muh) Cancer of the tissues that form white blood cells.

lysogenic cycle (lī´-sō-jen´-ik) A type of bacteriophage replication cycle in which the viral genome is incorporated into the bacterial host chromosome as a prophage. New phages are not produced, and the host cell is not killed or lysed unless the viral genome leaves the host chromosome.

lysosome (lī-sō-sōm) A digestive organelle in eukaryotic cells; contains hydrolytic enzymes that digest the cell's food and wastes.

lytic cycle (lit´-ik) A type of viral replication cycle resulting in the release of new viruses by lysis (breaking open) of the host cell.

M

macroevolution Evolutionary change on a grand scale, encompassing the origin of new taxonomic groups, evolutionary trends, adaptive radiation, and mass extinction.

macromolecule A giant molecule in a living organism formed by the joining of smaller molecules: a protein, carbohydrate, or nucleic acid.

macronutrient A chemical substance that an organism must obtain in relatively large amounts. *See also* micronutrient.

macrophage (mak´-rō-fāj) A large, amoeboid, phagocytic white blood cell that functions in innate immunity by destroying microbes and in acquired immunity as an antigen-presenting cell.

major depression Depressive mental illness characterized by experiencing a low mood most of the time.

major histocompatibility complex (MHC) *See* self protein.

malignant tumor An abnormal tissue mass that can spread into neighboring tissue and to other parts of the body; a cancerous tumor.

malnourishment The long-term absence from the diet of one or more essential nutrients.

mammal Member of the class Mammalia, amniotes that possess mammary glands and hair.

mantle In a mollusc, the outgrowth of the body surface that drapes over the animal. The mantle produces the shell and forms the mantle cavity.

marsupial (mar-sū´-pē-ul) A pouched mammal, such as a kangaroo, opossum, or koala. Marsupials give birth to embryonic offspring that complete development while housed in a pouch and attached to nipples on the mother's abdomen.

mass number The sum of the number of protons and neutrons in an atom's nucleus.

mast cell In vertebrates, a type of circulating body cell that produces histamine, triggering the inflammatory response.

matter Anything that occupies space and has mass.

maximum sustained yield The level of harvest that produces a consistent yield without forcing a population into decline.

mechanoreceptor (mek´-uh-nō-ri-sep´-ter) A sensor (sensory receptor) that detects physical deformations in the environment associated with pressure, touch, stretch, motion, or sound.

medulla oblongata (meh-duh´-luh ob´-long-got´-uh) Part of the vertebrate hindbrain continuous with the spinal cord; passes data between the spinal cord and forebrain and controls autonomic, homeostatic functions, including breathing, heart rate, swallowing, and digestion.

medusa (med-ū´-suh) (plural, **medusae**) One of two types of cnidarian body forms; an umbrella-like body form.

meiosis (mī-ō´-sis) In a sexually reproducing organism, the division of a single diploid nucleus into four haploid daughter nuclei. Meiosis and cytokinesis produce haploid gametes from diploid cells in the reproductive organs of the parents.

membrane potential The charge difference between a cell's cytoplasm and extracellular fluid due to the differential distribution of ions.

memory The ability to store and retrieve information. *See also* long-term memory, short-term memory.

memory cell A clone of long-lived lymphocytes formed during the primary immune response; remains in a lymph node until activated by exposure to the same antigen that triggered its formation. When activated, a memory cell forms a large clone that mounts the secondary immune response.

meninges (muh-nin´-jēz) Layers of connective tissue that enwrap and protect the brain and spinal cord.

menstrual cycle (men´-strū-ul) The hormonally synchronized cyclic buildup and breakdown of the endometrium of some primates, including humans.

menstruation (men´-strū-ā´-shun) Uterine bleeding resulting from shedding of the endometrium during a menstrual cycle.

meristem (mār´-eh-stem) Plant tissue consisting of undifferentiated cells that divide and generate new cells and tissues.

mesoderm (mez´-ō-derm) The middle layer of the three embryonic cell layers in a gastrula; gives rise to muscles, bones, the dermis of the skin, and most other organs in the adult.

mesophyll (mes´-ō-fil) The green tissue in the interior of a leaf; a leaf's ground tissue system; the main site of photosynthesis.

messenger RNA (mRNA) The type of ribonucleic acid that encodes genetic information from DNA and conveys it to ribosomes, where the information is translated into amino acid sequences.

metabolic pathway A series of chemical reactions that either builds a complex molecule or breaks down a complex molecule into simpler compounds.

metabolic rate The total amount of energy an animal uses in a unit of time.

metabolism The totality of an organism's chemical reactions.

metamorphosis (met´-uh-mōr´-fuh-sis) The transformation of a larva into an adult. *See* complete metamorphosis; incomplete metamorphosis.

metaphase (met´-eh-fāz) The third stage of mitosis, during which all the cell's duplicated chromosomes are lined up at an imaginary plane equidistant between the poles of the mitotic spindle.

metastasis (muh-tas´-tuh-sis) The spread of cancer cells beyond their original site.

methanogens A type of Archaea that produces methane as a metabolic waste product.

methyl group In an organic molecule, a carbon bonded to three hydrogens.

microevolution A change in a population's gene pool over generations.

microfilament The thinnest of the three main kinds of protein fibers making up the cytoskeleton of a eukaryotic cell; a solid, helical rod composed of the globular protein actin.

micrograph A photograph taken through a microscope.

micronutrient An element that an organism needs in very small amounts and that functions as a component or cofactor of enzymes. *See also* macronutrient.

microtubule The thickest of the three main kinds of fibers making up the cytoskeleton of a eukaryotic cell; a straight, hollow tube made of globular proteins called tubulins. Microtubules form the basis of the structure and movement of cilia and flagella.

microvillus (plural, **microvilli**) A microscopic projection on the epithelial cells in the lumen of the small intestine that increase its surface area.

midbrain One of three ancestral and embryonic regions of the vertebrate brain; develops into sensory integrating and relay centers that send sensory information to the cerebrum.

middle ear One of three main regions of the vertebrate ear; a chamber containing three small bones (the hammer, anvil, and stirrup) that convey vibrations from the eardrum to the oval window.

migration The regular back-and-forth movement of animals between two geographic areas at particular times of the year.

millipede A terrestrial arthropod that has two pairs of short legs for each of its numerous body segments and that eats decaying plant matter.

mineral In nutrition, a simple inorganic nutrient that an organism requires for proper body functioning.

mineralocorticoid (min´-er-uh-lō-kort´-uh-koyd) A corticosteroid hormone secreted by the adrenal cortex that helps maintain salt and water homeostasis and may increase blood pressure in response to long-term stress.

mitochondrial matrix (mī´-tō-kon´-drē-ul mā´-triks) The fluid contained within the inner membrane of a mitochondrion.

mitochondrion (mī´-tō-kon´-drē-on) (plural, **mitochondria**) An organelle in eukaryotic cells where cellular respiration occurs. Enclosed by two concentric membranes, it is where most of the cell's ATP is made.

mitosis (mī´-tō-sis) The division of a single nucleus into two genetically identical daughter nuclei. Mitosis and cytokinesis make up the mitotic (M) phase of the cell cycle.

mitotic phase (M phase) The part of the cell cycle when the nucleus is divided (via mitosis), its chromosomes are distributed to the daughter nuclei, and the cytoplasm divided (via cytokinesis), producing two daughter cells.

mitotic spindle A football-shaped structure formed of microtubules and associated proteins that is involved in the movements of chromosomes during mitosis and meiosis.

mold A rapidly growing fungus that reproduces asexually by producing spores.

molecular biology The study of the molecular basis of genes and gene expression; molecular genetics.

molecular clock Evolutionary timing method based on the observation that at least some regions of genomes evolve at constant rates.

molecular systematics A scientific discipline that uses nucleic acids or other molecules in different species to infer evolutionary relationships.

molecule A group of two or more atoms held together by covalent bonds.

mollusc (mol´-lusk) A soft-bodied animal characterized by a muscular foot, mantle, mantle cavity, and radula; includes gastropods (snails and slugs), bivalves (clams, oysters, and scallops), and cephalopods (squids and octopuses).

molting The process of shedding an old exoskeleton or cuticle and secreting a new, larger one.

monoclonal antibody (mon´-ō-klōn´-ul) An antibody secreted by a clone of cells and, consequently, specific for the one antigen that triggered the development of the clone.

monocot (mon´-ō-kot) A flowering plant whose embryos have a single seed leaf, or cotyledon.

monoculture The cultivation of a single plant variety in a large land area.

monogamous Referring to a type of relationship in which one male mates with just one female, and both parents care for the children.

monohybrid cross An experimental mating of individuals differing at one genetic locus.

monomer (mon´-uh-mer) A chemical subunit that serves as a building block of a polymer.

monophyletic (mon´-ō-fī-let´-ik) Pertaining to a taxon derived from a single ancestral species that gave rise to no species in any other taxa.

monosaccharide (mon´-ō-sak´-uh-rīd) The simplest carbohydrate; a simple sugar with a molecular formula that is generally some multiple of CH_2O. Monosaccharides are the building blocks of disaccharides and polysaccharides.

monotreme (mon´-uh-trēm) An egg-laying mammal, such as the duck-billed platypus.

morning after pill (MAP) Birth control pill taken within three days of unprotected intercourse to prevent fertilization or implantation.

morphological species concept A definition of species in terms of measurable anatomical criteria.

motor neuron A nerve cell that conveys command signals from the central nervous system to effector cells, such as muscle cells or gland cells.

motor output The conduction of signals from a processing center in a central nervous system to effector cells.

motor unit A motor neuron and all the muscle fibers it controls.

mouth An opening through which food is taken into an animal's body.

movement corridor A series of small clumps or a narrow strip of quality habitat (usable by organisms) that connects otherwise isolated patches of quality habitat.

mRNA *See* messenger RNA.

muscle fiber Muscle cell.

muscle tissue Tissue consisting of long muscle cells that are capable of contracting when stimulated by nerve impulses; the most abundant tissue in a typical animal. *See* skeletal muscle; cardiac muscle; smooth muscle.

muscular system All the skeletal muscles in the body. (Cardiac muscle and smooth muscle are components of other organ systems.)

mutagen (myū'-tuh-jen) A chemical or physical agent that interacts with DNA and causes a mutation.

mutagenesis (myū'-tuh-jen'-uh-sis) The creation of a mutation.

mutation A change in the nucleotide sequence of an organism's DNA; mutation also can occur in the DNA or RNA of a virus; the ultimate source of genetic diversity.

mutualism An interspecific relationship in which both partners benefit.

mycelium (mī-sē'-lē-um) (plural, **mycelia**) The densely branched network of hyphae in a fungus.

mycorrhiza (mī'-kō-rī'-zuh) (plural, **mycorrhizae**) A close association of plant roots and fungi that is beneficial to both partners.

myelin sheath (mī'-uh-lin) A series of cells, each wound around, and thus insulating, the axon of a nerve cell in vertebrates. Each pair of cells in the sheath is separated by a space called a node of Ranvier.

myofibril (mī'-ō-fī'-bril) A contractile strand in a muscle cell (fiber) made up of many sarcomeres. Longitudinal bundles of myofibrils make up a muscle fiber.

myosin A type of protein filament that interacts with actin filaments to cause cell contraction.

N

NAD⁺ Nicotinamide adenine dinucleotide; a coenzyme that can accept electrons during the redox reactions of cellular metabolism. The plus sign indicates that the molecule is oxidized and ready to pick up hydrogens; the reduced, hydrogen- (electron-) carrying form is NADH.

natural family planning A form of contraception that relies on refraining from sexual intercourse when conception is most likely to occur; also called the rhythm method.

natural killer cell A cell type that provides an innate immune response by attacking cancer cells and infected body cells, especially those harboring viruses.

natural selection A process in which organisms with certain inherited characteristics are more likely to survive and reproduce than are organisms with other characteristics.

nearsightedness An inability to focus on distant objects; occurs when the eyeball is longer than normal and the lens focuses distant objects in front of the retina. Also called myopia.

negative feedback A common control mechanism in which a chemical reaction, metabolic pathway, or hormone-secreting gland is inhibited by the products of the reaction, pathway, or gland. As the concentration of the products builds up, the product molecules themselves inhibit the process that produced them.

negative pressure breathing A breathing system in which air is pulled into the lungs.

nematode (nem'-uh-tōde) A roundworm, characterized by a pseudocoelom, a cylindrical, wormlike body form, and a tough cuticle.

nephron The tubular excretory unit and associated blood vessels of the vertebrate kidney; extracts filtrate from the blood and refines it into urine.

nerve A cable-like bundle of neuron fibers (axons and dendrites) tightly wrapped in connective tissue.

nerve cord An elongated bundle of axons and dendrites, usually extending longitudinally from the brain or anterior ganglia. One or more nerve cords and the brain make up the central nervous system in many animals.

nerve net A weblike system of neurons, characteristic of radially symmetrical animals such as a hydra.

nervous system The organ system that forms a communication and coordination network between all parts of an animal's body.

nervous tissue Tissue made up of neurons and supportive cells.

neural tube (nyūr'-ul) An embryonic cylinder that develops from ectoderm after gastrulation; gives rise to the brain and spinal cord.

neuron (nyūr'-on) A nerve cell; the fundamental structural and functional unit of the nervous system, specialized for carrying signals from one location in the body to another.

neurosecretory cell A nerve cell that synthesizes hormones and secretes them into the blood and also conducts nerve signals.

neurotransmitter A chemical messenger that carries information from a transmitting neuron to a receiving cell, either another neuron or an effector cell.

neutral variation Genetic variation that does not appear to provide a selective advantage or disadvantage.

neutron An electrically neutral particle (a particle having no electrical charge), found in the nucleus of an atom.

neutrophil (nyū'-truh-fil) An innate, defensive, phagocytic white blood cell that can engulf bacteria and viruses in infected tissue; has a multilobed nucleus.

nitrogen fixation The conversion of atmospheric nitrogen (N_2) into nitrogen compounds (NH_4^+, NO_3^-) that plants can absorb and use.

node The point of attachment of a leaf on a stem.

node of Ranvier (ron'-vē-ā) An unmyelinated region on a myelinated axon of a nerve cell, where nerve signals are regenerated.

nodule A swelling on a plant root consisting of plant cells that contain nitrogen-fixing bacteria.

noncompetitive inhibitor A substance that impedes the activity of an enzyme without entering an active site. By binding elsewhere on the enzyme, a noncompetitive inhibitor changes the shape of the enzyme so that the active site no longer functions.

nondisjunction An accident of meiosis or mitosis in which a pair of homologous chromosomes or a pair of sister chromatids fail to separate at anaphase.

nonpolar covalent bond A covalent bond in which electrons are shared equally between two atoms of similar electronegativity.

nonself molecule A foreign antigen; a protein or other macromolecule that is not part of an organism's body. *See also* self protein.

norepinephrine (nor'-ep-uh-nef'-rin) An amine hormone (also called noradrenaline) secreted by the adrenal medulla that prepares body organs for action (fight or flight); also serves as a neurotransmitter.

notochord (nō'-tuh-kord) A flexible, cartilage-like, longitudinal rod located between the digestive tract and nerve cord in chordate animals; present only in embryos in many species.

nuclear envelope A double membrane, perforated with pores, that encloses the nucleus and separates it from the rest of the eukaryotic cell.

nuclear transplantation A technique in which the nucleus of one cell is placed into another cell that already has a nucleus or in which the nucleus has been previously destroyed.

nucleic acid (nū-klā'-ik) A polymer consisting of many nucleotide monomers; serves as a blueprint for proteins and, through the actions of proteins, for all cellular structures and activities. The two types of nucleic acids are DNA and RNA.

nucleic acid probe In DNA technology, a labeled single-stranded nucleic acid molecule used to find a specific gene or other nucleotide sequence within a mass of DNA. The probe hydrogen-bonds to the complementary sequence in the targeted DNA.

nucleoid (nū'-klē-oyd) A dense region of DNA in a prokaryotic cell.

nucleolus (nū-klē' ō lus) A structure within the nucleus of a eukaryotic cell where ribosomal RNA is made and assembled with proteins imported from the cytoplasm to make ribosomal subunits.

nucleosome (nū'-klē-ō-sōm) The bead-like unit of DNA packaging in a eukaryotic cell; consists of DNA wound around a protein core made up of eight histone molecules.

nucleotide (nū'-klē-ō-tīd) An organic monomer consisting of a five-carbon sugar covalently bonded to a nitrogenous base and a phosphate group. Nucleotides are the building blocks of nucleic acids.

nucleus (plural, **nuclei**) (1) An atom's central core, containing protons and neutrons. (2) The genetic control center of a eukaryotic cell.

O

obligate anaerobes An organism that only carries out fermentation; such organisms cannot use oxygen and also may be poisoned by it.

ocean current One of the riverlike flow patterns in the oceans.

omnivore An animal that eats animals as well as plants or algae.

oncogene (on'-kō-jēn) A cancer-causing gene; usually contributes to malignancy by abnormally enhancing the amount or activity of a growth factor made by the cell.

oogenesis (ō'-uh-jen'-uh-sis) The formation of ova (egg cells).

open circulatory system A circulatory system in which blood is pumped through open-ended vessels and bathes the tissues and organs directly. In an animal with an open circulatory system, blood and interstitial fluid are one and the same.

operator In prokaryotic DNA, a sequence of nucleotides near the start of an operon to which an active repressor can attach. The binding of a repressor prevents RNA polymerase from attaching to the promoter and transcribing the genes of the operon.

operculum (ō-per'-kyū-lum) (plural, **opercula**) A protective flap on each side of a fish's head that covers a chamber housing the gills.

operon (op'-er-on) A unit of genetic regulation common in prokaryotes; a cluster of genes with related functions, along with the promoter and operator that control their transcription.

opportunistic infections Infections that can be controlled by a normally functioning immune system but that cause illness in a person with an immunodeficiency.

opposable thumb An arrangement of the fingers such that the thumb can touch the ventral surface of the fingertips of all four fingers.

optimal foraging theory The basis for analyzing behavior as a compromise of feeding costs versus feeding benefits.

oral cavity The mouth of an animal.

oral contraceptive *See* birth control pills.

order In classification, the taxonomic category above family.

organ A structure consisting of several tissues adapted as a group to perform specific functions.

organ of Corti (kor'-tē) The hearing organ in birds and mammals, located within the cochlea.

organ system A group of organs that work together in performing vital body functions.

organelle (ōr-guh-nel') A membrane-enclosed structure with a specialized function in a cell.

organic compound A chemical compound containing the element carbon and usually synthesized by cells.

organism An individual living thing, such as a bacterium, fungus, protist, plant, or animal.

orgasm A series of rhythmic, involuntary contractions of the reproductive structures.

osmoconformer (oz'-mō-con-form'-er) An organism whose body fluids have a solute concentration equal to that of its surroundings. Osmoconformers do not have a net gain or loss of water by osmosis.

osmoregulation Method by which organisms regulate solute concentrations and balance the gain and loss of water.

osmoregulator An organism whose body fluids have a solute concentration different from that of its environment and that must use energy in controlling water loss or gain.

osmosis (oz mō'-sis) The diffusion of water across a selectively permeable membrane.

osteoporosis (os'-tē-ō-puh-rō'-sis) A skeletal disorder characterized by thinning, porous, and easily broken bones; most common among women after menopause.

outer ear One of three main regions of the ear in reptiles, birds, and mammals; made up of the auditory canal and, in many birds and mammals, the pinna.

outgroup In a cladistic study of evolutionary relationships among taxa of organisms, a taxon or group of taxa known to have diverged before the lineage that contains the group of species being studied. *See also* ingroup.

oval window In the vertebrate ear, a membrane-covered gap in the skull bone, through which sound waves pass from the middle ear into the inner ear.

ovarian cycle (ō-văr'-ē-un) Hormonally synchronized cyclic events in the mammalian ovary, culminating in ovulation.

ovary (1) In animals, the female gonad, which produces egg cells and reproductive hormones. (2) In flowering plants, the basal portion of a carpel in which the egg-containing ovules develop.

overnourishment The consumption of more food energy than the body needs for normal metabolism.

oviduct (ō'-vuh-dukt) The tube that conveys egg cells away from an ovary; also called a fallopian tube.

ovulation (ah'-vyū-lā'-shun) The release of an egg cell from an ovarian follicle.

ovum (ō'-vum) (plural, **ova**) The female gametes; the haploid, unfertilized egg.

oxidation The loss of electrons from a substance involved in a redox reaction; always accompanies reduction.

oxidative phosphorylation (fos'-fōr-uh-lā'-shun) The production of ATP using energy derived from the redox reactions of an electron transport chain; the third major stage of cellular respiration.

ozone layer The layer of ozone (O_3) in the upper atmosphere that protects life on Earth from the harmful ultraviolet rays in sunlight.

P

P generation The parent individuals from which offspring are derived in studies of inheritance. (P stands for parental.)

P site One of two of a ribosome's binding sites for tRNA during translation. The P site holds the tRNA carrying the growing polypeptide chain. (P stands for peptidyl tRNA.)

pacemaker The SA (sinoatrial) node; a specialized region of cardiac muscle in the right atrium that maintains the heart's pumping rhythm (heartbeat) by setting the rate at which the heart contracts.

paedomorphosis (pē'-duh-mōr'-fuh-sis) The retention in an adult of juvenile features of its evolutionary ancestors.

pain receptor A sensor (sensory receptor) that detects pain.

paleoanthropology (pā'-lē-ō-an'-thruh-pol'-uh-jē) The study of human origins and evolution.

paleontologist (pa'-lē-on-tol'-uh-jist) A scientist who studies fossils.

pancreas (pan'-krē-us) A gland with dual functions: The digestive portion secretes digestive enzymes and an alkaline solution into the small intestine via a duct. The endocrine portion secretes the hormones insulin and glucagon into the blood.

Pangaea (pan-jē'-uh) The supercontinent consisting of all the major landmasses of Earth fused together. Continental drift formed Pangaea near the end of the Paleozoic era.

parabasilid A heterotrophic protist that has modified mitochondria that generates some energy anaerobically.

parasite Organism that derives its nutrition from a living host, which is harmed by the interaction.

parasympathetic division A set of neurons in the autonomic nervous system that generally promotes body activities that gain and conserve energy, such as digestion and reduced heart rate. *See also* sympathetic division.

parathyroid glands (pãr'-uh-thī'-royd) Four endocrine glands embedded in the surface of the thyroid gland that secrete parathyroid hormone.

parathyroid hormone (PTH) A peptide hormone secreted by the parathyroid glands that raises blood calcium level.

parenchyma cell (puh-ren'-kim-uh) In plants, a relatively unspecialized cell with a thin primary wall and no secondary wall; functions in photosynthesis, food storage, and aerobic respiration and may differentiate into other cell types.

Parkinson's disease A motor disorder caused by a progressive brain disease and characterized by difficulty in initiating movements, slowness of movement, and rigidity.

parsimony (par'-suh-mō'-nē) In scientific studies, the search for the least complex explanation for an observed phenomenon.

partial pressure A measure of the relative amount of gas in a mixture.

passive immunity Temporary immunity obtained by acquiring ready-made antibodies; lasts only a few weeks or months because the immune system has not been stimulated by antigens.

passive transport The diffusion of a substance across a biological membrane, without any input of energy.

pathogen An agent such as a virus, bacteria, or fungus, that causes disease.

pattern formation During embryonic development, the emergence of a spatial organization in which the tissues and organs of the organism are all in their correct places.

pedigree A family tree representing the occurrence of heritable traits in parents and offspring across a number of generations.

pelagic realm (puh-laj'-ik) The region of an ocean occupied by seawater.

penis The copulatory structure of male mammals.

peptide bond The covalent linkage between two amino acid units in a polypeptide; formed by a dehydration reaction.

peptidoglycan (pep'-tid-ō-glī'-kan) A polymer of complex sugars cross-linked by short polypeptides; a material unique to bacterial cell walls.

per capita rate of increase The average contribution of each individual in a population to population growth.

perception The brain's meaningful interpretation, or conscious understanding, of sensory information.

perennial (puh-ren'-ē-ul) A plant that lives for many years.

peripheral nervous system (PNS) The network of nerves and ganglia carrying signals into and out of the central nervous system.

peristalsis (per'-uh-stal'-sis) Rhythmic waves of contraction of smooth muscles. Peristalsis propels food through a digestive tract and also enables many animals, such as earthworms, to crawl.

permafrost Continuously frozen ground found in the tundra.

peroxisome An organelle containing enzymes that transfer hydrogen from various substrates to oxygen, producing and then degrading hydrogen peroxide.

petal A modified leaf of a flowering plant. Petals are the often colorful parts of a flower that advertise it to pollinators.

pH scale A measure of the relative acidity of a solution, ranging in value from 0 (most acidic) to 14 (most basic). The letters pH stand for potential hydrogen and refer to the concentration of hydrogen ions (H).

phage (fāj) *See* bacteriophage.

phagocyte (fag'-ō-sīt) A white blood cell (for example, a neutrophil or a monocyte) that engulfs bacteria, foreign proteins, and the remains of dead body cells.

phagocytosis (fag'-ō-sī-tō'-sis) Cellular "eating"; a type of endocytosis whereby a cell engulfs macromolecules, other cells, or particles into its cytoplasm.

pharyngeal slit (fā-rin'-jē-ul) A gill structure in the pharynx; found in chordate embryos and some adult chordates.

pharynx (fãr'-inks) The organ in a digestive tract that receives food from the oral cavity; in terrestrial vertebrates, the throat region where the air and food passages cross.

phenotype (fē'-nō-tīp) The expressed traits of an organism.

phenotypic plasticity An individual's ability to change phenotype in response to local environmental conditions.

phloem (flō'-um) The portion of a plant's vascular tissue system that conveys phloem sap throughout a plant. Phloem tissue is made up of sieve-tube members.

phloem sap The solution of sugars, other nutrients, and hormones conveyed throughout a plant via phloem tissue.

phosphate group (fos'-fāt) A functional group consisting of a phosphorus atom covalently bonded to four oxygen atoms.

phospholipid (fos'-fō-lip'-id) A lipid made up of glycerol joined to two fatty acids and a phosphate group, giving the molecule a nonpolar hydrophobic tail and a polar hydrophilic head. Phospholipids form bilayers that function as biological membranes.

phosphorylation (fos'-fōr-uh-lā'-shun) The transfer of a phosphate group, usually from ATP, to a molecule. Nearly all cellular work depends on ATP energizing other molecules by phosphorylation.

photic zone (fō'-tik) The region of an aquatic ecosystem into which light penetrates and where photosynthesis occurs.

photoautotroph An organism that obtains energy from sunlight and carbon from CO_2 by photosynthesis.

photoheterotroph An organism that obtains energy from sunlight and carbon from organic sources.

photon (fō'-ton) A fixed quantity of light energy. The shorter the wavelength of light, the greater the energy of a photon.

photoperiod The length of the day relative to the length of the night; an environmental stimulus that plants use to detect the time of year.

photophosphorylation (fō'-tō-fos'-fōr-uh-lā'-shun) The production of ATP by chemiosmosis during the light reactions of photosynthesis.

photopsin (fō-top'-sin) One of a family of visual pigments in the cones of the vertebrate eye that absorb bright, colored light.

photoreceptor A type of electromagnetic sensor (sensory receptor) that detects light.

photorespiration In a plant cell, the breakdown of a two-carbon compound produced by the Calvin cycle. The Calvin cycle produces the two-carbon compound, instead of its usual three-carbon product G3P, when leaf cells fix O_2, instead of CO_2. Photorespiration produces no sugar molecules or ATP.

photosynthesis (fō'-tō-sin'-thuh-sis) The process by which plants, autotrophic protists, and some bacteria use light energy to make sugars and other organic food molecules from carbon dioxide and water.

photosystem A light-capturing unit of a chloroplast's thylakoid membrane, consisting of a reaction center complex surrounded by numerous light-harvesting complexes.

phototropism (fō'-tō-trō'-pizm) The growth of a plant shoot toward (positive phototropism) or away from (negative phototropism) light.

phyla In classification, the taxonomic category above class.

phylogenetic species concept A definition of species as the smallest group of individuals that shares a common ancestor and forms one branch on the tree of life.

phylogenetic tree (fī'-lō-juh-net'-ik) A branching diagram that represents a hypothesis about the evolutionary history of a group of organisms.

phylogeny (fī-loj'-uh-nē) The evolutionary history of a species or group of related species.

physiology (fi'-zi-ol'-uh-ji) The study of the functions of an organism's structures.

phytochrome (fī'-tuh-krōm) A colored protein in plants that contains a special set of atoms that absorbs light.

phytoplankton (fī'-tō-plank'-ton) Algae and photosynthetic bacteria that drift passively in aquatic environments.

pilus (pī'-lus) (plural, **pili**) A short projection on the surface of a prokaryotic cell that helps the prokaryote attach to other surfaces. Specialized sex pili are used in conjugation to hold the mating cells together.

pineal gland (pin'-ē-ul) An outgrowth of the vertebrate brain that secretes the hormone melatonin, which coordinates daily and seasonal body activities such as the sleep/wake circadian rhythm with environmental light conditions.

pinna (pin′-uh) The flap-like part of the outer ear, projecting from the body surface of many birds and mammals; collects sound waves and channels them to the auditory canal.

pinocytosis (pē′-nō-sī-tō′-sis) Cellular "drinking"; a type of endocytosis in which the cell takes fluid and dissolved solutes into small membranous vesicles.

pistil Part of the reproductive organ of an angiosperm, a single carpel or a group of fused carpels.

pith Part of the ground tissue system of a dicot plant. Pith fills the center of a stem and may store food.

pituitary gland An endocrine gland at the base of the hypothalamus; consists of a posterior lobe, which stores and releases two hormones produced by the hypothalamus, and an anterior lobe, which produces and secretes many hormones that regulate diverse body functions.

pivot joint A joint that allows precise rotations in multiple planes. An example in humans is the wrist.

placenta (pluh-sen′-tuh) In most mammals, the organ that provides nutrients and oxygen to the embryo and helps dispose of its metabolic wastes; formed of the embryo's chorion and the mother's endometrial blood vessels.

placental mammal (pluh-sen′-tul) Mammal whose young complete their embryonic development in the uterus, nourished via the mother's blood vessels in the placenta; also called a eutherian.

plasma The liquid matrix of the blood in which the blood cells are suspended.

plasma cell An antibody-secreting B cell.

plasma membrane The membrane that sets a cell off from its surroundings and acts as a selective barrier to the passage of ions and molecules into and out of the cell; consists of a phospholipid bilayer in which are embedded molecules of protein and cholesterol.

plasmid A small ring of independently replicating DNA separate from the main chromosome(s). Plasmids are found in prokaryotes and yeast.

plasmodesma (plaz′-mō-dez′-muh) (plural, **plasmodesmata**) An open channel in a plant cell wall through which strands of cytoplasm connect from adjacent cells.

plasmodial slime mold (plaz-mō′-dē-ul) A type of protist that has amoeboid cells, flagellated cells, and an amoeboid plasmodial feeding stage in its life cycle.

plasmodium (1) A single mass of cytoplasm containing many nuclei. (2) The amoeboid feeding stage in the life cycle of a plasmodial slime mold.

platelet A pinched-off cytoplasmic fragment of a bone marrow cell; platelets circulate in the blood and are important in blood clotting.

pleated sheet The folded arrangement of a polypeptide in a protein's secondary structure.

pleiotropy (plī′-uh-trō-pē) The control of more than one phenotypic characteristic by a single gene.

polar covalent bond A covalent bond between atoms that differ in electronegativity. The shared electrons are pulled closer to the more electronegative atom, making it slightly negative and the other atom slightly positive.

polar molecule A molecule containing polar covalent bonds.

pollen *See* pollen grain.

pollen grain The structure that will produce the sperm in seed plants; the male gametophyte.

pollination In seed plants, the delivery, by wind or animals, of pollen from the male parts of a plant to the stigma of a carpel on the female.

polychaete (pol′-ē-kēt) A member of the largest group of annelids. *See* annelid.

polygamous Referring to a type of relationship in which an individual of one sex mates with several of the other.

polygenic inheritance (pol′-ē-jen′-ik) The additive effect of two or more gene loci on a single phenotypic characteristic.

polymer (pol′-uh-mer) A large molecule consisting of many identical or similar molecular units, called monomers, covalently joined together in a chain.

polymerase chain reaction (PCR) (puh-lim′-uh-rās) A technique used to obtain many copies of a DNA molecule or part of a DNA molecule. A small amount of DNA mixed with a heat-resistant DNA polymerase, DNA nucleotides, and a few other ingredients replicates repeatedly in a test tube.

polynucleotide (pol′-ē-nū′-klē-ō-tīd) A polymer made up of many nucleotides covalently bonded together.

polyp (pol′-ip) One of two types of cnidarian body forms; a columnar, hydra-like body.

polypeptide A polymer (chain) of amino acids linked by peptide bonds.

polyploidy An organism that has more than two complete sets of chromosomes as a result of an accident of cell division.

polysaccharide (pol′-ē-sak′-uh-rīd) A carbohydrate polymer consisting of hundreds to thousands of monosaccharides (sugars) linked by dehydration synthesis.

pons (pahnz) Part of the vertebrate hindbrain that functions with the medulla oblongata in passing data between the spinal cord and forebrain and in controlling autonomic, homeostatic functions.

population A group of individuals belonging to one species and living in the same geographic area.

population density The number of individuals of a species per unit area or volume.

population ecology The study of how members of a population interact with their environment, focusing on factors that influence population density and growth.

population momentum In a population in which $r = 0$, the continuation of population growth as girls in the prereproductive age group reach their reproductive years.

positive feedback A control mechanism in which the products of a process stimulate the process that produced them.

post-anal tail A tail posterior to the anus; found in chordate embryos and most adult chordates.

posterior Pertaining to the rear, or tail, of a bilaterally symmetrical animal.

posterior pituitary An extension of the hypothalamus composed of nervous tissue that secretes hormones made in the hypothalamus; a temporary storage site for hypothalamic hormones.

postzygotic barrier A reproductive barrier that prevents hybrid zygotes produced by two different species from developing into viable, fertile adults. Includes reduced hybrid viability, reduced hybrid fertility, and hybrid breakdown.

potential energy The energy that matter possesses because of its location or arrangement. Water behind a dam and chemical bonds possess potential energy.

predation An interaction between species in which one species, the predator, eats the other, the prey.

prepuce (prē′-pyūs) A fold of skin covering the head of the clitoris and penis.

pressure flow mechanism The method by which phloem sap is transported through a plant from a sugar source, where sugars are produced, to a sugar sink, where sugars are used.

prevailing winds Winds that result from the combined effects of Earth's rotation and the rising and falling of air masses.

prezygotic barrier A reproductive barrier that impedes mating between species or hinders fertilization if mating between two species is attempted. Includes temporal, habitat, behavioral, mechanical, and gametic isolation.

primary consumer In the trophic structure of an ecosystem, an organism that eats plants or algae.

primary growth Growth in the length of a plant root or shoot, produced by an apical meristem.

primary immune response The initial immune response to an antigen, which appears after a lag of several days.

primary oocyte (ō′-uh-sīt) A diploid cell, in prophase I of meiosis, that can be hormonally triggered to develop into an ovum.

primary phloem *See* phloem.

primary production The amount of solar energy converted to chemical energy (in organic compounds) by autotrophs in an ecosystem during a given time period.

primary spermatocyte (sper-mat'-eh-sīt') A diploid cell in the testis that undergoes meiosis I.

primary structure The first level of protein structure; the specific sequence of amino acids making up a polypeptide chain.

primary succession A type of ecological succession in which a biological community arises in an area without soil. *See also* secondary succession.

primary xylem *See* xylem.

primers Short, artificially created, single-stranded DNA molecules that bind to each end of a target sequence to drive a PCR procedure.

prion An infectious form of protein that may multiply by converting related proteins into more prions. Prions cause several related diseases in different animals, including scrapie in sheep and mad cow disease.

problem solving The activity of applying past experiences to overcome obstacles in novel situations.

producer An organism that makes organic food molecules from CO_2, H_2O, and other inorganic raw materials: a plant, alga, or autotrophic prokaryote.

product An ending material in a chemical reaction.

progestin (prō-jes'-tin) One of a family of steroid hormones, including progesterone, produced by the mammalian ovary. Progestins prepare the uterus for pregnancy.

programmed cell death The timely death (and disposal of the remains) of certain cells, triggered by certain genes; an essential process in normal development; *also called* apoptosis.

prokaryotic cell (prō-kār'-ē-ot'-ik) A type of cell lacking a membrane-enclosed nucleus and other membrane-enclosed organelles; found only in the domains Bacteria and Archaea.

prolactin (PRL) (prō-lak'-tin) A protein hormone secreted by the anterior pituitary that stimulates different responses in different animals.

prometaphase The second stage of mitosis, during which the nuclear envelope fragments and the spindle microtubules attach to the kinetochores of the sister chromatids.

promiscuous Referring to a type of relationship in which mating occurs with no strong pair-bonds or lasting relationships.

promoter A specific nucleotide sequence in DNA located at the start of a gene that is the binding site for RNA polymerase and the place where transcription begins.

prophage (prō'-fāj) Phage DNA that has inserted by genetic recombination into the DNA of a prokaryotic chromosome.

prophase The first stage of mitosis, during which the chromatin condenses to form structures (sister chromatids) visible with a light microscope and the mitotic spindle begins to form, but the nucleus is still intact.

prostate gland (pros'-tāt) A gland in human males that secretes an acid-neutralizing component of semen.

protein A functional biological molecule consisting of one or more polypeptides folded into a specific three-dimensional structure.

proteobacteria A diverse clade of gram-negative bacteria that includes five subgroups known as alpha, beta, gamma, delta, and epsilon.

proteomics The study of whole sets of proteins and their interactions.

protist A member of the Kingdom Protista. Most protists are unicellular, though some are colonial or multicellular.

protobiont An aggregate of abiotically produced molecules surrounded by a membrane or membrane-like structure.

proton A subatomic particle with a single positive electrical charge, found in the nucleus of an atom.

proto-oncogene (prō'-tō-on'-kō-jēn) A normal gene that can be converted to a cancer-causing gene.

protostome An animal with a coelom that develops from solid masses of cells that arise between the digestive tube and the body wall of the embryo. The protostomes include the molluscs, annelids, and arthropods.

protozoan (prō'-tō-zō'-un) (plural, **protozoa**) A protist that lives primarily by ingesting food; a heterotrophic, "animal-like" protist.

proximal tubule In the vertebrate kidney, the portion of a nephron immediately downstream from Bowman's capsule that conveys and helps refine filtrate.

proximate cause In animal behavior, a condition in an animal's internal or external environment that is the immediate reason or mechanism for a behavior.

pseudocoelom (sū'-dō-sē'-lōm) A body cavity that is in direct contact with the wall of the digestive tract.

pseudopodium (sū'-dō-pō'-dē-um) (plural, **pseudopodia**) A temporary extension of an amoeboid cell. Pseudopodia function in moving cells and engulfing food.

pulmonary artery A large blood vessel that conveys blood from the heart to a lung.

pulmonary circuit One of two main blood circuits in terrestrial vertebrates; conveys blood between the heart and the lungs. *See also* systemic circuit.

pulmonary vein A blood vessel that conveys blood from a lung to the heart.

pulse The rhythmic stretching of the arteries caused by the pressure of blood during contraction of ventricles in systole.

punctuated equilibria In the fossil record, long periods of apparent stasis in which a species undergoes little or no morphological change interrupted by relatively brief periods of sudden change.

Punnett square A diagram used in the study of inheritance to show the results of random fertilization.

pupil The opening in the iris that admits light into the interior of the vertebrate eye. Muscles in the iris regulate the pupil's size.

Q

quaternary consumer (kwot'-er-ner-ē) An organism that eats tertiary consumers.

quaternary structure The fourth level of protein structure; the shape resulting from the association of two or more polypeptide subunits.

R

R plasmid A bacterial plasmid that carries genes for enzymes that destroy particular antibiotics, thus making the bacterium resistant to the antibiotics.

radial symmetry An arrangement of the body parts of an organism like pieces of a pie around an imaginary central axis. Any slice passing longitudinally through a radially symmetrical organism's central axis divides it into mirror-image halves.

radioactive isotope An isotope whose nucleus decays spontaneously, giving off particles and energy.

radiolarian A protist that moves and feeds by means of threadlike pseudopodia and has a mineralized support structure composed of silica.

radiometric dating A method for determining the absolute ages of fossils and rocks, based on the half-life of radioactive isotopes.

radula (rad'-yū-luh) A toothed, rasping organ used to scrape up or shred food; found in many molluscs.

random Describing a dispersion pattern in which individuals are spaced in a patternless, unpredictable way.

ray-finned fish A bony fish having fins supported by thin, flexible skeletal rays.

reabsorption In the vertebrate kidney, the reclaiming of water and valuable solutes from the filtrate.

reactant A starting material in a chemical reaction.

reaction center complex In a photosystem in a chloroplast, the chlorophyll *a* molecules and the primary electron acceptor that trigger the light reactions of photosynthesis. The chlorophyll donates an electron excited by light energy to the primary electron acceptor, which passes an electron to an electron transport chain.

reading frame The way in which a cell's mRNA-translating machinery groups the mRNA nucleotides into codons.

receptor potential The electrical signal produced by sensory transduction.

receptor-mediated endocytosis (en'-dō-sī-tō'-sis) The movement of specific molecules into a cell by the inward budding of membranous vesicles. The vesicles contain proteins with receptor sites specific to the molecules being taken in.

GLOSSARY

recessive allele An allele that has no noticeable effect on the phenotype of a gene when the individual is heterozygous for that gene.

reciprocal altruism (al'-trū-izm) In animal behavior, a selfless act repaid at a later time by the beneficiary or by another member of the beneficiary's social system.

recombinant DNA A DNA molecule carrying genes derived from two or more sources.

recombination frequency With respect to two given genes, the number of recombinant progeny from a mating divided by the total number of progeny. Recombinant progeny carry combinations of alleles different from those in either of the parents as a result of independent assortment of chromosomes or crossing over.

Recommended Dietary Allowance (RDA) A recommendation for daily nutrient intake established by nutritionists.

rectum The terminal portion of the large intestine where the feces are stored until they are eliminated.

red alga A member of a group of marine, mostly multicellular, autotrophic protists, which includes the reef-building coralline algae.

red blood cell *See* erythrocyte.

red bone marrow A specialized tissue found in cavities in the ends of bones that produces blood cells.

red-green color blindness A category of common, sex-linked human disorders involving several genes on the X chromosome; characterized by a malfunction of light-sensitive cells in the eyes; affects mostly males but also homozygous females.

redox reaction Short for oxidation-reduction; a chemical reaction in which electrons are lost from one substance (oxidation) and added to another (reduction). Oxidation and reduction always occur together.

reduction The gain of electrons by a substance involved in a redox reaction; always accompanies oxidation.

reflex An automatic reaction to a stimulus, mediated by the spinal cord or lower brain.

regeneration The regrowth of body parts from pieces of an organism.

regulatory gene A gene that codes for a protein, such as a repressor, that controls the transcription of another gene or group of genes.

releasing hormone A kind of hormone released from the hypothalamus that makes the anterior pituitary secrete hormones.

renal cortex The outer portion of the vertebrate kidney.

renal medulla The inner portion of the vertebrate kidney, beneath the renal cortex.

repetitive DNA Nucleotide sequences that are present in many copies in the DNA of a genome. The repeated sequences may be long or short and may be located next to each other (tandomly) or dispersed in the DNA.

repressor A protein that blocks the transcription of a gene or operon.

reproduction The creation of new individuals from existing ones.

reproductive barrier A biological feature of a species that prevents it from interbreeding with other species even when populations of the two species live together.

reproductive cloning Using a somatic cell from a multicellular organism to make one or more genetically identical individuals.

reproductive isolation The existence of biological factors (barriers) that impede members of two species from producing viable, fertile hybrids.

reproductive system The body organ system responsible for reproduction.

reptile Member of the clade of amniotes that includes snakes, lizards, turtles, crocodilians, and birds, along with a number of extinct groups such as dinosaurs.

respiratory system The organ system that functions in exchanging gases with the environment. It supplies the blood with O_2 and disposes of CO_2.

resting potential The voltage across the plasma membrane of a resting neuron.

restoration ecology The use of ecological principles to develop ways to return degraded ecosystems to conditions as similar as possible to their natural, predegraded state.

restriction enzyme A bacterial enzyme that cuts up foreign DNA (at specific *restriction sites*), thus protecting bacteria against intruding DNA from phages and other organisms. Restriction enzymes are used in DNA technology to cut DNA molecules in reproducible ways.

restriction fragment length polymorphism (RFLP) (rif'-lips) The differences in homologous DNA sequences that are reflected in different lengths of restriction fragments produced when the DNA is cut up with restriction enzymes.

restriction fragments Molecules of DNA produced from a longer DNA molecule cut up by a restriction enzyme; used in genome mapping and other applications.

restriction site A specific sequence on a DNA strand that is recognized as a "cut site" by a restriction enzyme.

retina (ret'-uh-nuh) The light-sensitive layer in an eye, made up of photoreceptor cells and sensory neurons.

retrovirus An RNA virus that reproduces by means of a DNA molecule. It reverse-transcribes its RNA into DNA, inserts the DNA into a cellular chromosome, and then transcribes more copies of the RNA from the viral DNA. HIV and a number of cancer-causing viruses are retroviruses.

reverse transcriptase (tran-skrip'-tās) An enzyme used by retroviruses that catalyzes the synthesis of DNA on an RNA template.

rhizome (rī'-zōm) A horizontal stem that grows below the ground.

rhodopsin (ro-dop'-sin) A visual pigment that is located in the rods of the vertebrate eye and that absorbs dim light.

ribonucleic acid (RNA) (rī-bō-nū-klā'-ik) A type of nucleic acid consisting of nucleotide monomers with a ribose sugar and the nitrogenous bases adenine (A), cytosine (C), guanine (G), and uracil (U); usually single-stranded; functions in protein synthesis and as the genome of some viruses.

ribosomal RNA (rRNA) (rī'-buh-sōm'-ul) The type of ribonucleic acid that, together with proteins, makes up ribosomes; the most abundant type of RNA in most cells.

ribosome (rī'-buh-sōm) A cell structure consisting of RNA and protein organized into two subunits and functioning as the site of protein synthesis in the cytoplasm. The ribosomal subunits are constructed in the nucleolus.

ribozyme (rī'-bō-zīm) An enzyme-like RNA molecule that catalyzes chemical reactions.

RNA interference (RNAi) A biotechnology technique used to silence the expression of specific genes. Synthetic RNA molecules with sequences that correspond to particular genes trigger the breakdown of the gene's mRNA.

RNA polymerase (puh-lim'-uh-rās) An enzyme that links together the growing chain of RNA nucleotides during transcription, using a DNA strand as a template.

RNA splicing The removal of introns and joining of exons in eukaryotic RNA, forming an mRNA molecule with a continuous coding sequence; occurs before mRNA leaves the nucleus.

rod A photoreceptor cell in the vertebrate retina, enabling vision in dim light.

root cap A cone of cells at the tip of a plant root that protects the root's apical meristem.

root hair An outgrowth of an epidermal cell on a root, which increases the root's absorptive surface area.

root pressure The upward push of xylem sap in a vascular plant, caused by the active pumping of minerals into the xylem by root cells.

root system All of a plant's roots, which anchor it in the soil, absorb and transport minerals and water, and store food.

rough endoplasmic reticulum (reh-tik'-yuh-lum) A network of interconnected membranous sacs in a eukaryotic cell's cytoplasm. Rough ER membranes are studded with ribosomes that make membrane proteins and secretory proteins.

rRNA *See* ribosomal RNA.

r-selection The concept that in certain (*r*-selected) populations, a high reproductive rate is the chief determinant of life history.

rule of addition A rule stating that the probability that an event can occur in two or more alternative ways is the sum of the separate probabilities of the different ways.

rule of multiplication A rule stating that the probability of a compound event is the product of the separate probabilities of the independent events.

ruminant (rū′-min-ent) An animal, such as a cow or sheep, with a multichambered stomach housing microorganisms that can digest cellulose.

S

SA (sinoatrial) node (sī-nō′-ā′-trē-ul) The pacemaker of the heart, located in the wall of the right atrium, that sets the rate and timing at which all cardiac muscle cells contract. *See* pacemaker.

sac fungus Member of a group of fungi characterized by saclike structures called asci that produce spores in sexual reproduction.

saliva Salivary gland secretion that contains substances to lubricate food, buffers, antibacterial agents, and the digestive enzyme amylase.

salivary glands Glands associated with the oral cavity that secrete substances to lubricate food and begin the process of chemical digestion.

salt A compound resulting from the formation of ionic bonds; also called an ionic compound.

sapwood Light-colored, water-conducting secondary xylem in a tree. *See also* heartwood.

sarcoma (sar-kō′-muh) Cancer of the supportive tissues, such as bone, cartilage, and muscle.

sarcomere (sar′-kō-mēr) The fundamental unit of muscle contraction, composed of thin filaments of actin and thick filaments of myosin; in electron micrographs, the region between two narrow, dark lines, called Z lines, in a myofibril.

saturated Pertaining to fats and fatty acids whose hydrocarbon chains contain the maximum number of hydrogens and therefore have no double covalent bonds. Saturated fats and fatty acids solidify at room temperature.

savanna A biome dominated by grasses and scattered trees.

scanning electron microscope (SEM) A microscope that uses an electron beam to study the surface architecture of a cell or other specimen.

schizophrenia Severe mental disturbance characterized by psychotic episodes in which patients lose the ability to distinguish reality from hallucination.

sclera (sklār′-uh) A layer of connective tissue forming the outer surface of the vertebrate eye. The cornea is the frontal part of the sclera.

sclereid (sklār′-ē-id) In plants, a very hard, dead sclerenchyma cell found in nutshells and seed coats; a stone cell.

sclerenchyma cell (skluh-ren′-kē-muh) In plants, a supportive cell with rigid secondary walls hardened with lignin.

scrotum A pouch of skin outside the abdomen that houses a testis; functions in cooling sperm, thereby keeping them viable.

search image The mechanism that enables an animal to find a particular kind of food efficiently.

second law of thermodynamics The principle whereby every energy conversion reduces the order of the universe, increasing its entropy. Ordered forms of energy are at least partly converted to heat.

secondary consumer An organism that eats primary consumers.

secondary endosymbiosis A process by which protist diversity is hypothesized to have evolved from a symbiotic association that arose when an autotrophic eukaryotic protist was engulfed by a heterotrophic eukaryotic protist.

secondary growth An increase in a plant's girth, involving cell division in the vascular cambium and cork cambium.

secondary immune response The immune response elicited when an animal encounters the same antigen at some later time. The secondary immune response is more rapid, of greater magnitude, and of longer duration than the primary immune response.

secondary oocyte (ō′-uh-sīt′) A haploid cell resulting from meiosis I in oogenesis, which will become an ovum after meiosis II.

secondary phloem *See* phloem.

secondary spermatocyte (sper-mat′-uh-sīt′) A haploid cell resulting from meiosis I in spermatogenesis, which will become a sperm cell after meiosis II.

secondary structure The second level of protein structure; the regular local patterns of coils or folds of a polypeptide chain.

secondary succession A type of ecological succession that occurs where a disturbance has destroyed an existing biological community but left the soil intact. *See also* primary succession.

secondary xylem *See* xylem.

secretion (1) The discharge of molecules synthesized by a cell. (2) In the vertebrate kidney, the discharge of wastes from the blood into the filtrate from the nephron tubules.

seed A plant embryo packaged with a food supply within a protective covering.

seed coat A tough outer covering of a seed, formed from the outer coat (integuments) of an ovule. In a flowering plant, the seed coat encloses and protects the embryo and endosperm.

seed dormancy The temporary suspension of growth and development of a seed.

seedless vascular plants The informal collective name for lycophytes (club mosses and their relatives) and pterophytes (ferns and their relatives).

segmentation Subdivision along the length of an animal body into a series of repeated parts called segments.

selective permeability (per′-mē-uh-bil′-uh-tē) A property of biological membranes that allows some substances to cross more easily than others and blocks the passage of other substances altogether.

self protein A protein on the surface of an antigen-presenting cell that can hold a foreign antigen and display it to helper T cells. Each individual has a unique set of self proteins that serve as molecular markers for the body. Lymphocytes do not attack self proteins unless the proteins are displaying foreign antigens; therefore, self proteins mark normal body cells as off-limits to the immune system. The technical name for self proteins is *major histocompatibility complex (MHC) proteins. See also* nonself molecule.

self-fertilize The fusion of sperm and egg produced by the same individual organism.

semen (sē′-mun) The sperm-containing fluid that is ejaculated by the male during orgasm.

semicircular canals Fluid-filled channels in the inner ear that detect changes in the head's rate of rotation or angular movement.

semiconservative model Type of DNA replication in which the replicated double helix consists of one old strand, derived from the old molecule, and one newly made strand.

seminal vesicle (sem′-uh-nul ves′-uh-kul) A gland in males that secretes a fluid component of semen that lubricates and nourishes sperm.

seminiferous tubule (sem′-uh-nif′-uh-rus) A coiled sperm-producing tube in a testis.

sensation A feeling, or general awareness, of stimuli resulting from sensory information reaching the central nervous system.

sensitive period A limited phase in an individual animal's development when learning of particular behaviors can take place.

sensory adaptation The tendency of sensory neurons to become less sensitive when they are stimulated repeatedly.

sensory input The conduction of signals from sensory receptors to processing centers in the central nervous system.

sensory neuron A nerve cell that receives information from sensory receptors and conveys signals into the central nervous system.

sensory receptor A specialized cell or neuron that detects stimuli and sends information to the central nervous system.

sensory transduction The conversion of a stimulus signal to an electrical signal by a sensory receptor.

sepal (sē′-pul) A modified leaf of a flowering plant. A whorl of sepals encloses and protects the flower bud before it opens.

sessile An organism that is anchored to its substrate.

sex chromosome A chromosome that determines whether an individual is male or female.

sex-linked gene A gene located on a sex chromosome. In humans, the vast majority of sex-linked genes are located on the Y chromosome.

sexual dimorphism (dī-mōr'-fizm) Marked differences between the secondary sex characteristics of males and females.

sexual reproduction The creation of offspring by the fusion of two haploid sex cells (gametes), forming a diploid zygote.

sexual selection A form of natural selection in which individuals with certain inherited characteristics are more likely than other individuals to obtain mates.

sexually transmitted disease (STD) A contagious disease spread by sexual contact.

shared ancestral characters A character, shared by members of a particular clade, that originated in an ancestor that is not a member of that clade.

shared derived characters An evolutionary novelty that is unique to a particular clade.

shoot system All of a plant's stems, leaves, and reproductive structures.

short-day plant A plant that flowers in late summer, fall, or winter, when day length is short. Short-day plants actually flower in response to long nights (and so are sometimes called long-night plants).

short-term memory The ability to hold information, anticipations, or goals for a time and then release them if they become irrelevant.

sieve plate An end wall in a sieve-tube member that facilitates the flow of phloem sap.

sieve-tube member A food-conducting cell in a plant. Chains of sieve-tube members make up phloem tissue.

signal In behavioral ecology, a stimulus transmitted by one animal to another animal.

signal transduction pathway In cell biology, a series of molecular changes that converts a signal on a target cell's surface to a specific response inside the cell.

silencer A eukaryotic DNA sequence that functions to inhibit the start of gene transcription; may act analogously to an enhancer by binding a repressor.

single-lens eye The camera-like eye found in some jellies, polychaetes, spiders, many molluscs, and in vertebrates.

sister chromatid (krō'-muh-tid) One of the two identical parts of a duplicated chromosome in a eukaryotic cell.

skeletal muscle Striated muscle attached to the skeleton. The contraction of striated muscles produces voluntary movements of the body.

skeletal system The organ system that provides body support and protects body organs such as the brain, heart, and lungs.

small intestine The longest section of the alimentary canal. It is the principal site of the enzymatic hydrolysis of food macromolecules and the absorption of nutrients.

smooth endoplasmic reticulum A network of interconnected membranous tubules in a eukaryotic cell's cytoplasm. Smooth ER lacks ribosomes.

smooth muscle Muscle made up of cells without striations, found in the walls of organs such as the digestive tract, urinary bladder, and arteries.

SNP (single nucleotide polymorphism) A variation in DNA sequence found within the genomes of at least 1% of a population.

social behavior Any kind of interaction between two or more animals, usually of the same species.

social learning Modification of behavior through the observation of other individuals.

sociobiology The study of the evolutionary basis of social behavior.

sodium-potassium (Na-K) pump A membrane protein that transports sodium ions out of, and potassium ions into, a cell against their concentration gradients. The process is powered by ATP.

solute (sol'-yūt) A substance that is dissolved in a solution.

solution A liquid consisting of a homogeneous mixture of two or more substances, consisting of a dissolving agent, called the solvent, and a substance that is dissolved, called the solute.

solvent The dissolving agent of a solution. Water is the most versatile solvent known.

somatic cell (sō-mat'-ik) Any cell in a multicellular organism except a sperm or egg cell or a cell that develops into a sperm or egg.

somatic nervous system The component of the vertebrate peripheral nervous system that carries signals to and from skeletal muscles.

spatial learning Modification of behavior based on experience of the spatial structure of the environment.

speciation The evolution of a new species.

species A group whose members possess similar anatomical characteristics and have the ability to interbreed and produce viable, fertile offspring. *See* biological species concept.

species diversity The variety of species that make up a community; includes both species richness (the total number of different species) and the relative abundance of the different species in the community.

sperm A male gamete.

spermatogenesis (sper-mat'-ō-jen'-uh-sis) The formation of sperm cells.

spermicide A sperm-killing chemical (cream, jelly, or foam) that works with a barrier device as a method of contraception.

sphincter (sfink'-ter) A ringlike valve, consisting of modified muscles in a muscular tube, that regulates passage between some compartments of the alimentary canal.

spinal cord The dorsal hollow nerve cord in vertebrates, located within the vertebral column; with the brain, makes up the central nervous system.

spinal nerve In the vertebrate peripheral nervous system, a nerve that carries signals to or from the spinal cord.

spirochete A member of a group of helical bacteria that spiral through the environment by means of rotating, internal filaments.

sponge An aquatic animal characterized by a highly porous body.

sporangium (spuh-ranj'-ē-um') (plural, **sporangia**) A structure in fungi and plants in which meiosis occurs and haploid spores develop.

spore (1) In plants and algae, a haploid cell that can develop into a multicellular individual without fusing with another cell. (2) In prokaryotes, protists, and fungi, any of a variety of thick-walled life cycle stages capable of surviving unfavorable environmental conditions.

sporophyte (spōr'-uh-fīt) The multicellular diploid form in the life cycle of organisms undergoing alternation of generations; results from a union of gametes and meiotically produces haploid spores that grow into the gametophyte generation.

stabilizing selection Natural selection that favors intermediate variants by acting against extreme phenotypes.

stamen (stā'-men) A pollen-producing male reproductive part of a flower, consisting of a filament and an anther.

starch A storage polysaccharide found in the roots of plants and certain other cells; a polymer of glucose.

start codon (kō'-don) On mRNA, the specific three-nucleotide sequence (AUG) to which an initiator tRNA molecule binds, starting translation of genetic information.

stem The part of a plant's shoot system that supports the leaves and reproductive structures.

stem cell An unspecialized cell that can divide to produce an identical daughter cell and a more specialized daughter cell, which undergoes differentiation.

steroid (ster'-oyd) A type of lipid whose carbon skeleton is in the form of four fused rings with various chemical groups attached; examples are cholesterol, testosterone, and estrogen.

steroid hormone A lipid made from cholesterol that acts as a regulatory chemical, activating the transcription of specific genes in target cells.

stigma (stig'-muh) (plural, **stigmata**) The sticky tip of a flower's carpel, which traps pollen grains.

stimulus (plural, **stimuli**) (1) In the context of a nervous system, a factor that triggers sensory transduction. (2) In behavioral biology, a factor that triggers a specific response.

stoma (stō´-muh) (plural, **stomata**) A pore surrounded by guard cells in the epidermis of a leaf. When stomata are open, CO_2 enters a leaf, and water and O_2 exit. A plant conserves water when its stomata are closed.

stomach A pouch-like organ in a digestive tract that grinds and churns food and may store it temporarily.

stop codon In mRNA, one of three triplets (UAG, UAA, UGA) that signal gene translation to stop.

STR analysis (short tandem repeat analysis) A method of DNA profiling that involves the comparison of the lengths of short tandem repeat (STR) sequences selected from specific sites within the genome.

stramenopile A member of a clade of protists that includes water mold, diatoms, and brown algae and is characterized by a "hairy" flagellum.

strata Rock layers formed when new layers of sediment cover older ones and compress them.

stretch receptor A type of mechanoreceptor sensitive to changes in muscle length; detects the position of body parts.

stroke The death of nervous tissue in the brain, usually resulting from rupture or blockage of arteries in the head.

stroma (strō´-muh) The fluid of the chloroplast surrounding the thylakoid membrane; involved in the synthesis of organic molecules from carbon dioxide and water; Sugars are made in the stroma by the enzymes of the Calvin cycle.

stromatolite (strō-mat´-uh-līt) Layered rocks that result from the activities of prokaryotes that bind thin films of sediment together.

STRs (short tandem repeats) Short DNA sequences that are repeated many times in a row in the genome.

substrate (1) A specific substance (reactant) on which an enzyme acts. Each enzyme recognizes only the specific substrate or substrates of the reaction it catalyzes. (2) A surface in or on which an organism lives.

substrate feeder An organism that lives in or on its food source, eating its way through the food.

substrate-level phosphorylation The formation of ATP by an enzyme directly transferring a phosphate group to ADP from an organic molecule (for example, one of the intermediates in glycolysis or the citric acid cycle).

sugar sink A plant organ that is a net consumer or storer of sugar. Growing roots, shoot tips, stems, and fruits are sugar sinks supplied by phloem.

sugar source A plant organ in which sugar is being produced by either photosynthesis or the breakdown of starch. Mature leaves are the primary sugar sources of plants.

sugar-phosphate backbone The alternating chain of sugar and phosphate to which the DNA and RNA nitrogenous bases are attached.

superior vena cava (vē´-nuh kā´-vuh) A large vein that returns O_2-poor blood to the heart from the upper body and head. *See also* inferior vena cava.

surface tension A measure of how difficult it is to stretch or break the surface of a liquid. Water has a high surface tension because of the hydrogen bonding of surface molecules.

surfactant A substance secreted by alveoli that decreases surface tension in the fluid that coats the alveoli.

survivorship curve A plot of the number of members of a cohort that are still alive at each age; one way to represent age-specific mortality.

suspension feeder An aquatic animal that sifts small food particles from the water.

sustainable agriculture Long-term productive farming methods that are environmentally safe.

sustainable development The long-term prosperity of human societies and the ecosystems that support them.

sustainable resource management Management of a natural resource so as not to damage the resource.

swim bladder A gas-filled internal sac that helps bony fishes maintain buoyancy.

symbiosis A close association between organisms of two or more species.

sympathetic division A set of neurons in the autonomic nervous system that generally prepares the body for energy-consuming activities, such as fleeing or fighting. *See also* parasympathetic division.

sympatric speciation The formation of new species in populations that live in the same geographic area.

synapse (sin´-aps) A junction between two neurons, or between a neuron and an effector cell. Electrical or chemical signals are relayed from one cell to another at a synapse.

synaptic cleft (sin-ap´-tik) In a chemical synapse, a narrow gap separating the synaptic terminal of a transmitting neuron from a receiving neuron or an effector cell.

synaptic terminal The tip of a transmitting neuron's axon, where signals are sent to another neuron or to an effector cell.

synaptic vesicle A membranous sac containing neurotransmitter molecules at the tip of the presynaptic axon.

systematics A scientific discipline focused on classifying organisms and determining their evolutionary relationships.

systemic acquired resistance A defensive response in plants infected with a pathogenic microbe; helps protect healthy tissue from the microbe.

systemic circuit One of two main blood circuits in terrestrial vertebrates; conveys blood between the heart and the rest of the body. *See also* pulmonary circuit.

systems biology An approach to studying biology that aims to model the dynamic behavior of whole biological systems.

systole (sis´-tō-lē) The contraction stage of the heart cycle, when the heart chambers actively pump blood. *See also* diastole.

T cell A type of lymphocyte that matures in the thymus and is responsible for the cell-mediated immune response; also involved in humoral immunity. *See also* B cell.

tapeworm A parasitic flatworm characterized by the absence of a digestive tract.

target cell A cell that responds to a regulatory signal, such as a hormone.

taxis (tak´-sis) (plural, **taxes**) Virtually automatic orientation toward or away from a stimulus.

taxon A named taxonomic unit at any given level of classification.

taxonomy The branch of biology that identifies, names, and classifies species.

technology The practical application of scientific knowledge.

telomere (tel´-uh-mēr) The repetitive DNA at each end of a eukaryotic chromosome.

telophase The fifth and final stage of mitosis, during which daughter nuclei form at the two poles of a cell. Telophase usually occurs together with cytokinesis.

temperate broadleaf forest A biome located throughout midlatitude regions where there is sufficient moisture to support the growth of large, broadleaf deciduous trees.

temperate grassland A grassland region maintained by seasonal drought, occasional fires, and grazing by large mammals.

temperate zones Latitudes between the tropics and the Arctic Circle in the north and the Antarctic Circle in the south; regions with milder climates than the tropics or polar regions.

temperature A measure of the intensity of heat in degrees, reflecting the average kinetic energy or speed of molecules.

tendon Fibrous connective tissue connecting a muscle to a bone.

tendril A modified leaf used by some plants to climb around a fixed structure.

terminal bud Embryonic tissue at the tip of a shoot, made up of developing leaves and a compact series of nodes and internodes.

terminator A special sequence of nucleotides in DNA that marks the end of a gene. It signals RNA polymerase to release the newly made RNA molecule and then to depart from the gene.

territory An area that one or more individuals defend and from which other members of the same species are usually excluded.

tertiary consumer (ter'-shē-ār-ē) An organism that eats secondary consumers.

tertiary structure The third level of protein structure; the overall, three-dimensional shape of a polypeptide due to interactions of the R groups of the amino acids making up the chain.

testcross The mating between an individual of unknown genotype for a particular characteristic and an individual that is homozygous recessive for that same characteristic.

testis (plural, testes) The male gonad in an animal; produces sperm and, in many species, reproductive hormones.

testosterone (tes-tos'-tuh-rōn) An androgen hormone that stimulates an embryo to develop into a male and promotes male body features.

tetrad A paired set of homologous chromosomes, each composed of two sister chromatids. Tetrads form during prophase I of meiosis.

tetrapod A vertebrate with two pairs of limbs. Tetrapods include mammals, amphibians, and birds and other reptiles.

thalamus (thal'-uh-mus) An integrating and relay center of the vertebrate forebrain; sorts and relays selected information to specific areas in the cerebral cortex.

theory A widely accepted explanatory idea that is broad in scope and supported by a large body of evidence.

therapeutic cloning The cloning of human cells by nuclear transplantation for therapeutic purposes, such as the generation of embryonic stem cells. *See* nuclear transplantation; reproductive cloning.

thermodynamics The study of energy transformation that occurs in a collection of matter. *See* first law of thermodynamics; second law of thermodynamics.

thermoreceptor A sensor (sensory receptor) that detects heat or cold.

thermoregulation The maintenance of internal temperature within a range that allows cells to function efficiently.

thick filament A filament composed of staggered arrays of myosin molecules; a component of myofibrils in muscle fibers.

thigmotropism (thig'-mō-trō'-pizm) Growth movement of a plant in response to touch.

thin filament The thinner of the two myofilaments, consisting of two strands of actin and two strands of regulatory protein coiled around each other.

threatened species As defined in the U.S. Endangered Species Act, a species that is likely to become endangered in the foreseeable future throughout all or a significant portion of its range.

three-domain system A system of taxonomic classification based on three basic groups: Bacteria, Archaea, and Eukarya.

threshold The minimum change in a membrane's voltage that must occur to generate a nerve signal (action potential).

thylakoid (thī'-luh-koyd) One of a number of disk-shaped membranous sacs inside a chloroplast. Thylakoid membranes contain chlorophyll and the enzymes of the light reactions of photosynthesis. A stack of thylakoids is called a granum.

thymine (T) (thī'-min) A single-ring nitrogenous base found in DNA.

thymus gland (thī'-mus) An endocrine gland in the neck region of mammals that is active in establishing the immune system; secretes several hormones that promote the development and differentiation of T cells.

thyroid gland (thī'-royd) An endocrine gland that secretes thyroxine (T_4), triiodothyronine (T_3), and calcitonin.

thyroid-stimulating hormone (TSH) A protein hormone secreted by the anterior pituitary that stimulates the thyroid gland to secrete its hormones.

thyroxine (T_4) (thī-rok'-sin) An amine hormone secreted by the thyroid gland that stimulates metabolism in virtually all body tissues.

Ti plasmid A bacterial plasmid that induces tumors in plant cells that the bacterium infects; often used as a vector to introduce new genes into plant cells. Ti stands for tumor-inducing.

tissue An integrated group of cells with a common function, structure, or both.

tissue system One or more tissues organized into a functional unit within a plant or animal.

tonicity The ability of a solution surrounding a cell to cause that cell to gain or lose water.

topsoil A mixture of particles derived from rock, living organisms, and humus.

trace element An element that is essential for life but required in extremely minute amounts.

trachea (trā'-kē-uh) (plural, **tracheae**) The windpipe; the portion of the respiratory tube that has C-shaped cartilagenous rings and passes from the larynx to two bronchi.

tracheal system A system of branched, air-filled tubes in insects that extend throughout the body and carry oxygen directly to cells.

tracheid (trā'-kē-id) A tapered, porous, water-conducting and supportive cell in plants. Chains of tracheids or vessel elements make up the water-conducting, supportive tubes in xylem.

trade winds The movement of air in the tropics (those regions that lie between 23.5° north latitude and 23.5° south latitude).

trait A variant of a character found within a population, such as purple flowers in pea plants.

transcription factor In the eukaryotic cell, a protein that functions in initiating or regulating transcription. Transcription factors bind to DNA or to other proteins that bind to DNA.

transcription The synthesis of RNA on a DNA template.

transduction (1) The transfer of bacterial genes from one bacterial cell to another by a phage. (2) *See* sensory transduction. (3) *See* signal transduction.

transfer RNA (tRNA) A type of ribonucleic acid that functions as an interpreter in translation. Each tRNA molecule has a specific anticodon, picks up a specific amino acid, and conveys the amino acid to the appropriate codon on mRNA.

transformation The incorporation of new genes into a cell from DNA that the cell takes up from the surrounding environment.

transgenic organism An organism that contains genes from another species.

translation The synthesis of a polypeptide using the genetic information encoded in an mRNA molecule. There is a change of "language" from nucleotides to amino acids.

translocation (1) During protein synthesis, the movement of a tRNA molecule carrying a growing polypeptide chain from the A site to the P site on a ribosome. (The mRNA travels with it.) (2) A change in a chromosome resulting from a chromosomal fragment attaching to a nonhomologous chromosome; can occur as a result of an error in meiosis or from mutagenesis.

transmission electron microscope (TEM) A microscope that uses an electron beam to study the internal structure of thinly sectioned specimens.

transpiration The evaporative loss of water from a plant.

transpiration-cohesion-tension mechanism A transport mechanism that drives the upward movement of water in plants: transpiration exerts a pull that is relayed downward along a string of molecules held together by cohesion and helped upward by adhesion.

transport vesicle A tiny membranous sac in a cell's cytoplasm carrying molecules produced by the cell. The vesicle buds from the endoplasmic reticulum or Golgi and eventually fuses with another membranous organelle or the plasma membrane, releasing its contents.

transposable element (tranz-pō'-zon) A transposable genetic element, or "jumping gene"; a segment of DNA that can move from one site to another within a cell and serve as an agent of genetic change.

TRH-releasing hormone A peptide hormone that triggers the release of TSH (thyroid-stimulating hormone), which in turn stimulates the thyroid gland.

trial-and-error learning Learning to associate a particular behavioral act with a positive or negative effect.

triiodothyronine (T₃) (trī′-ī-ō-dō-thī′-rō-nīn) An amine hormone secreted by the thyroid gland that stimulates metabolism in virtually all body tissues.

trimester In human development, one of three 3-month-long periods of pregnancy.

triplet code A set of three-nucleotide-long "words" that specify the amino acids for polypeptide chains. *See* genetic code.

trisomy 21 *See* Down syndrome.

tRNA *See* transfer RNA.

trophoblast (trōf′-ō-blast) In mammalian development, the outer portion of a blastocyst. Cells of the trophoblast secrete enzymes that enable the blastocyst to implant in the endometrium of the mother's uterus.

tropical forest A terrestrial biome characterized by high levels of precipitation and warm temperatures year-round.

tropics Latitudes between 23.5° north and south.

tropism (trō′-pizm) A growth response that makes a plant grow toward or away from a stimulus.

true-breeding Referring to organisms for which sexual reproduction produces offspring with inherited traits identical to those of the parents; the organisms are homozygous for the characteristics under consideration.

tubal ligation A means of sterilization in which a woman's two oviducts (fallopian tubes) are tied closed to prevent eggs from reaching the uterus; a segment of each oviduct is removed.

tuber An enlargement at the end of a rhizome in which food is stored.

tumor An abnormal mass of cells that forms within otherwise normal tissue.

tumor-suppressor gene A gene whose product inhibits cell division, thereby preventing uncontrolled cell growth.

tundra A biome at the northernmost limits of plant growth and at high altitudes, characterized by dwarf woody shrubs, grasses, mosses, and lichens.

tunicate One of a group of invertebrate chordates.

U

ultimate cause In animal behavior, the evolutionary reason for a behavior.

ultrasound imaging A technique for examining a fetus in the uterus. High-frequency sound waves echoing off the fetus are used to produce an image of the fetus.

undernourishment A condition that results from a diet that consistently supplies less chemical energy than the body requires.

uniform Describing a dispersion pattern in which individuals are evenly distributed.

unsaturated Pertaining to fats and fatty acids whose hydrocarbon chains lack the maximum number of hydrogen atoms and therefore have one or more double covalent bonds. Unsaturated fats and fatty acids do not solidify at room temperature.

uracil (U) (yū′-ruh-sil) A single-ring nitrogenous base found in RNA.

urea (yū-rē′-ah) A soluble form of nitrogenous waste excreted by mammals and most adult amphibians.

ureter (yū-rē′-ter or yū′-reh-ter) A duct that conveys urine from the kidney to the urinary bladder.

urethra (yū-rē′-thruh) A duct that conveys urine from the urinary bladder to the outside. In the male, the urethra also conveys semen out of the body during ejaculation.

uric acid (yū′-rik) An insoluble precipitate of nitrogenous waste excreted by land snails, insects, birds, and some reptiles.

urinary bladder The pouch where urine is stored prior to elimination.

urinary system The organ system that forms and excretes urine while regulating the amount of water and ions in the body fluids.

urine Concentrated filtrate produced by the kidneys and excreted by the bladder.

uterus (yū′-ter-us) In the reproductive system of a mammalian female, the organ where the development of young occurs; the womb.

vaccination (vak-suh-nā′-shun) A procedure that presents the immune system with a harmless variant or derivative of a pathogen, thereby stimulating the immune system to mount a long-term defense against the pathogen.

vaccine (vak-sēn′) A harmless variant or derivative of a pathogen used to stimulate a host organism's immune system to mount a long-term defense against the pathogen.

vacuole (vak′-ū-ōl) A membrane-enclosed sac that is part of the endomembrane system of a eukaryotic cell, having diverse functions.

vagina (vuh-jī′-nuh) Part of the female reproductive system between the uterus and the outside opening; the birth canal in mammals; also accommodates the male's penis and receives sperm during copulation.

vas deferens (vas def′-er-enz) (plural, **vasa deferentia**) Part of the male reproductive system that conveys sperm away from the testis; the sperm duct; in humans, the tube that conveys sperm between the epididymis and the common duct that leads to the urethra.

vascular bundle (vas′-kyū-ler) A strand of vascular tissues (both xylem and phloem) in a plant stem.

vascular cambium (vas′-kyū-ler kam′-bē-um) During secondary growth of a plant, the cylinder of meristematic cells, surrounding the xylem and pith, that produces secondary xylem and phloem.

vascular cylinder The central cylinder of vascular tissue in a plant root.

vascular plant A plant with xylem and phloem, including club mosses, ferns, gymnosperms, and angiosperms,

vascular tissue Plant tissue consisting of cells joined into tubes that transport water and nutrients throughout the plant body.

vascular tissue system A system formed by xylem and phloem throughout the plant, serving as a transport system for water and nutrients, respectively.

vasectomy (vuh-sek′-tuh-mē) Surgical removal of a section of the two sperm ducts (vasa deferentia) to prevent sperm from reaching the urethra; a means of sterilization in the male.

vector In molecular biology, a piece of DNA, usually a plasmid or a viral genome, that is used to move genes from one cell to another.

vein (1) In animals, a vessel that returns blood to the heart. (2) In plants, a vascular bundle in a leaf, composed of xylem and phloem.

ventilation A mechanism that provides contact between an animal's respiratory surface and the air or water to which it is exposed.

ventral Pertaining to the underside, or bottom, of a bilaterally symmetrical animal.

ventricle (ven′-truh-kul) (1) A heart chamber that pumps blood out of a heart. (2) A space in the vertebrate brain, filled with cerebrospinal fluid.

venule (ven′-yūl) A vessel that conveys blood between a capillary bed and a vein.

vertebra (ver′-tuh-bruh) (plural, **vertebrae**) One of a series of segmented skeletal units that enclose the nerve cord, making up the backbone of a vertebrate animal.

vertebral column backbone; composed of a series of segmented units called vertebrae.

vertebrate (ver′-tuh-brāt) A chordate animal with a backbone. Vertebrates include lampreys, chondricthyans, ray-finned fishes, lobe-fin fishes, amphibians, reptiles (including birds), and mammals.

vesicle A sac made of membrane in the cytoplasm of a eukaryotic cell.

vessel element A short, open-ended, water-conducting and supportive cell in plants. Chains of vessel elements or tracheids make up the water-conducting, supportive tubes in xylem.

vestigial organ A structure of marginal or no importance to an organism. Vestigial organs are historical remnants of structures that had important function in ancestors.

villus (vil′-us) (plural, **villi**) (1) A fingerlike projection of the inner surface of the small intestine. (2) A fingerlike projection of the chorion of the mammalian placenta. Large numbers of villi increase the surface areas of these organs.

viriod (vī'-royd) A plant pathogen composed of molecules of naked, circular RNA several hundred nucleotides long.

virus A microscopic particle capable of infecting cells of living organisms and inserting its genetic material. Viruses are generally not considered to be alive because they do not display all of the characteristics associated with life.

visceral mass (vis'-uh-rul) One of the three main parts of a mollusc, containing most of the internal organs.

visual acuity The ability of the eyes to distinguish fine detail.

vital capacity The maximum volume of air that a mammal can inhale and exhale with each breath.

vitamin An organic nutrient that an organism requires in very small quantities. Vitamins generally function as coenzymes.

vitreous humor (vit'-rē-us hyū'-mer) A jellylike substance filling the space behind the lens in the vertebrate eye; helps maintain the shape of the eye.

vocal cord One of a pair of bands of elastic tissues in the larynx. Air rushing past the tensed vocal cords makes them vibrate, producing sounds.

W

water mold A fungus-like protist in the stramenopile clade.

water vascular system In echinoderms, a radially arranged system of water-filled canals that branch into extensions called tube feet. The system provides movement and circulates water, facilitating gas exchange and waste disposal.

water-conducting cell A specialized, dead plant cell with lignin-containing secondary walls, arranged end to end, forming xylem tissue. *See also* tracheid; vessel element.

wavelength The distance between crests of adjacent waves, such as those of the electromagnetic spectrum.

westerlies Winds that blow from west to east.

wetland An ecosystem intermediate between an aquatic ecosystem and a terrestrial ecosystem. Wetland soil is saturated with water permanently or periodically.

white blood cell *See* leukocyte.

white matter Tracts of axons within the central nervous system.

whole-genome shotgun method A method for determining the DNA sequence of an entire genome. After a genome is cut into small fragments, each fragment is sequenced and then placed in the proper order.

wood ray A column of parenchyma cells that radiates from the center of a log and transports water to its outer living tissues.

wood Secondary xylem of a plant. *See also* heartwood; sapwood.

X

X chromosome inactivation In female mammals, the inactivation of one X chromosome in each somatic cell.

xylem (zī'-lum) The nonliving portion of a plant's vascular system that provides support and conveys xylem sap from the roots to the rest of the plant. Xylem is made up of vessel elements and/or tracheids, water-conducting cells. Primary xylem is derived from the procambium. Secondary xylem is derived from the vascular cambium in plants exhibiting secondary growth.

xylem sap The solution of inorganic nutrients conveyed in xylem tissue from a plant's roots to its shoots.

Y

yeast A single-celled fungus that inhabits liquid or moist habitats and reproduces asexually by simple cell division or by the pinching of small buds off a parent cell.

yellow bone marrow A tissue found within the central cavities of long bones, consisting mostly of stored fat.

yolk sac An extraembryonic membrane that develops from endoderm; produces the embryo's first blood cells and germ cells and gives rise to the allantois.

Z

zoned reserve An extensive region of land that includes one or more areas that are undisturbed by humans. The undisturbed areas are surrounded by lands that have been altered by human activity.

zooplankton (zō'-ō-plank'-tun) Animals that drift in aquatic environments.

zygomycete Member of a group of fungi characterized by a sturdy structure called a zygosporangium during sexual reproduction.

zygote (zī'-gōt) The fertilized egg, which is diploid, that results from the union of a sperm cell nucleus and an egg cell nucleus.

zygote fungus *See* zygomycete.

GLOSSARY

Animal(s) (*continued*)
    mammals, 392–93, 399
    medicinal plants used by, 676
    movement in (*see* Movement)
    nervous systems, 572–76
    nutrition in (*see* Animal nutrition)
    organs and organ systems of, 419–21
    pathogens in, 203
    phylogenetic tree for, 369, 369 *fig.*
    phylogeny of, 384–85
    plant species diversity in community and, 748
    primates, 400–402
    regulation of internal environment by (*see*
        Homeostasis; Regulatory systems, animal)
    reproduction in (*see* Asexual reproduction;
        Human reproduction; Sexual reproduction)
    respiration in (*see* Respiration)
    seed dispersal by, 352 *fig.*
    senses of (*see* Senses)
    signaling behavior in, 713
    speciation in (*see* Speciation)
    structural organization in hierarchy of, 414–23
    superhuman senses in, 587
    transgenic, 239–40
    vertebrates, 390–408
Animal body. *See also* Bilateral symmetry; Body
        cavity, of animals
    body symmetry of, and nervous system
        coordination, 572
    characteristics, 368
    of mollusc, 374 *fig.*
    organs of (*see* Organ(s))
    pattern formation in, 552–53
    radial, 371
    segmented, 376–77, 376 *fig.*
    senses of (*see* Senses)
    temperature of (*see* Body temperature)
    tissues of (*see* Tissues, animal)
Animal cells, 56–57, 56 *fig.*
    cleavage, 132 *fig.*, 548
    cytokinesis in, 132
    meiosis with diploid number of 4, 138–39 *fig.*
    organelles of (*see* Organelles)
    osmoregulation of water balance in,
        76–77, 77 *fig.*
    plasma membrane of, 74 *fig.*
    surfaces and junctions, 68 *fig.*
Animal development. *See* Embryonic
    development in animals
Animal disease. *See* Disease; Human disease
Animalia (kingdom), 7, 7 *fig.*, 314, 384–85, 389.
    See also Animal(s)
Animal nutrition, 428–51
    chemical conversions and, 29
    chemical energy for body and, 442
    diets and digestive adaptations in, 441
    digestion and, 431, 431 *fig.*, 432
    essential amino acids, vitamins, and
        minerals, 443–45
    feeding, ingestion, and, 366, 430–32
    food labels and, 446
    human digestive system, 433–41
    human disease, diet, and, 449
    human healthy diet, 443–49
    obtaining and processing food and, 430–32
    weight loss plans and, 448
    in whales, 429
Annelid (Annelida), 376–77, 572, 572 *fig.*
Annuals, 630
Ant(s)
    fungi and, 360–61, 360 *fig.*
Antagonistic hormones, 525
Antagonistic muscles, 611 *fig.*
Anterior pituitary, 522, 523
    hormones of, 523 *fig.*
Anterior surface of animals, 368, 368 *fig.*, 372
Anthers, 350, 634

Anthrax, 323, 323 *fig.*
    as biological weapon, 328
Anthropoids, 401
Antibiotics
    bacterial resistance to, 205, 272, 323
    cellular respiration and effects of, 99
    enzymes and effects of, 85
    fungi and production of, 361
    gram-negative bacteria insensitivity to, 322
Antibody(ies), 489
    antigen-binding sites on, 491
    antigens marked for elimination by, 495, 495 *fig.*
    binding to antigenic determinants, 491 *fig.*
    computer graphic of, 494 *fig.*
    monoclonal, 496, 496 *fig.*
    structure of, 494, 494 *fig.*
    as weapons of humoral immunity, 494
Anticodons, 195
Antidiuretic hormone (ADH), 513, 522
Antigen(s), 489
    allergies and environmental, 501
    antibody binding to, 494 *fig.*
    marking of, by antibodies, 495
Antigen-binding sites, 491, 491 *fig.*, 494
Antigenic determinants, 491, 491 *fig.*
Antigen-presenting cells (APCs), 497, 497 *fig.*
Antigen receptors, 490
Antihistamines, 501
Anus, 432
Aorta, 470
Apes, relationship of humans to, 400–401, 402
Aphids
    abiotic effects on population size in, 730, 730 *fig.*
    as parasites, 745 *fig.*
    study of transport in phloem tissue using,
        648–49, 649 *fig.*
Aphotic zone, 688
Apical dominance, 624
Apical meristems, 342
    primary growth and, 630, 630 *fig.*, 631 *fig.*
Apicomplexans, 333
Apoptosis, 552, 552 *fig.*
Appendicular skeleton, 608, 608 *fig.*
Appendix, 440
Aquaporins, 77, 78
Aquatic animals, 688
    excretion in, 509 *fig.*
    at hydrothermal vents, 681, 681 *fig.*
    osmoregulation in, 508 *fig.*
    respiration and gas exchange in, 455, 455 *fig.*,
        456–57, 456 *fig.*
Aquatic ecosystems, 688–90
    coral reefs, 688, 689, 689 *fig.*
    eutrophication in, 759
    freshwater, 690
    gills as adaptation to, 455, 456–57
    global water cycle connecting terrestrial and,
        697, 697 *fig.*
    hydrothermal vents in, 681
    oceans, 681, 688–89
    overexploitation of, 766
Aquatic food chain, 746 *fig.*
Aqueous humor, 595 *fig.*, 596
Aqueous solutions, 26
Arabidopsis thaliana (mustard plant), 247,
    674, 674 *fig.*
Arachnids, 378
Arbuscular mycorrhizal fungi, 356 *fig.*
Archaea (domain), 6, 7 *fig.*, 314
    bacteria compared to, 320–21, 321 *table*
    extreme habitats of select, 325
    insensitivity of gram-negative bacteria to, 322
Archaean eon, 298
Archaeopteryx fossil, 398, 398 *fig.*
Ardipithecus, 403
Aristotle, 154, 256, 644
Arousal, brain regulation of sleep and, 580

Arteries, 468
    atherosclerosis of, 473, 473 *fig.*
    coronary, 473, 473 *fig.*
    pulmonary, 470
    pulse of blood in, 475
    structure of, 474 *fig.*
Arterioles, 468, 474 *fig.*
Arthritis, rheumatoid, 500
Arthropods (Arthropoda), 378–79
    exoskeleton of, 606, 606 *fig.*, 607
    nervous system of, 572 *fig.*
    structure of, 378 *fig.*
Artificial pacemaker, 472, 472 *fig.*
Artificial selection, 258, 258 *fig.*
Ascomycetes, 356 *fig.*, 357, 357 *fig.*
Asexual reproduction, 126
    in animals, 534
    in fungi, 356
    mitosis and, 136
    in plants, 638–39, 639 *fig.*
Aspartame, 267
Aspartic acid, 42, 42 *fig.*
Aspirin, 473, 481, 675
Assisted reproductive technology (ART), 559
Associative learning, 710
Astigmatism, 597
Astronauts, motion sickness and, 594
Atherosclerosis, 473, 473 *fig.*
Athletes
    growth hormone and, 522
    muscle fiber characteristics of performance
        of, 616, 616 *table*
    red blood cell levels and, 480
Athlete's foot, 359
Atmosphere
    greenhouse effect in, 119, 768–69, 769 *fig.*
    origin of life and Earth's early, 294
    ozone layer depletion in, 120, 120 *fig.*, 767
Atomic mass, 20
Atomic number, 20
Atoms, 2–3, 2 *fig.*, 20, 20 *fig.*
    chemical reactions and rearrangements of, 29
    covalent bonds and molecule formation from, 23
    electron arrangement and properties of, 22
    electronegativity of, 24
    ionic bonds formed between, 22–23
    structure of, 19
ATP (adenosine triphosphate), 35
    active transport and need for, 83
    cellular respiration and synthesis of, 82, 89,
        91 *fig.*, 93, 95 *fig.*, 98, 100 *fig.*
    as chemical energy shuttle in cells, 83, 83 *fig.*
    mitochondria and, 63
    muscle contraction and, 613, 615
    photosynthesis and synthesis of, 111, 114 *fig.*,
        115, 115 *fig.*
    photosynthesis and synthesis of sugars using, 116
    structure and hydrolysis of, 83 *fig.*
ATP cycle, 83 *fig.*
ATP synthases, 93
    poisons as disruptors of, 99
Atria (atrium), 468
Attention deficit hyperactivity disorder (ADHD)
    medications, 571
Auditory canal, 592
Australia, animal diversity in, 388–89, 399, 404,
    408, 408 *fig.*
Australopithecus afarensis, 403, 404
Australopithecus africanus, 403
Australopithecus anamensis, 404
Australopiths, 403
Autoimmune disease, 500
    diabetes (Type I) as, 527
    multiple sclerosis, 565
Automatic external defibrillators (AEDs), 472
Autonomic nervous system, 574, 575, 575 *fig.*
Autosomes, 137

Autotrophs, 108, 324
Auxins, 663, 664 *table*, 669
    antagonistic interactions of, 666, 669
    cell elongation in shoots regulated by, 664–65, 665 *fig.*
AV (atrioventricular) node, 472
Avian flu, 202, 202 *fig.*
Axial skeleton, 608, 608 *fig.*
Axillary buds, 624
Axolotl, 304, 304 *fig.*
Axons, 418, 565, 565 *fig.*
    propagation of action potential along, 568, 568 *fig.*

B

Bacilli, 321, 321 *fig.*
Bacillus anthracis, 323, 323 *fig.*, 326, 328
Bacillus coagulans, 55 *fig.*
Bacteria (domain), 6, 7 *fig.*, 314
    antibiotic resistance in, 205, 272, 323
    archaea compared to, 320–21, 321 *table*
    binary fission in, 127, 127 *fig.*
    bioterrorism using, 328
    cell structure and size in, 54
    chromosomes in, 127 *fig.*
    customization using plasmids, 232
    cyanobacteria, 319
    as denitrifiers, 757
    disease causing, 327, 328, 437, 437 *fig.*, 487
        See also Disease; Human disease
    diversity of, 326
    flagella and cilia, 66, 322
    at hydrothermal vents, 681
    mutation rates in, 265
    natural means of DNA transfer in, 204
    nitrogen cycle and, 756–57, 757 *fig.*
    nitrogen-fixing, 655, 656, 756–57, 757 *fig.*
    oil spill remediation with, 778
    plasmids of (*see* Plasmids)
    recycling and cleaning environment with, 329
    as tool for manipulating DNA, 232–38
Bacterial cell wall, 55
Bacteriophage(s), 182
    genomic library of, 235, 235 *fig.*
    Hershey and Chase experiments on, 182–83, 183 *fig.*
    lambda, 200
    reproductive cycle of, 183 *fig.*, 200 *fig.*
Bacteriorhodopsin, 325
Balance, 592–94
Balancing selection, 272–73
Ball-and-socket joints, 611, 611 *fig.*
Bamboo, 103
Banff National Park, Canada, animal bridge in, 773 *fig.*
Bark, 633, 633 *fig.*
Barnacles, 379, 379 *fig.*
Barr body, 213
Barrier methods (contraception), 545
Basal body, 66
Basal ganglia, 577, 577 *fig.*
Basal lamina, 416
Basal metabolic rate (BMR), 442
Base, 27
    nitrogenous, 46, 47 *fig.*
Basidiomycetes, 356 *fig.*, 357, 357 *fig.*
Basilar membrane, 592, 593, 593 *fig.*
Basophils, 479, 479 *fig.*
Bateson, William, 172
Bats, 293, 399, 505, 587, 587 *fig.*
B cells (B lymphocytes), 490–91, 490 *fig.*
Bdellovibrio bacteriophorus, 51, 326, 326 *fig.*
Beadle, George, 190
Bears
    global warming and polar, 770, 770 *fig.*
    systematics of raccoons and, 312, 312 *fig.*
    thermoregulation in, 505

Bees. *See also* Honeybees
Beetles, 408, 771
Behavior, 700–723
    abnormal, chemical pollutants causing, 716
    innate, 702–3
    learning, 705–11
    scientific study of, 702–5
    sociobiology and social, 717–21
    survival and reproductive success, 712–16
    thermoregulation and, 507
Behavioral ecology/ecologists, 701, 702
    animal movement, 709
    feeding behavior, 712
Behavioral isolation, 280, 280 *fig.*
Belding's ground squirrel, 720, 720 *fig.*
Benign tumors, 135
Benthic realm, 688
Benzene, 34 *fig.*
Bernard, Claude, 425
Beta-carotene, conversion to vitamin A, 239
Biennials, 630
Big bang theory, 294
Bilateral symmetry, 368, 368 *fig.*, 372, 572
Bilaterians, 369, 372, 373, 384
Bilbies, 408, 408 *fig.*
Bile, 438, 440
Binary fission, 127
Binomial naming system, 308–9
Biodiversity
    in communities, 749
    endangered species protection and, 763
    evolution of (*see* Evolution)
    human activities as threat to, 764
    human welfare and, 764
    in plants as irreplaceable resource, 354
    protected areas to slow loss of, 774
Biodiversity crisis, 764–71
    endangered species and, 429, 763
    global climate change and, 768–69
    habitat destruction, invasive species, and overexploitation as causes of, 766
    ozone layer depletion and, 120, 120 *fig.*, 767
    reasons for concern about, 764
    technology and human overpopulation as factors in, 354
    (E. O.) Wilson on, 764
Biodiversity hotspots, 774, 774 *fig.*
Biofilms, 324, 324 *fig.*
Biogenic amines, 570–71
Biogeochemical cycles, 754–55, 755 *fig.*
Biogeography, evidence for evolution in, 262
Biological clocks, 577, 671
    phytochromes and, 673
    plant circadian rhythms, 671
    in plant guard cells, 647
    seasonal, in plants, 672
Biological control, 751
Biological magnification, 767, 767 *fig.*
Biological species concept, 279
Biological weapons, 328
Biological Weapons Convention, 328
Biology, 1, 2. *See also* Conservation biology; Ecology; Molecular biology
    at atomic and molecular level, 18
    everyday life and, 10, 12
    scope of, 2–3
Bioluminescence, 73
Biomass, 752–53, 769
Biomass energy, 107
Biomes, 687
    chaparral, 694
    coniferous forests, 696, 696 *fig.*
    deserts, 693
    estuary, 689
    freshwater, 690
    global climate change and, 770–71

global terrestrial, 691 *fig.*
global water cycle connecting, 697, 697 *fig.*
oceans, 688–89
savannas, 692–93, 692 *fig.*
temperate broadleaf forests, 695, 695 *fig.*
temperate grasslands, 694–95
tropical forest, 692
tundra, 696, 696 *fig.*
wetlands, 689
Biophilia, 764
Bioremediation, 329, 778
Biosafety Protocol, 240
Biosphere, 2, 2 *fig.*, 680–99
    abiotic and biotic factors in, 682, 685
    aquatic ecosystems of, 681, 688–90
    autotrophs and producers in, 108
    chemical cycling in, 754–58
    climate and distribution of communities in, 686–87
    definition of, 680
    ecology as study of, 681
    environmental problems, ecology and insights into, 683
        See also Environmental problems
    global water cycle and, 697, 697 *fig.*
    physical and chemical factors in, 684
    terrestrial ecosystems of, 691–97
Biotechnology, 232
    biodiversity and bioprospecting for, 764
    yeasts and, 361
Biotic components of ecosystems. *See also* Organisms
Biotic factors, 682, 752
    adaptation to, 685
Bipedalism, 404, 404 *fig.*
Bipolar disorder, 582
Birds, 398. *See also* names of individual birds
    alimentary canal of, 432 *fig.*
    blue-footed booby, 254–55, 266–67
    bones of, 306
    breathing in, 461
    cardiovascular system, 469, 469 *fig.*
    chemical pesticides and, 767
    courtship and mating behaviors of, 280, 280 *fig.*, 714, 714 *fig.*
    digestion in, 432
    edge-adapted species of, 773
    evolution of, 293, 306
    excretion in, 509 *fig.*
    extinct, 398 *fig.*
    finches, 259, 285, 287, 288 *fig.*
    flight in, 605, 605 *fig.*
    foraging behavior of, 712, 712 *fig.*
    habituation in, 705
    in high altitudes, 453
    lungs of, 461
    migration and navigation in, 709
    phylogenetic tree of, 311, 311 *fig.*
    problem-solving behavior in, 711, 711 *fig.*
    ptarmigan, 425, 425 *fig.*
    respiration and gas exchange in, 461
    respiratory system of, 458
    songbird species, 706
    song sparrow populations, 730, 730 *fig.*, 731, 731 *fig.*
    territorial behavior of, 717 *fig.*
    thermoregulation in, 506–7
    wing formation in, 553, 553 *fig.*
Bird song, imprinting and learning of, 706
Birth control pills, 545
Birth defects, 148
Birth rates, human population growth and, 735
Births, multiples, 532–33
Bishop, J. Michael, 224
Bivalves, 374, 375, 375 *fig.*
Blastocoel, 548, 548 *fig.*

Blastocyst(s), 554
  embryonic stem cells in, 222
  implantation of, 554 *fig.*
Blastopore, 549, 549 *fig.*
Blastula, 366, 548, 548 *fig.*, 549, 549 *fig.*
Bleaching, 770
Blind spot, 595, 595 *fig.*
Blood, 479–81. *See also* Red blood cells
    (erythrocytes); White blood cells
    (leukocytes)
  ABO groups, 167, 265
  buffers, 462–63
  clotting, 480–81, 480 *fig.*, 487
  composition of, 479 *fig.*
  as connective tissue, 417, 417 *fig.*
  diffusion between tissues and, 468 *fig.*
  distribution of, controlled by smooth muscle, 477
  exchanges between interstitial fluid and, 478,
    478 *fig.*
  fetal, 463
  flow path of, through cardiovascular system,
    470 *fig.*
  flow path of, through heart, 470 *fig.*
  gravity and circulation of, 467
  hemoglobin in (*see* Hemoglobin)
  liver function and, 440
  plasma, 479
  platelets, 479
  stem cells and diseases of, 481
  transport of respiratory gases by, 462–63
  velocity and pressure of, 475–77, 475 *fig.*
Blood-brain barrier, 573
Blood fluke (*Schistosoma*), 372
Blood pressure, 475, 475 *fig.*
  measuring, 476–77, 476 *fig.*
Blood tests for genetic disorders, 165
Blood vessels. *See also* Capillaries
  blood pressure and velocity in, 475–77, 475 *fig.*
  cardiovascular system and, 468, 469 *fig.*,
    470 *fig.*, 474
  control of blood flow through, 477
  structure and function of, 474
Blue-footed booby, 254–55
  gene pool and microevolution in, 266–67
Body. *See* Animal body; Plant body
Body cavity, of animals, 368
  cnidarian, 371
  flatworm, 372
  nematodes, 373
Body segmentation, 376–77
Body temperature
  regulation of, 426, 426 *fig.*, 506–8
  thermoreceptors and sensation of, 590
Bolus, 434
Bone(s), 609–11
  bird, 306
  breaks and healing of, 610
  as connective tissue, 417, 417 *fig.*
  structure of arm, 609 *fig.*
Bone marrow, 481, 609
  cell replacement in, 136 *fig.*
Boom-and-bust population growth cycles, 731,
    731 *fig.*
Borrelia burgdorferi, 326, 327
Bottleneck effect, 268, 268 *fig.*
Botulism, 323
Bound ribosomes, 59
Bowman's capsule, 510 *fig.*, 511, 512 *fig.*
Boysen-Jensen, Peter, 662, 663 *fig.*
Brain, 573
  cerebral cortex of, 578
  development of vertebrate, 576, 576 *fig.*
  evolution of, 404–5
  fluid-filled spaces of CNS and, 573 *fig.*
  fMRI scans of, 580, 580 *fig.*
  human, 576–83
  lateralization, 578

regulation of breathing by, 461
  sensory inputs and, 588
Brainstem, 576
Brassinosteroids, 664
Bread mold, black (*Rhizopus stolonifer*), 357, 357 *fig.*
  life cycle, 358
Bread mold, *Neurospora crassa*, 190
Breast cancer, 135 *fig.*
  diet and, 449
Breathing, 454, 460–61
  automatic control of, 461
  in birds, 461
  cellular respiration and, 90, 90 *fig.*
  in humans, 460 *fig.*, 461, 461 *fig.*
  oxygen supplied and carbon dioxide removed
    by, 462–63
Breathing control centers, 461, 461 *fig.*
Bronchi, 458
Bronchioles, 459
Brown algae, 334, 334 *fig.*
Brown tree snake (*Boiga irregularis*), 766, 766 *fig.*
Bryophytes, 344, 344 *fig.*
Bubonic plague, 328 *fig.*
Budding, 136, 534
Buffers, 27
  blood, 462–63
Bulbourethral glands, 538
Bulk feeders, 430, 430 *fig.*
Bushmeat trade, 766, 766 *fig.*
Butane, 34, 34 *fig.*
Butene, 34, 34 *fig.*
Butterflies, 381, 381 *fig.*
  monarch, 709

C

C_3 plants, 118
C_4 plants, 118
Caecilian, 396, 396 *fig.*
Caenorhabditis elegans (nematodes), 247, 373
Caffeine, 571
Calcitonin, 524–25
Calcium
  homeostasis of, 524–25, 525 *fig.*
  in the human body, 18 *table*
  muscle contraction, motor neurons, and, 614
  as plant nutrient, 650
  storage of, in smooth ER, 60
Calvin, Melvin, 111
Calvin cycle of photosynthesis, 111, 111 *fig.*, 116,
    116 *fig.*, 117, 117 *fig.*
Cambrian period, animal evolution and, 367
Camouflage, 259 *fig.*, 365, 381, 381 *fig.*, 744, 744 *fig.*
CAM plants, 118
Cancer
  breast (*see* Breast cancer)
  chromosomal alterations as cause of, 148,
    148 *fig.*, 225 *fig.*
  colon, 225, 225 *fig.*
  death rates from, in United States, 227 *table*
  faulty cell–cell control system leading to, 135
  leukemia(s), 135, 481
  lung, 460, 460 *fig.*
  monoclonal antibodies as treatment for, 496
  multiple genetic changes underlying
    development of, 225
  mutations in genes controlling cell division
    and, 224–25
  oncogene proteins, faulty tumor-suppressor
    proteins and, 226
  radioactive isotopes for detection of, 21
  reducing risk of, by diet and lifestyle changes,
    227, 449, 449 *table*
  viruses as cause of, 224
Cancer cells, 135
Cancer drugs, mechanism of action in, 85
Cancer Genome Project, 225

Canines. *See also* Dogs
Capillaries, 468
  control of blood flow through, 477, 477 *fig.*
  lymphatic, 488, 488 *fig.*
  in muscle tissue, 474, 474 *fig.*
  structure/function of blood vessels and, 474
  substance transfer through walls of, 474 *fig.*,
    478, 478 *fig.*
Capillary beds, 468
Capsid, 200
Capsule, 55 *fig.*
Capsule, prokaryotic cells, 55, 322, 322 *fig.*
Carbohydrates
  biosynthesis of, 103 *fig.*
    See also Photosynthesis
  digestion of, 438–39, 438 *table*
  disaccharides, 37, 38
  as fuel for cellular respiration, 102, 102 *fig.*
  human perception of sweetness and, 38
  monosaccharides as, 37
  polysaccharides, 39
  problems of diets extremely low in, 448, 448 *table*
Carbon
  atom, 20 *fig.*
  in human body, 18, 18 *table*, 19
  isotopes of, 20 *table*
  organic compounds and properties of, 34
Carbon–14, for radiometric dating, 298
Carbon cycle, 755, 755 *fig.*
Carbon dioxide (CO_2)
  breathing and release of, 90, 454
  exchange of oxygen and, at respiratory surfaces,
    454–55
  global warming and atmospheric, 119, 119 *fig.*,
    769, 769 *fig.*
  as plant nutrient, 644
Carbon fixation, 111, 116, 116 *fig.*
Carboniferous period, 348, 396
Carbon monoxide (CO) as disruptor of cellular
    respiration, 99, 99 *fig.*
Carbon skeleton, 34
  variations, 34 *fig.*
Carbonyl group, 35, 35 *fig.*
Carboxyl group, 35, 35 *fig.*
Carboxylic acids, 35
Carcinogens, 227
Carcinomas, 135
Cardiac cycle, 471, 471 *fig.*
Cardiac muscle, 418, 418 *fig.*
Cardiac output, 471
Cardiovascular disease, 473
  blood pressure and diagnosis of, 476–77
  diet and, 449
Cardiovascular system, 468
  gas exchange and role of, 462–63
  mammalian, 469 *fig.*, 470–78
  of vertebrates, 469, 469 *fig.*
Carnivores, 430
  relationship of classification and phylogeny
    for select, 309 *fig.*
Carnivorous plants, 657, 657 *fig.*
Carotenoids, 112, 113
Carpels, 350, 634
Carriers, genetic, 162
Carroll, Sean, 385
Carrying capacity (K), 729, 729 *table*
Carson, Rachel, 683, 683 *fig.*
Cartilage, 417, 417 *fig.*
Cartilaginous fishes, 392
Casparian strip, 645, 645 *fig.*
Cat(s)
  classification of domestic, 309 *fig.*
  X chromosome and tortoiseshell pattern,
    213, 213 *fig.*
Cation exchange, root hair uptake of nutrients
    by, 652, 652 *fig.*
CC (cloned cat), 222, 223 *fig.*

Cecum, 440
Celera Genomics, 248, 249
Cell(s), 2, 2 *fig.*, 50–87. *See also* Chemistry of life
    chemical signals and
        See also Hormone(s), animal; Hormone(s),
            plant
    cytoskeleton and related structures, 65–66
    differentiation of (*see* Cellular differentiation)
    embryonic development and changes in shape
        of, 552
    energy and, 80–83
        See also Energy
    energy transformations in, 73
    enzyme functions and, 84–85
    eukaryotic, 56–57, 69
        See also Eukaryotic cells
    life structure, functions and, 4
    membrane structure and function in, 74–79
    microscopy and study of, 52–54
    molecules of, 33
    organelles, 59–62, 63, 66, 69
    prokaryotic, 55
        See also Prokaryotic cells
    respiration (*see* Cellular respiration)
    size of, 54
    surfaces and junctions, 68
Cell body, neuron, 565, 565 *fig.*
Cell–cell recognition, 74
Cell cycle, 129
    cytokinesis in, 131 *fig.*, 132
    growth factor as signal for, 133,
        134, 134 *fig.*
    phases of, 129 *fig.*
Cell cycle control system
    cancer and faulty, 135, 224
    growth factors and function of, 134
    mechanical model for, 134 *fig.*
Cell division, 125, 127
    anchorage dependence of, 133
    cancer caused by faulty, 135, 224
    cell cycle and, 129
    controlling factors in, 133
    cytokinesis and, 131 *fig.*, 132
    cytokinins and plant, 666
    in eukaryotes, 128–36
    evolution and errors in, 147
    growth factors and, 134
    mitosis in, 130–31
    in prokaryotes, 127
    stages of, 130–31 *fig.*
Cell junctions, 68, 68 *fig.*
Cell-mediated immunity, 490, 497
    T cells and, 497, 497 *fig.*
Cell migration, embryonic development and,
    549, 549 *fig.*, 552
Cell movement
    cytoskeleton fibers and, 65 *fig.*
    flagella and cilia and, 66, 67, 69
Cell plate, 132, 132 *fig.*
Cell theory, 52
Cell-to-cell signaling, animal embryonic
    development and role of, 220
Cellular differentiation
    cloning and, 221
    definition of, 221
    genetic potential of differentiated cells, 221
    specialized cells produced by, 221
Cellular metabolism, 56
    chemical energy in body, nutrition, and, 442
    disposal of nitrogenous wastes from, 509
    endergonic and exergonic reactions of, 82
Cellular respiration, 81 *fig.*, 88–105. *See also* Gas
    exchange in animals
    ATP production in, 91
    basic mechanisms of energy release and storage
        and, 92–94, 95 *fig.*
    breathing and, 90, 90 *fig.*

carbon cycle and, 755, 755 *fig.*
    definition of, 89
    equation for, 91 *fig.*
    as exergonic reaction, 82
    glycolysis stage of, 94, 94 *fig.*, 100
    interconnection between molecular breakdown
        and synthesis in, 102–3
    introduction to, 90–92
    overview of, 93, 93 *fig.*
    oxidative phosphorylation for ATP production
        in, 98
    photosynthesis as origin of fuels for,
        90, 90 *fig.*
    poisons and disruption of, 99
    as redox reaction, 92, 110 *fig.*
Cellular slime molds, 335
Cellulose, 39, 39 *fig.*
Cell walls, 55 *fig.*
    plant, 57 *fig.*, 68, 68 *fig.*, 628, 628 *fig.*
    prokaryotic, 55
Cenozoic era, 298
Centipedes, 379, 379 *fig.*
Central canal, of spinal cord, 573
Centralization of nervous system, 572, 573
Central nervous system (CNS), 564, 572, 573,
    573 *fig.*
    brain and, 576–83
    fluid-filled spaces in, 573 *fig.*
    sensory input into, and response of, 588, 600
Central vacuole, 57 *fig.*, 62, 62 *fig.*
Centrioles, 56 *fig.*, 65
Centromere, 128, 128 *fig.*
Centrosomes, 131
Cephalization, 572, 573
Cephalopods, 375, 375 *fig.*
Cerebellum, 577
Cerebral cortex, 578, 578 *fig.*
Cerebral hemispheres, 577
Cerebrospinal fluid, 573
Cerebrum, 576, 577 *fig.*
    cerebral cortex, 578, 578 *fig.*
    hemispheres of, 577
Cervix, 537
Chaparral, 694, 694 *fig.*
Chara (green alga), 342, 342 *fig.*, 343 *fig.*
Character, 154
Chargaff, Erwin, 186
Chargaff's rules on base pairing, 186
Charophyceans, 336
Charophytes, 342
Chase, Martha, 182–83, 184
Cheddar Man, 245, 245 *fig.*
Cheese production, 361, 361 *fig.*
Cheetah (*Acinonyx jubatus*)
    low genetic variability of, 269, 269 *fig.*
    territorial behavior of, 717 *fig.*
Chelicerates, 378–79
Chemical bonds, 22, 23 *fig.*
    covalent, 23
    double, 23
    ionic, 22–23
    polar covalent, 24
Chemical cycling in ecosystems, 752, 754–55
    alteration of, 758, 758 *fig.*
Chemical defenses
    in animals, 744, 744 *fig.*
    in plants, 674–76, 744
Chemical elements, 18
    compounds, 19
    emergent properties of, 19 *fig.*
    in human body, 18 *table*
    as plant nutrients, 650
Chemical energy, 80
    ATP as shuttle in cells for, 83
    nutrition, diet, and, 442
Chemically-gated ion channels, 569
Chemical mutagens, 199

Chemical reactions, 29
    energy stored or released by, 82
    matter and atoms rearranged by, 29
    redox, in cellular respiration, 110
    redox, in photosynthesis, 110–11
Chemical regulation in animals, 516–31
    nature of, 518–19
    vertebrate endocrine system and, 520–23
Chemical signals. *See also* Hormone(s)
    coordination of body functions by, 518
Chemical synapses, 569
    action of stimulants and depressants on, 571
    complex information processing possible
        because of, 570
    neurotransmitter activity at, 569 *fig.*
Chemiosmosis, 93, 98 *fig.*
    ATP generation during photosynthesis from, 115
    oxidative phosphorylation and, 98
Chemistry of life, 16–31. *See also* Chemical
    reactions
    atoms and molecules, 18–24
    carbohydrates, 37–39
    lipids, 40–41
    nucleic acids, 46–47
    organic compounds, 34–36
    Pauling's contributions to study of, 46
    proteins, 42–46
    water, 25–29
Chemoautotrophs, 324
Chemoheterotrophs, 324
Chemoreceptors, 590–91, 599
Chemotherapy, 135
Chernobyl (Ukraine) nuclear disaster, 21, 643
Chiasma (chiasmata), 142, 142 *fig.*
Chief cells, 436, 436 *fig.*
Childbirth, 558–59, 558 *fig.*
Chimpanzees, 247, 402 *fig.*
    dominance hierarchies and reconciliation
        behavior in, 719, 719 *fig.*
    genome of, 250
    human relationship to, 402
    problem solving by, 711, 711 *fig.*
    vocalizations of, 407
Chitin, 39
Chlamydias, 326, 544, 544 *table*
Chlamydia trachomatis, 326
Chlamydomonas (unicellular green alga),
    336, 336 *fig.*
Chlorofluorocarbons (CFCs), 120, 767
Chlorophyll, 109
    chlorophyll a, 112, 113
    chlorophyll b, 112, 113
    photosynthesis and, 113 *fig.*
Chloroplasts, 57 *fig.*, 64, 64 *fig.*
    origins and evolution of, 64, 64 *fig.*
    photosynthesis in, 109, 112–17
    structure and location of, 109 *fig.*
Choanocytes, 370
Choking, Heimlich maneuver and, 435, 435 *fig.*
Cholesterol, 41, 79–80
    cardiovascular disease and, 473
    structure of, 41 *fig.*
Chondrichthyes (cartilaginous fishes), 392
Chordates (Chordata)
    four features of, 383
    invertebrate, 383
    phylogenetic tree, 390 *fig.*
    vertebrate, 390–99
Chorion, 554, 555, 555 *fig.*
Chorionic villi, 555
Chorionic villus sampling (CVS), 164 *fig.*, 165
Choroid, 596 *fig.*
Chory, Joanne, 674, 674 *fig.*
Chromatids, 128
Chromatin, 58, 128
Chromosomal DNA, transfer of, by plasmids,
    205 *fig.*

Chromosomal theory of inheritance, 170–74, 171 *fig.*
crossing over and new allele combinations, 172–73
gene mapping and, 174, 174 *fig.*
linked genes and, 172
Mendelian laws explained by, 170
sex chromosomes and, 174–76
Chromosome(s), 55, 56 *fig.*, 57 *fig.*, 58, 126, 187. *See also* Sex chromosome(s); X chromosome; Y chromosome
alteration in number and structure of, 144–48
bacteria (prokaryotic), 127
daughter, 131 *fig.*
deletions, duplications, inversions, and translocations in, 148, 148 *fig.*
duplication and distribution of, 128 *fig.*
eukaryotic, 128
in gametes, 137
gene regulation aided by DNA packing in eukaryotic, 212, 213 *fig.*
homologous, 136–37, 137 *fig.*
See also Homologous chromosomes
in human genome, 248
independent orientation of, in meiosis, 141
karyotype of, 144, 144 *fig.*, 145 *fig.*
mapping, 248
meiosis and reduction of, to haploid number, 138–39
mitosis and duplication of, in eukaryotes, 128–31
mutations in, and creation of genetic variation, 265
sex determination by number of, 175, 175 *fig.*
in somatic cells, 136–37
Chronic myelogenous leukemia (CML), 148, 148 *fig.*
Chronic obstructive pulmonary diseases (COPD), 459
Chyme, 437
Chytrids, 356–57, 356 *fig.*
Cichlid fish, 277
Cilia (cilium), 66, 66 *fig.*
Ciliary body, 595 *fig.*, 596
Ciliary dyskinesia (PCD), 67
Ciliates, 333, 333 *fig.*
Ciprofloxacin (Cipro), 328
Circadian rhythms, 577, 671
Circulatory system, 420, 420 *fig.*, 466–83
adaptations in, for thermoregulation, 507
of arthropods, 378
blood in, 479–81
See also Blood
body tissues and, 468
closed, 376
gas exchange and transport of gases by, 454, 462–63
gravity and, 467
in high altitudes, 453
mammalian cardiovascular system and, 470–78
mechanisms of internal transport and, 468–70
of mollusc, 374
open, 376
Circumcision, 539
Citric acid cycle
cellular respiration and process of, 93, 96–97, 100
details of, 97 *fig.*
overview of, 96 *fig.*
pyruvate groomed for, 96, 96 *fig.*
Clades, 310
Cladistics, 310, 314
Classes (taxonomy), 309
Class I and Class II proteins, 500
Classification
phylogeny and, 309 *fig.*
Clay surfaces, polymer formation on, 296
Cleavage, 548
Cleavage furrows, 132, 132 *fig.*

Climate
distribution of terrestrial communities linked to, 686–87
global warming of, 119, 768–69
terrestrial biomes and variations in, 691
Clinton (Bill) impeachment, 245
Clitoris, 537
Clonal selection, 492–93, 492 *fig.*
Clones and cloning
animal, 209, 222–23
gene, 232–36, 233 *fig.*
nuclear transplantation and, 222, 222 *fig.*
plant, 221–22, 638–39, 639 *fig.*
reproductive, 222–23
therapeutic, 222, 223
Closed circulatory system, 376, 468, 468 *fig.*
See also Cardiovascular system
Clostridium botulinum, 323, 328
Club fungi, 356 *fig.*, 357, 357 *fig.*
Club mosses, 344, 345 *fig.*
Clumped population-dispersion pattern, 726, 726 *fig.*
Cnidarians (Cnidaria), 371
digestion and gastrovascular cavity of, 371, 432
habituation in, 705
hydrostatic skeleton of, 606, 606 *fig.*
internal transport in, 468
nerve net in, 572, 572 *fig.*
Cnidocytes, 371, 371 *fig.*
Coal, formation of, 348
Cocaine, 571
Cocci, 321, 321 *fig.*
Coccidioidomycosis, 359
Cochlea, 592, 593, 593 *fig.*
Codominance, genetic, 167
Codons, 191
anticodons, 195
conversion of, by transfer RNA, 194–95
start, and initiation of translation, 196–97
stop, and termination of translation, 197
translation and transcription of, 191 *fig.*
Coelacanth, 393
Coelom, 551, 551 *fig.*
true, 368, 368 *fig.*
Coenzymes, 85
Coevolution, 744, 751
Cofactors, 85
Cognition, 711
Cognitive maps, 709
Cohesion of water, 25
plant transpiration and, 646–47, 646 *fig.*
Coleochaete (green alga), 342, 342 *fig.*
Collagen, quaternary structure of, 44, 44 *fig.*
Collecting duct, of kidney nephron, 510 *fig.*, 511, 512–13, 512 *fig.*
Collenchyma cells, 628, 628 *fig.*
Colon, 440–41
Colon cancer, 225, 225 *fig.*, 449
Colonial algae, 336, 336 *fig.*
Color blindness, 177
Columnar epithelium, simple, 416, 416 *fig.*
Combined DNA Index System (CODIS) database, 244
Communication, among animals, 713, 713 *fig.*
Community(ies), 2, 740–51. *See also* Biodiversity; Ecology; Ecosystem(s)
competition in, 742, 743
definition of, 2, 742
disturbance as feature of, 750
food chains in, 747
food webs in, 747
global climate change and, 770–71
interaction of, with environment, 682, 682 *fig.*
See also Ecology
invasive species in, 751
mutualism in, 742, 743
predation in, 744

regional climate and distribution of, 686–87
species diversity of, 748
structure and dynamics, 742–51
trophic structure and dynamics of, 746
Companion cells, 629, 629 *fig.*
Comparative anatomy, evidence for evolution in, 262
Competition in communities, 742, 743
agonistic animal behaviors and, 718, 719
Competitive inhibitors of enzymes, 85
Complementary DNA (cDNA), 235
Complement system
activation of, by humoral immune system, 495, 495 *fig.*
innate immunity and, 486
Complete digestive tract, in nematodes, 373
Complete dominance, 166
Complete metamorphosis, 380, 380 *fig.*
Compost, 651, 651 *fig.*
Compound(s)
formation of, 19
hydrophilic, 35
hydrophobic, 40
organic, 34–36
Compound events, rule of probability and, 160
Compound eyes, 595, 595 *fig.*
Computed tomography (CT), 422, 422 *fig.*
Concentration gradient, 75
Conception, 554
Conduction, heat gains or losses by, 506, 506 *fig.*
Cones, pine, 348, 349 *fig.*
Cones, retina, 598, 598 *fig.*
Coniferous forests, 696, 696 *fig.*
Conifers, 348, 621
pine life cycle, 348–49, 349 *fig.*
redwoods, 621
Conjugation, bacterial, 204, 205
Conjunctiva, 596
Conjunctivitis (pink eye), 596
Connective tissue, 417, 417 *fig.*
Conservation biology, 762–81
biodiversity crisis and, 764–71
ecosystem management and restoration, 772–79
Myanmar tigers and, 763
protecting endangered populations as a goal of, 772
Consumers, in communities, 3, 3 *fig.*, 746
Continental drift, 300–302, 300 *fig.*, 301 *fig.*
Continental shelves, 688
Contour farming, 653, 653 *fig.*
Contraception, 545, 545 *table*
Contractile proteins, 42
Control centers
breathing, 461, 461 *fig.*
homeostasis and, 426
Controlled experiments, 11
Control sequences, DNA, 210
Convection, heat gains or losses and, 506, 506 *fig.*
Convergent evolution, 308
Cookiecutter shark (*Isistius brasiliensis*), 73, 73 *fig.*
Copulation, 535
Coral reefs, 688, 689, 689 *fig.*, 749, 749 *fig.*, 765, 765 *fig.*
mutualism between dinoflagellates and corals, 743, 743 *fig.*
Corals, 371
Cork, 632, 633, 633 *fig.*
Cork cambium, 632, 633 *fig.*
Corn
seed germination of, 638, 638 *fig.*
seed structure of, 636, 636 *fig.*
Cornea, 596 *fig.*
Corn smut, 359, 359 *fig.*
Corn syrup, high-fructose, 38
Coronary arteries, 473, 473 *fig.*
Coronavirus, 202
Corpus callosum, 577

INDEX

Corpus luteum, 536
Cortex, plant tissue, 626
Corticosteroids, 529
Costa Rica
    zoned reserves in, 775, 775 *fig.*
Cotton cloth, 284
Cotyledons, 623
Countercurrent exchange, 456–57
Countercurrent heat exchanger, 507, 507 *fig.*
Counter-illumination, 73
Courtship rituals, 280, 280 *fig.*, 704, 704 *fig.*,
    714–15, 714 *fig.*
Covalent bonds, 23
    polar, 24
Cowbirds as edge-adapted species, 773, 773 *fig.*
Coyotes, trial-and-error learning by, 710, 710 *fig.*
Cranial nerves, 573
Craniates, 390
Crawling as locomotion, 604–5
Cretaceous mass extinction, 302, 303,
    303 *fig.*, 397
Crick, Francis, 46, 186–87, 186 *fig.*
Cri du chat syndrome, 148
Crime scene investigations, DNA technology
    and, 231
Cristae, 63
Crocodiles, 311
Cro-Magnon humans, 405
Crop (animal), 432
Crop plants
    improving protein content of, 655
Crop rotation, 656
Cross (genetic), 155–59
    dihybrid, 158–59
    monohybrid, 156
Cross fertilization in plants, 154–55, 155 *fig.*
Crossing over, 142–43, 143 *fig.*
    mapping genes using data from, 174, 174 *fig.*
    new allele combinations produced by, 172–73
Crustaceans, 379, 379 *fig.*
CT (computed tomography), 422, 422 *fig.*
CT-PET scanner, 422, 422 *fig.*
Cuboidal epithelium, simple, 416, 416 *fig.*
Cultural eutrophication, 759
Cuticle, 342, 373, 378, 626
Cyanea kuhihewa, 125, 125 *fig.*
Cyanide, 99, 99 *fig.*
Cyanobacteria, 108, 319, 326
    chemical cycling and, 329
    chloroplasts and, 331
    as photoautotrophs, 108 *fig.*
Cycads, 345
Cyclohexane, 34 *fig.*
Cystic fibrosis, 162, 222
Cytokinesis, 129, 131 *fig.*
    in animal versus plant cells, 132
    telophase I and, 139 *fig.*
Cytokinins, 664 *table*, 666
Cytoplasm, 55
Cytosine (C), 185, 185 *fig.*
Cytoskeleton, 56 *fig.*, 57 *fig.*, 65–66
Cytotoxic T cells, 497, 497 *fig.*
    destruction of infected cell by, 498, 498 *fig.*

D

Daphnia, 432
Darwin, Charles R., 8, 8 *fig.*, 385
    evolutionary theory of, 256–63
    modern systematics and, 310
    sea voyage and studies of, 256–57, 257 *fig.*
    studies of phototropism and hormones by,
        662, 663 *fig.*
Darwin, Francis, 662, 663 *fig.*
Daughter cells
    in meiosis, 139
    in mitosis, 132, 132 *fig.*

Daughter DNA, 188, 188 *fig. See also*
    DNA polymerases
DDT (pesticide), 683, 697, 767
Deafness, 162, 593
Death rates, human population growth
    and lower, 734
Decomposers, 3–4, 361, 746
Decomposition, 746
Deductive reasoning, 9
Deep-sea firefly squid (*Watasenia scintillans*),
    73, 73 *fig.*
Defenses, animal, 744, 744 *fig.*
Defenses, plant, 674–76, 744–45
Defensive proteins, 42. *See also* Antibody(ies)
Deforestation, 354, 692, 758, 765, 766, 769
Dehydration reactions, 36, 36 *fig.*, 38 *fig.*, 39
Dehydrogenase, 92
Deinonychus (dinosaur), 397, 397 *fig.*
Deletion, chromosomal, 148, 148 *fig.*
Delta proteobacteria, 326
Demographic transition, 734–35, 734 *table*
Denaturation, 43
Dendrites, 418, 565, 565 *fig.*
Density-dependent factors limiting population
    growth, 730
Density-dependent inhibition of cell division,
    133, 133 *fig.*
Dental plaque, 324 *fig.*
Deoxyribonucleic acid, 46. *See also* DNA
Deposit feeders, 688
Depression, 582
Derived characters, shared, 310–11
Dermal tissue system, plants, 626
Dermis, 423, 423 *fig.*
Descent with modification, principle of, 257, 293
Desertification, 693
Deserts, 693, 693 *fig.*
Determinate growth, 630
Detritivores, 746
Detritus, 746, 757 *fig.*
Deuterostomes, 368, 369, 384
"Devil's garden", 17, 17 *fig.*
Devonian period, 393
Diabetes mellitus, 527
    insulin-dependent, 500
Dialysis, kidney, 480, 513, 513 *fig.*
Diaphragm, respiratory, 458
Diastole, 471, 476
Diatoms, 334, 334 *fig.*
Dicots, 623. *See also* Eudicots
Dictyostelium (cellular slime mold), 335
Diet, animal, 430–32
    adaptations of digestive system reflect, 441
    as chemical energy, 442
    needs satisfied by healthy, 442
Diet, human
    cancer and, 449, 449 *table*
    cardiovascular disease and, 473
    meat in, 754
    nutrition and, 442–49
    obesity and, 447
    soy in, 661
    vitamin and mineral supplements in, 446
Differential interference-contrast microscopy,
    53, 53 *fig.*
Differentiation. *See* Cellular differentiation
Diffusion, 75 *fig.*
    between blood and tissue cells, 474 *fig.*
    facilitated, 77
    passive, 75
Digestion, 431, 431 *fig. See also* Digestive system
Digestive system, 421, 421 *fig.*
    diet and adaptations of vertebrate, 441
    exchanges with environment and role of,
        424–25, 424 *fig.*
    human, 433–41, 433 *fig.*
    in nematodes, 373

nutrition and (*see* Nutrition)
    pharynx and, 458
    specialized compartments of animal, 432, 432 *fig.*
Dihybrid cross, 158–59
Dinitrophenol (DNP) as disruptor of cellular
    respiration, 99, 99 *fig.*
Dinoflagellates, 333, 333 *fig.*
    corals and, 743, 743 *fig.*
Dinosaurs, 306, 397
    tracks, 260 *fig.*
Dipeptides, 43
Diploid cells, 137
    plant, 346, 349 *fig.*, 634–35
    See also Sporophytes
Diploid organisms, balancing selection and, 272–73
Diplomonads, 332–33
Directional selection, 270, 270 *fig.*
Disaccharides, 38, 38 *fig.*
Discovery science, 9
Disease. *See also names of specific diseases;*
        Human disease
    amoebic dysentery, 334
    bacterial, 205, 272, 320, 322, 326, 327, 437, 437
        fig., 487
    bioterrorism, 328
    fungal, 359
    immune system malfunctions and, 500–501
    viral, 202–3
Dispersion patterns, population, 726–27
Disruptive selection, 270, 270 *fig.*
Distal tubule, of kidney nephron, 510 *fig.*, 511,
    512, 512 *fig.*
Disturbances, in biological communities, 750
DNA (deoxyribonucleic acid), 46
    bacterial plasmids and transfer of, 234–36
    bacterial transfer of, in nature, 204
    complementary, 235
    double helix structure of, 186, 187 *fig.*
    experiments demonstrating, as genetic
        material, 182–83, 183 *fig.*
    gel electrophoresis of, 243, 246
    gene regulation aided by packing of, in
        eukaryotes, 212, 213 *fig.*
    genotype of, expressed as proteins, 190
    human evolution and mitochondrial, 406
    microarrays, 219, 219 *fig.*
    molecular structure of, 5
    Neanderthal, 405
    nitrogenous bases of, 185 *fig.*
    as nucleotide polymer, 184–85
    polynucleotide, 184 *fig.*
    repetitive, 244, 248
    replication of, and multiple "bubbles" and
        daughter strands, 189, 189 *fig.*
    replication of, dependent on base pairing,
        188–89, 188 *fig.*
    replication of, in cell cycle, 129
    restriction enzymes used to create
        recombinant, 234, 234 *fig.*
    transcription of, into RNA, 190, 193, 198
    viruses, 201
DNA chip, 219, 219 *fig.*
DNA fingerprints, 242 *fig.*
DNA ligase, 189, 232
DNA polymerases, 189
DNA probes, 236
DNA profiling, 242–46
    with STR analysis, 244, 244 *fig.*
DNA sequence(s)
    amplifying, by PCR method, 242, 243 *fig.*
    analysis of, in systematics, 312–13
    analysis of, using restriction fragments, 246
    enhancer, 214, 214 *fig.*
    mutations in, 199
    operator, 210, 211 *fig.*
    promoter, 193, 210, 211 *fig.*
    silencer, 214

DNA sequencing
  in Human Genome Project, 248
  by restriction fragment analysis, 246
DNA strands
  opposite orientation of, 189 *fig.*
  sticky ends on, 234
DNA structure, 47 *fig.*, 186, 187 *fig.*
DNA technology, 230–52
  in agriculture, 239–40
  bacteria as tool for manipulating
    DNA, 232–36
  DNA microarrays test, 219, 219 *fig.*
  gel electrophoresis, 243
  gene cloning, 232–36
  gene therapy and, 241
  genomics and, 230–52
  human genome and, 241, 247, 248, 249, 250
  legal and forensic applications of, 242
  mass production of gene products
    using, 236–37
  medical uses of, 238, 241
  nucleic acid probes, 236, 236 *fig.*
  PCR technique and DNA sequence
    amplification, 242, 243 *fig.*
  pharmaceuticals and, 238
  restriction fragment analysis, 246
  reverse transcriptase and gene cloning, 235
  risks of, 240
Dodd, Diana, 285
Dogs. *See also* Canines
  artificial and natural selection in, 153
  independent assortment of two genes in,
    159 *fig.*
  testcross to determine genotype of, 159 *fig.*
Doldrums, 686
Dolly (cloned sheep), 209, 222
Domains (classification), 6, 309
Dominance hierarchies, 718, 719
Dominant alleles, 156, 161
Dominant traits
  codominance, 167
  genetic disorders as, 162–63, 163 *table*
  incomplete dominance, 166–67
Donkey, hybrid sterility in cross between horse
    and, 281 *fig.*
Dormancy, in bears, 505
Dorsal, hollow nerve cord, 383, 383 *fig.*
Dorsal surface of animals, 368, 368 *fig.*
Double bonds, 23
Double circulation, 469
Double fertilization, 635, 635 *fig.*
Double helix, 47, 186
Down, John Langdon, 145
Down syndrome, 145, 146
Drosophila melanogaster (fruit fly), 247
  crossing over and recombinant gametes
    of, 173 *fig.*
  evolution of reproductive barriers among,
    285, 285 *fig.*
  genetic control of development in, 218
  head-tail polarity, 218 *fig.*
  homeotic genes in, 553, 553 *fig.*
  mapping genes of, 174 *fig.*
  sex-linked traits in, 176 *fig.*
Drought, 770
Drugs. *See also* Pharmaceuticals
  AIDS-retarding, 499
  effects of, on nervous system, 571
  hypothalamus and addiction to, 577
  placenta-crossing, 555
  tolerance to, 60
Duchenne muscular dystrophy, 177
Duodenum, 438
Duplication, chromosomal, 148, 148 *fig.*
Dwarfism, pituitary, 522
Dynein arms, 66
Dysentery, amoebic, 334

E

E. coli. See Escherichia coli
Ear(s)
  balance and inner, 594
  hearing and, 592–93
  route of sound through, 593 *fig.*
  structure of, 592 *fig.*, 593 *fig.*
Eardrum, 592
Earth
  atmosphere of (*see* Atmosphere)
  biodiversity hotspots on, 774, 774 *fig.*
  biosphere of (*see* Biosphere)
  climate and distribution of terrestrial
    communities on, 686–87
  continental drift and plate tectonics of,
    300–302, 300 *fig.*, 301 *fig.*
  crustal plates of, 301–2, 302 *fig.*
  fossil record and macroevolution on,
    298, 299 *table*
  major episodes in early history of,
    297, 297 *fig.*
  origin of life on, 294–96
Earthworms, 368, 368 *fig.*, 376–77, 376 *fig.*
  alimentary canal of, 432 *fig.*
  body segmentation in, 376 *fig.*
  hydrostatic skeleton of, 606
  peristalsis locomotion in, 605, 605 *fig.*
  reproduction in, 535 *fig.*
Eastern coral snake, 11 *fig.*
Ebola virus, 202
Ecdysis, 384
Ecdysozoans, 384
Echidnas (spiny anteaters), 399
Echinoderms (Echinodermata), 382, 572.
    See also Sea star
Echolocation, 587
Ecological footprint, human, 736–37, 737 *fig.*
  carrying capacity and, 737 *fig.*
Ecological niche, 743
Ecological Society of America, 779
Ecological species concept, 279
Ecological succession, 750
Ecology, 681. *See also* Community(ies);
    Conservation biology; Population
    dynamics
  behavioral, 712
  biosphere and study of, 682
  fungus and, 361
  restoration, 772, 778
Ecosystem(s), 2, 2 *fig.*, 682, 682 *fig.*
  alteration of, 758
  aquatic, 681, 688–90, 759
    See also Aquatic ecosystems
  bioremediation of, 778
  carbon cycle in, 755
  carrying capacity of, 729
  chemical cycling in, 754–58
  definition of, 752
  diversity in, 765
  ecology and study of, 681, 682
    See also Ecology
  economic value for services of, 764
  energy flow and chemical cycling in, 752
  energy supply and food chains in, 753
  fragmentation of, 772, 772 *fig.*
  global climate change and, 770–71
  human meat-eating and production pyramid
    in, 754
  interactions in, 3, 3 *fig.*
  landscape ecology and, 773
  managing and restoring, 772–79
  net primary production of various, 753 *fig.*
  nitrogen cycle in, 756–57
  phosphorus cycle in, 756
  primary production as energy
    budget for, 752
  protection of biodiversity hotspots,
    774, 774 *fig.*
  structure and dynamics of, 752–59
  terrestrial biomes, 691–97
  Yellowstone to Yukon Conservation Initiative
    (Y2Y), 776–77, 776 *fig.*
  zoned reserves, 775, 775 *fig.*
Ectoderm, 366, 368, 368 *fig.*, 548–49
  neural tube formation from, 550, 550 *fig.*
  organ and tissue derivatives of, 549 *table*
Ectopic pregnancy, 537
Ectothermic animals, 397
  thermoregulation in, 506–7
Edges of landscapes, 773, 773 *fig.*
Effector cells, 493, 564
Effector mechanisms, humoral immunity,
    495, 495 *fig.*
Effectors, nervous system, 564
Egg(s) (ova/ovum), 534, 540–41. *See also* Gametes
  amniotic, 397, 398
  fertilization of animal, 535
  human, surrounded by sperm, 546 *fig.*
  plant, 635 *fig.*
Ejaculation, 538–39
  two stages of male, 539 *fig.*
Ejaculatory duct, 538
Eldredge, Niles, 289
Electrical synapses, 569
Electrocardiogram, heart rhythm and, 472, 472 *fig.*
Electroencephalogram (EEG), 580
Electromagnetic energy, 112
Electromagnetic receptors, 591
Electromagnetic spectrum, 112
Electron(s), 20
  cellular respiration and energy release from, 92
  chemical properties of atoms determined by
    arrangement of, 22, 22 *fig.*
Electronegativity of atoms, 24
Electron microscopes (EMs), 52
Electron shells, 22, 22 *fig.*
Electron transport chain
  in cellular respiration, 92, 93, 98, 98 *fig.*, 100
  disruption of, by poison, 99
  in photosynthesis, 114, 114 *fig.*
Electroreception, 587
Elements, chemical. *See* Chemical elements
Elimination, 431, 431 *fig.*
Elodea, 51
Embryo(s), 537
  development of (*see* Embryonic development
    in animals)
  human, 554–55
  plant (*see* Sporophytes)
Embryonic development in animals, 546–53
  brain, 576, 576 *fig.*
  cell shape, cell migration, and programmed cell
    death in, 552, 552 *fig.*
  cleavage, 548
  fertilization, zygote formation, and initiation
    of, 546–47
  gastrulation, 548–49, 549 *fig.*, 554
  genetic control of, 218
  human, 554–59
  induction and, 552
  organ formation, 550–51, 550–52 *fig.*
  pattern formation in, 552–53
Embryonic development in plants, 636,
    636 *fig.*, 637
Embryonic stem cells (ES cells), 222, 563
Embryophytes, 343
Embryo sac, plant, 635, 635 *fig.*
Emergent properties, 3, 4
Emerging viruses, 202
Emotions, limbic system and, 581
Emphysema, 459, 460
Emu, 398, 398 *fig.*
Encephalitis, 202

Endangered species
  biodiversity crisis and, 763
  cheetahs, 269
  reduced genetic variation in, 268
  U.S. Endangered Species Act's definition of, 765
  whales as, 429
Endemic species, 774
Endergonic reactions, 82, 82 *fig.*
Endless Forms Most Beautiful: The New Science of Evo Devo (Carroll), 385
Endocrine disruptors, abnormal behavior caused by, 716
Endocrine glands, 518
  adrenal, 528–29
  disorders of, 527
  glucocorticoids and, 529
  gonads, 529
  human, 520 *fig.*
  hypothalamus and pituitary, 522–23
  major, and hormones of, 521 *table*
  pancreas, 526–27
  pineal, 520
  thymus, 520
  thyroid and parathyroid, 524–25
Endocrine system, 420, 420 *fig.*, 518
  disruptions of, 517
  hormones of, 518 *fig.*, 521 *table*
  nervous system and, 518
  vertebrate, 520–23
Endocytosis, 79, 79 *fig.*
Endoderm, 366, 368, 368 *fig.*, 548–49
  organ and tissue derivatives of, 549 *table*
Endodermis, 626
Endomembrane system, 59
  organelles of, 59–63
Endometrium, 537
Endoplasmic reticulum (ER), 56 *fig.*, 59, 60–61
Endorphins, 522–23
Endoskeletons, 607
  bones of, 609–11
  echinoderm, 382
  human, 608–9
Endosperm, 635, 636
Endospore, 323, 323 *fig.*
Endosymbiosis, 64, 64 *fig.*, 330
  primary, 331
  secondary, 331, 331 *fig.*
Endothermic animals, 397, 398, 399
  thermoregulation in, 506–7
Endotoxins, 327
Energy. *See also* Solar energy
  ATP as shuttle in cells for chemical, 83
  cells and, 80–83
  cellular harvesting of (*see* Cellular respiration)
  chemical reactions and release or storage of, 82
  definition of, 80
  electromagnetic, 112
  enzymes and, 84–85
  forms of, 80, 80 *fig.*
  human activities and consumption of, 91 *table*
  laws on conversion of, 81
  organelles and conversion of, 63–64
Energy conservation, laws on, 81
Energy coupling, 82
Energy flow in ecosystems, 752
Energy of activation (E$_A$), 84
Energy processing, 5
Energy supply in ecosystems, 753
Energy utilization as property of all organisms, 5
Enhancer DNA sequence, 214
Enteric division, autonomic nervous system, 575
Entomology, 380
Entropy, 81
Environment. *See also* Biosphere; Ecology
  abiotic factors in, 682
  adaptations to changes in (*see* Behavior)
  animal behavior resulting from genes and, 704–5

animal exchanges with external, 424–26
animal regulation of internal, 425
    See also Homeostasis; Regulatory systems, animal
  biotic factors in, 682
  genetic influences of, 170
  human behavior and, 721
  response to, as property of all organisms, 5, 682
  risks of genetically modified organisms to, 240
Environmental problems. *See also* Biodiversity crisis
  acid precipitation, 28, 759
  deforestation, 692, 765, 765 *fig.*, 766, 769
  desertification, 693
  ecosystem alteration, 758
  greenhouse effect and global warming, 119
  human overpopulation and, 736–37
  introduced (exotic) species as, 408, 725, 766
  nitrogen cycle balance, 757
  oil spills, 329, 329 *fig.*
  ozone layer depletion, 120, 120 *fig.*, 767
  science of ecology and insight into, 683
  technology and, 12
Enzyme(s), 84–85
  as catalyst, 84, 84 *fig.*
  chemical reactions controlled by, 73
  cofactors of, 85
  definition of, 36, 42, 84
  digestion in small intestine and, 438–39, 438 *table*
  digestion in stomach and, 436, 436 *fig.*
  energy and, 84–85
  function of, 84, 84 *fig.*
  inhibitors of, 85, 85 *fig.*
  membrane proteins as, 74
  milk-digesting, 33 *fig.*
  pesticides and antibiotics effects on, 85
  restriction, 234
  temperature, salt, and pH effects on, 85
Eosinophils, 479, 479 *fig.*
Epidemiology, 449
Epidermis, 423, 423 *fig.*
  animal (*see* Skin)
  plant, 626
Epididymis, 538
Epinephrine, 472, 501, 518, 528
Epiphytes, 657
Epithelial tissue (epithelium), 416, 416 *fig.*
Epstein-Barr virus (EBV), 485, 489, 490
Equilibrium, sense of, 594
Ergots, 359, 359 *fig.*
Erythrocytes, 479, 479 *fig. See also* Red blood cells (erythrocytes)
Erythropoietin (EPO), 237, 480
Escherichia coli (E. coli)
  chromosome, 127
  of gamma proteobacteria group, 326
  infection of, by virus, 182–83, 200
  pathogenic, 327
  recombinant DNA technology and genetics research in, 232
  regulation of gene transcription in, 210–11
Esophagus, 432
  human, 434–35, 435 *fig.*
Essential amino acids, 443, 443 *fig.*
Essential elements, 650
Essential fatty acids, 443
Essential minerals, 444–45, 445 *table*
Essential nutrients, 443
Estivation, 505
Estradiol, 35 *fig.*
Estrogen(s), 517, 519, 529
  childbirth and, 558 *fig.*
  osteoporosis and, 610
  ovarian and menstrual cycles and, 542–43, 543 *fig.*
Estrogen mimics, 517

Estuaries, 689, 689 *fig.*
Ethane, 34, 34 *fig.*
Ethanol as product of alcohol fermentation, 101, 101 *fig.*
Ethics
  fetal imaging or testing and, 163
  gene therapy and, 241
  human reproductive cloning and, 222–23
  reproductive technology and, 559
Ethylene, 664 *table*, 668–69
  fruit ripening and, 668, 668 *fig.*
  leaf fall and, 668–69, 668 *fig.*
Eudicots, 623, 623 *fig.*
  embryo development in, 636, 636 *fig.*
  monocots versus, 623 *fig.*
  seed germination in, 638, 638 *fig.*
  tissues in, 625 *fig.*, 626, 627 *fig.*
Euglena spp., 333, 333 *fig.*
Euglenozoans, 333, 333 *fig.*
Eukarya (domain), 6, 7 *fig.*, 314
Eukaryotes, 6, 314
  balancing selection in diploid, 272–73
  fungi, 355–61
  gene regulation in, 212–17
  origin of multicellular, 297
  origin of single-celled, 297
  plants, 341–57
  tentative phylogeny of, 332, 332 *fig.*
Eukaryotic cells, 4, 4 *fig.*, 55
  cell cycle and cell division of, 128–36
  cilia and flagella of, 66 *fig.*, 333
  cytoskeleton and, 66
  energy-converting organelles in, 63
  flow of genetic information in, 190 *fig.*, 198
  functional categories of organelles in, 69 *table*
  gene regulation in, 212–17
  messenger RNA in, 194
  mitosis, cytokinesis, and chromosome duplication in, 128–31
  organelles as functional compartments in, 56–57
  organelles of endomembrane system in, 59–63
  surfaces and junctions of, 68
Eumetazoans, 369, 384
Eustachian tubes, 592
Eusthenopteron, 394
Eutherians, 399, 399 *fig.*
Eutrophication in freshwater ecosystems, 759
Evaporative cooling, 25, 25 *fig.*, 506, 506 *fig.*, 507
"Evo-devo" research field, 304
Evolution, 8–9, 254–339
  of angiosperm plants, 353
  of animal diversity, 364–65, 384–85, 392–93
  of birds, 306
  of cardiovascular system, 469
  cell division errors and, 147
  of cell signaling systems, 220–21
  convergent, 308
  Darwin's theory of, 256–63
  definition of, 255
  domains of life and, 314
  everyday life and, 12
  evidence for, 260–63
  of fungi, 341, 355
  genetic variation, natural selection, and, 270
  genomes and, 250, 312
  of glycolysis, 102
  of HIV, 499
  of horses, 307 *fig.*
  of invertebrate animals, 370–83
  life history of organisms and, 732–33
  macroevolution and, 300–307
  macroevolution and Earth history, 298, 299 *table*
  microevolution (in gene pools), 267
  of multicellular organisms, 337, 337 *fig.*
  natural selection as mechanism of, 259
    See also Natural selection

Evolution (*continued*)
  phylogenetic trees as symbol of, 309, 309 *fig.*
  of plants, 118, 342–43, 344 *fig.*, 345
  population as units of, 264
  of prokaryotes (bacteria), 320–29
  as property of all organisms, 5
  of protists, 332, 332 *fig.*
  of reproductive barriers, 285
  sociobiology and, 717
  speciation and, 277, 282–89
  species concepts and, 278–81
  systematics, phylogenetic biology, and, 308–14
  of tetrapods, 394–95, 394 *fig.*
  variation and natural selection, 270
  of vertebrate animals, 390–99
  Y chromosome and male, 177
Evolutionary adaptations, 5, 8, 255, 259. *See also*
      Mass extinctions
  natural selection and, 259, 259 *fig.*
Evolutionary fitness, 270
Evolutionary history. *See* Phylogeny
Evolutionary tree, 263, 263 *fig.*
Exaptation, 306
Excretion, 505
  nitrogenous waste disposal via, 509
  osmoregulation and, 508–13
  as urinary system function, 511
Excretory system, 421, 421 *fig.*, 510 *fig.*
  exchanges with external environment and role
      of, 424–25, 424 *fig.*
  key processes of, 510–11, 510 *fig.*
  kidney function in, 512–13, 512 *fig.*
Exercise
  aerobic, 615
  cardiovascular disease and, 473
  energy consumed by various activities of, 91 *table*
  food equivalents of, 442 *table*
  genetic influences of, 170
Exergonic reactions, 82, 82 *fig.*
Exocytosis, 79
Exons, 194
Exoskeletons, 378, 606–7, 606 *fig.*
Exotic species, 408
Exotoxins, 327
Experimental group, 11
Exponential growth model of population
      growth, 728
  logistic growth versus, 729 *fig.*
External fertilization, 535
Extinction, 258, 765
Extinct species, 398 *fig.*
Extracellular matrix, 67, 67 *fig.*
Extraembryonic membranes, 554–55, 555 *fig.*
Extreme halophiles, 325, 325 *fig.*
Extreme thermophiles, 325, 325 *fig.*
Eye(s)
  corrective lens and surgery for, 597
  induction during development of, 552
  photoreceptor cells in vertebrate, 598, 598 *fig.*
  types of invertebrate, 595
  vertebrate single-lens, 595–98
Eye cups, 595, 595 *fig.*
Eyespots, 381

F

F_1 generation, 155
F_2 generation, 155
Facilitated diffusion, 77
Factor VIII, 237
Facultative anaerobes, 101
FAD, cellular respiration and, 96–99 *fig.*, 100
$FADH_2$ (flavin adenine dinucleotide), cellular
      respiration and, 93, 96, 97 *fig.*
Fallopian tubes, 536
Family(ies) (taxonomy), 309
Family size, human, 735

Farming
  contour, 653, 653 *fig.*
  organic, 654
Farsightedness, 597, 597 *fig.*
Fat, body, 447
Fats, 40. *See also* Lipids
  biosynthesis of, 103 *fig.*
  digestion of, 438 *table*, 439
  as fuel for cellular respiration, 102 *fig.*, 103
  problems of diets extremely low in, 448, 448 *table*
Fat-soluble vitamins, 444 *table*
Fatty acids, 40
  essential, 443
Feathers, 398
Feces, 440–41
Feedback inhibition, 85. *See also* Negative feedback
Feeding
  animal behaviors associated with, 712
  animal ingestion for, 366, 366 *fig.*, 370, 430
  humpback whales, 429
  sponge, 370 *fig.*
Females, human
  childbirth in, 558–59
  contraception in, 545, 545 *table*
  hormonal regulation of reproductive cycle in,
      542–43, 543 *fig.*
  ovulation in, 536, 536 *fig.*
  pregnancy in, 536–37
  reproductive anatomy of, 536–37, 536 *fig.*, 537 *fig.*
Fermentation, 101, 102
Ferns, 344, 345 *fig.*, 347
  life cycle of, 347 *fig.*
Fertile Crescent, 622
Fertility, 532–33
Fertility drugs, 532–33
Fertilization, 125, 137
  animal, 546–47, 547 *fig.*
  external versus internal, 535
  after nondisjunction in the mother, 146 *fig.*
  plant, 350–51, 351 *fig.*, 635 *fig.*
  random, as cause of genetic variety, 141, 171
Fertilization envelope, 547, 547 *fig.*
Fertilizers, 651
  genetically modified plants and, 653
  inorganic, 651, 683
  nutrient deficiencies prevention and, 651
  organic, 651, 653, 654
Fetus, human, 537
  development of, 556–57, 556–57 *fig.*
  diagnosis of genetic disorders by testing of,
      164–65, 164 *fig.*, 165 *fig.*
  gas exchange in, 463
  placental and embryonic development of,
      554–55, 554–55 *fig.*
F factor, transfer of chromosomal DNA by, 205,
      205 *fig.*
Fibers (sclerenchyma cells), 628, 629 *fig.*
Fibrin, 480–81, 480 *fig.*, 481 *fig.*
Fibrinogen, 480–81
Fibroblasts, human-engineered tissue from, 419
Fibrous connective tissue, 417, 417 *fig.*
"Fight or flight" stress response, 704, 705
Filtrate, 510, 512–13, 512 *fig.*
Filtration function of urinary system, 511, 511 *fig.*
First law of thermodynamics, 81
Fishes, 392–93
  cardiovascular system, 469, 469 *fig.*
  cartilaginous, 392
  electroreception in, 587
  gills of, 455 *fig.*, 456–57, 456 *fig.*
  locomotion in, 604 *fig.*
  osmoregulation in saltwater and freshwater,
      508, 508 *fig.*
  population collapse, 733, 733 *fig.*
  salmon sensing and migration, 706
  signaling behavior among, 713
Fission, 534

Fitness, evolutionary, 269, 270
Five-kingdom classification scheme, 314
Fixed-action patterns (FAPs), 702–3, 703 *fig.*
Flagella, 66
  cell movement by eukaryotic, 66 *fig.*
  in euglenozoans, 333
  prokaryotic, 55, 55 *fig.*, 322, 323 *fig.*
  in stramenopiles, 334
Flatworms, 368, 368 *fig.*, 372
  digestion and gastrovascular cavity of, 432
  nervous system of, 572, 572 *fig.*
Flight, 398
  feathers and, 306
  as form of locomotion, 605, 605 *fig.*
Flower(s), 350
  attractiveness of, to animals, 353
  correspondence between fruit and, 637 *fig.*
  parts of, 350 *fig.*
  structure of, 634 *fig.*
Flowering, photoperiodic control of, 672, 672 *fig.*
Flowering plants, 345. *See also* Angiosperms
Fluid feeders, 430, 430 *fig.*
Fluid mosaic, membranes as, 74
Flukes, 372
Fluorescence and confocal microscopy, 53, 53 *fig.*
Fluoride, 19
Flying. *See* Flight
Follicles, ovarian, 536, 541, 541 *fig.*
Follicle-stimulating hormone (FSH), 522, 529,
      542, 543, 543 *fig.*
Food
  artificial chemicals in production of, 669
  cancer risk reduction by changes in, 227
  digestion of (*see* Digestive system)
  exercise equivalent of, 442 *table*
  four stages of food processing, 431, 431 *fig.*
  as fuel for chemical energy in body, 102–3
  fungi and production of, 361
  harvesting of chemical energy from, 92
      See also Cellular respiration
  meat as, 754
  obtaining and processing, in animals, 430–32
      See also Feeding
  overpopulation and shortages of, 736, 737
  photosynthesis and production of, 117
  production of, using lactic acid fermentation, 101
  soy products as, 661
Food chain(s), 746
  biological magnification of pesticides in,
      767, 767 *fig.*
  energy supply and limits to, 753
  interconnecting, food webs' formation
      and, 747
  terrestrial, and aquatic, 746 *fig.*
Food-conducting cells, 629, 629 *fig.*
Food labels, 446, 446 *fig.*
Food plants
  improving protein content of, 655
  polyploid plants as, 284
Food webs
  biological magnification of PCBs in,
      767, 767 *fig.*
  formation of, 747, 747 *fig.*
Foolish seedling disease, 666
Foot, mollusc, 374
Foraging, 712
Foraminiferans, 335, 335 *fig.*
Forebrain, 576, 577, 577 *fig.*
Forensic science
  DNA technology applied to, 242, 245
  restriction fragments analysis to detect
      differences in DNA sequences for, 246
  STR analysis, 244, 244 *fig.*
Forest(s). *See also* Tree(s); Tropical rain forests
  acid precipitation effects on, 28
  chemical cycling and alterations in, 758
  coniferous (taiga), 696, 696 *fig.*

INDEX

deforestation of, 354, 692, 758, 765, 765 *fig.*, 766, 769
  medicinal plants in tropical rain, 676
  temperate broadleaf, 695, 695 *fig.*
Formic acid, 17
Formula diets, 448 *table*
Fortified foods, 19, 19 *fig.*
Fossil(s), 256. *See also* Fossil record
  age of rocks and dating of, 298
  as evidence for evolution, 260–61
  human, 404
  macroevolution chronicled in, 298
  Neanderthal, 405, 405 *fig.*
Fossil fuels, 348
  global warming and, 119, 769
Fossil record, 260–61
  evidence of evolution in, 289
  evolutionary divergence chronicled in, 312
  evolutionary temporal patterns in, 289
  macroevolution chronicled in, 298
  mass extinctions recorded in, 302
  of mycorrhizal fungus, 341
Founder effect, 268, 269
Fovea, 595, 595 *fig.*
Fox, Michael J., 583 *fig.*
FOXP2 gene, speech development and, 250, 407
Fragmentation, asexual reproduction by, 534, 638
Franklin, Rosalind, 186, 186 *fig.*, 187
Frederickson, Megan, 17
Free-living flatworms, 372, 372 *fig.*
Free ribosomes, 59
Frequency-dependent selection, 272–73
Freshwater biomes, 690
  eutrophication in, 759
Frigate bird, 398, 398 *fig.*
Frogs, 396
  embryonic development in, 550–51, 550 *fig.*
  endoskeleton of, 607, 607 *fig.*
  gastrulation in, 549, 549 *fig.*
  metamorphosis in, 396 *fig.*
  reproduction in, 535 *fig.*
Fructose, 37, 37 *fig.*, 38
Fruit, 352
  auxins and development of, 665, 669
  correspondence between flower and, 637 *fig.*
  development of, 637 *fig.*
  dry and fleshy, 637
  ethylene and ripening of, 668, 668 *fig.*
  gibberellins and development of, 666
  seed dispersal and, 352 *fig.*
Fruit flies. *See* Drosophila melanogaster
FSH (follicle-stimulating hormone), 522, 529, 542, 543, 543 *fig.*
Functional groups, 35
  common, 35 *table*
  differences in sex hormones, 35 *fig.*
Functional magnetic resonance imaging (fMRI), 580, 580 *fig.*
Fungi, 355–61
  ants and, 360–61, 360 *fig.*
  colonization of land by plants and, 355
  as detritivores, 746
  ecological and practical impacts of, 361
  feeding and nutrition of, 355
  lichens and, 360, 360 *fig.*
  life cycle phases of, 356 *fig.*
  mycorrhiza, 341, 355, 656, 656 *fig.*
  parasitic, 359
  plant disease caused by, 359, 666 *fig.*
  yeast, 101, 355
Fungi (kingdom), 6, 7 *fig.*, 314, 355

G

G3P (glyceraldehyde 3-phosphate)
  as intermediate in glycolysis, 103
  photosynthesis and, 116

Gage, Phineas, brain injury to, 579, 579 *fig.*
Galápagos Islands
  Darwin's studies of life on, 255
  finches of, 259, 285, 287, 288 *fig.*
Gallbladder, 438
Galls, 359
Gametangia, 342, 343
Gametes, 137. *See also* Egg(s) (ova/ovum)
  animal, 534, 540
  crossing over and production of recombinant, 143, 172–73, 173 *fig.*
  formation of, by meiosis, 540–41
  genetic variation in (*see* Genetic variation)
  plant, 346, 634–35, 635 *fig.*
Gametic isolation, 281, 281 *fig.*
Gametogenesis, 540
Gametophytes, 336, 346
  in angiosperm, 350–51, 635, 635 *fig.*
  moss, 346 *fig.*, 347
  pine, 348–49, 349 *fig.*
Gamma proteobacteria, 326
Ganglia, 564
Gap junctions, 68, 68 *fig.*
Garrod, Archibald, 190
Gas exchange in animals, 420, 453. *See also* Respiration
  fetal, 463
  mechanisms of, 454–61
  three phases of, 454 *fig.*
  transport of gases in the body and, 462–63
Gastric glands, 436, 436 *fig.*
Gastric juice, 436, 436 *fig.*
Gastric ulcers, 437
Gastrin, 436, 436 *fig.*
Gastroesophageal reflux disease (GERD), 437
Gastropods, 374, 374 *fig.*
Gastrovascular cavity, 432
  cnidarian, 371
  flatworm, 372
Gastrula, 366, 548
Gastrulation, 548
  embryonic tissues formed in, 548–49, 549 *fig.*, 549 *table*, 554
  organ formation after, 550–51
Gause, G. F., 743
Gecko(s), 413 *fig.*
  locomotion in, 413
Gel electrophoresis
  analyzing restriction fragments by, 246 *fig.*
  sorting DNA molecules by size with, 243
Genbank, 248
Gene(s), 4, 187
  alleles of, 167
    See also Alleles
  behavior resulting from environment and, 704–5
  cascades of expressed, in animal embryonic development, 218
  cloning of (*see* Gene cloning)
  controls on expression of (*see* Gene regulation)
  developmental, and evolution, 304–5
  DNA as genetic material in, 46, 182–83
    See also DNA
  DNA technology and mass-produced products of, 236–37
  expression of, in proteins (*see* Gene expression)
  homeotic, 218, 385, 553, 553 *fig.*
  horizontal gene transfer, 314
  Hox, 366
  in human genome, 248
  hypothesis for first, 296, 296 *fig.*
  linked, 172, 176–77
  locus, 137
  mapping, 174, 174 *fig.*
  mutations in, 199, 224–25, 225 *fig.*
  p53 tumor-suppressor gene, 226
  pattern formation during embryonic development controlled by ancient, 552–53

pleiotropy as influence of single, 168, 168 *fig.*
polygenic inheritance and influence of many, 169
ras proto-oncogene, 226
sex-linked, 176–77
transcription of, 190, 193 *fig.*
transfer of, by plasmids, 205
tumor-suppressor, 224
Gene chip, 219, 219 *fig.*
Gene clones
  genomic libraries of, 235, 235 *fig.*
  identifying, with nucleic acid probes, 236
Gene cloning
  overview of, 233 *fig.*
  in recombinant plasmids, 232, 233 *fig.*
  reverse transcriptase and production of genes for, 235
Gene duplication, 313
Gene expression, 209–29
  adult stem cells and, 223
  animal cloning, 209
  cancer and faulty, 224–26
  cascade of, in animal embryonic development, 218
  cellular differentiation and, 221
  cloning of nonhuman animals and, 222
  definition of, 210
  embryonic development and, 218
  regulation of, in eukaryotes, 212–17
  regulation of, in prokaryotes, 210–11
  reproductive cloning and, 222–23
  small RNAs' multiple roles in controlling, 215
  summary of mechanisms regulating eukaryotic, 217, 217 *fig.*
  therapeutic cloning, embryonic stem cells, and, 223
Gene flow, 269
Gene pools
  Hardy-Weinberg equilibrium in, 266–67
  microevolution in, 264
Gene regulation
  embryonic development and, 219
  in eukaryotes, 212–17
  evolution and, 305
  in prokaryotes, 210–11
Genesis, Book of, 256
Gene therapy, 241
Genetically-modified (GM) organisms, 236–41, 654–55
  in agriculture, 239
  nutrients in soil and, 653
  potential risks of, 240
  protein yield in crops and, 655
  tolerant to herbicides, 654
Genetic code, RNA codons as, 192
Genetic disorders. *See also names of specific disorders*, e.g. Cystic fibrosis
  autosomal, 163 *table*
  carriers of, 162
  detecting, through fetal testing, 164–65
  detecting, with restriction fragment analysis, 246
  dominant, 162–63
  Down syndrome, 145
  gene therapy for, 241
  hypercholesterolemia, 79, 166
  incomplete dominance and, 166–67
  lysosomal storage disease, 62
  recessive, 162
  sex-linked, 177
Genetic diversity, 764, 765. *See also* Biodiversity
Genetic drift, 268–69, 772
Genetic engineering, 232. *See also* Clones and cloning; DNA technology; Genetically-modified (GM) organisms
Genetic markers, 246
Genetic recombination, crossing over and, 143, 143 *fig.*

Genetics, 153. *See also* Chromosome(s); Gene(s); Inheritance
  ancient roots of, 154
  animal behavior as result of environment and, 704–5
  DNA (*see* DNA)
  human behavior and, 721
  human disorders in (*see* Genetic disorders)
  molecular (*see* Molecular biology)
Genetic testing, 164
  for disease-causing alleles, 246
  legal and forensic applications of, 242, 242 *fig.*
Genetic variation
  crossing over between homologous chromosomes as cause of, 142–43
  differing genetic information of homologous chromosomes and, 142
  independent orientation of chromosomes in meiosis as cause of, 141
  mutations as cause of
    See also Mutation(s)
  random fertilization as cause of, 141
Genital herpes, 544, 544 *table*
Genome(s), 125, 247. *See also* Human genome; Human Genome Project
  completed, 247 *table*
  evolution of, 312
Genomic libraries, 235, 235 *fig.*
Genomics, 247–50. *See also* Human Genome Project (HGP)
  defined, 247
  whole-genome shotgun method, 249, 249 *fig.*
Genotype, 157
  expression of DNA, as proteins, 190
  relationship of, to phenotype, 157, 166
  using testcross to determine, 159
Genus, 308–9
Geographical isolation and speciation, 282
Geologic record (time scale), 298, 299 *table*
GERD (gastroesophageal reflux disease), 437
Germination, of seeds, 635, 638, 638 *fig.*
  abscisic acid and, 667
  gibberellins and, 666–67
Gestation, 554
GH (growth hormone), human, 522
  DNA technology for synthesis of, 238
Giant tortoise, 256 *fig.*
Giardia intestinalis, 332
Gibberellins, 664 *table*, 666–67, 669
Gibbons, 402, 402 *fig.*
Gigantism, 522
Gill(s), 455, 455 *fig.*, 456–57
  structure of, 456, 456 *fig.*
Giraffes
  gravity and circulatory system of, 467
Gizzards, 432
Glacier retreat, 768, 768 *fig.*
Glacier retreat, primary succession after, 750
Glans, 537, 539
Glia, 565
Global warming, 119, 768–69
  atmospheric CO_2 and, 119 *fig.*, 769, 769 *fig.*
  natural selection and, 771
  terrestrial biomes, 691
Glomeromycetes, 356 *fig.*, 357, 357 *fig.*
Glomeruli (glomerulus), 511
Glucagon, 526–27
Glucocorticoids, 529
Glucose, 37
  cellular respiration and metabolism of, 89–102
  homeostasis in blood levels of, 440, 526–27, 526 *fig.*
  structure of, 37 *fig.*
Glucose-tolerance test, 527 *fig.*
Glycogen, 39, 39 *fig.*
  epinephrine and breakdown of, 528, 528 *fig.*
  homeostasis and, 526 *fig.*

Glycolysis
  aerobic cellular respiration and process of, 93, 94, 94 *fig.*, 95 *fig.*, 100
  anaerobic cellular respiration and process of, 101, 615
  evolution of, 102
Glycoprotein, 60
Goiter, 18–19, 18 *fig.*, 524
  iodine deficiency and, 524 *fig.*
Golgi, Camillo, 61
Golgi apparatus, 56 *fig.*, 57 *fig.*, 61, 61 *fig.*
Gonads, 529. *See also* Ovaries; Testes
Gondwana, 300
Goodall, Jane, 402, 719, 719 *fig.*
Goose, graylag
  fixed action patterns in, 703, 703 *fig.*
  imprinting in, 706, 706 *fig.*
Goose bumps, 423
Gordon, Deborah, 17
Gorillas, 402, 402 *fig.*
Gould, Stephen Jay, 289
Gradualism model of speciation, 289, 289 *fig.*
Gram-positive bacteria, 326
Gram stain, bacterial identification using, 322
Grana (granum), 64, 109, 109 *fig. See also* Thylakoids
Grand Canyon, 261 *fig.*, 282, 282 *fig.*
Grant, Peter and Rosemary, 259, 287, 287 *fig.*
Grapes, gibberellins effect on, 666, 667 *fig.*
Grasshopper, 380 *fig.*
  alimentary canal, 432 *fig.*
  digestion in, 432
Grasslands, 692–93, 694–95, 694 *fig.*
  temperate, 694–95, 694 *fig.*
Graves disease, 524, 524 *fig.*
Gravitropism, 670, 670 *fig.*
Gravity
  blood circulation and effects of, 467
  plants and effects of, 670
Gray matter, central nervous system, 573
Gray tree frogs, 271, 271 *fig.*
Gray wolves, Yellowstone to Yukon Conservation Initiative and, 776–77, 776 *fig.*
Greater prairie chicken, 268, 268 *fig.*, 269
Great tit (*Parus major*), 771, 771 *fig.*
Green algae, 336, 336 *fig.*
  comparison of plants to multicellular, 343 *fig.*
Greenhouse effect, 119, 768–69
Green revolution, 622
Griffith, Frederick, 182, 204
Grinell Glacier, 768, 768 *fig.*
Ground tissue system, 626
Growth
  development and, as property of all organisms, 5
  mitosis, cell division and, 136
  plant, 630–33, 670
Growth factor(s)
  cell-cycle control system signaled by, 134
  cell division affected by, 133, 133 *fig.*
  proto-oncogenes and coding for, 226 *fig.*
Growth-factor proteins, 563
Growth hormone (GH), human, 522
  DNA technology for synthesis of, 238
Growth-inhibiting factor, 226, 226 *fig.*
Guanine (G), 185, 185 *fig.*
Guard cells, 626
  transpiration control by, 647
Guppy populations, predation and evolution of, 732–33, 732 *fig.*
Gymnosperms, 345, 345 *fig.*, 621
  coniferous forests, 348, 696, 696 *fig.*
  pine, 348–49, 349 *fig.*

H

Habitat(s), 682. *See also* Global warming
  archaea living in extreme, 325
  loss of, biodiversity crisis and, 766
  restoring degraded, 778–79
Habitat isolation, 280, 280 *fig.*
Habituation, 705
Haemophilus influenzae, 247
Hagfishes, 391, 391 *fig.*
Hair, 423
Hair cells (sensory receptors), 590, 590 *fig.*
  mechanoreception by, 591 *fig.*
Haldane, J. B. S., 295
Hales, Stephen, 644
Halobacterium halobium, 325
Halophiles, 325, 325 *fig.*
Hammerhead shark, 587
Hapalochlaena, 365
Haploid cells, 137
  in humans, 346
    See also Egg(s) (ova/ovum); Sperm
  in plants, 346, 349, 349 *fig.*, 634–35
    See also Gametophytes
Harcombe, William, 10, 11
Hardy-Weinberg equilibrium, 266–67
  conditions required for, 268
  public health science and use of, 267
Hearing, 592–94
Heart, 468, 470–73
  cardiac cycle and contraction of, 471, 471 *fig.*
  cardiac muscle, 418, 418 *fig.*
  cardiovascular system and, 469, 469 *fig.*, 470
  diseases of, and attack in, 473, 473 *fig.*
  path of blood flow through human, 470 *fig.*
  radioactive isotopes for detection of disorders in, 21
  tempo and rhythm of heartbeat, 472
Heart attack, 473, 473 *fig.*
Heart murmur, 471
Heart rate, 471
Heartwood, 633, 633 *fig.*
Heartworms, 373, 373 *fig.*
Heat
  definition of, 25
  as form of energy, 75, 80
  thermoregulation and gains or losses of, 506–7
Heimlich, Henry, 435
Heimlich maneuver, 435, 435 *fig.*
Helicobacter pylori, 437, 437 *fig.*
Helium, atomic structure of, 20 *fig.*
Helper T cells, 497, 497 *fig.*, 498–99
Hemings, Sally, 245
Hemispherectomy, 579, 579 *fig.*
Hemoglobin, 462–63
  gene regulation and synthesis of, 216
  mutation in, causing sickle-cell disease, 46
  oxygen loading/unloading by, 463 *fig.*
  Pauling's research on, 46
Hemophilia, 177, 481
Hemorrhagic fever, 202
Hepatic portal system, 440 *fig.*
Hepatic portal vein, 440
Herbicides, 669
Herbivores, 430, 674
  alimentary canal, 441, 441 *fig.*
  digestive adaptations, 441
  plant defenses against, 674–75, 675 *fig.*, 744–45
Herbivory, 742, 744–45
Herceptin, 496
Heredity, science of. *See* Genetics
Hermaphroditism, 535, 535 *fig.*
Herpesvirus, 181, 201
Hershey, Alfred, 182–83, 184
Heterokaryotic stage, fungal life cycle, 356
Heterotrophs, 324
Heterozygote advantage, 272

Heterozygous organisms, 156
Hibernation, 505
High altitudes, respiration and circulation in, 453
High-density lipoproteins (HDLs), 449
Himalayas, alpine meadows of, 680–81
Hindbrain, 576, 577 *fig.*
Hinge joints, 611, 611 *fig.*
Hippocampus, 581
Hippocrates, 154
Hippopotamuses (*Hippopotamus amphibious*), communities and ecosystems involving, 741
Histamines
    allergies and release of, 501
    inflammatory response and, 487
Histones, 212
HIV (human immunodeficiency virus), 202, 203
    behavior and structure of, 203 *fig.*
    drug-resistant strains of, 499
    molecular clock to date origin of infection in humans, 313, 313 *fig.*
    placenta-crossing by, 555
    T cell destruction by, 498–99, 499 *fig.*
Hodgkin, A. L., 566
Hodgkin's disease, 500
Homeoboxes, 553
Homeostasis, 425
    animal regulatory systems and, 506–8
    brain and, 573
    calcium, 525 *fig.*
    chemical signals and, 518
    circulatory system and, 474
    endocrine system and, 520–23
    glucose, 526–27, 526 *fig.*
    model of, 425 *fig.*
    negative feedback mechanisms of, 426, 426 *fig.*
    neurotransmitters in, 570–71
    osmoregulation, excretion, and, 508–13
    somatic and autonomic nervous systems and, 575
    urinary system and, 510–11, 510 *fig.*
Homeotic gene(s)
    animal embryonic development and role of, 218, 366
    evolution and, 305, 385
    of fruit fly versus mouse, 553 *fig.*
Hominids, 403–8
    timeline for, 403 *fig.*
Hominoids, 401
Homo erectus, 260 *fig.*, 405, 406
Homo ergaster, 404
Homo floresiensis, 405
Homo habilis, 404
Homo heidelbergensis, 406
Homologous chromosomes, 136–37, 137 *fig.*
    crossing over between, 142–43, 143 *fig.*
    gene alleles carried by, 157
    reduction of number from diploid to haploid, 138–39
Homology (homologous structure), 262–63
    analogy versus, 308
    phylogenetic relationships indicated by, 308
    wings and limbs, 262 *fig.*
Homo sapiens. See also Human(s)
    evolution of, 403, 406
    FOXP2 gene and speech development in, 407
    migration of, 406, 406 *fig.*
    oldest known fossil of, 406
Homozygous organisms, 156
Honeybees
    pattern recognition by, 711
    signaling behavior in, 713, 713 *fig.*
    thermoregulation in, 506
Hooke, Robert, 51
Hookworms, 373
Hopping locomotion, 604
Horizontal gene transfer, 314

Hormone(s), animal, 517, 518
    adrenal gland, 528–29
    anabolic steroids, 41
    antagonistic, 525
    DNA technology and production of therapeutic, 238
    from endocrine glands, 518 *fig.*
    of hypothalamus and pituitary, 522, 523 *fig.*
    insulin, 216 *fig.*
    labor and childbirth regulated by, 558–59, 558 *fig.*
    melatonin, 520
    from neurosecretory cell, 518 *fig.*
    ovarian and menstrual cycles regulated by, 542–43, 543 *fig.*
    for pain relief, 529
    of pancreas, 526–27
    prairie vole behavior and, 701, 704
    sexual reproduction and, 536, 539, 539 *fig.*, 542–43
    signaling mechanisms of, 519
    steroid, 519, 520
        See also Sex hormones
    of thyroid and parathyroid, 524–25
Hormone(s), plant, 662–69
    abscisic acid (ABA), 667
    agricultural uses of, 669
    auxin, 663, 664–65, 665 *fig.*, 669
    cytokinins, 666
    discovery of, 662–63
    ethylene, 668–69
    five major, 664 *table*
    gibberellins, 666–67, 669
    phytoestrogens, 661
Hornworts, 344, 344 *fig.*
Horse(s)
    hybrid sterility in cross between donkey and, 281 *fig.*
    Man versus Horse Marathon, 603
    trends in evolution of, 307 *fig.*
Horseshoe crab, 378, 378 *fig.*
Hox genes, 366, 609, 609 *fig.*
Hubbard Brook Experimental Forest, New Hampshire, ecosystem alteration in, 758, 758 *fig.*
Human(s). *See also Homo sapiens*; Fetus, human; *specific aspect under* Human
    breathing in, 90, 460 *fig.*, 461, 461 *fig.*
    cloning, 223
    global warming and ozone depletion caused by activities of, 120
    smell and chemoreceptors in, 599 *fig.*
    species, 279 *fig.*
Human behavior
    biodiversity crisis and, 766
    environmental and genetic factors in, 721
    fixed-action patterns of behavior in, 703
Human body. *See also* Human health
    ATP use by, 91
    blood types, 167
    body fat, 448
    bones, 609–11
    cardiovascular system and blood, 470–78
    chemical composition of, 18 *table*
    development of (*see* Human development)
    digestive system, 433–41
    endocrine glands in, 520 *fig.*
    endocrine system and hormones, 521 *table*
    energy consumed by various activities of, 91 *table*
    gas exchange in, 458–59, 459 *fig.*, 462–63
    imaging technology for viewing inner, 422
    immune response (*see* Immune response)
    lungs, 425 *fig.*, 459, 459 *fig.*, 460–61, 460 *fig.*
    lungs, healthy and cancerous, 460 *fig.*
    lymphatic system, 488, 488 *fig.*
    muscles and muscle contraction, 611–16

    organs and organ systems, 419–21
    poisons and disruption of cellular respiration in, 99
    respiratory system, 458–59, 459 *fig.*
    senses (*see* Senses)
    skeleton, 608, 608 *fig.*
    somatic cells, 136–37
    tissues, 415–19
Human brain, 576–83
    cerebral cortex, 578, 578 *fig.*
    cerebral hemispheres, 577 *fig.*
    embryonic development of, 576, 576 *fig.*
    evolution of, 404–5
    injuries in, and study of, 579
    lateralization, 578
    limbic system, 581, 581 *fig.*
    neurological disorders and physiology of, 582
    sleep and arousal regulation in, 580
    structure of, 576–77, 577 *fig.*
    structure of, linked to function, 577 *table*
Human chorionic gonadotropin (HCG), 555
Human development, 554–59
    childbirth and, 558–59
    embryo and placenta formation, 554–55
    three trimesters of, 556–57, 556–57 *fig.*
Human disease. *See also* Genetic disorders
    AIDS, 202, 203, 485, 498–99, 500
    allergies as, 501
    amoebic dysentery, 334
    bacterial, 205, 272, 320, 327, 487
    bioterrorism, 328
    blood, 481
    cancer (*see* Cancer)
    cardiovascular and heart disease, 473
    chronic obstructive pulmonary diseases (COPD), 459
    diabetes mellitus, 527
    diet effects on, 449
    DNA technology for diagnosis and treatment of, 238
    fungal, 359
    gastric ulcers, 437
    hypercholesterolemia, 79, 166–67
    hypoglycemia, 527
    immune system malfunctions and, 500–501
    lysosomal storage disease, 62
    malaria (Plasmodium), 168, 333, 683
    mononucleosis, 485
    multiple sclerosis, 565
    osteoporosis, 610, 610 *fig.*
    parasitic, 359, 372, 373
    Parkinson's disease, 571
    pesticides and, 683
    sexually transmitted, 544, 544 *table*
    sickle cell disease and malaria, 168
    skeletal and bone, 610
    viral, 202–3
Human evolution
    bipedalism and, 404
    fossils, 404
    hominids and, 403–8
    primate diversity and, 400–402
    relationship of Neanderthals to, 405
    skin pigmentation, 407
    speech, 407
    theories on locations of, 406
Human genetics. *See also* Genetics; Inheritance
    environmental influences of, 170
    family pedigrees and, 161
    speech development and, 407
Human genome, 248
Human Genome Project (HGP), 215, 248, 249
Human growth hormone, 522
    DNA technology for synthesis of, 238

Human health. *See also* Medicine(s)
  anabolic steroids and, 41
  application of Hardy-Weinberg equation to, 267
  gene therapy for, 241
  threat of bacterial resistance to antibiotics to, 205, 272, 323
  threat of poisons to, 99
  threat of smoking to, 460
  threat of viruses to, 202–3
Human population, 734–37
  age structure and growth of, 735, 735 *fig.*, 736, 736 *fig.*
  biodiversity and, 764
  centers of, in North America, 264 *fig.*
  environmental problems caused by, 119
  growth of, 734–35, 734 *fig.*
  life tables for U.S., 727, 727 *table*
Human reproduction, 536–45. *See also* Embryonic development in animals
  contraception, 545, 545 *table*
  embryonic development and, 554–60
  female reproductive anatomy, 536–37, 536 *fig.*, 537 *fig.*
  fertilization and zygote formation, 137
  hormones and, 539 *fig.*, 542–43, 543 *fig.*
  male reproductive anatomy, 538–39, 538 *fig.*, 539 *fig.*
  sex determination in, 176
  sexually transmitted diseases, 544, 544 *table*
  sperm and ova formation, 540–41, 540 *fig.*, 541 *fig.*
  technology of, 559
Humboldt Redwoods State Park, 621
Humoral immunity, 490
  antibodies as weapons of, 494
  antibody marking of antigens by, 495
  antigen sites for antibody binding, 491
  clonal selection and, 492–93
  effector mechanisms of, 495, 495 *fig.*
  monoclonal antibodies and, 496, 496 *fig.*
  T cells and, 497, 497 *fig.*
Humus, 652
Huntington's disease, 163
Huxley, A. F., 566
Hybrid(s), 155
Hybrid breakdown, 281
Hybrid inviability, 281
Hybrid zones, 286, 286 *fig.*, 288
Hydra, 371, 371 *fig.*
  asexual reproduction of, 136 *fig.*
  digestion in, 432, 432 *fig.*
  exchanges between environment and, 424, 424 *fig.*
  hydrostatic skeleton, 606, 606 *fig.*
  nerve net, 572, 572 *fig.*
Hydrocarbons, 34
Hydrochloric acid (HCl), 436
Hydrogen
  cellular respiration and electron release from, 92, 92 *fig.*, 98, 98 *fig.*
  in human body, 18, 18 *table*, 19
Hydrogen bonds, properties of water based on, 24, 24 *fig.*, 25
Hydrolysis, 36, 36 *fig.*
  digestion as, 431
Hydrophilic amino acids, 42, 42 *fig.*
Hydrophilic compounds, 35
Hydrophilic head, 58, 58 *fig.*
Hydrophobic amino acids, 42, 42 *fig.*
Hydrophobic compounds, 40
Hydrophobic tails, 58, 58 *fig.*
Hydroponic culture, 650, 650 *fig.*
Hydrostatic skeletons, 368, 606, 606 *fig.*
Hydrothermal vents, 295, 681, 681 *fig.*
Hydroxyl group, 35, 35 *fig.*
Hymen, 537
Hyperaccumulators, 643

Hypercholesterolemia, 79, 166–67
Hypertension, 476–77
Hyperthyroidism, 524, 524 *fig.*
Hypertonic solutions, 76, 77 *fig.*
Hyphae, 355
Hypodermis, 423, 423 *fig.*
Hypoglycemia, 527
Hypothalamus, 522, 577 *fig.*
  biological clocks and, 577
  drug addiction and, 577
  location of pituitary and, 522 *fig.*
  nervous system, endocrine system and, 522–23
Hypothesis, definition of, 9
Hypothesis-based science, 9, 10–11, 10 *fig.*
Hypothyroidism, 524
Hypotonic solutions, 76, 77 *fig.*
Hyracotherium fossil, 307, 307 *fig.*

I

"Ice Man," 260, 260 *fig.*
Ichthyostega, 394
Iguana, marine, 256 *fig.*
Imaging technology, 422
Imitation, learning by, 710–11
Immune response, 489
  primary and secondary, 492 *fig.*, 493, 493 *fig.*
  specific immunity (*see* Immune system)
Immune system, 421 *fig.*, 484–503
  acquired immunity, 489–500
  antibodies and humoral immunity, 494
  antibody binding to antigens and, 495, 495 *fig.*
  antigens and, 491
  cell-mediated immunity, 490, 497
  clonal selection and, 492–93, 492 *fig.*
  cytotoxic T cells and, 498
  disorders of, 500–501
  HIV and AIDS effects on, 203, 498–99
  humoral immunity, 490
  inflammatory response, 487, 487 *fig.*
  innate immunity, 486–88
  lymphatic system and, 488, 488 *fig.*
  lymphocyte B cells and T cells of, 490–91, 490 *fig.*
  memory of, 489
  monoclonal antibodies and, 496, 496 *fig.*
  overview of, 486 *fig.*
  self-recognition and nonself-recognition in, 497, 500
Immunity, 489
  acquired, 489–500
  active and passive, 489
  cell-mediated, 490, 497
  humoral, 490
  innate, 486–88
  stress and, 501
Immunodeficiency diseases, 500. *See also* AIDS; HIV
Immunoglobulins. *See also* Antibody(ies)
  classes of, 494
Imperfect fungi, 356
Implantation of blastocyst, 554, 554 *fig.*
Impotence, 559
Imprinting, 706–7, 706 *fig.*
Inbreeding, 162, 772
Inclusive fitness, altruism and, 720
Incomplete dominance, 166–67
Incomplete metamorphosis, 380
Independent assortment, law of, 158–59, 159 *fig.*, 171
Independent events, rule of probability and, 160
Indeterminate growth, 630
India, ecological footprint of, 737
Indigo bunting, star navigation by, 709, 709 *fig.*
Individual variation, 8
Indoleacetic acid (IAA), 664, 665 *fig.*
Induced fit, of substrate binding to enzymes, 84
Induction, organ formation and embryonic, 552

Inductive reasoning, 9
Infants, newborn
  diagnosis of genetic disorders by testing of, 165
  multiple, 532–33
Infection, innate defenses against, 486–88
Inferior vena cava, 470
Infertility, 532–33, 559
Inflammatory response, 487, 487 *fig.*
Influenza virus, 202
Ingestion, 366, 366 *fig.*, 430, 431, 431 *fig.*
Ingroup, cladistic analysis and, 310
Inheritance. *See also* Genetics
  of behavior patterns, 704–5
  chromosomal theory of, 170–74
    See also Chromosome(s); Gene(s)
  Mendel's laws of, 154–65
  polygenic, 169
  sex chromosomes and sex-linked genes related to, 174–77
  study of, 154
  variations on Mendel's laws, 166–70
Inhibiting hormones, 522
Injuries
  brain, 579
  spinal cord, 563
Innate behavior, 702–3
Innate immunity, 486–88
  inflammatory response, 487, 487 *fig.*
  lymphatic system and, 488, 488 *fig.*
Inner ear, 592, 592 *fig.*, 593 *fig.*
  balance and, 594, 594 *fig.*
Innocence Project, 245
Insect(s), 378, 380–81
  aphids, 648–49, 649 *fig.*
  body plan of, modular, 380–81
  butterflies, 709
  camouflage in, 259 *fig.*
  chemoreceptors in, 591, 591 *fig.*
  compound eye in, 595, 595 *fig.*
  excretion in, 509 *fig.*
  exoskeleton of, 606–7
  fossilized, 260, 260 *fig.*
  fruit flies (*see Drosophila melanogaster*)
  grasshopper, 380, 432 *fig.*, 457, 457 *fig.*
  honeybees (*see* Honeybees)
  nervous system, 572 *fig.*
  pesticide resistance in, 259 *fig.*
  plant pollination and, 353, 353 *fig.*
  protective color patterns of, 381, 381 *fig.*
  sex determination in, 175, 175 *fig.*
  tracheal system, 455, 455 *fig.*, 457, 457 *fig.*
  wasps (*see* Wasps)
Insulation, thermoregulation and, 506–7
Insulin
  diabetes and, 527
  DNA technology for synthesis of, 238
  glucose homeostasis and, 526 *fig.*
  production of, 526
  regulation of gene expression and synthesis of, 216 *fig.*
Insulin-dependent diabetes mellitus, 500, 527
Integrated pest management (IPM), 733
Integration, nervous system, 564
Integrins, 67
Integumentary system, 420, 420 *fig.*, 423
Interferons
  innate immunity and, 486
  mechanism of action against viruses, 486 *fig.*
Intergovernmental Panel on Climate Change (IPCC), 768, 769, 771
Interleukin-2, 497, 497 *fig.*
Intermediate compounds in cellular respiration, 94, 95 *fig.*
  biosynthesis from, 103 *fig.*

Intermediate filaments, 56 fig., 57 fig.,
     65, 65 fig.
Intermembrane space, 63
Internal environment, animal regulation of. See
     also Body temperature; Osmoregulation;
     Water balance
  excretion, 505, 508–13
  homeostatic functions of liver, 511
  sympathetic and parasympathetic neurons
     and, 574–75
  thermoregulation, 505
Internal fertilization, 535
Internal transport, mechanisms of animal,
     468–69. See also Circulatory system
Interneurons, 564
Internodes, 624
Interphase
  meiosis, 138 fig.
  mitosis, 129, 129 fig., 130, 130 fig.
Intersexual selection, 271
Interspecific interactions, 742, 742 table, 743
Interstitial fluid, 424
  exchanges between blood and, 478, 478 fig.
  urine production and, 512
Intertidal zones, 689
Intestines, 432
Intrasexual selection, 271
Introduced (exotic) species, 408, 725, 766
Introns, 194
  making gene with no, 235 fig.
Invasive species, 751, 766
Inversion, chromosomal, 148, 148 fig.
Invertebrates, 370–83
  annelids, 376–77
  arthropods, 378–79
  body plans of, 368, 369, 371, 371 fig.,
     372, 374 fig.
  body segmentation in, 376–77, 376 fig.
  as chordates, 383
  cnidarians, 371
  diversity of, 365, 370–83
  echinoderms, 382
  evolution of, from protists, 367 fig.
  eyes of, 595
  flatworms, 372
  innate immunity in, 486
  insects, 380–81
  molluscs, 374–75
  nervous system of, 572 fig.
  roundworms, 373
  sponges, 370
In vitro fertilization (IVF), 559, 559 fig.
Iodine, as trace element, 18
Ion channels, chemically-gated, 569
Ionic bonds, 22–23
Iris (eye), 595, 595 fig.
Iron, as trace element, 18
Irrigation, 653, 653 fig.
Islets of Langerhans, 526
Isobutane, 34, 34 fig.
Isoflavones, 661
Isomers, 34
Isotonic solutions, 76, 77 fig.
Isotopes, 20
  carbon, 20 table
  radioactive, 20, 21

J

Jacob, François, 210
Jaws
  hinged, 391
  human evolution and, 404
Jefferson, Thomas, 245
Jeffreys, Alec, 231
Jellies (jellyfish), 371
Joints, three types of, 611 fig.

K

Kahn, Genghis, 177
Kangaroo, 389, 399 fig.
  locomotion in, 604, 604 fig.
Kaposi's sarcoma, 499
Karyotype, 144, 144 fig., 145 fig.
Katrina, Hurricane, 643
Kelp, 108, 108 fig., 334
Keystone species, 749, 749 fig.
Kidneys
  conversion of blood filtrate to urine by, 511
  dialysis of, 480, 513, 513 fig.
  nephron structure and orientation in, 510 fig.
  structure of, 510 fig.
  urinary system and, 510–11
Killer whales, 9, 9 fig.
Killifish, predation on guppy populations by,
     732–33, 732 fig.
Kilocalories, 91, 442
  expense of, in select activities, 91 table
Kinesis, 708
Kinetic energy, 80, 80 fig.
Kingdoms (classification), 6, 309
Kin selection, altruism and, 720
Kissimmee River Restoration Project,
     778–79, 778 fig.
Kittiwakes, fixed action patterns in, 703
Kiwa hirsuta, 681, 681 fig.
Klinefelter syndrome, 147, 147 table
Knee-jerk reflex, 564 fig.
Koalas, foraging behavior of, 712
Krebs, Hans, 96
Krebs cycle, cellular respiration and process of,
     96–97. See also Citric acid cycle
Krill, 429
K-selection, 732

L

Labia majora, 537
Labia minora, 537
Labor stages in childbirth, 558–59, 558 fig.
lac operon, 210–11, 211 fig.
Lactase, 33, 42, 47
Lactic acid fermentation, 101, 101 fig., 615
Lactose, metabolism of, in prokaryotes, 210–11
Lactose intolerance, 33, 47
Lakes and streams
  acid precipitation and, 28, 759
  eutrophication in, 759
  as freshwater ecosystem, 690
Lamarck, Jean Baptiste, 256
Lamellae, 456
Lampreys, 391, 391 fig.
Lancelets, 383, 383 fig.
Land
  animal locomotion on, 604–5
  climate and landforms, 687
  plant colonization of, 297
  vertebrates and life on, 396, 458
Landmarks, animal behavior using, 708
Landscape ecology
  edges and corridors affecting, 773
  habitat restoration, 778–79
Landscapes, 682
Language, evolution of human, 407
Large intestine, 440–41
Larva, 366
Larynx, 458
Laser-assisted in situ keratomileusis (LASIK), 597
Lateralization, brain, 578
Lateral line system, 392
Lateral meristems, 632
Laurasia, 300–301
Law of independent assortment, 158–59, 171.
     See also Mendelian inheritance, laws of

Law of segregation, 156–57, 171. See also
     Mendelian inheritance, laws of
Laws of thermodynamics, 81
Lead contamination, phytoremediation of, 643
Leaf (leaves), 624–26
  falling of, 667, 668–69, 668 fig.
  modified, 625, 625 fig.
  stomata on (see Stomata)
  tissue systems in, 627, 627 fig.
  veins of, 626
Learning, 705–11
  associative, 710
  cognition and problem-solving behavior in, 711
  habituation, 705
  imprinting, 706–7, 706 fig.
  limbic system role in, 581
  sleep and, 580
  social, 710–11
  trial-and-error, 710, 710 fig.
  types of, 705 table
Lederberg, Joshua, 232
Leeches, 376, 377, 377 fig.
  nervous system, 572, 572 fig.
Legal applications of DNA technology, 231, 242,
     244, 245
Legumes, 443 fig.
  nitrogen-fixing bacteria on, 656
Lemba people, 177
Lemon ant (Myrmelachista schumanni), 17
Lemon ant tree (Duroia hirsute), 17
Lemurs, 400, 401, 713, 713 fig.
Lens (eye), 595, 595 fig.
  accommodation in, 596 fig.
  corrective, 597
Leopard (Panthera pardus), 1, 779, 779 fig.
Leptin, obesity and, 447
Leucine, 42, 42 fig.
Leukemia(s), 135, 481
Leukocytes, 479, 479 fig. See also White blood
     cells (leukocytes)
LH (luteinizing hormone), 522, 529, 542–43, 543 fig.
Lichens, 360, 778
Life. See also Organisms
  arranging, into kingdoms, 314
  cells as structural and functional units of, 4
  chemistry of (see Chemistry of life)
  common features, 4–5
  diversity of, 6–7
  evolution of, 8–9
     See also Evolution
  levels of organization in, 2–3, 2 fig., 414
  prokaryote evolution and, 320–29
  scope of biology and, 2–4
Life cycle, 125
  angiosperm, 350–51, 351 fig., 634 fig., 635 fig.
  fern, 347 fig.
  fungi, 356, 356 fig.
  moss, 346 fig., 347
  mushrooms, 358, 358 fig.
  pine, 348–49, 349 fig.
  sea star, 366 fig.
  zygote fungi, 358, 358 fig.
Life history of organisms, evolution and, 732–33
Life tables, population survivorship tracked in,
     727, 727 table
Light
  distribution of marine organisms and, 688–89
  Earth's tilt as cause of variations in, 686 fig.
  phytochromes as detector of, 673, 673 fig.
  plant responses to, 662–63, 670, 674
  vision and, 598, 598 fig.
Light microscopes (LMs), 52, 52 fig., 53
Light reactions of photosynthesis, 111,
     111 fig., 112–15
  ATP synthesis through chemiosmosis in,
     115 fig.
  mechanical analogy of, 114 fig.

Lignin, 343
Limbic system, 581, 581 *fig.*
Limiting factors, 728–29
Linked genes, 172
Linnaeus, Carolus, 278, 308, 309
Lipids, 40–41
    dehydration reaction and formation of, 40 *fig.*
    synthesis of, in smooth ER, 60
Liver
    blood processing by, 440
    digestion and role of, 438
Liverworts, 344, 344 *fig.*
Lizards, 397
    geckos, 413, 413 *fig.*
Lobe-fins, 392, 393, 394
Lobster, 378 *fig.*
Local regulators, 518
Locomotion, 604–5. *See also* Movement
    flying as, 605, 605 *fig.*
    on land, 604–5
    muscle contraction for, 611–16
    skeletal support for, 606–11
    swimming as, 604
Locus of gene, 137
Logistic growth model of population growth, 728–29, 729 *fig.*
Long-day plants, 672, 672 *fig.*, 673 *fig.*
Long-term memory, 581
Loon, courtship and mating behaviors of, 714, 714 *fig.*
Loop of Henle, of kidney nephron, 510 *fig.*, 511, 512, 512 *fig.*
Loose connective tissue, 417, 417 *fig.*
Lophotrochozoans, 384
Lorenz, Konrad, 702, 703, 706, 706 *fig.*
Loris, 400 *fig.*
Low-density lipoproteins (LDLs), 79, 449
LSD, 359
Luciferase, 73
Luciferin, 73
Lucy, fossilized skeleton, 404
Lung(s), 392
    bird, 461
    breathing and ventilation of, 460–61
    evolution of, 458
    human, 425 *fig.*, 459, 459 *fig.*, 460–61, 460 *fig.*
    smoking effects on, 460
    surfactants in, 459
    in terrestrial vertebrates, 455, 455 *fig.*
    vital capacity of, 461
Lung cancer, 460, 460 *fig.*
Lungfishes, 393
    geographic distribution of, 301, 301 *fig.*
Lupus (systemic lupus erythematosus), 500
Luteinizing hormone (LH), 522, 529, 542–43, 543 *fig.*
Lycophytes, 344, 348
Lyell, Charles, 257
Lyme disease, 327, 327 *fig.*
Lymph, 488
Lymphatic system, 420, 421 *fig.*, 488, 488 *fig.*
Lymph nodes, 488, 488 *fig.*
Lymphocytes, 479, 479 *fig.*, 490–91
    clonal selection of, 492–93, 492 *fig.*
    development of B cell and T cell, 490 *fig.*
    immune response and, 488
Lymphomas, 135
Lysogenic cycle, viral, 200, 200 *fig.*
Lysosomal storage disease, 62
Lysosomes, 56 *fig.*, 62, 62 *fig.*
Lysozyme, shape and function of, 43, 43 *fig.*
Lytic cycle, viral, 200, 200 *fig.*

M

Macroevolution, 277, 278, 293–316
    continental drift and, 300–302, 300 *fig.*, 301 *fig.*
    early earth and origin of life, 294–97
    "evo-devo" and role of genes in, 304
    fossil record and, 298, 299 *table*
    geologic record (time scale) and, 298, 299 *table*
    mass extinctions and, 302–3
    mechanisms of, 300–307
    origins single-celled and multicelled organisms and colonization of land, 297
    phylogenetic trees as representation of, 308–11
    trends versus goals in, 307
Macromolecules, 36
    abiotic synthesis of, 296
    biosynthesis of, as cellular respiration intermediates, 103 *fig.*
    polymer chains and formation of, 36
Macronutrients, plant, 650
Macrophages
    acquired immunity and, 497, 497 *fig.*
    in alveoli, 459
    innate immunity and, 486
Madagascar, biodiversity in, 764
Magnesium as plant nutrient, 650
Magnetic resonance microscopy (MRM), 422
Magnetoreception, 587
Magnification of microscopes, 52
Major depression, 582
Major histocompatibility complex (MHC), 500
Malaria. *See also* Plasmodium
    pesticides and, 683
    sickle-cell disease and, 168
Malathion, as pesticide, 85
Males, human
    contraception in, 545, 545 *table*
    evolution of, Y chromosome and, 177
    formation of sperm in, 540 *fig.*
    hormonal control of testis, 539 *fig.*
    reproduction anatomy of, 538–39, 538 *fig.*, 539 *fig.*
    sex-linked genetic disorders in, 177
Malignant tumors, 135
Malnutrition, 443
Malthus, Thomas, 258
Maltose, 38, 38 *fig.*
Mammal(s) (Mammalia), 399
    cardiovascular system, 469, 469 *fig.*, 470–78
    cloning, 222–23
    excretion in, 509 *fig.*
    respiratory system, 458–59
    thermoregulation in, 506–7
    X chromosome inactivation in female, 213
Mantle, mollusc, 374
Man versus Horse Marathon, 603
Marijuana, 571
Marsupials, 389, 399, 399 *fig.*
Mass extinctions, 302–3, 337, 397
Mass number, 20
Mast cells, 501
Mating
    courtship rituals, 704, 704 *fig.*, 714, 714 *fig.*
    in hermaphroditic animals, 535, 535 *fig.*
    patterns, 701
    reproductive barriers to, 280–81, 285
    reproductive success, behaviors enhancing, 715
    sexual selection and sexual dimorphism in, 271
Matter, definition of, 18
Maturation model, 61
Maximum sustained yield, 733
Mayr, Ernst, 279
Measurement equivalents, 52 *table*
Mechanical isolation, 279, 281, 281 *fig.*
Mechanoreceptors, 590
Medicinal plants, 354, 354 *table*, 676

Medicine(s)
    applications of reproductive cloning to, 222–23
    cancer treatment, 496
    fungi as source of, 361
    imaging technology, 422
    leeches used in, 377
    monoclonal antibodies and, 496
    plants as source of, 354, 354 *table*, 676, 764
    problem of R plasmids and antibiotic resistance in bacteria to, 272
    use of radioactive isotopes in, 21
Medulla oblongata, 576, 577 *fig.*
Medusa, 371
Meiosis, 136–43
    in angiosperm plants, 350–51, 351 *fig.*
    errors in, and altered chromosome number, 146
    gamete formation and, 137
    genetic variety produced by, 141, 142–43
    homologous chromosomes and, 136–39
    human reproduction, 540–41
    mitosis versus, 140, 140 *fig.*
    nondisjunction in, 146 *fig.*
    in oogenesis, 541 *fig.*
    phase I and II, 138–40, 138 *fig.*
    reduction of chromosome number by, 138–39
    in spermatogenesis, 540 *fig.*
    stages of, 138–39 *fig.*
Melatonin, 520
Membrane potential, 566
    nerve signal transmission and changes in, 566–67
Membrane(s), cellular, 74–79
    enzyme-controlled chemical reactions in, 73
    fluid mosaic model of plasma, 74
    phospholipid bilayer of plasma, 74, 75
    transport across, 75–77, 75 *fig.*
Memory
    immunological, 489
    limbic system and, 581
    sleep and, 580
Memory cells, 493
Mendel, Gregor, genetic studies conducted by, 154–55, 264
Mendelian inheritance, laws of, 154–65
    chromosomal basis of, 170–77
    homologous chromosomes, alleles, and, 157
    human genetic disorders based on, 162–63
    law of independent assortment, 158–59, 171
    law of segregation, 156–57, 171
    Mendel's first experiments and, 154–55
    as revealed in family pedigrees, 161
    rule of probability and, 160
    use of testcross to determine genotype and, 159
    variations on, 166–70
Meninges, 573
Menstrual cycle, 542–43, 543 *fig.*
    hormones of, 542 *table*
Menstruation, 542, 543 *fig.*
Mercury, environmental degradation from, 767
Meristems
    primary growth in, 630, 630 *fig.*, 631 *fig.*
    secondary growth in, 632–33
Mescaline, 744
Mesoderm, 366, 368, 368 *fig.*, 548–49
    organ and tissue derivatives of, 549 *table*
Mesophyll, 109, 109 *fig.*, 626
Mesozoic era, 298, 300–301
Messenger RNA (mRNA)
    initiation codon and, 196–97
    lac operon and production of, 211
    production of eukaryotic, 194
    RNA splicing and production of, from same gene, 215 *fig.*
    translation and, 194–95, 216
Metabolic heat production, 506
Metabolic pathway, 82
Metabolic rate, 442, 505

INDEX

Metabolism. *See* Cellular metabolism
Metal accumulators, plants as, 643
Metals, bioremediation of toxic, 778
Metamorphosis, 366, 380
Metaphase
    cell division II, of meiosis, 139 *fig.*
    cell division I of meiosis I, 138 *fig.*
    of mitosis, 130–31, 131 *fig.*
Metastasis, 135
Methane, 34, 34 *fig.*
    alternate ways to represent, 23 *table*
    structure of, 34 *fig.*
Methanogens, 325
Methyl group, 35, 35 *fig.*
Mexico
    demographic transition in, 734, 735 *fig.*
    population momentum in, 735, 735 *fig.*
Microarrays, DNA, 219, 219 *fig.*
Microevolution, 264, 277, 278
    gene pool and, 267
    Hardy-Weinberg equilibrium in gene pools
        and, 267
    mechanisms of, 268–73
    in phenotypic plasticity, 771
    potential causes of, 269
Microfilaments, 56 *fig.*, 57 *fig.*, 65, 65 *fig.*
Micrographs, 51, 52, 53 *fig.*
Micronutrients, plant, 650
MicroRNAs (miRNAs), 215
Microscopes, 52–53
Microtubule-organizing centers, 131
Microtubules, 56 *fig.*, 57 *fig.*, 65, 65 *fig.*, 131
    bending of, in cilia and flagella, 66
Microvilli, 439, 439 *fig.*
Midbrain, 576, 577 *fig.*
Middle ear, 592–93, 592 *fig.*
Migration
    electromagnetic receptors and, 587, 591
Migration, internal maps and animal, 709
Milk, mammalian production of, 399
Miller, Stanley, 295
Millipedes, 379, 379 *fig.*
Mimicry, 10–11, 11 *fig.*
Mineralocorticoids, 529
Minerals, essential, 444–45, 445 *table*
Mining wastes, bioremediation of, 778
Mitchell, Peter, 93
Mites, 378, 379, 379 *fig.*
Mitochondria, 56 *fig.*, 57 *fig.*, 63, 63 *fig.*
    chemiosmosis and ATP synthesis
        in, 98 *fig.*
    origins and evolution of, 64, 64 *fig.*
    poisons and function of, 99
Mitochondrial matrix, 63
Mitosis, 128–36
    interphase and, 129
    meiosis versus, 140, 140 *fig.*
    review of, 136
    stages of, 130–31, 130–31 *fig.*
Mitotic phase (M phase) of cell cycle,
    129, 130–31 *fig.*
Mitotic spindle, 130–31
Mold, 356
Molecular biology, 180–207
    DNA and RNA as nucleotide
        polymers, 184–85
    DNA as genetic material, 182–83
    DNA replication, 188–89
    DNA structure, 186–87
    evidence for evolution in, 262–63
    genetic information flow from DNA to RNA to
        protein, 190–99
    phylogenetic tree based on, 384 *fig.*
    as tool in systematics, 312
    of viruses, 200–205
    yeasts and research in, 361
Molecular clock, 313

Molecules, 2–3, 2 *fig.*
    alternative ways to represent, 23, 23 *table*
    covalent bonds and, 23
    polar and nonpolar, 24
Mole rats, altruism among, 720, 720 *fig.*
Molina, Mario, 120
Molluscs (Mollusca), 374–75
    exoskeleton of, 607, 607 *fig.*
    nervous system, 572, 572 *fig.*
    range of eye complexity among, 306, 306 *fig.*
Molting, 378
Monera (kingdom), 314
Monkey flower, 285
Monkeys, 400, 401, 401 *fig.*
    alarm calls of vervet, 710–11, 710 *fig.*
Monoclonal antibodies, 496, 496 *fig.*
Monocots
    embryo development in, 636, 636 *fig.*
    eudicots versus, 623 *fig.*
    seed germination in, 638, 638 *fig.*
    tissues in, 626, 627 *fig.*
Monocytes, 479, 479 *fig.*
Monod, Jacques, 210
Monogamous mating behavior, 701, 715
Monohybrid cross, 156
Monomers, 36
Mononucleosis, 485
Monophyletic taxa, 310
Monosaccharides, 37, 37 *fig.*
Monotremes, 388–89, 399, 399 *fig.*
Morgan, Thomas Hunt, 173, 174 *fig.*
Morning after pills (MAPs), 545
Morphine, 744
Morphological species concept, 279
Mosquito(es), 771
Mosquitofish, effect of endocrine disruptors
        on, 716, 716 *fig.*
Mosses, 344, 344 *fig.*
    life cycle of, 346 *fig.*, 347
Moths, 380
    chemoreceptors in, 591 *fig.*
Motion sickness, 594
Motor neurons, 564
    muscle contraction stimulated by, 614–15
    relationship of muscle fibers to, 614 *fig.*
    structure of, 565 *fig.*
Motor output, nervous system, 564
Motor units, 614 *fig.*
Mountains, effect of, on rainfall, 687, 687 *fig.*
Mount Hood National Forest, 772, 772 *fig.*
Mouth, 432
    human, 434, 434 *fig.*
Movement, 602–18
    animal locomotion and, 604–5
    cell, 65–66, 66 *fig.*, 69, 549 *fig.*, 552
    internal maps in animal, 709
    muscles and animal, 611–16
        See also Muscle
    skeletal support for animal, 606–11
    stimuli, landmarks, and animal, 708
Movement corridors, 773
Mucous cells (stomach), 436, 436 *fig.*
Mucous membrane, 416
Multicellular green algae, 336, 336 *fig.*
Multicellular organisms
    evolution of, from unicellular protists,
        337, 337 *fig.*
    seaweed as, 334
Multiple sclerosis (MS), 500, 565
Muscle
    antagonistic pairs of, 611, 611 *fig.*
    blood distribution controlled by
        smooth, 477
    contractile apparatus of, 612
    interaction of skeleton and, in movement, 611
    motor neurons and contraction of, 614
    types of, 418 *fig.*

Muscle cells
    aerobic function in slow muscle, 89
    anaerobic function in slow muscle, 89
    contractile apparatus in each, 612
Muscle contraction, 612–13
    motor neurons and, 614
    sliding filament model of, 612–13, 613 *fig.*
Muscle fibers, 612
    characteristics of, 616 *table*
    relationship between motor neurons
        and, 614 *fig.*
    slow versus fast, 89, 616
Muscle tissue, 418
    capillaries in, 474 *fig.*
    contraction of, 612–13
    motor neurons and, 614
    types of, 418 *fig.*
Muscular dystrophy, Duchenne, 177
Muscular system, 420, 420 *fig.*
Mushrooms, 357, 357 *fig.*, 361
    life cycle, 358, 358 *fig.*
Mus musculus (mouse), 247
Mustard plant (*Arabidopsis thaliana*), 247
Mutagenesis, 199
Mutagens, 199
Mutation(s), 199
    cancer caused by, 224–25, 225 *fig.*, 226
    emerging viruses due to, 202–3
    in gene expression in Drosophila, 218
    genetic variation due to, 199, 265
    by HIV virus, 499
    types of, and effects of, 199 *fig.*
Mutualism, 742. *See also* Symbiosis
    benefits to both partners, 743
    fungi and animals, 360, 360 *fig.*
    lichens and algae, 360, 360 *fig.*
    mycorrhiza and plants association as, 341
Myanmar tigers, conservation of, 763
Mycelium, 355, 355 *fig.*
Mycoplasmas, 326
Mycorrhiza, 341, 355, 656, 656 *fig.*
Mycosis, 359
Myelin sheath, 565, 565 *fig.*
Myofibrils, 612
Myosin filaments, muscle contraction and, 612,
    612 *fig.*, 613, 613 *fig.*, 616
Myxobacteria, 326

N

NAD^+ (nicotinamide adenine dinucleotide),
        cellular respiration and, 92, 100, 101
NADH, cellular respiration and role of, 92, 92 *fig.*,
        93, 93 *fig.*, 94, 96, 97 *fig.*
$NADP^+$, photosynthesis and, 111, 115
NADPH, photosynthesis and, 111, 114, 115, 116
Nails, 423
Naked mole rats, altruism among, 720, 720 *fig.*
Natural family planning, 545
Natural killer cells, 486
Natural selection, 8–9, 8 *fig.*
    adaptations to abiotic or biotic factors and, 685
    allele frequencies in population and, 268
    animal's form as reflection of, 415
    evolutionary adaptation resulting from, 259,
        259 *fig.*, 269
    general outcomes of, 270, 270 *fig.*
    genetic variation in populations affected by,
        272–73
    global climate change as agent of, 771
    as mechanism of evolution, 258
    perfection not produced by, 273
    population variation through, 270
    reproductive success and, 715
    scientific observation of, 259
Neanderthals, 405, 406
Nearsightedness, 597, 597 *fig.*

Negative feedback. *See also* Feedback inhibition
homeostasis and mechanisms of, 426, 426 *fig.*
Negative pressure breathing, 460–61, 460 *fig.*
Nematodes (*Caenorhabditis elegans*), 247, 373
Nephrons, 511
  detailed structure of, 510 *fig.*
  orientation within kidney of, 510 *fig.*
  reabsorption and secretion in, 512, 512 *fig.*
Nerve(s), 564
  cranial and spinal, 573
Nerve cords, 572
  dorsal, hollow, 383, 383 *fig.*
Nerve gases, enzymes' effects on, 85
Nerve net, 572, 572 *fig.*
Nerve signals, transmission of, 566–71
Nervous systems, 421, 421 *fig.*, 562–85. *See also*
    Central nervous system; Peripheral
    nervous system
  of animals, 572–76
  autonomic, 574, 575 *fig.*
  body symmetry and organization of, 572
  brain of vertebrate (human), 576–83
  disorders of, 582–83
  endocrine system and, 518
  immune system and, 501
  invertebrate, 572 *fig.*
  nerve signal transmission, 566–71
  neurons as functional units of, 565
    See also Neuron(s)
  organization of, 564 *fig.*
  parasympathetic and sympathetic,
    574 *fig.*, 575 *fig.*
  sensory input and response of, 588, 600
  somatic, 574
  spinal cord, 563, 575 *fig.*
  structural and functional overview of, 564–65
  vertebrate, 573–83
Nervous tissue, 418
Neural folds, 550, 550 *fig.*
Neural tube
  development of brain from, 576
  formation of, 550, 550 *fig.*
Neurological disorders, 582–83
Neuron(s), 418, 418 *fig.*, 564
  action potential propagation along, 568, 568 *fig.*
  communication between, at synapses,
    569–71, 569 *fig.*
  electrical potential in plasma membrane of, 566
  as functional units of nervous system, 565
  nerve signal transmission and changes in
    membrane potential of, 566–67
  structure and function of, 565 *fig.*
Neurosecretory cells, 518, 518 *fig.*
Neurotransmitter(s), 518, 518 *fig.*, 569
  chemical synapses and, 569 *fig.*
  small molecules functioning as, 570–71
Neutralization of pathogens, 495, 495 *fig.*
Neutral variation, 273
Neutrons, 20
Neutrophils, 479, 479 *fig.*, 486
New Guinea, animal diversity in, 388
New World monkeys, 401, 401 *fig.*
Ngege (*Oreochromis esculentus*), 724, 725
Niall of the Nine Hostages, 177
Niches, 743
Nicotine, 571, 744
Nile perch, introduction into Lake Victoria, 725
Nirenberg, Marshall, 192
Nitrogen
  in human body, 18, 18 *table*, 19
  as plant nutrient, 644, 650, 651, 651 *fig.*
Nitrogen cycle, 756–57, 757 *fig.*
Nitrogen fixation, 655, 656, 756–57
Nitrogenous base(s), 47, 47 *fig.*
  Chargaff's rules on pairing of, 186
  of DNA and RNA, 185 *fig.*
  DNA replication dependent upon pairing of
    complementary, 188

mutations in, 199
sequences of (*see* DNA sequence(s))
triplet code of, 191
  See also Codons
Watson and Crick's rules on, 187
Nitrous oxide, atmospheric, 769, 769 *fig.*
Nodes, stem, 624
Nodes of Ranvier, 565, 565 *fig.*
Noncompetitive inhibitors of enzymes, 85
Nondisjunction in meiosis, 146, 146 *fig.*
Non-native (exotic) species, 408, 725, 766
Nonpolar covalent bonds, 24
Nonself molecules, 497
Norepinephrine, stress and release of, 528, 528 *fig.*
North America, human population centers
  in, 264 *fig.*
Northern spotted owl (*Strix occidentalis caurina*),
  772, 772 *fig.*
Norway rats, influence of environment on
  behavior of, 704–5, 705 *fig.*
Notochord, 383, 383 *fig.*, 550, 550 *fig.*
Nuclear envelope, 56 *fig.*, 57 *fig.*, 58–59
Nuclear transplantation, 222, 222 *fig.*
Nucleic acid probes, 236, 236 *fig.*
Nucleic acids, 36. *See also* DNA; RNA
  digestion of, 438 *table*, 439
  as nucleotide polymers, 46
Nucleoid region, 55 *fig.*
  of prokaryotic cells, 55
Nucleolus, 56 *fig.*, 57 *fig.*, 59
Nucleosomes, 212
Nucleotides, 46–47, 47 *fig.*, 184. *See also* DNA; RNA
  DNA and RNA as polymers of, 46, 184–85
  homeobox sequences of, 553
  nitrogenous bases of (*see* Nitrogenous base(s))
  noncoding (introns, exons), 194, 248
  promoter sequence of, 193
  reading frame, 199
  restriction fragment length polymorphism
    analysis of, 246
  sequences of (*see* DNA sequence(s))
Nucleus (atom), 20
Nucleus (cell), 56 *fig.*, 58, 58 *fig.*
  cloning techniques using, 222, 222 *fig.*
Nutrient pollution in ecosystems, 759
Nutrients, as abiotic factor, 684
Nutrition
  animal (*see* Animal nutrition)
  fungal, 355
  genetic influences of, 170
  plant (*see* Plant nutrition)
  reducing cancer risk by changes in, 227

O

Obesity, human, 38, 447
Obligate anaerobes, 101
Ocean(s), 688–89
  climate and, 687
  coral reefs, 688, 689 *fig.*
  currents, 687, 687 *fig.*
  hydrothermal vents in, 295, 681, 681 *fig.*
  pH increase in, 769
  sulfate-consuming bacteria and
    methane-consuming archaea in, 324
  zones of, 688–89, 688 *fig.*
Octopus, 365, 375, 375 *fig.*
Oil spills, 329, 329 *fig.*, 361, 778
Old World monkeys, 401, 401 *fig.*
Olfactory receptors, 599
Oligomycin, 99, 99 *fig.*
Omnivores, 430
Oncogenes, 224
  alternative ways of making, from
    proto-oncogenes, 224 *fig.*
  interference by, in signal-transduction
    pathways, 226
One gene-one polypeptide hypothesis, 190

Onion root, cell division in, 136 *fig.*
*On the Origin of Species by Means of Natural
    Selection* (Darwin), 8, 154, 257,
    258, 264, 278, 385
Oocytes, primary and secondary, 541, 541 *fig.*
Oogenesis, 540–41, 541 *fig.*, 542
Oparin, A. I., 295
Open circulatory system, 376, 468, 468 *fig.*
Operation Migration, 707, 707 *fig.*
Operator DNA segment, 210, 211 *fig.*
Operculum, 393
Operons, 210–11
  activator controlled, 211
  lac, 210–11, 211 *fig.*
  repressor controlled, 210–11, 211 *fig.*
  trp, 211, 211 *fig.*
Opiates, 571
Opportunistic infections, 499
Opposable thumbs, 401
Optimal foraging theory, 712
Oral cavity, human, 434, 434 *fig.*
Oral contraceptives, 545
Orangutans, 402, 402 *fig.*
Order as property of all organisms, 5
Orders (taxonomy), 309
Ordovician period, 392
Organ(s), 2, 2 *fig.*, 419. *See also names of
    specific organs*
  embryonic formation of, 550–53
  plant, 624
  structural hierarchy and, 414
  systems of, 419 *fig.*, 420–21 *fig.*
Organelles, 2, 2 *fig.*, 55, 56
  of endomembrane system, 59–63
  energy-converting, 63–64
Organic compounds, 34–36
  carbohydrates, 37–39
  carbon-based, 34
  functional groups, 35, 35 *table*
  lipids, 40–41
  nucleic acids and, 46–47
  polymers, of, and molecule formation, 36
  proteins, 42–46
Organic farming, 654
Organic molecules, origin of, 295
Organisms, 2, 2 *fig. See also* Animal(s);
    Life; Plant(s)
  adaptation of, to biospheric factors, 685
  arranging, into kingdoms, 314
  chemistry of (*see* Chemistry of life)
  classification of, 308–9
  communities of (*See* Community(ies))
  evolution of (*see* Evolution)
  genetically modified, 239–40
  interaction of, with environment, 682
    See also Ecology
  levels of organization in, 2–3
  life history of, 732–33
  multicellular, 337, 337 *fig.*
  reproduction in (*see* Reproduction)
  structural hierarchy of, 414, 414 *fig.*
  transgenic, 239
Organ of corti, 592, 593 *fig.*
Organ systems, 2, 2 *fig.*
  human body, 419 *fig.*, 420–21 *fig.*
  structural hierarchy and, 414
Orgasm, 538–39
Origins of replication, 189
Orrorin, 403
Oryza sativa, 247
Osmoconformers, 508
Osmoregulation, 76–77, 505, 508–13
Osmoregulators, 508–9
Osmosis, 76, 76 *fig.*
Osteoporosis, 610, 610 *fig.*
Outer ear, 592
Outgroup, cladistic analysis and, 310
Ova. *See* Egg(s) (ova/ovum)

INDEX

Oval window, 592
Ovarian cycle, 542–43, 543 fig.
  hormones of, 542 table
Ovaries, 536
Ovary, plant, 350, 634
  fruit development from, 637
  ovule development in, and fertilization, 349, 635, 635 fig.
Overconsumption, 737
Overnourishment, 447
Overproduction and competition, 8
Oviduct (fallopian tube), 536
Oviraptor, 311, 311 fig.
Ovulation, 536, 536 fig., 537 fig., 554 fig.
  hormonal events at and after, 542–43
  hormonal events before, 542
Ovules, plant, 349, 634–35
  development of, and fertilization, 635, 635 fig.
  pine tree, 349, 349 fig.
  seed development from, 636, 636 fig., 637
Ovum. See Egg(s) (ova/ovum)
Oxidation, 92
Oxidative phosphorylation
  in cellular respiration, 93, 98, 98 fig., 100
  photophosphorylation versus, 115
Oxygen
  breathing and intake of, 90, 454
  double bonds in, 23
  exchange of carbon dioxide and, through respiratory surfaces, 454–55, 462–63
  hemoglobin and loading/unloading of, 463 fig.
  in human body, 18, 18 table, 19
  photosynthetic light reactions and, 114
  plant production of, by splitting water, 110
Oxygen debt, 615
Oxytocin, 522
  childbirth and role of, 558 fig.
Ozone layer depletion, 120, 120 fig., 767

P

p53 tumor-suppressor gene, 226
Pacemaker, 472, 472 fig.
Pacific yew, pharmaceuticals from, 135
Paedomorphosis, 304, 304 fig.
Pain
  glucocorticoids for relief of, 529
  nervous system and perception of, 590
Paine, Robert, 749
Pain receptors, 590
Pakicetus, 261, 261 fig.
Paleoanthropology, 403
Paleontologists, 260
Paleozoic era, 298
  mass extinction and, 302, 337
Pancreas, 438, 526–27
Pancreatic hormones, 526–27
Pandas, 103
Panderichthyes, 394–95
Pangea, 300–301
Pangenesis, 154
Pangolin, 8–9, 9 fig.
Pan troglodytes (chimpanzee), 247
Parabasalids, 332–33, 333 fig.
Paramecium, 51, 52–53, 52 fig., 53 fig., 62, 62 fig.
Paramecium, 743
Parasite(s), 332
  community composition and, 745
  flukes (flatworms) as, 372
  fungi as, 355
  of plants, 359
  plants as, 657, 657 fig.
  roundworms as, 373 fig.
  tapeworms as, 372, 372 fig.
Parasympathetic division, autonomic nervous system, 574 fig.
  regulation of internal environment and, 574
Parathion, as pesticide, 85

Parathyroid glands, 524–25
  calcium homeostasis regulated by, 525 fig.
Parathyroid hormone (PTH), 524–25
Parenchyma cells, 628, 628 fig.
Parental care, reproductive success and, 715, 715 fig.
Parietal cells, 436, 436 fig.
Parkinson's disease, 248, 571, 583
Parsimony, cladistics and, 311
Partial pressure, 462
Passive immunity, 489
Passive transport, 75, 75 fig.
Pasteur, Louis, 294
Paternity, certainty of, 715
Pathogens, 320, 485. See also Disease; Human disease
  bacterial, 326, 327, 328, 437, 487
  community composition and, 745
  plant defenses against, 675, 675 fig.
  species diversity and, 748
  viral, 202–3
Pattern formation, 552–53
Pauling, Linus, 46, 46 fig., 186
PCBs (toxic compound), 767
PCR (polymerase chain reaction), amplifying DNA sequences using, 242, 243 fig.
Peas, Mendel's studies on genetics of, 154–60
Pecking order, 718, 718 fig.
Pedigree, human genetic traits tracked through, 161
Pelagic realm, 688
Pelicans, 2
  structural hierarchy in, 414 fig.
Penguin, 415 fig.
Penicillin, 85, 272, 361 fig.
Penis, 539
Pepsin, 436, 436 fig.
Pepsinogen, 436, 436 fig.
Peptide bonds, 42–43
  formation of, 43 fig., 197
Peptide hormones, 519
Peptidoglycans, 321
Per capita rate of increase, 728
Perception, 588
Perennials, 630
Perforin, 498
Peripheral nervous system (PNS), 564, 572, 573 fig.
  cranial nerves and spinal nerves of, 573
  functional hierarchy of, 574, 574 fig.
Peristalsis
  in alimentary canal, 433, 434, 435 fig.
  earthworm locomotion by, 605, 605 fig.
Periwinkle, pharmaceuticals from, 135, 764 fig.
Permafrost, 696
Permian mass extinction, 302, 303
Peroxisome, 56 fig., 57 fig.
Pesticides, 63, 683
  biological magnification and environmental damage caused by, 767, 767 fig.
  enzymes' effects on, 85
  pest populations resistant to, 259 fig.
Pests
  biological control of, 751
  pesticide resistance in, 259 fig.
  wasps and control of, 674–75
Petals, 350, 634
PET (positron-emission tomography) imaging, 422, 422 fig.
  scanner, 21 fig.
Petrification, 260, 260 fig.
Pfennig, David and Karin, 10
P generation, 155
pH, 27
  enzymes' effects on, 85
  scale, 27, 27 fig.
Phages, 182–83. See also Bacteriophage(s)
  lambda, 200
  T2, 182–83, 182 fig.

Phagocytes, 479
  inflammatory response and, 487, 487 fig.
Phagocytosis, 79, 79 fig., 486
Pharmaceuticals
  antibiotics, 326
  applications of reproductive cloning to, 222–23
  for chemotherapy, 135
  DNA technology and production of, 238
  plants as source of, 354, 354 table, 676
Pharyngeal slits, 383, 383 fig.
Pharynx, 432, 458
  human, 434, 434 fig.
Phenotype, 157
  environmental influence on, 170
  genotype and, 157, 166
  incomplete dominance and intermediate, 166–67
  influence of single genes on (pleiotropy), 168, 168 fig.
  proteins as molecular basis for traits of, 190
Phenotypic plasticity, 771
Phenylalanine (Phe), 192
Phenylketonuria (PKU), Hardy-Weinberg equation and incidence of, 267
Phenylketonuria screening, 165
Philadelphia chromosome, 148, 148 fig.
Phloem, 342, 629
  food-conducting cells of, 648 fig.
  primary, 631
  secondary, 632–33
  transport of sugars in, 648–49
Phloem sap, 648
Phosphate group, 35, 35 fig., 46–47, 47 fig.
Phospholipid bilayer of membranes, 58, 58 fig., 74
Phospholipids, 41
  as main components of membranes, 74, 74 fig.
Phosphorus
  cultural eutrophication and, 759
  in the human body, 18 table
  as plant nutrient, 650, 651
Phosphorus cycle, 756, 756 fig.
Phosphorylation, 83
  active transport and, 78, 78 fig.
  oxidative, in cellular respiration, 93, 98, 98 fig.
  substrate-level, 94, 94 fig.
Photic zone, 688
Photoautotrophs, 108, 108 fig., 324
Photoheterotrophs, 324
Photons, 112
Photoperiod, 672
Photophosphorylation, 115
Photopsins, 598
Photoreceptors, 591, 595
  rods and cones in vertebrate eye, 598, 598 fig.
Photorespiration, 118
Photosynthesis, 106–22
  adaptations of C_3, C_4, and CAM plants, 118
  ATP and NADPH production in, 111, 114
  ATP production in, 111
  autotrophs as producers and, 108
  Calvin cycle in, 111, 116
  carbon cycling and, 755, 755 fig.
  cellular respiration and, 90, 90 fig.
  chemical equation for, 110
  chloroplast as site of, 109
  cyanobacteria as generator of, 326
  definition of, 107
  as endergonic reaction, 82
  light reactions of, 111, 112–15
  overview of, 108–11
  oxygen production in, 110
  radioactive isotopes for research on, 21
  as redox process, 110–11
  review of, 117
  solar radiation, Earth's atmosphere, and, 119–20
  stages of, linked by ATP and NADPH, 111
  summary of chemical processes of, 117 fig.
Photosynthetic bacteria, 319. See also Cyanobacteria
Photosynthetic prokaryotes, 322, 323 fig.

INDEX

Photosynthetic protists (algae), 330
Photosystem, 113
    components, 113 *fig.*
    I (P700), 113, 114, 114 *fig.*, 117 *fig.*
    II (P680), 113, 114, 114 *fig.*, 117 *fig.*
Phototropism, 662–63, 662 *fig.*, 663 *fig.*, 670
pH scale, 27, 27 *fig.*
Phthalates, 67
Phyla (taxonomy), 309
Phylogenetic species concept, 279
Phylogenetic trees, 309
    of animals, 369, 369 *fig.*
    based on molecular data, of bears and
        raccoons, 312 *fig.*
    of chordates, 390 *fig.*
    construction of, 310
    of fungi, 356–57, 356 *fig.*
    molecular, of animal kingdom, 384 *fig.*
    of plants, 344 *fig.*
    of primates, 400 *fig.*
    of reptiles, 311 *fig.*
Phylogeny, 308–14
    bacterial, 326
    classification of organisms and, 309 *fig.*
    of eukaryotes (tentative), 332, 332 *fig.*
    homologous structures and, 308
    systematics and, 308
Physarum (plasmodial slime mold), 335 *fig.*
Physical laws, evolution of animal form and, 415
Physiology, 414
Phytochromes, as light detector, 673, 673 *fig.*
Phytoestrogens, 661
Phytoplankton, 688
Phytoremediation, 643
Pied flycatcher, 286, 286 *fig.*
Pigments
    carotenoids, 112, 113
    chlorophyll (*see* Chlorophyll)
    vision-related, 598
Pili/pilus, 55, 322, 322 *fig.*
Pine, life cycle of, 348–49, 349 *fig.*
Pineal gland, 520
Pinna, 592
Pinocytosis, 79, 79 *fig.*
Piper nigrum, 352 *fig.*
Pitch (sound), 593
Pitchfork, Colin, 231
Pith, 626
Pituitary gland, 522
    hormones of, 523 *fig.*
Pitx1 gene, 305
Pivot joints, 611, 611 *fig.*
Placenta, 399, 463, 463 *fig.*
    formation of, 554, 555–56, 555 *fig.*
Placental mammals, 399
Planarians, 372, 372 *fig.*
    eye cups of, 595, 595 *fig.*
    nervous system, 572, 572 *fig.*
Plant(s), 340–57
    adaptations for life on land, 342–43
    agriculture and, 352, 653, 653 *fig.*, 654, 669
    analogous structures of, 308 *fig.*
    angiosperm (*see* Angiosperms)
    as autotrophs, 108
    biological rhythms in, 671–74
    C₃, 118
    C₄ and CAM, 118
    carnivorous, 657, 657 *fig.*
    cells of (*see* Plant cells)
    defenses of, 674–76, 744–45
    diseases and pests of (*see* Plant diseases
        and pests)
    diversity of, 344–45, 354
    DNA technology and enhanced, 239–40
    eudicot and monocot, 623, 623 *fig.*
    evolution of, 342–43, 344 *fig.*, 345
    fungi association with, 341, 355

genetically engineered, 239, 622
growth of, 630–33, 670
growth responses (tropisms) in, 662–63, 670
gymnosperms (*see* Gymnosperms)
hormones of, 662–69
life cycles of, 346–54
medicinal, 354, 354 *table*, 676
multicellular green alga compared to, 343 *fig.*
mycorrhizal fungus and, 341, 355
nutrition (*see* Plant nutrition)
organs, 624
parasitic, 657, 657 *fig.*
pathogens in, 203
photosynthesis in (*see* Photosynthesis)
phytoremediation by, 643
polyploidy and sympatric speciation in,
    283 *fig.*, 284
red algae and green algae as relatives of, 336
reproduction in (*see* Plant reproduction)
seed, 344–45
    See also Seed(s)
self-fertilizing, 154
structure and function of, 622–29
transgenic, 239
trees (*see* Tree(s))
Plantae (kingdom), 6, 7 *fig.*, 314. *See also* Plant(s)
Plant body, 624 *fig.*
    cells and tissues of, 628–29
    roots, stems, and leaves of, 624–25
    tissue systems of, 626
Plant cells, 57, 57 *fig.*, 628–29
    auxin and elongation of, 665, 665 *fig.*
    cell division in, 128 *fig.*
    cell plate formation in, 132 *fig.*
    chloroplast (*see* Chloroplasts)
    cytokinesis in, 132
    cytokinins and division of, 666
    osmoregulation of water balance in, 77 *fig.*
    structure of, 628 *fig.*
    types of, 628 *fig.*, 629 *fig.*
    vacuoles of, 62
    walls and junctions of, 68 *fig.*
Plant diseases and pests
    defenses against, 674–76, 744–45
    foolish seedling disease, 666
    fungal, 359
    parasites and pathogens causing, 745
    viral, 202
Plant growth, 630–33
    hormone regulation of, 664
    primary, 630, 630 *fig.*, 631 *fig.*
    secondary, 632–33, 632 *fig.*
Plant nutrition, 642–59
    agriculture and, 654
    deficiencies in, 651
    fungi and, 341, 656
    metal accumulators, 643
    nitrogen-fixing bacteria and, 655, 656
    nutrient uptake, 644–45
    phloem transport and, 648–49
    plants as epiphytes, parasites and carnivores
        and, 657, 657 *fig.*
    soil and, 650–55
    symbiosis and, 655–57
    water transpiration and, 646–47
Plant reproduction, 634–40
    alternation of generation and cycles of, 346–54
    angiosperm, 350–51, 351 *fig.*, 634–40
    asexual, 638–39, 639 *fig.*
    flower in, 350, 634 *fig.*, 635, 635 *fig.*
    fruit and, 352, 637
    gymnosperm, 348, 349 *fig.*
    reproductive isolation in, 281
    seed, 344–45, 636, 636 *fig.*, 637
    seed germination, 635, 638, 638 *fig.*
    sexual life cycle, 634 *fig.*, 635 *fig.*
Plant tissues. *See* Tissue systems, plant

Plasma, blood, 479
    composition of, 479 *fig.*
Plasma cells, 493
Plasma membrane, 55, 55 *fig.*, 56 *fig.*, 57 *fig.*, 68 *fig.*
    of animal cell, 74 *fig.*
    cellular water balance and, 76–77
    fluid mosaic model of, 74
    phospholipid bilayer of, 58, 58 *fig.*
    of prokaryotic cell, 55
    proteins of, 74
    spontaneous formation of, 75
    structure and function of, 58
    transport across, 75–79
Plasma-membrane receptor, hormones binding
        to, 519 *fig.*
Plasmids
    as carriers for gene transfer, 205
    cloning genes in recombinant, 232, 233 *fig.*
    F-factor, 205, 205 *fig.*
    genomic library of, 235, 235 *fig.*
    Ti, 239, 239 *fig.*
Plasmodesmata, 57 *fig.*, 68, 68 *fig.*, 201
Plasmodial slime mold, 334, 335 *fig.*
Plasmodium, 333
Plasmodium (cytoplasm mass), 334–35
Plasmolysis, 77
Plasticity, phenotypic, 771
Platelets, 479
    blood clotting and, 480–81, 480 *fig.*
Platyhelminthes, 372
Platypus, 388, 399, 399 *fig.*, 591
Pleated sheet protein structure, 44, 45 *fig.*, 46
Pleiotropy, 168
Pneumocystis pneumonia, 499
Poison arrow frogs, 396, 396 *fig.*
Poisons as disruptors of cellular respiration, 99
Polar covalent bonds, 24
Polar molecules, 24 *fig.*
Poliovirus, 201
Politics, science and, 120
Pollen, 344
Pollen grains, 343, 349
Pollination, 349, 635, 635 *fig.*
    animals and, 353, 353 *fig.*
Pollution, environmental, 767. *See also*
        Air pollution
    chemical, abnormal behavior caused by, 716
    cleanup efforts, 643
    habitat destruction and, 766
    by nutrients, 759
Polychaetes, 376, 377
Polygamous mating behavior, 701, 715
Polygenic inheritance, 169
Polymerase chain reaction (PCR), amplifying
        DNA sequences using, 242, 243 *fig.*
Polymers, 36
    abiotic synthesis of, 296
    breaking, 36
    diversity of, 36
    making, 36
    of nucleotides, DNA and RNA as, 47
Polynucleotides, 184–85
Polyp(s), 371
Polypeptides, 43, 45 *fig.* *See also* Amino acids;
        Protein(s)
    synthesis of, 198, 198 *fig.*
    translation and elongating chains of, 197 *fig.*
Polyploid cells, 283
Polysaccharides, 39, 39 *fig.*
Pons, 576, 577 *fig.*
Population(s), 2, 2 *fig.*
    Darwin's theory of evolution in, 258
    definition of, 264, 726
    fragmentation of, 772, 772 *fig.*
    global climate change and, 770–71
    growth of (*see* Population growth)
    human (*see* Human population)

interaction of, with environment, 682
  See also Ecology
life tables of survivorship in, 727, 727 *table*
natural selection and evolution of, 258
as units of evolution, 264
Population density, 726–27
  factors limiting population growth dependent on, 730–31
Population dynamics
  behavior and (*see* Social behavior)
Population ecology, 724–39. *See also* Population dynamics
  human, 734–37
  life histories and evolution in, 732–33
  non-native species and, 725
  practical applications of principles of, 733
  structure of populations and, 726–33
Population growth
  boom-and-bust cycles of, 731, 731 *fig.*
  density-dependent factors limiting, 730–31
  exponential growth model of, 728, 728 *fig.*
  human, 734–37
  logistic growth model and limiting factors in, 728–29
  social and economic trends, age structures and, 736, 736 *fig.*
Population momentum, 735, 735 *fig.*
Porifera, 370
Porpoises, 399, 587
Post-anal tail, 383, 383 *fig.*
Posterior pituitary, 522
  hormones of, 523 *fig.*
Posterior surface of animals, 368, 368 *fig.*
Postzygotic barriers, 280 *table*, 281
Potassium–40, for radiometric dating, 298
Potassium as plant nutrient, 650, 651
Potential energy, 80, 80 *fig.*
Pottos, 400
Prairies, 694–95, 694 *fig.*
Prairie voles, behavior in, 704
  monogamy, 701
Precambrian period, 337
Precapillary sphincters, 477, 477 *fig.*
Precipitation
  acid, 28
  climate change and, 768
  in deserts, 693
  of dissolved antigens, 495, 495 *fig.*
  mountains' effects on, 687, 687 *fig.*
  uneven heating as cause of, 687 *fig.*
Predation
  adaptations of prey/predators for, 744
  coevolution and, 744
  group foraging behaviors and, 712
  as interspecific interaction, 742
  life history shaping through evolution and, 732–33, 732 *fig.*
  plant defenses against, 674–75, 675 *fig.*, 744–45
  population density and, 730
Predators
  coevolution and prey interactions with, 744–45
  group foraging behaviors of, 712
  plant recruitment of predatory animals, 674–75, 675 *fig.*
  population cycles and, 731
  prey defenses against, 744
  scientific method and study of prey and, 10–11
Pregnancy, human, 536–37
  childbirth and, 530, 558–59
  development of embryo and placenta, 554–55
  prolactin and, 530
  trimesters of, 556–57, 556–57 *fig.*
Pregnancy tests, home, 496
Prenatal testing, 164–65
Prepuce, 537, 539
Pressure-flow mechanism in plant phloem tissue, 648, 649 *fig.*

Prevailing winds, 686–87
Prey
  coevolution and predator interactions with, 744–45
  population cycles and, 731
  predator defenses by, 744
  scientific method and study of predators and, 10–11
Prezygotic barriers, 280–81, 280 *table*
Primary consumers, 746, 746 *fig.*, 747, 747 *fig.*
Primary endosymbiosis, 331
Primary immune response, 492 *fig.*, 493, 493 *fig.*
Primary oocytes, 541, 541 *fig.*
Primary phloem, 631
Primary production, 752–53, 753 *fig.*
Primary spermatocytes, 540
Primary structure of proteins, 44, 45 *fig.*
Primary succession, 750
Primary xylem, 631
Primates, 400–402
  apes as closest relatives of humans, 402
  hominid branch of, 403
  hominid evolution and, 403–8
  phylogenetic tree of, 400 *fig.*
  reasoning in, 711
  signaling behavior in, 713, 713 *fig.*
Primers, 242
Principles of Geology (Lyell), 257
Prions, 44, 203
PRL (prolactin), 522
Probability, Mendelian inheritance and rules of, 160
Probes, nucleic acid, 236, 236 *fig.*
Problem solving, 711
Producers, 3, 3 *fig.*, 108, 746, 746 *fig.*
Production, pyramid of, 753 *fig.*
Products of chemical reactions, 29
Progesterone, ovarian and menstrual cycles and, 542–43, 543 *fig.*
Progestins, 529
Programmed cell death, 552, 552 *fig.*
Progressive retinal atrophy (PRA), 158
Prokaryotes, 6, 314, 320–29
  archaea and bacteria as main branches in evolution of, 320–21
  cyanobacteria, 319
  as detritivores, 701, 746
  diversity and extent of, 320
  early origins of, 297
  fossilized, 261
  gene regulation in, 210–11
  genetic variation in, 265
  nutritional modes of, 324, 324 *fig.*
  recycling and cleaning environment using, 329
  shapes of, 321, 321 *fig.*
  structural features of, 322–23
Prokaryotic cells, 4, 4 *fig.*, 55 *fig.*
  binary fission of, 127, 127 *fig.*
  size and structure of, 55, 322–23
Prokaryotic flagella, 55, 55 *fig.*, 322, 323 *fig.*
Prolactin (PRL), 522, 530
Prometaphase, mitosis, 130–31, 130 *fig.*
Promiscuous mating behavior, 701, 715
Promoter DNA sequences, 193, 210, 211 *fig.*
Pronghorn antelopes, 685, 685 *fig.*
Propagation, vegetative, 638
Propane, 34, 34 *fig.*
Prophages, 200
Prophase
  cell division I, of meiosis I, 138 *fig.*
  cell division II, of meiosis II, 139 *fig.*
  mitosis, 130, 130 *fig.*
Propylthiouracil, 599
Prostaglandins, 558, 558 *fig.*
Prostate gland, 538
Protease inhibitors, 85

Protein(s), 36, 42–45. *See also* Amino acids
  amino acids and formation of, 42–43
  biosynthesis of, 103 *fig.*
  classes of, 42
  Class I and II, 500
  comparison of, in systematics, 312
  denaturation of, 43
  digestion of, 438 *table*, 439
  DNA technology and mass production of, 237 *table*
  essential amino acids and, 443
  as essential to life, 42
  as fuel for cellular respiration, 102–3, 102 *fig.*
  in membranes, 74
  nucleic acids as polymer blueprints for, 46
  peptide bonds in, 43 *fig.*
  post-translational breakdown of, 216
  post-translational controls on activation of, 216
  receptors, 74
  secretory, 60, 60 *fig.*
  self and nonself, 497, 500
  shape and function, 43
  shape and function of, 43
  signal transduction and role of, 220
  structure of, 44
  structures, 44–45
  translation of RNA information into, 190
Protein hormones, 519
Proteobacteria, 326
Proteomics, 249
Proterozoic eon, 298
Proteus (bacterium), 322 *fig.*
Protista (kingdom), 314
Protists, 7 *fig.*, 330–37, 330 *fig.*
  alveolates, 333
  amoebozoans, 334–35
  classification of, 332, 332 *fig.*
  diplomonads, 332–33
  euglenozoans, 333, 333 *fig.*
  evolution of animal kingdom from colonial, 367
  foraminiferans, 335, 335 *fig.*
  multicellular life originating in, 337
  Paramecium, 62, 62 *fig.*, 743
  radiolarians, 335, 335 *fig.*
  red algae and green algae, 336, 336 *fig.*
  secondary endosymbiosis in, 331, 331 *fig.*
  stramenopiles, 334
  as unicellular eukaryotes, 330, 330 *fig.*
Protobionts, 296
Protons, 20
Proto-oncogenes, 224
  ras, 226
Protostomes, 368, 369, 384
Protozoans, 6, 330
Provirus, 203
Proximal tubule, of kidney nephron, 510 *fig.*, 511, 512, 512 *fig.*
Proximate causes, of behavior, 702
Pseudocoelom, 368, 368 *fig.*
Pseudopodia (pseudopodium), 334, 335
Pseudostratified epithelium, 416
Ptarmigan, 425, 425 *fig.*
Pterophytes, 344
Pterosaurs, 293
Public health science, Hardy-Weinberg equation useful in, 267
Pulmocutaneous circuit, 469
Pulmonary arteries, 470
Pulmonary circuit, 469
Pulmonary veins, 470
Pulse, 475
Punctuated equilibrium model of speciation, 289, 289 *fig.*
Punnett, Reginald, 172
Punnett square, 157
Pupil (eye), 595, 595 *fig.*

INDEX

Purines, 185, 185 *fig.*
Pyramid of production
    human meat-eating as luxury explained by, 754
    idealized, 753, 753 *fig.*
Pyrimidines, 185, 185 *fig.*
Pyruvate
    cellular respiration and production of,
        93, 94, 95 *fig.*
    chemical grooming for citric acid cycle,
        96, 96 *fig.*
Python, *Hox* gene expression in, 609, 609 *fig.*

Q

Quaternary consumers in communities, 746,
    746 *fig.*, 747 *fig.*
Quaternary structure of proteins, 44, 45 *fig.*
Quolls, 389, 408, 408 *fig.*

R

Rabbits
    exponential growth model applied to,
        728, 728 *fig.*
    as non-native pest species, 408
Raccoons, systematics of bears and, 312, 312 *fig.*
Radial keratotomy (RK), 597
Radial symmetry, 368, 368 *fig.*, 371
Radiation
    heat gains or losses by, 506, 506 *fig.*
    as mutagen, 199
Radiation therapy, 135
Radioactive isotopes, 20, 21
Radiolarians, 335, 335 *fig.*
Radiometric dating, 298, 298 *fig.*
Radon, 21
Radula, mollusc, 374
Rainfall. *See* Precipitation
Rain forests. *See* Tropical rain forests
Random population-dispersion patterns,
    726 *fig.*, 727
Ras proto-oncogene, 226
Ray-finned fishes, 393, 393 *fig.*
Reabsorption function of excretory system,
    511, 511 *fig.*, 512–13, 512 *fig.*
Reactants in chemical reactions, 29
Reaction center of photosynthetic pigments, 113
Reading frame, 199
Receptor-mediated endocytosis, 79, 79 *fig.*
Receptor potential, 588–89
Receptors, protein, 42
Receptors for hormones, 519, 519 *fig.*
Recessive alleles, 156, 161
Recessive traits, genetic disorders as, 162, 162 *fig.*,
    163 *table*
Reciprocal altruism, 720
Recombinant cells and organisms, 236–37
Recombinant DNA, use of restriction enzymes
    and DNA ligase to create, 234, 234 *fig.*
Recombinant DNA technology, 232. *See also*
    DNA technology
Recombinant gametes, production of,
    143, 172, 173 *fig.*
Recombination frequency, 173
Recommended Daily Allowances (RDAs), 446
Reconciliation behavior, 719
Rectum, 440 *fig.*, 441
Red algae, 336, 336 *fig.*
Red blood cells (erythrocytes), 479, 479 *fig.*, 480 *fig.*
    healthy body function and levels of, 480
Red bone marrow, 609
Red-cockaded woodpecker (*Picoides borealis*),
    772, 772 *fig.*
Red-green color blindness, 177
Redox reactions, 92 *fig.*, 95 *fig.*, 97 *fig.*
    of cellular respiration, 92, 110 *fig.*
    of photosynthesis, 110–11, 116, 116 *fig.*

Red squirrel (*Tamiasciurus hudsonicus*),
    771, 771 *fig.*
Red-tide dinoflagellates, 333
Reduced hybrid fertility, 281
Reduced hybrid viability, 281
Reduction, 92, 116, 116 *fig.*
Redwoods (*Sequoia sempervirens*), 620–21
Reeve, Christopher, 563, 563 *fig.*
Reflexes, 564
    knee-jerk, 564 *fig.*
Regeneration, 221, 534
    by sea stars and echinoderms, 382
Regulation, as property of all organisms, 5
Regulatory genes, 211, 211 *fig.*
Regulatory systems, animal, 504–15
    chemical regulation, overview of, 518–19
    endocrine system as, 520–23
    homeostasis and (*see* Homeostasis)
    hormones and, 521 *table*
    osmoregulation and excretion as, 508–13
    sympathetic and parasympathetic nervous
        systems and, 574–75
    thermoregulation as, 505, 506–8
Regulatory systems, plant, 660–78
    defenses, 674–76
    growth responses, 670
    hormones, 662–69
    internal clocks, 671–74
Releasing hormones, 522
REM sleep, 580
Renal cortex, 510 *fig.*, 511
Renal medulla, 510 *fig.*, 511
Repetitive DNA, 244, 248
Repressor protein, 210–11
Reproduction, 532–61. *See also* Inheritance
    alterations of chromosome number and
        structure during, 144–48
    asexual, 126, 534
    cellular (cell division), 126–27
    connections between cell division and, 126–27
    endocrine disruptors effects on, 716
    in green algae, 336, 336 *fig.*
    human, 536–45
    meiosis and crossing over in, 136–43
    mitosis and eukaryotic cell cycle in, 128–36
    natural selection success in, 715
    plant, 634–40
    of prokaryotes, 322
    as property of all organisms, 5
    sexual, 125, 534–35
        See also Sexual reproduction
    of viruses, 201 *fig.*
Reproductive barriers, 280–81, 280 *table*
    evolution of, 285
    hybrid zones and, 286, 286 *fig.*
    speciation and, 282
Reproductive cloning, 222–23
    applications of, 222–23
Reproductive isolation, 279, 286, 286 *fig.*
Reproductive systems, 421, 421 *fig.*
Reptiles (Reptilia), 397
    cardiovascular system, 469
    dinosaurs, 397
    excretion in, 509 *fig.*
    gravity and circulatory system of, 467
    lizards, 397
    phylogenetic tree of, 311 *fig.*
    respiratory system of, 458
    snakes, 397, 397 *fig.*
Research
    applications of reproductive cloning
        to, 222–23
    radioactive isotopes used in, 21
Resolution, of microscopes, 52
Resources
    competition over shared, 743
    human overexploitation of, 766

Respiration, 452–65. *See also* Cellular respiration
    aerobic, 615
    in birds, 461
    breathing and, 90, 460–61
    gas exchange and, overview of, 454
    gas exchange through moist body surfaces as,
        454–55, 455 *fig.*
    gills in aquatic animals and, 456–57, 456 *fig.*
    in high altitudes, 453
    insect tracheal system and, 457, 457 *fig.*
    lungs in terrestrial animals and
        See also Lung(s)
    smoking effects on, 460
    transport of gases in body and, 462–63
Respiratory surfaces, 454–55, 455 *fig.*
Respiratory system, 420, 420 *fig.*, 454–55
    exchanges with external environment and role
        of, 424 *fig.*, 425
    in high altitudes, 453
    human, 458–59, 459 *fig.*
    smoking as assault on, 460
Resting potential, neuron membrane,
    566, 566 *fig.*
    nerve signal and changes in, 566–67
Restoration ecology, 772, 778–79
    Kissimmee River Project, 778–79, 778 *fig.*
Restriction enzymes, creating recombinant DNA
    with, 234
Restriction fragment length polymorphisms
    (RFLPs), 246, 246 *fig.*
Restriction fragments, 234, 246
    analyzing, to detect differences in DNA
        sequences, 246, 246 *fig.*
    detecting harmful alleles using, 246
    sticky ends and, 234
Restriction sites, 234
Reticular formation, 580
Retina, 595, 595 *fig.*
    photoreceptor cells (rods and cones)
        in, 598 *fig.*
Retinitis pigmentosa, 269
Retrovirus, 203, 241 *fig.*
Reverse transcriptase, 203
    gene cloning and role of, 235
Rheumatoid arthritis, 500
Rhizobium spp., 326, 656, 656 *fig.*
Rhizomes, 625, 625 *fig.*
Rhodopsin, 598
Rhythm method (contraception), 545
Ribonucleic acid (RNA), 46. *See also* RNA
Ribosomal RNA (rRNA), 196
    in bacteria vs. in archaea, 320
Ribosomes, 55, 55 *fig.*, 56 *fig.*, 57 *fig.*, 59 *fig.*
    as factories for polypeptides, 196
    protein synthesis by, 59
Ribozymes, 296
Rice (*oryza sativa*), 247
Ringworm, 359
Rituals
    agonistic behaviors and, 718
    courtship, 280, 280 *fig.*, 714–15, 714 *fig.*
Rivers. *See* Lakes and streams
RNA (ribonucleic acid), 47
    comparing DNA and, in systematics, 312
    messenger RNA (mRNA), 194
    as nucleotide polymer, 185 *fig.*
    polynucleotide, 184–85, 185 *fig.*
    roles in controlling gene expression, 215
    self-replicating, 296
    transcription of DNA into, 190, 193
    translation of, into protein, 190
    viruses, 201, 202–3
RNA interference, 215, 215 *fig.*
RNA polymerase, 193, 211
RNA splicing, 194
    alternative, 214–15
RNA world, 296

Rocks
  age of, and geologic time, 298
  phosphorus cycle and weathering of, 758
Rodhocetus, 261, 261 *fig.*
Rodriguez, Eloy, 676, 676 *fig.*
Rods, retina, 598, 598 *fig.*
Romer, Alfred, 394
Root(s)
  modified, 625, 625 *fig.*
  mycorrhiza on, 341, 355
  nutrient uptake by, 645, 645 *fig.*
  primary growth in, 630–31, 631 *fig.*
  tissue systems in, 626, 627 *fig.*
Root cap, 630, 631 *fig.*
Root hairs, 624, 624 *fig.*
  in soil, 652, 652 *fig.*
  solute uptake and, 645, 645 *fig.*
Root nodules, nitrogen-fixing bacteria on,
  656, 656 *fig.*
Root pressure, 646
Root system, 624, 624 *fig.*, 625
Rotenone as disruptor of cellular respiration,
  99, 99 *fig.*
Rough endoplasmic reticulum (rough ER), 56 *fig.*,
  57 *fig.*, 60–61, 60 *fig.*
Roundworms, 368, 368 *fig.*, 373
R plasmids, 205
r-selection, 732
Rubisco, 118
  Calvin cycle and, 116, 116 *fig.*
RuBP, Calvin cycle and regeneration of,
  116, 116 *fig.*
Rule of addition, 160
Rule of multiplication, 160
Runners, as modified stems, 625, 625 *fig.*
Runners, sprinter versus marathoner, 89
Running as locomotion, 603, 604
Rusts, 359

S

Saccharomyces cerevisiae (yeast), 220–21,
  221 *fig.*, 247
Saccule, 594, 594 *fig.*
Sac fungi, 357
Safe sex, 499, 544, 545
Sage grouse, courtship and mating behaviors of,
  714–15, 714 *fig.*
Sahelanthropus tchadensis, 403
Salamanders, 396, 396 *fig.*
  paedomorphic axolotl, 304, 304 *fig.*
Saliva, 434
Salivary glands, 434, 434 *fig.*
Salmon, sense perception and migration in, 706
Salmonella, of gamma proteobacteria group, 326
Salt
  ionic bonds as, 23, 23 *fig.*
San Andreas fault, 302, 302 *fig.*
Sapwood, 633, 633 *fig.*
Sarcomas, 135
Sarcomeres, 612–13
SARS (severe acute respiratory syndrome), 202
SA (sinoatrial) node, 472
Saturated fats, 40
Savannas, 692–93, 692 *fig.*
Scale-eating fish, 273, 273 *fig.*
Scanning electron microscopes (SEMs), 52–53
Scarlet king snake, 11 *fig.*
Schindler, David, 759, 759 *fig.*
Schistosomiasis, 372
Schizophrenia, 571, 582
Schweickart, Rusty, 680, 697
Science. *See also* Biology
  discovery, using inductive reasoning, 9
  hypothesis-based, 9
  politics and, 120
  theories and, 8

Sclera, 595 *fig.*, 596, 596 *fig.*
Sclereids, 628, 629 *fig.*
Sclerenchyma cells, 628, 629 *fig.*
Scolex, 372
Scorpions, 378, 379 *fig.*
Scrotum, 538
Scypha (sponge), 370, 370 *fig.*
Sea anemones, 371
  fission in, 534 *fig.*
Sea cucumbers, 382
Sea ice, melting of, 768
Seals, 415 *fig.*
  combat between male elephant, 529 *fig.*
  population-limiting factors on fur,
    728–29, 729 *fig.*
Search image, 712
Seasonal cycles, plant, 672
Season(s), Earth's tilt as cause of, 686 *fig.*
Sea star, 366, 382, 382 *fig.*
  endoskeleton of, 607
  as keystone species, 749, 749 *fig.*
  life cycle of, 366 *fig.*
Sea turtles, conservation efforts for, 774, 774 *fig.*
Sea urchins, 382, 382 *fig.*
  egg fertilization in, 546, 547 *fig.*
  endoskeleton of, 607, 607 *fig.*
  as keystone species, 749, 749 *fig.*
  zygote cleavage in, 548 *fig.*
Seaweeds, 334
Secondary consumers in communities, 746,
  746 *fig.*, 747, 747 *fig.*
Secondary endosymbiosis, 331, 331 *fig.*
Secondary growth in plants, 632–33, 632 *fig.*
Secondary immune response, 492 *fig.*, 493, 493 *fig.*
Secondary oocytes, 541, 541 *fig.*
Secondary phloem, 632–33
Secondary spermatocytes, 540
Secondary structure of proteins, 44, 45 *fig.*
Secondary succession, 750, 750 *fig.*
Secondary xylem, 632
Second law of thermodynamics, 81
Secretion function of urinary system, 511,
  511 *fig.*, 512, 512 *fig.*
Secretory proteins, 60, 60 *fig.*
Sedimentary rock, strata of, 261, 261 *fig.*
Seed(s), 344–45
  abscisic acid and dormancy of, 667
  development of, 636, 636 *fig.*, 637
  fruits and dispersal of, 352 *fig.*
  germination of, 638, 638 *fig.*, 666–67
  structure of, 636 *fig.*
Seed coat, 636
Seed dormancy, 636, 667
Seedless plants, 348
  carboniferous coal forests formed by, 348
Seedless vascular plants, 344–45, 345 *fig.*
Seed plants, 345, 345 *fig. See also* Angiosperms;
  Gymnosperms
Segmentation, animal body, 376–77, 376 *fig.*
Segregation, Mendel's law of, 156–57, 171
Selective breeding, 153
Selective permeability of plasma membrane,
  74, 76
Selective serotonin uptake inhibitors (SSRIs),
  571, 582
  prescriptions in U.S. by year, 582, 583 *fig.*
Self-fertilizing plants, 154–55
Self proteins, 497
  Class I and II, 500
Self-recognition and non-self recognition,
  immune system and, 497, 500
Semen, 538–39
Semicircular canals, 594, 594 *fig.*
Semiconservative model of DNA replication, 188
Seminal vesicles, 538
Seminiferous tubules, 540, 540 *fig.*
Sensations, 588

Senses, 586–601
  hearing and balance, 592–94
  movement and, 587
  sensory inputs into nervous system and, 588, 600
  sensory reception, 588–91
  taste and smell, 599
  vision, 595–98
Sensitive period, 706
Sensory adaptation, 589
Sensory input, central nervous system, brain, and,
  564, 588
Sensory neurons, 564
Sensory organ, platypus bill as, 388
Sensory receptors, 588–89, 590 *fig.*
  for balance, 594
  for electromagnetism, 591
  for light (vision), 595–98
  for pain, 590
  in skin, 423
  for sound (hearing), 592–93
  specialized, for five categories of stimuli, 590–91
  stimuli converted into action potentials by,
    588–89
  for taste and smell, 589 *fig.*, 599
  for temperature and touch, 590
Sensory transduction, 588, 589 *fig.*
Sepals, 350, 634
September 11 terrorist attacks, 245
Septic shock, 487
Septuplets, Iowa, 532–33
Serine, 42, 42 *fig.*
Serotonin, 580
Sessile organisms, 370
Setae, 413, 413 *fig.*
Set point, homeostasis and, 426
Severe acute respiratory syndrome (SARS), 202
Severe combined immunodeficiency disease
  (SCID), 500
  gene therapy for, 241
Sewage treatment, 329, 329 *fig.*
Sex, safe, 499, 544, 545
Sex chromosome(s), 137, 174–75
  abnormal numbers of, 146–47, 147 *table*
  sex determination due to, 174–75
  sex-linked genes and unique inheritance
    patterns, 176
  sex-linked genetic disorders, 177
Sex determination, 175, 175 *fig.*
Sex hormones, 67, 520, 529
  functional group differences in, 35 *fig.*
  steroids and, 41
Sex-linked genes, 176–77
Sex pili, 322
Sexual dimorphism, 271
Sexually transmitted diseases (STDs),
  544, 544 *table*
Sexual reproduction, 125, 126
  in animals, 534–35
  description of, 534
  in fungi, 356
  genetic variation from, 265, 265 *fig.*
  in humans, 536–45
  meiosis and, 540–41, 540 *fig.*, 541 *fig.*
  in plants, 346, 634–40
  prezygotic and postzygotic barriers to, 280–81,
    280 *table*
  sexual selection and sexual dimorphism in, 271
  zygote fungi, 358, 358 *fig.*
Sexual selection, 271
Shared ancestral characters, 310
Shared derived characters, 310–11
Sharks, 392, 392 *fig.*, 415 *fig.*, 587
Shoots
  auxin stimulation of cell elongation in, 664–65,
    665 *fig.*
  modified, 625, 625 *fig.*
  primary growth in, 630–31, 631 *fig.*

Shoot system, 624, 624 *fig.*
Short-day plants, 672, 672 *fig.*, 673 *fig.*
Short tandem repeats (STRs), 244, 244 *fig.*
Short-term memory, 581
Siamese fighting fish (*Betta splendens*), agonistic behavior of, 718
Sickle-cell disease, 44, 46
    base pair mutation causing, 199
    as genetic pleiotropy, 168, 168 *fig.*
    molecular basis of, 199 *fig.*
Sieve plates, 629, 629 *fig.*, 648, 648 *fig.*
Sieve-tube members, 629, 629 *fig.*, 648, 648 *fig.*
Sifaka, 401 *fig.*
Signaling behavior in animals, 713, 713 *fig.*
Signal proteins, 42
Signal transduction, 74, 74 *fig.*
    cell-cycle control system utilizing, 134
Signal transduction pathways
    cell-to-cell signaling and initiation of, 220, 220 *fig.*
    faulty proteins interfering with normal, 226
    hormones and creation of, 519
    light and hormones effects on plants and, 674
Silencer DNA sequence, 214
Silent Spring (Carson), 683
Simple epithelium, 416
Simpson (O. J.) murder trial, 245
Single-lens eye, 595–98
    corrective lenses and surgery for, 597
    focusing of, 596, 596 *fig.*
    photoreceptors in, 598
    structure of, 595 *fig.*
Single nucleotide polymorphism (SNP), 246
Sister chromatids, 128, 128 *fig.*, 137 *fig.*
Skeletal muscle, 418, 418 *fig.*, 612
    contractile apparatus of, 612
Skeletal system, 420, 420 *fig.*
Skeleton
    bones of, 609–11
    endoskeleton, 607
    exoskeleton, 378, 606–7
    human, 608–9, 608 *fig.*
    hydrostatic, 368, 606, 606 *fig.*
    muscle interaction with, in movement, 611
    support, movement, and protection provided by, 606–7
Skin
    artificial, 419
    cell replacement in, 136
    epithelial tissue of, 416
    functions of, 423
    polygenic inheritance of color, 169, 169 *fig.*, 170
    sensory receptors in, 590 *fig.*
    structure of, 423, 423 *fig.*
Skin pigmentation, adaptation to sunlight amounts in humans and, 407
Skull, 390, 392 *fig.*
Skunks, eastern spotted and western spotted, 278, 278 *fig.*
Sleep
    brain regulation of arousal and, 580
    plant sleep movements, 671, 671 *fig.*
Sliding-filament model of muscle contraction, 612–13, 613 *fig.*
Slime molds, 335, 335 *fig.*
Small intestine, 438–39, 438 *fig.*
    enzymatic digestion in, 438 *table*
    relationship of, to large intestine, 440–41, 440 *fig.*
    structure of, 439, 439 *fig.*
    tissue layers in wall of, 419 *fig.*
Smell sense
    chemoreceptors for, 590–91, 599
    in salmon, 706
Smoking
    birth defects and, 555
    damage to respiratory system caused by, 460

Smooth endoplasmic reticulum (smooth ER), 56 *fig.*, 57 *fig.*, 60, 60 *fig.*
Smooth muscle, 418, 418 *fig.*
    blood distribution controlled by, 477
Smuts, 359
Snails, Japanese land, 285
Snakes, 11 *fig.*
    agonistic behavior in, 718, 718 *fig.*
    electromagnetic receptors in, 591, 591 *fig.*
    gravity and circulatory system of, 467
    hox genes in, 609, 609 *fig.*
    locomotion in, 604–5
    mimicry in, 10
Social behavior, 717–21. *See also* Rituals
    agonistic, 718
    altruistic, 720
    communication among animals, 713
    dominance hierarchies, 718
    Goodall on chimpanzee dominance hierarchies and reconciliation behaviors, 719
    human, 721
    mating, 714–15
        See also Mating
    territorial, 717
Social learning, 710–11
Social memories, behavior and, 701
Sociobiology, 717, 721
Sodium chloride, 19, 19 *fig.*, 22, 23, 23 *fig.*
Sodium potassium pumps (Na$^+$-K$^+$), 78
    in neuron membrane, 566, 567, 570
Soil
    characteristics of, 652
    conservation of, 653, 653 *fig.*
    fungal absorption of nutrients from, 656
    organic farming and, 654
    plant nutrients acquired from, 644, 650–55
Soil conservation, 653, 653 *fig.*
Soil horizons, 652, 652 *fig.*
Solar energy
    as biospheric abiotic factor, 684
    as electromagnetic energy, 112
    greenhouse effect in Earth's atmosphere and, 119
    photosynthetic light reactions and, 113
Solutes, 26
    animal osmoregulation and balance of dissolved, 508
    plant uptake of, 645, 645 *fig.*
Solutions, 26, 26 *fig.*
    acidic, basic, and neutral, 27 *fig.*
    hypertonic, hypotonic, and isotonic, 77 *fig.*
Solvents, 26
Somatic cells, 136–37
    mutations in, and development of cancer, 225
Somatic nervous system, 574, 575
Somites, 551, 551 *fig.*
Sound, route through ear of, 593 *fig.*
Sow bugs, kinesis in, 708, 708 *fig.*
Soy foods, 661
Sparrows
    imprinting in white-crowned, 706, 706 *fig.*
    population fluctuations, 730, 730 *fig.*, 731, 731 *fig.*
Spatial learning, animal behavior and, 708
Spatulae, 413, 413 *fig.*
Speciation, 278 *fig.*, 282–89
    of Darwin's finches on Galápagos Islands, 287, 288 *fig.*
    definition of, 277
    geographical isolation and allopatric, 282
    polyploidy and plant, 284
    sympatric, 283, 283 *fig.*
    tempo (models) of, 289, 289 *fig.*
Species, 6. *See also* Biodiversity
    binomial classifications and, 309
    classifying (*see* Classification; Systematics; Taxonomy)

community described by species composition, 742
    concepts of, 278–81
    of Darwin's finches on Galápagos Islands, 287, 288 *fig.*
    deep-sea, 681, 681 *fig.*
    definition of, 277, 278
    diversity, 748, 749, 764, 765
    endangered (*see* Endangered species)
    endemic, 774
    extinct, 398 *fig.*
    global climate change and distributions of, 770
    invasive, 751
    keystone, 749
    mass extinctions and, 303
    mechanisms in development of, 282–89
    naming, 308–9
    new, from errors in cell division, 147
    non-native (exotic), 408, 725, 751, 751 *fig.*
    relative abundance, 748, 748 *table*
    reproductive barriers between, 280–81, 280 *table*
    richness, 748
    threatened, 765
Speech, *FOXP2* gene and human, 407
Sperm. *See also* Gametes
    animal, 534
    fertilization and, 546, 547 *fig.*
    human, 540–41, 540 *fig.*
    motility, 67
    plant, 635, 635 *fig.*
    properties of, 546
    structure of human, 546 *fig.*
Spermatocytes, primary and secondary, 540
Spermatogenesis, 540, 540 *fig.*, 541
Spermicides, 545
Sperry, Roger, 579
Sphincters, 433, 436 *fig.*
Sphyma mokarran, 587
Spiderman, 412 *fig.*, 413
Spiders, 378–79, 379 *fig.*
Spider silk proteins, uses of, 44
Spinal cord, 573
    fluid-filled spaces in, 573 *fig.*
    injured, 563
    neurons in, 418 *fig.*
Spinal nerves, 573
Spirilla, 321
Spirochetes, 321, 321 *fig.*, 326
Sponges, 370, 370 *fig.*, 432
Sporangia (sporangium), 343
Spores, 343, 356, 358, 358 *fig.*
Sporophytes, 336, 346, 346 *fig.*, 634–35
    angiosperm plant as, 350–51
    fern, 347
    pine, 348–49, 349 *fig.*
Squamous epithelium, simple or stratified, 416, 416 *fig.*
Squid, 375, 375 *fig.*
    courtship rituals of, 714, 714 *fig.*
    eye of, 595
    giant axons of, 566–67
    nervous system of, 572, 572 *fig.*
Squirrels, geographically isolated species of antelope, 282, 282 *fig.*
SRY gene, 175
SSRIs (selective serotonin uptake inhibitors), 571, 582
    prescriptions in U.S. by year, 582, 583 *fig.*
Stabilizing selection, 270, 270 *fig.*
Stamens, 350, 634
Staphylococcus, 321, 321 *fig.*, 326, 327, 327 *fig.*
Starch, 39, 39 *fig.*
Starlet sea anenome, 535 *fig.*
Star navigation in birds, 709, 709 *fig.*
Start codon, translation initiated by, 196–97

Stem cells, 563
  adult, 223
  blood cell diseases and, 481
  differentiation of blood cells from, 481 *fig.*
  differentiation of cultured, 223 *fig.*
  embryonic, 222, 222 *fig.*
Stems, 624–25
  gibberellins and elongation of, 666–67
  modified, 625, 625 *fig.*
  secondary growth in woody, 632 *fig.*
  tissue systems in, 626, 627 *fig.*, 629
Stentor, 333 *fig.*
Steroid hormones, 519, 520
Steroids, 41
  anabolic, as health risk, 41
  spinal injuries and, 563
Steward, F. C., 221
Stickleback fish, 305, 305 *fig.*
Stigmas, 351, 634
Stimulants, effects of, on nervous system, 571
Stimuli, 702
Stimulus, nerve signal, 566–67
  intensity of, 589
  sensory, 588, 600
Stolons, 625, 625 *fig.*
Stomach(s), 432
  bacterial infection and ulcers in, 437
  gastric glands in, 436, 436 *fig.*
  human, 434, 436–37
Stomata, 109, 342, 626
  closing of, and reduced water loss, 118
  guard cell regulation of opening/closing of, 647 *fig.*
Stop codon, 197
Storage proteins, 42
Stramenopiles, 334
STR analysis, 244, 244 *fig.*
Strata, of sedimentary rock, 261, 261 *fig.*
Stratified epithelium, 416
Streptococcus, 326
Streptomyces, 326, 326 *fig.*
Stress
  adrenal glands and, 528–29
  immunity and, 501
  responses to, 528–29, 704–5
Stretch receptors, 590
Strict anaerobes, 101
Stroke, 473
Stroma, 64, 109, 109 *fig.*
  Calvin cycle and photosynthesis in, 111
Stromatolites, 294, 294 *fig.*, 318, 320
Structural proteins, 42
Structure and function, relationship of, in animals, 414
Strychnine, 744
Sturtevant, Alfred H., 174
Subatomic particles, 20
Substrate feeders, 430, 430 *fig.*
Substrate-level phosphorylation, 94, 94 *fig.*
Substrates, enzyme, 84
Sucrose, 38
Sugar-phosphate backbone of nucleotides, 184
Sugars, 35
  photosynthesis and production of, 116
  transport of, by phloem tissue in plants, 648–49
Sugar sinks, 648, 649 *fig.*
Sugar sources, 648, 649 *fig.*
Sulfur bacteria, 326
Sunflowers, 643
Sun-tanning, genetic influences on, 170
Superior vena cava, 470
Supertasters, 599
Supplements, vitamin and mineral, 446
Supporting cells, neuron, 565
Surface tension, 25, 25 *fig.*
Surface-to-volume ratio in cells, 54, 54 *fig.*
Surfactants, 459

Surrogate motherhood, 559
Surroundings, scientific definition of, 81
Survivorship curves, population, 727, 727 *fig.*
Suspension feeders, 370, 383, 430, 430 *fig.*
Sustainable agriculture, 654
Sustainable Biology Initiative, 779
Sustainable development, 775, 779
Sustainable resource management, 733
Swallowing reflex, 434, 434 *fig.*
  Heimlich maneuver and disrupted, 435, 435 *fig.*
Sweating. *See also* Evaporative cooling
Swim bladder, 393
Swimming as locomotion, 604
Symbiosis, 330. *See also* Mutualism
  of mycorrhiza and plants, 656, 656 *fig.*
  in nitrogen-fixing bacteria and plants, 655, 655 *fig.*, 656
  plant nutrition and, 655–57
Sympathetic division, autonomic nervous system, 574 *fig.*
  regulation of internal environment and, 574–75
Sympatric speciation, 283, 283 *fig.*
Synapses, 565, 569
Synapsis, 138 *fig.*
Synaptic cleft, 569
Synaptic terminals, 565, 565 *fig.*, 570 *fig.*
Systematics, 308–13
  classifying and naming species as, 308–9
  homologies and study of, 308
  molecular biology as tool in, 312
Systemic acquired resistance, 675, 675 *fig.*
Systemic circuit, 469
Systemic lupus erythematosus (lupus), 500
Systems, 4
  definition of, 81
Systems biology, 4
Systole, 471, 476

T

T2 phage, 182–83, 182 *fig.*
T_3 (triiodothyronine), 524
T_4 (thyroxine), 523, 524
  secretions of, 523 *fig.*
Tadpole, 551, 551 *fig.*
Taiga, 696
Tannin, 744
Tapeworms, 372, 372 *fig.*
Taproot, 625, 625 *fig.*
Target cells, 518, 520
  hormone signaling mechanisms affecting, 519
Tarsiers, 400, 401, 401 *fig.*
Tasmanian tiger, 389
Taste
  action potentials and sensation of, 589 *fig.*
  chemoreceptors for, 590–91, 599
Taste buds, sensory transduction at, 589 *fig.*
Tatum, Edward, 190, 232
Taxis, 708, 708 *fig.*
Taxol (drug), 135
Taxonomy, 6, 278
Tay-Sachs disease, 62
T cells (T lymphocytes), 490–91, 490 *fig.*, 497
  cytotoxic, 498, 498 *fig.*
  development of, 490 *fig.*
  helper, 498–99
  HIV destruction of, 498–99, 499 *fig.*
Tears, 596
Technology, 12
  DNA (*see* DNA technology)
  science applications using, 12
Teeth, human, 434, 434 *fig.*
Telomeres, 248
Telophase
  cell division I, cytokinesis and, 139 *fig.*
  mitosis, 130, 131 *fig.*
Temperate broadleaf forests, 695, 695 *fig.*

Temperate grasslands, 694–95, 694 *fig.*
Temperate zones, 686
Temperature. *See also* Body temperature
  as biospheric abiotic factor, 684
  definition of, 25
  enzymes' effects on, 85
  global climate change and, 768, 768 *fig.*, 769
Temporal isolation, 280
Tendons, 611
Tendrils, 625, 625 *fig.*
Terminal bud, 624
Terminator nucleotide sequence, 193
Terrarium ecosystem, 752, 752 *fig.*
Terrestrial animals
  cardiovascular system of, 469, 469 *fig.*, 470–78
  gravity effects on, 467
  lungs of, 455 *fig.*
Terrestrial biomes, 691–97
  global water cycle connecting aquatic and, 697, 697 *fig.*
  human disruption of, 759
Terrestrial food chain, 746 *fig.*
Territorial behavior, 717
Tertiary consumers in communities, 746, 746 *fig.*, 747 *fig.*
Tertiary structure of proteins, 44, 45 *fig.*
Testcross, determining genotype using, 159
Testes, 538
Testosterone, 35 *fig.*, 519, 529
  anabolic steroid as synthetic, 41
Tetrads, 140
Tetraploidy, 283
Tetrapods, 263, 263 *fig.*, 390, 395–96, 397
  evolution of lungs in, 458
Thalamus, 577
Thaumoctopus mimicus, 365
Theories, definition of, 9
Therapeutic cloning, 222, 223
Thermal energy, 80
Thermodynamics, laws of, 81
Thermophiles, 325, 325 *fig.*
Thermoreceptors, 590
Thermoregulation, 505, 506–7
  heat gains or losses and, 506–7
  reducing metabolic rate for energy savings and, 505
Theropods, feathered, 398. *See also* Archaeopteryx fossil
THG (tetrahydrogestrinone), 41
Thick filaments, myosin, 612, 612 *fig.*, 613 *fig.*
Thigmotropism, 670, 670 *fig.*
Thin filaments, actin, 612, 612 *fig.*, 613 *fig.*
Thinking, brain and, 578. *See also* Thought, symbolic
Thiobacillus, 329
Thiomargarita namibiensis, 326 *fig.*
Thought, symbolic. *See also* Thinking, brain and
  human evolution and, 406
Threatened species, 765. *See also* Endangered species
Three-domain classification scheme, 314, 314 *fig.*, 320
Threshold, nerve signal, 567, 567 *fig.*
Thylakoids, 64, 109, 109 *fig.*
  light reactions of photosynthesis in, 111, 112–15, 117
Thymine (T), 185, 185 *fig.*
Thymus gland, 520
Thyroid gland, 524
  calcium homeostasis regulated by, 524–25, 525 *fig.*
  development and metabolism regulation by, 524
Thyroid-stimulating hormone (TSH), 522
Thyroxine (T_4), 523, 524
  secretions of, 523 *fig.*
Ticks, 378

Tigers
  conservation of Myanmar, 763
  Tasmanian, 389
Tight junctions, 68, 68 *fig.*
Tiktaalik, 395, 458, 458 *fig.*
Tinbergen, Niko, 702, 703, 708
Ti plasmid, 239, 239 *fig.*
Tissues, 2, 2 *fig.*, 414, 626
Tissues, animal, 415–19
  artificial, 419, 419 *fig.*
  circulatory system and, 468
  embryonic, 549 *fig.*, 549 *table*, 550
  gas exchange in (*see* Gas exchange in animals)
Tissue systems, plant, 626, 627 *fig. See also*
      Phloem; Xylem
Toads, 396
  cane, 408, 408 *fig.*
Tobacco
  birth defects and, 555
  as carcinogen, 227, 460
Tongue, human, 434, 434 *fig.*
Tonicity, 76
Tools, complex, human evolution and, 404, 406
Topsoil, 652
Torpor, 505
Touch
  plant response to, 670
  sensory receptors of, 590, 590 *fig.*
Toxins
  bioremediation of metallic, 778
  chemical, as animal defense, 744, 744 *fig.*
  chemical, as plant defense, 674–76, 744
  endotoxins and exotoxins, 327
  environmental degradation from, 767
  food crops and, 669
  fungal, 359
  phytoremediation of, 643
Trace elements, 18–19, 18 *table*
Trachea (windpipe), 434, 434 *fig.*, 458
Tracheal system, insect, 455, 455 *fig.*, 457, 457 *fig.*
Tracheids, 629, 629 *fig.*, 646
Tracheoles, 457
Trade winds, 686
Trait, 154, 161
Tranquilizers, 571
Transcription, 190, 193, 193 *fig.*
  codons and, 191 *fig.*
  codons and genetic code, 192
  DNA microarray tests for, 219
  messenger RNA and, 194
  regulating eukaryotic genes with regulatory
     proteins (transcription factors) during,
     214, 214 *fig.*
  regulating prokaryotic genes by turning on and
     off, 210
  summary, 198, 198 *fig.*
Transcription factors, 214, 214 *fig.*
Transduction, bacterial, 204
Trans fats, 40, 449
Transfer RNA (tRNA)
  structure of, 195 *fig.*
  translation and, 194–95
Transformation, bacterial, 204
Transgenic organism, 239–40
Translation, 190
  of codons, 191 *fig.*
  initiation codon for, 196–97, 197 *fig.*
  regulating eukaryotic genes during, 216
  stop codon for termination of, 197
  summary, 198, 198 *fig.*
  transfer RNA and, 194–95
Translocation
  chromosomal, 148, 148 *fig.*
  polypeptide chain formation and, 197
Transmission electron microscope (TEM), 53
Transpiration, 646–47
  guard cells and control of, 647

Transpiration-cohesion-tension mechanism, 647
Transport across membranes, 74, 75–79
  exocytosis, endocytosis and, 79
  osmosis, 76
  passive, 75
  transport proteins and, 77
  water balance and, 76–77
Transport in animal bodies, 468–70
Transport in plant tissues
  of sugars, 648–49
  of water, 646–47
Transport proteins, 42
  facilitated diffusion and, 77, 77 *fig.*
Transport vesicles, 60–61
Transposable elements, 780
Transthyretin, molecular structure of, 44, 45 *fig.*
Tree(s). *See also* Forest(s)
  citrus, 341
  Dutch elm disease, 359, 359 *fig.*
  of life, 308–14
  pine, 348–49, 349 *fig.*
  redwoods, 620–21
  water flow up, 646 *fig.*
Treponema pallidum, 326
TRH (TSH-releasing hormones), 523
Trial-and-error learning, 710, 710 *fig.*
Trichinella spiralis, 373
Trichinosis, 373
Trichomonas vaginalis, 332–33, 333 *fig.*
Triglycerides, 40
Triiodothyronine (T_3), 524
Trimesters, pregnancy, 556–57, 556–57 *fig.*
Triplet code, 191
Trisomy 21, 145, 146
Triticale, 240
Trophic structure of communities
  ecosystem dynamics and, 746
  food chains and, 746–47, 746 *fig.*, 747 *fig.*
  pyramid of production and, 754
Trophoblast, 554
Tropical rain forests, 692. *See also* Forest(s)
  deforestation of, 354, 692, 765
  global climate change and, 770
  medicinal plants in, 676
Tropics, 686
Tropisms, plant, 662–63, 670
trp operon, 211, 211 *fig.*
True-breeding varieties, 155
Trypanosoma, 333, 333 *fig.*
Tryptophan, 195, 580
  repressor-controlled operons and, 211, 211 *fig.*
TSH (thyroid-stimulating hormone), 523
TSH-releasing hormone (TRH), 523
Tubal ligation, 545
Tuberculosis, 250
Tubers, 625, 625 *fig.*
Tubulins, 65
Tumors, 135
Tumor-suppressor genes, 224
  interference of faulty, in signal-transduction
     pathways, 226
  p53, 226
Tundra, 696, 696 *fig.*
Tunicates, 383, 383 *fig.*
Turner syndrome, 147, 147 *table*
Turtles, sea, conservation efforts for, 774, 774 *fig.*
Twins, 170, 532–33
Twin studies of human behavior, 721, 721 *fig.*
Tyrannosaurus rex, 415

U

Ulcers, gastric, 437
Ultimate causes of behavior, 702
Ultrasound imaging, 165, 165 *fig.*
Ultrastructure, cellular, 52
Ultraviolet light, 227, 407, 407 *table*

Ulva (multicellular green alga), 336, 336 *fig.*
Uncouplers as poisons, 99
Undernourished individuals, 443
Unequal reproductive success, 8
Unicellular green algae, 336, 336 *fig.*
Uniform population-dispersion pattern, 726 *fig.*, 727
United States
  Biological Weapons Convention and, 328
  cardiovascular disease in, 473
  human population centers in, 264 *fig.*
  population age structure for, 736, 736 *fig.*
  regulatory agencies, 41, 91, 240
Unsaturated fats, 40
Uracil (U), 185, 185 *fig.*
Urea, excretion of, 509
Ureters, 510, 510 *fig.*
Urethra, 510 *fig.*, 511, 539
Urey, Harold, 295
Uric acid, excretion of, 509
Urinary bladder, 510
Urinary system, 421, 421 *fig.*, 510–11
Urine, 508
  production of, 510–12, 511 *fig.*
Uterus, 463 *fig.*, 536 *fig.*, 537, 537 *fig.*
Utricle, 594, 594 *fig.*

V

Vaccination, 489
Vaccines, 489
  DNA technology and development of, 238
Vacuoles, 62
Vagina, 537
Van der Waals forces, 413
van Helmont, Jan Baptista, 644
van Leeuwenhoek, Anton, 51
Varmus, Harold, 224
Vascular bundles, 626
Vascular cambium, 632
Vascular cylinder, 626
Vascular plants, 344–45
Vascular tissue system, 342, 626
Vas deferens, 538
Vasectomy, 545
Vector, gene, 232
Vegetarians, human
  essential amino acids for, 443, 443 *fig.*
  as primary consumers, 754, 754 *fig.*
Vegetative propagation, 638
Veins, animal, 468
  blood flow in, 475 *fig.*
  pulmonary, 470
  structure of, 474, 474 *fig.*
Veins, leaf, 626
Venter, J. Craig, 249
Ventilation, 456. *See also* Breathing
Ventral surface of animals, 368, 368 *fig.*, 372
Ventricles
  of brain, 573
  of heart, 468
Venules, 468, 474, 474 *fig.*
Vertebrae, 390
Vertebral column, 390
Vertebrates, 390–99
  amphibians, 396
  birds, 398
  cardiovascular system, 469
  as chordates, 391
  digestive system adaptations of, 441
  endocrine system of, 520–23
  fish, 392
  without hinged jaws, 391
  innate immunity in, 486
  limb formation, 553, 553 *fig.*
  lungs of terrestrial, 458
  nervous system of, 573–83
  reptiles, 397

Vervet monkeys, alarm calls of, 710–11, 710 *fig.*
Vesicles, 59
Vessel elements, 629, 629 *fig.*, 646
Vestigial organs, 262
Vibrio cholerae, 326
Vibrios, 321
Victoria, Lake, biodiversity of, 724–25
Villi, intestinal, 439, 439 *fig.*
Vinblastin (drug), 135
Virchow, Rudolf, 127
Viroids, 203
Virus(es), 181, 200–205
    AIDS and HIV, 202, 203, 485, 498–99, 500–501
    animal disease caused by, 201
    cancer-causing, 224
    DNA of, 200
    emerging, 202–3
    herpes, 181
    infection of bacteria by (bacteriophage), 183, 200
    influenza, 202
    lytic and lysogenic cycles of phage, 200 *fig.*
    placenta-crossing, 555
    plant disease caused by, 201
    reproductive cycle of enveloped, 201 *fig.*
Visceral mass, 374
Vision, 595–98
    corrections for focusing problems with, 597
    invertebrate eye types and, 595
    photoreceptors for, 591, 598, 598 *fig.*
    single-lens eyes in vertebrates and, 595–98
Visual acuity, 597
Vital capacity, 461
Vitamin A
    beta-carotene converting to, 239
    as chemical compound, 19
Vitamin D synthesis, 407, 423
Vitamin(s), human requirements for, 444, 444 *table*
Vitreous humor, 595 *fig.*, 596
Vocal cords, 458
Voles, mating behavior of, 701
Voltage-gated channels, 567
Volume (sound), 593
Volvox (colonial alga), 336, 336 *fig.*
von Frisch, Karl, 702, 713

W

Walking locomotion, 604
Wallabies, 408
Wallace, Alfred, 257
Wasps
    behavior of digger, 708, 708 *fig.*
    plant recruitment of predatory, 674–75, 675 *fig.*
Water, 25–29
    acid precipitation, 28
    acids, bases and, 27
    alternate ways to represent, 23 *table*
    as biospheric abiotic factor, 684
    chemical reaction in formation of, 29
    cohesion of liquid, 25
    gas exchange in, 455, 456–57

hydrogen bonds in, 25
    osmosis and passive transport of, 76, 76 *fig.*
    plant adaptations for saving, 118
    plant nutrients acquired from, 644
    plant production of oxygen by splitting, 110
    plant xylem uptake/transport of, 645, 645 *fig.*, 646–47
    polar covalent bonds of, 24, 24 *fig.*
    as solvent, 26, 26 *fig.*
    states of, 26, 26 *fig.*
    temperature moderation and, 25
Water balance (osmoregulation), 76–77, 508–15
Water-channel proteins, 78
Water-conducting cells, 629, 629 *fig.*
Water cycle, global, 697, 697 *fig.*
Water molds, 334, 334 *fig.*
Water-soluble vitamins, 444 *table*
Water strider, 25, 25 *fig.*
Water vascular system, 382, 382 *fig.*
Watson, James D., 46, 186–87, 186 *fig.*
Wavelength of electromagnetic energy, 112
Wegener, Alfred, 300
Weight loss diets, 448, 448 *table*
Went, Frits, 662–63, 663 *fig.*
Westerlies, 686
West Nile virus, 202
Wetlands, 689, 690
    restoration of, 778–79
Whales
    evolution of, 261, 399
    extinct, 261 *fig.*
    feeding and nutrition in humpback, 429
    migration in gray, 709
Wheat (*Triticum* sp.), 284, 622
White blood cells (leukocytes), 479
    inflammatory response and, 487
    lymphocytes (*see* Lymphocytes)
    lysosomes in, 62
    types of, 479 *fig.*
White-crowned sparrows, imprinting in, 706, 706 *fig.*
White matter, central nervous system, 573
Whole-genome shotgun method, 249, 249 *fig.*
Whooping cranes, imprinting migratory behavior in, 707, 707 *fig.*
Wildfires, 770, 770 *fig.*
Wildlife populations, overexploitation of, 766
Wilkins, Maurice, 186, 187
Wilmut, Ian, 222
Wilson, Edward O., 764
Winds
    as biospheric abiotic factor, 684
    prevailing patterns of, 687 *fig.*
    seed dispersal by, 352, 352 *fig.*
    trade and prevailing, 686–87
    uneven heating as cause of, 687 *fig.*
Winemaking, yeast and, 101
Wings
    evolution of, 293
    pattern formation and development of, 553, 553 *fig.*

Withdrawal (contraception), 545
Wolves
    dominance hierarchies in, 718
    Yellowstone to Yukon Conservation Initiative and, 776–77
Womb, human, 537
Wood, 632–33, 633 *fig.*
Wood rays, 633, 633 *fig.*
World Health Organization, 447
World Trade Center terrorist attacks (9/11/2001), 245
Wrangham, Richard, 676

X

X chromosome, 137
    abnormal numbers of, 147
    inactive, 213
X-chromosome inactivation, 213
X-O chromosome system, sex determination and, 175, 175 *fig.*
X-rays, 227, 422
X-Y chromosome system, sex determination and, 175, 175 *fig.*
Xylem, 342, 629
    nutrient uptake to root, 645, 645 *fig.*
    primary, 631
    secondary, 632
    water transport in, 646–47
Xylem sap, 646

Y

Y chromosome, 137
    abnormal numbers of, 147
    human evolution and study of, 406
    sex determination and, 174–75, 175 *fig.*
Yeast, 355, 356, 361
    Saccharomyces cerevisiae, 220–21, 221 *fig.*, 247
Yeast infections, vaginal, 359
Yellow bone marrow, 609
Yellowstone to Yukon Conservation Initiative (Y2Y), 776–77, 776 *fig.*
Yersinia pestis, 328
Yolk sac, 554, 554 *fig.*, 555, 555 *fig.*

Z

Zebra, 399, 399 *fig.*
Zero population growth, 734
Zoned reserves, 775
Zoopharmacognosy, 676
Zooplankton, 688
Z-W chromosome system
    sex determination and, 175, 175 *fig.*
Zygomycetes, 356 *fig.*, 357, 357 *fig.*
Zygote(s), 137
    animal, 366, 534, 546–47
    plant, 349, 351, 635, 635 *fig.*, 636
Zygote fungi, 357
    life cycle, 358, 358 *fig.*